THE
ARTIST'S
YEARBOOK
2006

EDITOR: OSSIAN WARD

THE
ARTIST'S
YEARBOOK
2006

All the information and advice you
need to get ahead in the UK art world

Thames & Hudson

First published in the United Kingdom in 2005 by
Thames & Hudson Ltd, 181A High Holborn, London WC1V 7QX

www.thamesandhudson.com

British Library Cataloguing-in-Publication Data
A catalogue record for this book is available from the British Library

ISBN-13: 978-0-500-28577-0
ISBN-10: 0-500-28577-2

Printed and bound in Germany by Bercker

Contents

OO

Introduction

Introduction to
The Artist's Yearbook

Ossian Ward

The Artist's Yearbook has, to a large extent, come about in response to the frequently asked question, 'How do I become an artist?' – for which there is no single or simple answer. It is hoped that each reader will use these varied listings and inspirational essays on their individual paths towards this common goal. The task is made all the more complicated nowadays because the scope and very definition of the artist is open to interpretation. For instance, if you subscribe to the sort of utopian proclamations made by many post-war artists such as Joseph Beuys, an ambassador of socially conscious art in 1970s Germany, then anything can be art, anyone can make art and consequently everyone is an artist. However, whether you believe that art can consist of found objects such as sharks and bricks or whether you value a delicate brushstroke or a faithful likeness above all else, no one can deny another person's right to be an artist.

Among the many practitioners who make a conscious decision to be an artist, there are still varying levels of seriousness. With this in mind, *The Artist's Yearbook* is designed to be useful for everyone from the undecided undergraduate looking for the right degree or the best college, to the hobbyist painter in search of a local supplier of canvas and paints, as well as the established artist needing urgently to organize safe passage for their work to an exhibition in a Berlin gallery.

Nevertheless, this book does not discriminate or differentiate between the amateur and the professional artist. Andy Warhol, another influential figure in twentieth-century art, once said with typical irony, 'Why do people think artists are special? It's just another job', but how can you begin to measure professionalism in a wholly self-motivated occupation that has no job description or chances of promotion? Instead, the thousands

of visual arts contacts contained in this directory are for both full-timers and part-timers or indeed anyone who wants to experience, research, produce, study, exhibit or sell works of art in England, Scotland, Wales and Northern Ireland. In short, unlike Andy Warhol's philosophy, *The Artist's Yearbook* is all about the business of art, not the art of business.

Just as there is no orthodoxy governing what an artist should be, do or make, neither is there a secret to success in the art world – rather there are simultaneously many and none. Any quest for success as an artist only elicits more questions. What actually qualifies as success in an endeavour such as art that demands only that you be creative, original, passionate and dedicated in what you do? So, in addition to attaining these positive attributes, which even art history's finest exponents have struggled with, this then is the artist's lot – a world of doubt and uncertainty – but thankfully there is help at hand.

The first step is to realize that all but the most arrogant artists share these crises of confidence and purpose. After all, what is art but a continual observation and questioning of life? Facing public scrutiny is a key hurdle in any artist's development, so the first chapter is dedicated to the many commercial galleries spread throughout the UK. For many artists, this network of small exhibition spaces around the country is the first point of contact with contemporary art and its audience, which includes collectors, curators, agents, writers and other arts professionals. To help approach this minefield, respected and established gallery-owner Nicholas Logsdail clarifies the distinction between an art dealer that sells art as part of a commercial enterprise and a gallery that looks after an artist's career over a period of years. He also explains the importance of building your own community of like-minded artists that can provide a supplementary support structure as well as intellectual stimulus.

Elsewhere in this directory you will find an often-overlooked assortment of artistic communities that exists, readymade, in the guise of the many artists' societies and groups based in the UK. A prominent Royal Academician and president of the New English Arts Club, Ken Howard puts forward the case for membership and discusses what kind of person is most suited to the society world. Another less traditional meeting place for artists is the internet, and digital artist Nick Crowe, a pioneer in creating works of art on computers and online, prefaces a section of helpful websites with a discussion about the possibilities for artists interested in this ever-expanding and developing virtual culture.

Any significant time spent at art school is essential for developing and sustaining artistic practice and many courses offer the kind of vocational training that also increases the likelihood of making it as an artist. Whether you are looking for part-time study, a place on an art foundation or degree course, or even a postgraduate qualification, the essay by Janet Hand and Gerard Hemsworth of Goldsmiths College in London should be required reading, offering as it does a step-by-step guide to choosing the right course.

The stereotypical image of the starving artist toiling away in a grotty garret may be a hundred years out of date, but graduate artists often need to supplement their earnings in order to maintain a studio and their own production. Clearer, practical information is provided by the Arts Council's Artists Development officer, Tim Eastop, in the chapter devoted to securing funding for your practice or a commission to create new work. Financial concerns will soon be headline news for all artists when the new European directive on Artists' Resale Rights (also known as *droit de suite*) comes into force during 2006, which will give artists the right to a percentage of the revenue from any of their works of art resold on the art market.

Sourcing the right materials can also be a pursuit all of its own and the Mike Smith Studio has spent the past two decades designing and fabricating complex works of art for other artists, not least building Damien Hirst's famous shark tank, Rachel Whiteread's Trafalgar Square plinth and Michael Landy's replica house at Tate Britain. Mike Smith urges artists to explore the full diversity of materials and technologies available, even if this means seeking expert advice or enlisting the help of others in a work's manufacture. He also reveals a few secrets of the trade as well as some strategic guidance on budget, transportation and installation for anyone planning an ambitious work of art. While not all of the solutions can be found in *The Artist's Yearbook* (especially not the resources needed to pickle large fish in formaldehyde), within the wide range of art-material shops, printers, framers and founders, etc. there are many specialist suppliers that can be easily looked up by searching for your favoured material, media or subject matter in the subject index at the back of the book.

Creativity does not just apply to the conception and creation of your work, but also to its distribution. Career-minded artists hoping to sell and exhibit widely may need to learn the basics of self-publicity, taking helpful hints from the team at Brunswick Arts in London, who specialize in providing press coverage for major events in the art world and have written an introduction on how to conduct your own public relations campaign.

You may not see art as a competitive activity, but a recent boom in art prizes has added significantly to the number of opportunities for emerging artists to be seen by the wider public. However, with so many and varied awards it is worthwhile reading the foreword to the section on prizes, open competitions and residencies by Sacha Craddock, the chair of an annually selected prize for recent art-school-leavers called New Contemporaries, originally set up in 1949. She offers help on how to apply for prizes or residencies, how they function, who selects the entrants and what a place on the shortlist can mean for an artist's curriculum vitae.

Further outlets for artists' work include the UK's numerous art fairs and festivals. Contemporary art author and expert Louisa Buck surveys the landscape, from high-profile, international contemporary art gatherings such as the Frieze Art Fair in London and the Liverpool Biennial (next edition in 2006) to localized events such as the annual

Art Fortnight London and the Sunderland Art Weekender.

This constantly changing cultural landscape means that new exhibition spaces such as the Turner Centre, a new contemporary art gallery due to open in Margate in 2007, are springing up all over the UK, while existing museums expand and grow with the times. In this regard, it is fascinating to read the essay that heads the chapter on public museums and galleries by the Whitechapel's director Iwona Blazwick, as she prepares to open a new wing of east London's oldest art institution in 2007–8.

As the cycle of making, exhibiting, selling and appreciating art is such a restless process, it naturally follows that the art world itself is a moveable feast. We will update this book every year to account for this constant flux, weeding out the dead wood, adding in the new shoots and supplementing the current categories of information wherever possible. Whether you see being an artist as your calling in life, a professional vocation or just a pastime, then hopefully this book will provide a shortcut to success, allowing you more time to make more work.

A note on using *The Artist's Yearbook*

The Artist's Yearbook is divided into ten sections of listings, each preceded by an essay written by an authority on the topic. Within some of these sections are subdivisions, for instance the chapters on COMMERCIAL GALLERIES, DEALERS AND EXHIBITION SPACES or PUBLIC MUSEUMS AND GALLERIES are both divided by region and each venue is then listed alphabetically within each of these geographical areas. Another large section, SUPPLIERS AND SERVICES, is broken down into sub-categories, including art insurers, consultants, conservators, shippers, printmakers and so on. ART EDUCATION is divided into two sections: degree-giving institutions and foundation courses; within these two sections listings are geographical and alphabetical. The smaller sections, such as ART FAIRS AND FESTIVALS and ART MAGAZINES AND PUBLIC RELATIONS, are not regionalized but simply arranged alphabetically by company or event name. While this directory focuses on

England, Wales, Scotland and Northern Ireland, some of the sections, such as COMPETITIONS, RESIDENCIES AND PRIZES and ARTISTS' SOCIETIES AND ORGANIZATIONS, list a number of overseas artists' groups and opportunities for artists looking to work outside of the UK.

If you want to find an organization whose name you already know, turn to the 'General index'. If you know what kind of material, service or style of art you are interested in, but do not know where to find it, use the 'Subject index'. This index is designed to group specialist categories of art, working practices or media together and includes such general terms as painting and sculpture, as well as more particular kinds of media such as ceramics, photography and watercolours. As many galleries and museums cater to multimedia forms of art and do not actively distinguish between them nor specialize in one field, this 'Subject index' will by and large *not* refer you to the listings of non-specialist venues or services.

The listings are generally self-explanatory but where categories of information are missing – perhaps a website address or a gallery's submission criteria – it is because either the information does not exist or has not been provided. However, while we have made every effort to confirm that the correct contact details have been included for every entry within *The Artist's Yearbook*, as with all such directories, all addresses, numbers and emails are subject to change. To account for the art world's comings and goings, the book will be updated annually.

If you would like us to add a new entry, wish to update or correct an existing entry, or have a suggestion for improvement, please write to:

Ossian Ward
Editor
The Artist's Yearbook
Thames & Hudson Ltd
181A High Holborn
London WC1V 7QX

Or email:
artistsyearbook@thameshudson.co.uk

01

Commercial galleries, dealers and exhibition spaces

Dealing with the galleries:
How to build your own community

Nicholas Logsdail

There is no single pathway to being an artist. If there were it would be much like any other industry such as medicine, accountancy or the legal profession, where there is a structured and ordered process. By its very nature, the art world is both straightforward and yet also quite baffling until you have acquired 'the knowledge' (to use the analogy of the apprenticeship undertaken by every London taxi driver). For anyone who aspires to be an artist with a capital A, this is the only way.

Know your gallery

There is an extraordinary naivety among certain artists who believe that their lack of success is simply because they do not have a good gallery. This has nothing to do with it; the gallery does not make the difference, nor will a good gallery take on an artist unless the work and studio practice are sufficiently interesting.

There is no single system or specific way of discovering new artists. Good galleries are always trying to find the best interface with new art, but it is a complicated process; one can only be enquiring, open-minded and knowing, and hopefully make a decent judgment. You feel it when someone is really interesting, when you can envision the work carving out a place in history. This comes not only from the work itself but from the combination of your knowledge and an original mind. I have seldom encountered a talented artist who subsequently becomes important who was not knowledgeable or clever – not necessarily in the conventional sense, but a degree of artistic intelligence is necessary to any kind of creativity.

Artists are in a difficult position, but generally if they fit the criteria mentioned above they will find the path through their own skill. Just putting a foot in the door doesn't work because there are hundreds of people trying to

do that. Neither does cold-calling galleries, especially if you haven't been there or don't know the names of some of the artists they exhibit.

There is a great resentment among young artists who see galleries as snooty and uncaring, but it is not a closed world – go to openings, know your galleries. This is where knowledge and education come in. Artists should be informed and aware of what is happening. It must be a passion, an obsession.

Know your history

All young artists, particularly students and those in the formative phase of their careers, should immerse themselves in the art history of the past fifty years and come to terms with general art history. This way they can position and judge themselves against the best art out there, which has already been validated. My experience of students is that they are full of the arrogant, intellectual blossom of youth – which is very attractive and can be turned to great advantage – but as often as not, it is merely an excuse not to learn or inform themselves. An ignorant artist is not likely to go very far, because you need to be able to discuss your own work with a breadth and depth of reference that makes such a conversation interesting. There is an enormous difference between being able to talk about your work well and just being pushy or opportunistic.

Being able to convey artistic or intellectual information, and question it, forms part of the mechanics of becoming an artist, but the other part is doing the right thing, at the right time and in the right place, as well as meeting the right people. It is important to foster professional friendships, and building a community around you does this.

Create your own scene

Good art does not come without community. This community is built in many ways and begins, for most artists, when they join the art school system. The conceptual artists of the

1960s and 1970s, the British sculptors Cragg, Deacon, Kapoor et al, the YBAs or the Royal College situation before that – these were all small, intense young communities of like-minded artists.

My early history was about creating my own community. The Minimal/Conceptual art movement of the late 1960s, when I started, was a particular way of thinking about art that was specific to my generation. When one group forms and becomes powerful it takes a kind of insider control over the international contemporary art world, gaining the support of the serious critics, museums and collectors. Each subsequent generation takes a position that is contrary in some way to the previous one, and this engenders what we call 'movements' in art. Often these are not consciously created, they just happen, but they always happen through the formation of community.

Artists at heart

If you cannot create your own community, you can always look for a community to which you feel you belong. A gallery is one such place.

There is a major distinction between a gallery and an art dealer. Many dealers only manage to sustain their contemporary art programme through backroom sales of secondary-market material. On the other hand, galleries such as the Lisson Gallery aim to develop the careers of emerging or living artists – they are not dealers as such – and this sense of purpose was characteristic of many of the more serious galleries of the past. Clearly, conventional art dealing is the more profitable activity (even if you are only taking ten per cent) because the margins are smaller and all you need are knowledge and contacts. However, galleries whose prime preoccupation is dealing have less time to service or look after the interests of their artists.

Neither of these two different models is right or wrong. When I started the Lisson Gallery thirty-seven years or so ago, it began as an artist-curated space; that was always my idea of what a gallery should be. I came to the field

with no formal training or preconceptions: in fact, I was just over twenty years old when I got thrown out of art school for doing this, which is one of the reasons why I did not continue as an artist myself. Many people who enter the gallery scene come from the business side, the auction houses or the high-powered commercial galleries, and because of their experience and education they have a very different viewpoint.

The challenge or ideal of a gallery that sustains itself through its living artists should be self-fulfilling: if the central focus is on the quality of the artists, then they should be good enough to sustain the gallery economically. This is by no means the easiest path, but it fosters loyalty with artists. The other side of the business is when the gallery becomes a selling operation, rather than a nurturing one; any gallery can enter the scene once an artist has become well known or commercially viable. Loyalty of artist to gallery and vice versa is the only way to build a solid history with the right gallery or community.

Commerce and other dirty words

Unfortunately, the art world has changed so much in the past twenty years that the economic pressures are now greater than ever – everything costs more. Although we have to project ourselves as affluent organizations, galleries are not such profitable enterprises. We turn over relatively vast sums of money – many millions of pounds – but if you look at what we have to pay for, there is often not much surplus. A gallery runs essentially on its cash flow, so even as artists become more ambitious and grow with the gallery, we can afford only to share major fabrication costs and generally work to the international art world standard of fifty per cent commission on works of art.

Tying up vital capital in the long term can be problematic, but it is sometimes essential. Galleries' problems are thus linked to artists', because they are part of the same world; if a gallery's artists all have big commercial and financial worries, then so will the gallery.

Lisson is not commercial in the sense that it does not encourage artists to make work whose significance is only to supply the market. Inevitably, if an artist sells one piece of work they will then make two more – that is how the system works – but artists who continue to churn out their work like a product line, even if it is selling well, can be committing artistic suicide. The art world is full of exceptions and contradictions, of course: take Pablo Picasso, who made thousands of works without undermining his market.

Art, language and vision

Strategically, artists should begin with some vision of the end in mind – perhaps of where they want to be in five or ten years' time. The contemporary art world has become quite black and white, with not a lot of middle ground, so by the time an artist is in their late twenties they really need to be honest with themselves about how they feel about the quality of their work. Artists who blame others for their lack of success are very unlikely ever to do well.

Having said all of this, great artists are not overly concerned about how the world sees them and so make art for themselves rather than the marketplace. Success should not be the only reason why you want to be an artist in the first place, and maybe you should start

out with the idea that there is no such thing as success or failure. For example, some artists with MA qualifications choose to teach one or two days a week, even though they could make more money and be more productive, prolific and successful making art. This doesn't mean they have failed; some teach out of necessity, while others want to put something back into their community. It simply means they have taken a different pathway and understand the journey they have chosen to embark upon.

Instead of seeking 'success', an artist should make it their life's work to develop an original and personal language. It is then the job of the gallery to interpret that language so that it transcends everything the artist does. Although the chances of rising from art-school graduate to top international artist are depressingly small, if you want to be a serious artist then there is no point in aspiring to be something less than the best, at least until you find a level you are satisfied with.

Nicholas Logsdail is director of the Lisson Gallery in London, which he founded in 1967. He represents international and British artists, including Douglas Gordon, Anish Kapoor and Julian Opie.

Commercial galleries, dealers and exhibition spaces

East Anglia

Anne Jarman
The Old Fire Engine House,
25 St Mary's Street, Ely
CB7 5BW
T 01353 727160
F 01353 668364
E ofeh65@hotmail.com
W www.theoldfireenginehouse.co.uk
Contact Alice Johnson
Founded in 1968. All media shown. Artists
represented include Julia Ball, Anthony Day,
David Remfry, Terence Harjula, Richard Sell and
Simon Beer.
Submission policy No specific entry requirements
except gallery's approval of the work.
Price range £95–£2,000.
No of exhibitions annually 20

Big Blue Sky
Warham Road, Wells-next-the-Sea
NR23 1QA
T 01328 712023
F 01328 712024
E shop@bigbluesky.uk.com
W www.bigbluesky.uk.com
Opened in 2003, selling Norfolk works. Shows
contemporary, fresh work that represents the area
from which it comes. Artists include Pamela
Noyes, Cathy Layzell, Vanessa Vargo, Ben Johnson,
Jane Harper and John Barnard.
Submission policy Artists must be from Norfolk or
their work must represent something of Norfolk.
Price range £15–£3,000
No of exhibitions annually 6–8

Bircham Gallery
14 Market Place, Holt
NR25 6BW
T 01263 713312
E birchamgal@aol.com
W www.birchamgallery.co.uk
Contact Deborah Harrison or Gail Richardson
Specializes in contemporary British paintings,
original prints, modern British graphic works,
ceramics, glass, sculpture and jewelry. Artists
include Ros Loveday, Elaine Pamphilon, Nicholas
Homoky, Walter Keeler, Disa Allsopp and Elaine
Cox. Approved for Arts Council England's
Own Art scheme.

Submission policy Invites applications from artists
in any medium (UK only). Include images,
statement, CV and sae for return.
Price range £10–£10,000
No of exhibitions annually 10

Broughton House Gallery
98 King Street, Cambridge
CB1 1LN
T 01223 314960
E bhg@dircon.co.uk
W www.broughtonhousegallery.co.uk

Buckenham Galleries
81 High Street, Southwold
IP18 6DS
T 01502 725418
F 01502 722002
E info@buckenham-galleries.co.uk
W www.buckenham-galleries.co.uk
Contact Len Hodds
Founded in 1999 with the aim of showing
contemporary fine and applied art from local,
national and international artists. Seeks to
maintain a non-intimidating atmosphere in
which clients and artists can relax and discuss
the work. There are four galleries on two floors.
Submission policy Any living artist considered.
No photographic or digitally enhanced works.
Price range Usually up to £2,500
No of exhibitions annually 9

Byard Art
4 St Mary's Passage, Cambridge
CB2 3PQ
T 01223 464646
F 01223 464655
E info@byardart.co.uk
W www.byardart.co.uk
Contact Juliet Bowmaker or Ros Cleevely
Established in 1993. Runs an exhibition
programme of contemporary fine and applied art
in a series of solo and group shows throughout the
year. Exhibits figurative and abstract art ranging
from established names to young emerging artists.
Maintains a strong presence at selected art fairs in
London and New York.
Submission policy See website for details.
Price range From £100
No of exhibitions annually 8

Chappel Galleries
15 Colchester Road, Chappel, Colchester
CO6 2DE

T 01206 240326
F 01206 240326
E chappelgalleries@btinternet.com
W www.chappelgalleries.co.uk
Contact Edna Mirecka
Founded in 1986. Sells contemporary painting and sculpture of predominantly East Anglian artists or those with a strong regional connection. Artists represented include Roderic Barrett, Mory Griffiths, Jonathan Clarke, Bernard Meadows, Wlodyslow Mirecki and Paul Rumsey.
Submission policy By invitation only.
Price range Up to £30,000
No of exhibitions annually 13

Choyce Gallery

26A George Street, St Albans
AL3 4ES
T 01727 739931
F 01920 463003
E kaleemwalden@bt.co.uk
W www.choycegallery.co.uk
Housed in a building dating back to the fifteenth century. Exhibits glass art produced by contemporary artists mainly from Britain and Europe. Also contains a designer jewelry and fine-art secton.

Darryl Nantais Gallery

59 High Street, Linton, Cambridge
CB1 6HS
T 01223 891289
E enquiries@nantais-gallery.co.uk
W www.nantais-gallery.co.uk

Garden Gallery

64A High Street, Southwold
IP18 6DN
T 01502 723888
F 01502 723888
E mary@gardengallery.co.uk
W www.gardengallery.co.uk
Contact Peter Austin (Manager)
Established in the late 1990s, specializing in work related to Southwold, the surrounding area and the sea, mostly representational and traditional in style. Constantly rotating display of twenty-five artists in a variety of media including two-dimensional work, sculpture, ceramics and woodcarvings. Artists include John Tookey, John Lidzey, Matthew Garrard, Anne Paton, Geoffrey Wilson and Mary Gundry.
Submission policy No solo shows undertaken. Maximum of six works considered. Abstract work not appropriate. Large-scale work difficult due to lack of space.
Price range £150–£1,500

Harleston Gallery

37–39 The Thoroughfare, Harleston, Norfolk
IP20 9AS
T 01379 855366
F 01379 855366
E challis@harlestongallery.fsnet.co.uk
Founded in 2001, with the addition of a coffee shop in 2003. Aims to promote an enjoyment and understanding of the visual arts within the community. Areas of specialization include paintings, prints and contemporary crafts (ceramics, glass, jewelry, sculpture, textiles, wood, etc.).
Submission policy Artists residing in East Anglia are welcome to submit a CV and images of recent work by post.
Price range £5–£1,000
No of exhibitions annually 6

Head Street Gallery

1 Head Street, Halstead
CO9 2AT
T 01787 472705
E information@headstreetgallery.co.uk
W www.headstreetgallery.co.uk
Mainly shows contemporary work in all sizes, although representational work is exhibited from time to time. Exhibitions throughout the year last seven to eight weeks, with a private view during the first week. Two artists are featured each time, each occupying one room. A third room hosts an ongoing display by various local artists. There is also an art library. The gallery sells paintings, sculpture, glass, ceramics, jewelry, handmade gifts, toys and cards.
Submission policy Submissions from artists are welcome. A CV, statement and at least three images of work should be sent via post or email.
Price range All price ranges
No of exhibitions annually 7

Hertfordshire Gallery

6 St Andrew Street, Hertford
SG14 1JE
T 01992 503636
F 01992 503244
E info@hertfordshiregallery.com
W www.hertfordshiregallery.com
Contact Colin Gardner

Founded in 2003. Showcases original works by Hertfordshire artists and craftspeople, including paintings, ceramics and glass. Sponsors the Hertford Art Society and Welwyn Garden City Art Club Exhibitions.

Hunter Gallery
9 Hall Street, Long Melford, Sudbury
CO10 9JF
T 01787 466117
E info@thehuntergallery.com
W www.thehuntergallery.com
Contact Camilla Rodwell
Founded in 2001. Represents painters including Stephen Brown RBA, Andrew King ROI NS, John Lowrie Morrison, Julian Novorol, Alan Furneaux and John Tookey PS. Also shows sculpture by Nicola Toms and Kate Denton and fine contemporary furniture. The gallery is spread over five rooms and there is a large sculpture garden.
Submission policy Applications by email to camillarodwell@thehuntergallery.com or by post, including photos or CD.
Price range £40–£10,000
No of exhibitions annually 6

ICAS – Vilas Fine Art
8–10 Leys Avenue, Letchworth Garden City
SG6 3EU
T 01462 677455
E info@vilascollection.co.uk
W www.vilasart.co.uk
Contact Bipin Vilas
With more than twenty years' experience in fine art. Gallery artists include John W. Mills (British sculptor) and Gabriel Ellison (Zambian landscape and wildlife artist).
Submission policy Portfolio includes established British and international artists, sculptors and potters. New artists' enquiries welcome at BipinVilas@vilascollection.co.uk.
Price range £500–£65,000+
No of exhibitions annually 5

Letter 'A' Gallery
40 Whitmore Street, Whittlesey, Peterborough
PE7 1HE
T 01733 203595
W www.justfineart.net
Contact Caesar Smith
Founded in 1972, specializing in paintings by the owner Caesar Smith, whose work is published in limited editions only by the gallery.

Price range £150 for limited editions; £16,000 for originals.

Lynne Strover Gallery
High Street, Fen Ditton, Cambridge
CB5 8ST
T 01223 295264
W www.strovergallery.co.uk

McNeill Gallery
112 Watling Street, Radlett
WD7 7AB
T 01923 858594
E info@mcneillgallery.com
W www.mcneillgallery.com
Artists include Alex Rennie, Lawrie Williamson, Joan Somerville, Georgie Young, Pat Ames, Csaba Marcus, Rob Selkirk, John Luce Lockett and Kate Greenaway.

Patrick Davies Contemporary Art
Barley House, The Old Brewery, Furneux Pelham
SG9 0TS
T 01279 777070
E gallery@patrickdaviesca.com
W www.patrickdaviesca.com
Promotes the work of both emerging and established artists. Offers a consultancy service to corporate and private clients. Digital library with examples of work from over two thousand artists.
Submission policy Application by email with CV and no more than six digital images.
Price range £1,000–£25,000
No of exhibitions annually 6

Peterborough Art House Ltd
245 St Paul's Road, Peterborough
PE1 3RJ
T 01733 349024
E helen.mould@btinternet.com
W www.peterborougharthouse.com
Contact Helen Mould
Founded in 1996. The only independent gallery in Peterborough. Specializes in large Abstract Expressionist paintings by Helen Mould and the work of new graduate artists. Also has a collectors' room with nineteenth- and twentieth-century artists such as Alexander Graham Munro, Ainsley Bean, John Bellany, Mary Fedden and Anthony Green. Provides a consultancy service, art-search and advisory service.
Submission policy Artists graduated in the past seven years should submit no more than five photographs of their work to the address above.

Price range £100–£12,000
No of exhibitions annually 10

Picturecraft Gallery Ltd
23 Lees Courtyard, off Bull Street, Holt
NR25 6HS
T 01263 711040
F 01263 711040
E info@picturecraftgallery.com
W www.picturecraftgallery.com
Contact Adrian Hill
Art gallery and exhibition centre. Totally
refurbished gallery reopened in 2003. Offers
thirty-two display spaces for artists to rent on a
three-weekly, no-commission basis.

Primavera
10 King's Parade, Cambridge
CB2 1SJ
T 01223 357708
E infoprimavera@aol.com
W www.primaverauk.com

Regency Gallery
39 Fitzroy Street, Cambridge
CB1 1ER
T 01223 365454
F 01223 364515
E info@regencygallery.co.uk
W www.regencygallery.co.uk

Roar Art Gallery and Archive
9–10 Redwell Street, Norwich
NR2 4SN
T 01603 766220
E roar-art@hotmail.com
Contact Sarah Ballard
A registered charity founded in 2004 and
dedicated to the work of self-taught, marginalized
or Outsider artists.
Price range £40–£1,000
No of exhibitions annually 6–7

School House Gallery
Wighton, nr Wells-next-the-Sea
NR23 1AL
T 01328 820457
Founded in 1983 in the school where Henry Moore
lived and sculpted in the 1920s when his sister was
headmistress. Artists exhibiting include Norman
Ackroyd, Alfred Cohen, Derrick Greaves, Alison
Neville, Sula Rubens and Malcolm Weir.
Submission policy Hosts a mixed exhibition
every summer during July, August and

September and considers works submitted for
these shows.
Price range £250–£5,000
No of exhibitions annually 3

Skylark Studios
Hannath Road, Tydd Gote, Wisbech
PE13 5ND
T 01945 420403
E louise@skylarkstudios.co.uk
W www.skylarkstudios.co.uk
Founded in 1993. A small gallery set in quiet
Fenland countryside offering monthly exhibitions
by selection. Stocks original prints, photographs,
paintings and textiles. Workshops held in etching
and blockprinting.
Submission policy Professional artists working in
two dimensions may send slides or photographs of
work for consideration.
No of exhibitions annually 11

Storm Fine Arts
Church Street Barns, Great Shelford, Cambridge
CB2 5EL
T 01223 844786
F 01223 847871
E info@stormfinearts.com
W www.stormfinearts.com

Thompson Gallery
175 High Street, Aldeburgh
IP15 5AN
T 01728 453743
F 01728 452488
E john@thompsonsgallery.co.uk
Established in 1982. Specializes in early twentieth-
century and contemporary sculpture and paintings.
Artists include Fred Cuming, Terry Frost, Mary
Fedden, Edward Seags and Robert Kelsey.
Price range £500–£25,000
No of exhibitions annually 4

Waytemore Art Gallery
10–11 Florence Walk, Bishop's Stortford
CM23 2NZ
T 01279 506206
E info@waytemore-art-gallery.com
W www.waytemore-art-gallery.com
Founded in 2000. A contemporary gallery
selling originals, bronzes, ceramic and glass.
Offers bespoke framing service. Artists include
Terry McKivragan RI, Derek Hare, Kathryn
Thomas, Frank Taylor, Peter Heard and
Faye Haskins.

Submission policy Will consider contemporary abstracts, landscapes and figurative works in oil, acrylic and watercolour.
Price range £500–£10,000
No of exhibitions annually 4–5

Whittlesford Gallery
Old School Lane, High Street, Whittlesford, Cambridge
CB2 4YS
T 01223 836394
F 01223 290061
E johnshead@whitgallery.fsnet.co.uk
W www.whittlesfordgallery.co.uk

Wildlife Art Gallery
97 High Street, Lavenham
CO10 9PZ
T 01787 248562
F 01787 247356
E wildlifeartgallery@btinternet.com
W www.wildlifeartgallery.com
Founded in 1988, specializing in wildlife art, both twentieth-century and modern. Represents artists from Europe and the UK.
Price range Up to £10,000
No of exhibitions annually 4

Wildwood Gallery
40 Churchgate Street, Bury St Edmunds
IP33 1RG
T 01284 752938
F 01284 752938
E info@wildwoodgallery.co.uk
W www.wildwoodgallery.co.uk
A contemporary-art gallery, opened in 2002. Also sells limited-edition prints, sculptural furniture and ceramics. Offers a full picture-framing service. Exhibited artists include Francis Farmar, Samantha Toft, Anita Klein and Jenny Thompson.
Submission policy Send photos or CD with CV and artist's statement. Artists seen by appointment only.
Price range Up to £2,500
No of exhibitions annually 4

East Midlands

Belvoir Gallery
7 Welby Street, Grantham
NG31 6DY
T 01476 579498

Bottle Kiln Gallery
West Hallam, West Hallam
DE7 6HP
T 0115 9329442

Castle Ashby Gallery
The Byre, The Old Farmyard, Castle Ashby
NN7 1LF
T 01604 696787

Christopher Wren Gallery
St Marys Way, 40 Nottingham Street, Melton Mowbray
LE13 1NW
T 01664 480220
W www.christopherwrengallery.co.uk
Established in 1985. Stocks original paintings and fine-art, limited-edition prints by artists such as David Weston.

Clark Galleries
215 Watling Street West, Towcester
NN12 6BX
T 01327 352957
E sales@clarkgalleries.co.uk
W www.clarkgalleries.com
Established in 1963, specializing in figurative, marine, landscape and animal pictures. Also offers a full conservation service.

Croft Wingates
Wingates Walk, 44a St Mary's Road, Market Harborough
LE16 7DU
T 01858 465455
E shop@croftwingates.co.uk
W www.croftwingates.co.uk
Contact John Snape
Established since 1975. Stocks a wide range of images from popular artists including Mackenzie Thorpe, John Waterhouse, Paul James and Govinder Nazran. Carries both limited-edition prints and original work.
Price range £250–£5,000
No of exhibitions annually 6

Derek Topp Gallery
Chatsworth Road, Rowsley, Matlock
DE4 2EH
T 01629 735580
E info@derektoppgallery.com
W www.derektoppgallery.com

Evergreen Gallery
Sheaf Street, Daventry
NN11 4AB
T 01327 878117
E rsvp@egart.co.uk
W www.egart.co.uk

Fermynwoods Contemporary Art
The Water Tower, Fermyn Woods, Brigstock,
Kettering
NN14 3JA
T 01536 373469
E gallery@fermynwoods.co.uk
W www.fermynwoods.co.uk
An artist-led gallery that shows work by artists
of national and international standing alongside
others less well known at regional level. Areas of
interest include geometric abstraction and artists'
prints. Runs an educational programme alongside
exhibitions. Fermynwoods receives public and
private funding. Works are for sale.
Submission policy Artists usually invited.
Price range Up to £20,000
No of exhibitions annually Approx. 3

Focus Gallery
108 Derby Road, Nottingham
NG1 5FB
T 0115 9537575
E jjames@focus-gallery.co.uk
W www.focus-gallery.co.uk

Frank Haynes Gallery and Pottery
50 Station Road, Great Bowden, Market
Harborough
LE16 7HN
T 01858 464862
E enquiries@frankhaynesgallery.co.uk
W www.frankhaynesgallery.co.uk
Founded in 1987, offering original art works and
ceramics, much of it from the Midlands. Forty
potters in all including Roger Cockram FCPA and
several other Craft Potters Association members.
Submission policy Works by living artists and
potters only. No cold-calling. Write in advance.
Price range £100–£450 for paintings; £3–£350 for
ceramics.
No of exhibitions annually 10, each 4–5 weeks long

Gallery 52
Main Road, Brailsford, Ashbourne
DE6 3DA
T 01335 360368

Gallery 93
93 Belper Road, Derby
DE13 ER
T 01332 364574
Contact J.A. Thomas
Opened in 1990 in owner's home, showing
art within a domestic environment. Artists
represented include Ronald Pope, Walter Beizins,
Alan Smith, Ann Ellis, Keith Hayman and James
Brereton.
Submission policy Shows mostly work by living
artists, with preference for solo shows.
No of exhibitions annually 12

Granby Gallery
Water Lane, Bakewell
DE45 1EU
T 01629 813050

Harley Gallery
Welbeck, Worksop
S80 3LW
T 01909 501700
F 01909 501700
E info@harley-welbeck.co.uk
W www.harleygallery.co.uk
Funded by the Harley Foundation, which
was set up in 1977 by Ivy, Duchess of Portland.
The foundation aims to bring visual art and
craft to a wider audience and support artists.
To this end it provides subsidized studio space
at Welbeck and a platform for exhibiting and
selling at the Harley Gallery. The gallery was
built in 1994 on the site of the nineteenth-
century gas works for Welbeck Estate. It offers
a changing programme of contemporary art
and craft, a shop selling work by leading
British artists, a museum housing displays of
historical objects from the Portland Collection
and a café.
Submission policy To apply for an exhibition or
studio contact Lisa Gee (Director). To apply to sell
work in the shop contact Susan Sherrit (Gallery
Manager).
Price range £20–£1,000 in shop.
No of exhibitions annually 6

Hart Gallery
23 Main Street, Linby, Nottingham
NG15 8AE
T 0115 9638707
F 0115 9640743
E info@hartgallery.co.uk
W www.hartgallery.co.uk

Established in 1989. Represents artists, sculptors and studio ceramicists with national and international reputations, both up-and-coming and in mid-career.
Branches 113 Upper Street, Islington, London N1 1QN **T** 020 77041131; Brea, St Buryan, Penzance TR19 6JB.

Henry Brewer
3 Tudor Square, West Bridgford, Nottingham
NG2 6BT
T 0115 9811623

Hope Gallery
The Courtyard, Castleton Road, Hope Valley
S33 6RD
T 01433 621111

Little London Gallery
Nightingale House, Church Street, Holloway, Matlock
DE4 5AY
T 01629 534825
E info@littlelondongallery.co.uk
W www.littlelondongallery.co.uk
Established in 1991 by Chris and Krystyna Tkacz. A small private gallery in the village of Holloway, nestled in the hillside on the edge of the Peak District. Shows the work of local Derbyshire artists such as Carol Hill, Rosalind Forster, Shirley Anne Johnson, Sandy Bartle and Ursula Newell Walker. A picture-framing service is offered.
Submission policy Initial submission of CV and photographs of recent work, followed by invitation to bring work for a private selection with the gallery directors.
Price range From £40
No of exhibitions annually 8

Magpie Gallery
2 High Street West, Uppingham
LE15 9QD
T 01572 822212
F 01572 822212
E alan@themagpiegallery.com
W www.themagpiegallery.com

Manhattan Galleries
8 Flying Horse Walk, Nottingham
NG1 2HN
T 0115 9418916
F 0115 9418916

Mere Jelly
3rd Floor, Oldknows Factory Building, St Anns Hill Road, Nottingham
NG3 4GP
T 0115 9413160
E denisecweston@hotmail.com
Contact Denise Weston or Simon Withers
Established in 2003 to facilitate new opportunities for artists. Consists of a project space and gallery space. Seeks to broker interest between the artist and galleries, curators, critics and the public. Focuses on contemporary avant-garde work.

Miller Fine Arts
55 Station Road, Hugglescote, Coalville
LE67 2GB
T 01530 810469
E finearts@miller-art.co.uk
W www.miller-art.co.uk
Contact Pam and Michael Miller
Founded in 1989, specializing in fine-art animal portraits and paintings on commission.

Mosaic Gallery
10 Hall Bank, Buxton
SK17 6EW
T 01298 77557

Nest
43 Francis Street, Stoneygate, Leicester
LE2 2BE
T 0116 2709290
F 0116 2709290
A contemporary applied arts gallery founded in 2002. Aims to represent both established makers and new designers currently making in Britain. Permanent collections include the work of Chris Cornelis, Delan Bookson, Susan Nemeth, Shemara Carlow, Peter Davey and Roger Broady.
Submission policy Professional artists and makers are asked to submit CV, personal statement and images with an sae for return. No telephone submissions.
Price range £25–£300

Oakwood Ceramics
5 Kenmore Close, Mansfield
NG19 6RA
T 01623 635777
E oakwood.gallery@virgin.net
W www.oakwoodceramics.co.net
Formally known as the Oakwood Gallery, Oakwood Ceramics was founded in 2003 to

exhibit and promote contemporary ceramics by some of the most renowned potters of the day.
Submission policy Welcomes approaches from potters and makers. Send CV and images of typical work by email or post.
Price range £25–£1,500
No of exhibitions annually 2

Old Coach House
28–30 Nottingham Road, Nottingham
NG16 3NQ
T 01773 534030

Opus Gallery
34 St John's Street, Ashbourne
DE6 1GH
T 01335 348989
F 01335 348989
Contact Jill Stone
Established in 2000, offering monthly painting exhibitions and providing a showcase for British contemporary ceramics, glass, textiles, metalwork and handmade jewelry. Exhibited artists include Guilearia Lazzenni, Glyn Macey, Clare Caulfield and Peter Beard.
Price range £50–£2,500
No of exhibitions annually 10

Patchings Art Centre
Oxton Road, Calverton, Nottingham
NG14 6NU
T 0115 9653479
F 0115 9655308
E info@patchingsartcentre.co.uk
W www.patchingsartcentre.co.uk
Contact Liz or Chas Wood
Founded in 1988. A family business with facilities including three exhibition galleries, framing, art materials, an art school and eight studio workshops. Set in farm buildings within sixty acres of grounds.

Peter Robinson Fine Art
Bardney Road, Wragby, Market Rasen
LN8 5QZ
T 01673 858600

Pierrepoint Gallery
Thoresby Park, Newark
NG22 9EH
T 01623 822365
F 01623 822315
W www.emnet.co.uk/pierrepoint-gallery/

Piet's Gallery
102 Lawrence Court, Semilong
NN1 3HD
T 01604 624351

Sally Mitchell Fine Arts
Thornlea, Askham, Newark
NG22 0RN
T 01777 838234
F 01777 838198
E info@dogart.com
W www.dogart.com
Among the largest publishers of limited-edition dog, equestrian and countryside prints and cards for over twenty-five years. Artists represented include John Trickett, Mick Cawston, Malcolm Coward, Paul Doyle and Debbie Gillingham.
Submission policy Send a good selection of photos or low-res jpegs via email or CD.
Price range £1–£5,000
No of exhibitions annually 12

Small Plaice Modern Art Gallery
Lower Yard, Old Dairy Farm Centre, Main Street, Upper Stowe
NN7 4SH
T 01327 344422
E sales@smallplaiceart.co.uk
W www.smallplaiceart.co.uk

St John Street Gallery
50 St John Street, Ashbourne
DE6 1GH
T 01335 347425
E info@sjsg.co.uk
W www.sjsg.co.uk
Founded in 2000, showing sculpture, crafts and paintings by living contemporary artists, including Lewis Noble, Andrew Macara and Jiri Borsky.
Submission policy Submissions welcome. Contact gallery by email, post or phone.
Price range £500–£10,000 for paintings.
No of exhibitions annually 6

Treeline Gallery
Water Street, Bakewell
DE45 1EW

Watling Street Galleries
116 Watling Street East, Towcester
NN12 6BT
T 01327 351595
E info@picture-shop.co.uk
W www.picture-shop.co.uk

Established in 1975. Deals in the latest fine-art prints and originals. Offers an in-house framing service.

West End Gallery
4 West End, Wirksworth, Matlock
DE4 4EG
T   01629 822356

Woodbine Cottage Gallery
Back Bank, Whaplode Drive, nr Spalding
PE12 0TT
T   01406 330693
F   01406 331004
E   yorath@woodbinecontemporaryarts.co.uk
W   www.woodbinecottagegallery.co.uk
Established in 1996, showing fine arts and ceramics. Regularly exhibits the work of more than thirty established and emerging artists from Britain and abroad.

Yarrow Gallery
Glapthorn Road, Oundle
PE8 4JQ
T   01832 277170
W   www.oundleschool.org.uk/arts/yarrow/home.htm

London

1 000 000 mph projects
59 Old Bethnal Green Road, London
E2 6QA
T   020 77296557
E   info@1000000mph.com
W   www.1000000mph.com
Aims to provide a residency for artists, curators and writers to develop a project ending with an exhibition of the work produced. Works on an invitation basis with an emphasis on emerging and diverse projects.
No of exhibitions annually 6–8

198 Gallery
198 Railton Road, Herne Hill, London
SE24 0LU
T   020 79788309
F   020 77375315
E   gallery@198gallery.co.uk
W   www.198gallery.co.uk
Founded in 1988. A registered charity supporting contemporary art by emerging and mid-career artists from diverse cultural backgrounds working with a variety of media and issues, often giving artists their first solo exhibitions.
Submission policy Exhibition committee meets periodically to consider proposals made by artists. Proposals should include reproductions of work, CV and artist's statement.
Price range £50–£3,000
No of exhibitions annually 7

291 Gallery
291 Hackney Road, London
E2 8NA
T   020 76135676
F   020 76135692
E   admin@291gallery.com
W   www.291gallery.com
The grade II-listed, deconsecrated neo-Gothic Victorian church at 291 Hackney Road was restored and converted into an art gallery, restaurant and bar in 1998. Since then it has shown everything from music, digital work and sculpture to poetry, theatre and visual art.

96 Gillespie
96 Gillespie Road, London
N5 1LN
T   020 75033496
E   info@96gillespie.com
W   www.96gillespie.com
Founded in 2004. Specializes in photography and American art. Artists represented include Gee Vaucher, Melanie Standage, Pat Graham and Cynthia Connolly.
Submission policy Will accept submissions that include artist's past press, examples of work and ideas for the show. Directors will do their best to respond if possible. Gallery is booked up to one year in advance.
Price range £25–£1,000+
No of exhibitions annually 6

Abbott and Holder Ltd
30 Museum Street, opposite the British Museum, London
WC1A 1LH
T   020 76373981
F   020 76310575
E   abbott.holder@virgin.net
W   www.abbottandholder.co.uk
Contact Philip Athill
Founded in 1936 as a picture dealer and conservator. Renowned for selling watercolours, drawings, oils and prints from 1780 to 2005. A twentieth- century watercolour and drawings show

is held every September while the Christmas show has six hundred works priced between £5 and £250. **Submission policy** Artists should telephone and visit the gallery to establish whether the artist's work and the gallery are suitable for each other.
Price range £25–£10,000
No of exhibitions annually 8

Ackermann & Johnson Ltd

27 Lowndes Street, London
SW1X 9HY
T 020 72356464
F 020 78231057
E ackermannjohnson@btconnect.com
W www.artnet.com/ackermann-johnson.html
A two-floor gallery in the heart of Belgravia, just off Sloane Street. Specializes in eighteenth- and nineteenth-century British paintings, notably the Norwich School, English landscapes, sporting paintings, marine paintings and portraiture. Also exhibits bronzes, watercolours and works by contemporary artists including John King, Douglas Anderson and Peter Howell.
Price range From £300 for watercolours.

Adonis Art

1b Coleherne Road, Earls Court, London
SW10 9BS
T 020 74603888
E stewart@adonis-art.com
W www.adonis-art.com
Contact Stewart Hardman
Opened in 1995. Specializes in antique and contemporary art of the male form. Monthly exhibitions, plus a large selection of individual items – bronze figures, statues, nineteenth-century life study drawings, male figurative art of all types. Artists exhibited include Cornelius McCarthy, Peter Samuelson and Duncan Grant.
Submission policy Always interested in viewing the work of new artists, but the subject matter must be the male form.
Price range £100–£10,000
No of exhibitions annually 12

Advanced Graphics London

32 Long Lane, London
SE1 4AY
T 020 74072055
F 020 74072066
E gallery@advancedgraphics.co.uk
W www.advancedgraphics.co.uk
Contact Louise Peck

A print studio founded in 1967, specializing in screenprinting techniques combined, in some cases, with woodblock printing. Moved to current location near London Bridge in 2003. Shows contemporary artists' prints made in the advanced graphics studio and also paintings. Attends selected art fairs. Artists printed at the studio include Craigie Aitchison, Basil Beattie, Neil Canning, Anthony Frost, Albert Irvin, Anita Klein and Ray Richardson.
Price range £200–£20,000
No of exhibitions annually 10

The Agency

18 Charlotte Road, London
EC2A 3PD
T 020 77296249
E info@theagencygallery.co.uk
W www.theagencygallery.co.uk
Founded in 1993 as a space for installation art and new media with a focus on recent critical debates. Continues to launch the careers of young British talents and premieres international artists in Britain.

Agnew's

43 Old Bond Street, London
W1S 4BA
T 020 72909250
F 020 76294359
E agnews@agnewsgallery.co.uk
W www.agnewsgallery.co.uk
Founded in 1817, primarily as an Old Master paintings dealership, the gallery now also specializes in twentieth-century British art and represents a small selection of contemporary artists.

Air Gallery

32 Dover Street, London
W1S 4NE
T 020 74091255
F 020 74091856
E adminair@airgallery.co.uk
W www.airgallery.co.uk
Contact Clare Rea
Founded in 1996. Solely a hire gallery; does not represent artists. Has hosted a wide range of exhibitions, mainly but not only of contemporary art. Past clients include national and international artists and dealers, and also several art prizes.
Submission policy A hire gallery. Welcomes submissions from any interested artists.
No of exhibitions annually 35+

Alan Cristea Gallery

31 Cork Street, London
W1S 3NU
T 020 74398166
F 020 77341549
E info@alancristea.com
W www.alancristea.com
Founded in 1995 and the largest publisher
and dealer of contemporary prints in Europe.
Represents an international stable of artists
including Gillian Ayres, Ian Davenport, Richard
Hamilton, Jan Dibbets, Mimmo Paladino, Julian
Opie, Ian McKeever, Lisa Milroy and Howard
Hodgkin.
Submission policy Does not accept submissions
from artists.
Price range £1,000–£200,000
No of exhibitions annually 8

Albemarle Gallery

49 Albemarle Street, London
W1S 4JR
T 020 74991616
F 020 74991717
E info@albemarlegallery.com
W www.albemarlegallery.com
Focuses on contemporary figurative, still life and
trompe l'oeil work, together with urban and rural
landscapes. Presents group and solo shows of
established and emerging artists, supported by
full-colour catalogues.

Albion

8 Hester Road, London
SW11 4AX
T 020 78012480
F 020 78012488
E mhw@albion-gallery.com
W www.albion-gallery.com
Contact Michael Hue-Williams
Founded in 1993 on Cork Street and moved
in 2004 to a new Norman Foster-designed
space on the banks of the Thames. Comprises
12,500 sq. ft of exhibition space. Exhibited artists
include Mark di Suvero, James Turrell and
Andy Goldsworthy.
No of exhibitions annually 5

Alison Jacques Gallery

4 Clifford Street, London
W1X 1RB
T 020 72877675
E info@alisonjacquesgallery.com
W www.alisonjacquesgallery.com

Formerly known as Asprey Jacques when
it opened in 1998, this relatively young
contemporary gallery in the area around Cork
Street shows international and British artists
such as Ian Kiaer and Catherine Yass.

Anderson Hill

St Peter's House, 6 Cambridge Road,
Kingston-upon-Thames
KT1 3JY
T 020 85463800
F 020 85471227
E info@andersonhill.co.uk
W www.andersonhill.co.uk
Contact Annie Stevens
The gallery started in 2001 as an addition to
an existing commercial framing and corporate-
art business established in 1977. Framing
service available to artists, as well as
potential exposure to corporate clientele.
Gallery space is in a converted Edwardian
church-school building.
Price range £50–£10,000
No of exhibitions annually 6

Andipa Gallery

162 Walton Street, London
SW3 2JL
T 020 75892371
F 020 72250305
E art@andipa.com
W www.andipa.com
Dealers in fine art since 1593 [*sic.*]; London
gallery since 1969. Specializes in modern and
contemporary art (Picasso, Matisse, Chagall,
Warhol, Lichtenstein, Damien Hirst) and
Byzantine art. Offers restoration and valuation
services.
Price range £500–£100,000+
No of exhibitions annually 4

Andrew Coningsby Gallery

30 Tottenham Street, London
W1T 4RJ
T 020 76367478
F 020 75807017
E debutart@coningsbygallery.demon.co.uk
W www.coningsbygallery.com
Established in 1994. Specializes in exhibitions
for contemporary illustrators, photographers and
fine artists.
Price range £50–£10,000
No of exhibitions annually 52; one per week.

Andrew Mummery Gallery
Studio 1.04, Tea Building, 56 Shoreditch High
Street, London
E1 6JJ
T 020 77299399
F 020 77299399
E info@andrewmummery.com
W www.andrewmummery.com
Founded in 1996. Exhibits the work of
international contemporary artists including
Philip Akkerman, Ori Gersht, Alexis Harding,
Louise Hopkins, Merlin James and Carol Rhodes.
Submission policy Does not accept unsolicited
submissions from artists.
Price range £500–£15,000
No of exhibitions annually 7

Anne Faggionato
4th Floor, 20 Dering Street, London
W1S 1AJ
T 020 74936732
F 020 74939693
E info@annefaggionato.com
W www.anne-faggionato.com
Dealers in Impressionist, modern and
contemporary paintings, sculpture and works
on paper.
Submission policy Not open to submissions.
No of exhibitions annually 3

Annely Juda Fine Art
4th Floor, 23 Dering Street, London
W1S 1AW
T 020 76297578
F 020 74912139
E ajfa@annelyjudafineart.co.uk
W www.annelyjudafineart.co.uk
An established name on the gallery scene for over
forty years, showing major figures from the history
of twentieth-century art from Britain, Europe and
Japan, with a special interest in Russian
avant-garde and Constructivist art.

Anthony Reynolds Gallery
60 Great Marlborough Street, London
W1F 7BG
T 020 74392201
F 020 74391869
E info@anthonyreynolds.com
W www.anthonyreynolds.com
Established in 1985, the gallery moved to the
West End in 1990 and the current building was
opened in 2002. There are twenty-two artists
represented exclusively by the gallery, including
the Atlas Group, David Austen, Richard
Billingham, Leon Golub, Paul Graham and
Mark Wallinger.
Submission policy No submissions accepted.
No of exhibitions annually 9

AOP Gallery
81 Leonard Street, London
EC2A 4QS
T 020 77396669
F 020 77398707
E gallery@aophoto.co.uk
W www.the-aop.org
Contact Anna Roberts
Part of the Association of Photographers,
the gallery has been staging exhibitions and
events since 1986. Committed to heightening
awareness and promoting photography, exhibition
programmes represent advertising, fashion and
editorial photography, incorporating both
commercial and personal work from established
and up-and-coming photographers.
Submission policy Photography only.
Price range £70–£2,000
No of exhibitions annually 12

The Approach
1st Floor, 47 Approach Road, London
E2 9LY
T 020 89833878
F 020 89833919
E info@theapproach.co.uk
W www.theapproach.co.uk
Located on the first floor above a traditional
Victorian public house in the Bethnal Green area
since 1997, the gallery shows young British artists,
including recent graduates, as well as artists from
Europe and the USA.

Arcola Theatre
27 Arcola Street, London
E8 2DJ
T 020 75031646
E info@arcolatheatre.com
W www.arcolatheatre.com
Contact Leyla Nazli
Founded in 2001 to provide a much-needed
cultural venue in Dalston, Hackney, and has
become a well-respected fringe theatre. The
theatre's gallery space is designed to air new
and local work in need of a space.
Submission policy Open to a wide range of work.
The decision to exhibit is at the discretion of the
booker.

No of exhibitions annually 10–12; exhibitions run to coincide with performance runs, which usually last four weeks.

Arndean Gallery

23 Cork Street, London
W1S 3NJ
T 020 75897742
F 020 75893888
E info@arndeangallery.com
W www.arndeangallery.com
Contact Kate Sadler
High-profile gallery for hire in Cork Street, in the heart of London's art world. Approximately 900 sq. ft over two floors. With neighbours including Flowers Central, Waddingtons, Beaux Arts and the Royal Academy, the gallery is well placed to attract serious buyers.

Art First

1st Floor, 9 Cork Street, London
W1S 3LL
T 020 77340386
F 020 77343964
E artfirst@dircon.co.uk
W www.artfirst.co.uk
Established in 1991. A contemporary-art gallery exhibiting UK and international artists. Has a regular stable of artists, many of whom with works in public collections in the UK and worldwide.
Submission policy Contemporary painting and drawing. No video. Photographs or CDs (with relevant CV) by post only, with sae for any returns.
Price range £500–£20,000
No of exhibitions annually 10 major exhibitions in the main gallery and regular shows in the front-room project space.

artandphotographs

13 Mason's Yard, Duke Street, St James's, London
SW1Y 6BU
T 020 73210495
F 020 73210496
E info@artandphotographs.com
W www.artandphotographs.com
Opened in 2000 near St James's Park. American director Daniel Newburg shows mainly nineteenth- and twentieth-century photography, although there have been occasional shows of contemporary work and young artists. Also responsible for the photography listings magazine *pluk*, and a new art fair, photo-london.

artHester

5 Chartfield Avenue, Putney, London
SW15
T 01223 522489
E info@arthester.co.uk
W www.arthester.co.uk
Publishes limited editions by established figures and by younger, less well-known artists. Particular focus on British post-war work.

Arthouse Gallery

Lewisham Arthouse, 140 Lewisham Way, London
SE14 6PD
T 020 82443168
F 020 86949011
E arthouse@dircon.co.uk
W www.arthouse.dircon.co.uk
Contact Gallery Coordinator
Lewisham Arthouse, an artist-run studio cooperative, relocated its gallery to its current site in a listed Carnegie building in 1994. Aims to offer exhibitions to artists at the start of their careers. Not a commercial gallery and does not represent artists.
Submission policy Welcomes applications in any medium (subject to selection) on production of images, an exhibition proposal and a completed application form.
No of exhibitions annually Approx. 12

Artist Eye Space

1st Floor, 12 All Saints Road, Notting Hill, London
W11 1HH
T 020 77924077
E vlm@artisteye.com
W www.artisteye.com
Opened in 2003. Alongside established figures, the gallery introduces up-and-coming young artists. Runs a wide-ranging exhibition programme, including salon and corporate events. Exhibited artists include Michelle Molyneux, Paul Maffrett, Simeon Farrar, Amanda Couch, Anastasia Lewis and Jocelyn Clarke.
Submission policy Painting, sculptures, mixed media, video, and installations all considered.
Price range £1,000–£16,000
No of exhibitions annually 6

August Art

311 Royle Building, 31 Wenlock Road, London
N1 7SH
T 020 76081252
E info@augustart.co.uk
W www.augustart.co.uk

Founded by the director – herself a collector and artist – who decided to promote artists directly. Inaugural show held in 2004.
Submission policy Particularly interested in emerging work, whether of new artists or established artists looking in a new direction. Given appropriate opportunities, also interested in showing works of artists outside of Great Britain. Email jpegs of work and an artist's statement.
Price range £200–£3,000
No of exhibitions annually 6–8, including art fairs.

Austin/Desmond Fine Art Ltd
Pied Bull Yard, 68–69 Great Russell Street, London
WC1B 3BN
T 020 72424443
F 020 74044480
E gallery@austindesmond.com
W www.austindesmond.com
Contact Carlotta Graedel Matthai
Specializes in modern British paintings and prints by artists such as Ben Nicholson, Ivon Hitchens, Bridget Riley and Richard Hamilton, and regularly stages shows featuring ceramics by well-known British potters. The gallery also represents a number of contemporary artists, among whom are Margaret Mellis and Julian Perry.
Submission policy Painters and ceramic artists can apply either by email with jpegs or by post with images and sae enclosed.
Price range £100–£200,000
No of exhibitions annually Approx. 7

Barbara Behan Contemporary Art
50 Moreton Street, London
SW1V 2PB
T 020 78218793
F 020 78343933
E info@barbarabehan.com
W www.barbarabehan.com
Contact Barbara Behan
Opened in 2003 and devoted to the representation of Italian art in Britain. Gives voice to some of the most original, emerging and established artists of Italian descent and those with strong ties to the cultural heritage of Italy. Artists include Giuseppe Spagnulo, Claudio Olivieri, Rossella Bellusci, Salvatore Garau, Maria Morganti and Hans-Hermann. Programme set to include their British contemporaries in future exhibitions in order to generate discourses among the featured artists and the London art scene.

Submission policy Email cover letter with artist's statement, CV and examples of recent work. Visit the gallery or refer to the website to ensure that work is appropriate.
Price range £200–100,000
No of exhibitions annually 6

Barrett Marsden Gallery
17–18 Great Sutton Street, London
EC1V 0DN
T 020 73366396
E info@bmgallery.co.uk
W www.bmgallery.co.uk
Established in 1998. Exhibits contemporary studio ceramics, glass, metal and wood including work by Gordon Baldwin, Alison Britton, Caroline Broadhead, Tessa Clegg, Michael Rowe, Martin Smith and Emma Woffenden.

Baumkotter Gallery
63a Kensington Church Street, Kensington, London
W8 4BA
T 020 79375171
E art@baumkottergallery.com
W www.baumkottergallery.com
Specializes in seventeenth- to twenty-first-century paintings, English and European Old Master paintings, and fine oils of modern art. Subjects include hunting, sport, shipping, seascape and landscape. Nicholas Baumkotter has been in the London fine-art trade for twenty-seven years and provides restoration services for fine oil paintings and picture frames. A bespoke framing service is also offered.

Bayswater Road Art Exhibition
Bayswater Road, London
W2
T 01243 865454
E david.james@bayswater-road-artists.com
W www.bayswater-road-artists.com
Contact David James (Chairman)
Running every week for almost fifty years, the Sunday-only exhibition offers individual artists a unique opportunity to exhibit their own original work in person at a low cost. Exhibits range from miniatures to oils, acrylics, watercolours, pastels, sculpture and drawings. The Bayswater Road Artists' Association (BRAA) liaises with Westminster City Council, Royal Parks and Police. It offers support and advice to members including Public Liability Insurance, financial merchant benefits

through Barclays Business, and promotes the exhibition through listings and visitor advertising.
Submission policy No prints permitted in any medium. No agents or representatives allowed. Artists must exhibit their own original work in person.
Price range £5–£5,000
No of exhibitions annually 52, every Sunday.

Beaconsfield

22 Newport Street, London
SE11 6AY
T 020 75826465
F 020 75826486
E info@beaconsfield.ltd.uk
W www.beaconsfield.ltd.uk
An artist-run organization founded in 1994. The remaining wing of the former Lambeth Ragged School was restored and launched by Beaconsfield in 1995 as a developmental exhibition site with the aim of occupying a niche between the institution, the commercial and the 'alternative'. Over the past decade it has maintained a collaborative artistic direction in order to provide a laboratory and presentation facility for artists through a public programme of contemporary visual and combined art-form practice.
Submission policy Proposals can be submitted by either post or email. Enclose sae if return of material is required.
No of exhibitions annually 4

Bearspace

152 Deptford High Street, London
SE8 3PQ
T 020 86912085
E bearspace@thebear.tv
W www.thebear.tv/bearspace/
Contact Julia Alvarez
A contemporary-art gallery exhibiting the cutting edge of young international talent. Artists exhibited include Jonathan Callan and Steven Pippin as well as a range of recent graduates including Mandy Lee Jandrell and Samuel Herbert. The gallery attends art fairs on a regular basis and looks to promote and represent artists in London and internationally.
Submission policy Exhibits painting, photography, film and occasionally three-dimensional work. Contact the gallery for further information.
Price range £500–£5,000
No of exhibitions annually 11

Beaux Arts

22 Cork Street, London
W1S 3NA
T 020 74375799
F 020 74375798
E info@beauxartslondon.co.uk
W www.beauxartslondon.co.uk
Opened over twenty-five years ago in Bath; in 1993 expanded to Cork Street in London. Gallery policy is to show modern and contemporary British painting and sculpture, and to offer an opportunity to new and dynamic artists to exhibit in the heart of Mayfair.

Ben Brown Fine Arts

1st Floor, 21 Cork Street, London
W1S 3LZ
T 020 77348888
F 020 77348892
E info@benbrownfinearts.com
W www.benbrownfinearts.com
A newly founded gallery in Cork Street showing mainly twentieth-century masters and recent photography.

Blackheath Gallery

34A Tranquil Vale, Blackheath, London
SE3 0AX
T 020 88521802
E james@blackheath-gallery.co.uk
W www.blackheath-gallery.co.uk
Contact Sue Marshall
Established in 1975. Provides a showcase for artists from the UK, USA and Europe. Stocks fine prints by twentieth-century artists including Francis Bacon, David Hockney and Henry Moore. Exhibited artists include Graeme Wilcox, Mark Demsteader and Ray Donley.
Submission policy Painters, sculptors, printmakers and glass blowers are invited to submit applications via email with digital attachments or send CD or photographs and CV together with an sae.
Price range £50–£15,000
No of exhibitions annually 6–7

Blink Gallery

11 Poland Street, London
W1F 8QA
T 020 74398585
E info@blinkgallery.com
W www.blinkgallery.com
Contact Daniel Hay
Opened in 2002. A contemporary photography gallery specializing in music, celebrity and fashion

photography. Artists represented include Terry O'Neill, Michael Cooper, Sir Peter Blake, Gered Mankowitz and Dennis Morris.
Price range £300–£5,000
No of exhibitions annually 5

Bloxham Galleries

4–5 The Parade, St Johns Hill, London
SW11 1TG
T 020 79247500
F 020 75853901
E info@bloxhamgalleries.com
W www.bloxhamgalleries.com
Contact Julia Lister
John Bloxham, a respected London dealer involved in the arts for over thirty years, opened the galleries in 1994. There are two light and airy spaces at street level with a downstairs exhibition area for smaller, more intimate pieces. Specializes in sculpture and photography and figurative, landscape and abstract pieces.
Submission policy Welcomes all artists' submissions. Email CV and high-quality jpegs or send postal submissions (including sae) to Julia Lister.
Price range £400–£30,000
No of exhibitions annually 10–12

Blue Gallery

15 Great Sutton Street, London
EC1V 0BX
T 020 74903833
F 020 74905749
E info@thebluegallery.co.uk
W www.thebluegallery.co.uk
Founded in 1994 as a platform to exhibit, promote and sell 'innovative and interesting contemporary art', with particular emphasis on painting and photography.
Submission policy Suitable applications are welcome – initially by email, after which an invitation to make an appointment may be extended.
Price range Up to £20,000
No of exhibitions annually 8–10

Boundary Gallery – Agi Katz Fine Art

98 Boundary Road, London
NW8 0RH
T 020 76241126
F 020 76241126
E agi@boundarygallery.com
W www.boundarygallery.com
Contact Agi Katz or Louise Homes

Established for over nineteen years. Specializes in contemporary figurative work displaying good draughtsmanship and composition and a strong palette. Artists include Peter Prendergast, David Tress, June Redfern, Sonia Lawson, Anita Klein and David Breuer-Weil. Also specializes in modern British artists (1900–60) and immigrant artists of Jewish origin, including David Bomberg, Jacob Epstein, Josef Herman, Bernard Meninsky, Morris Kestelman and Alfred Wolmark.
Submission policy Figurative work (can be representational) with good draughtsmanship, strong composition and a strong palette. Accepts paintings and works on paper. No prints.
Price range £300–£40,000. Up to £10,000 for contemporary; £2,000–£40,000 for modern British.
No of exhibitions annually 7–8

Brixton Art Gallery

35 Brixton Station Road, London
SW9 8PB
T 020 77336957
E brixart@brixtonartgallery.co.uk
W www.brixtonartgallery.co.uk
Contact Ms D. Parker
Founded in 1983. Specializes in contemporary art. Artists represented include L. Postma, Kudzanai Chiurai, Amos Cherfil, Dubois, Sean Hasan, Teresa Nills. Offers training scheme for artists in schools.
Submission policy Submit statement, CV and images of work by post or through gallery website.
Price range Up to £1,000
No of exhibitions annually 8

Cabinet

Apartment 6, 3rd Floor 49–59 Old Street, London
EC1V 9HX
T 020 72516114
F 020 76082414
E art@cabinetltd.demon.co.uk
Contact Martin McGeown or Andrew Wheatley
Founded in 1992. Aims for 'informed, engaged and critical work by artists with an international perspective independent of art-world trends (economic/curatorial/editorial)'. Artists represented include Gillian Carnegie, Enrico David, Mark Leckey, Lucy McKenzie, Paulina Olowskan and Tariq Alvi.
Submission policy Unsolicited applications not sought.
No of exhibitions annually 6

Campbell Works

27 Belfast Road, London
N16 6UN
T 020 88060817
E info@campbellworks.org
W www.campbellworks.org
Founded in 1997. Provides studios,
a classroom, a project space for hire and a
gallery/presentation space offering a public
programme of contemporary, visual and
combined art-form practice. Exhibits new,
up-and-coming artists and experimental projects
as well as showcasing established artists.
The main gallery has good natural light and is
particularly suited to sculpture and installation
or project-based works.
Submission policy Applications welcomed from
curators and artists. Installation proposals
considered. Submissions should include up to
eight 35mm slides, DVD or VHS for media-based
works, a CV and brief statement, and an sae to the
correct amount if the work needs to be returned.
Price range £10–£10,000
No of exhibitions annually 7

Centre of Attention

67 Clapton Common, London
E5 9AA
T 020 88805507
F 020 88805507
E on@thecentreofattention.org
W www.thecentreofattention.org
Contact Pierre Coinde
Founded in 1999. A London-based contemporary-
art gallery examining the formalities of
production, distribution and consumption
of art. Exhibitions take place both in the UK
and overseas.
Submission policy Welcomes submissions from
artists and curators. Post a small number of non-
returnable slides, pictures, images or other
medium that give a fair idea of the work or project.
Can also view websites.
Price range £1–£10,000
No of exhibitions annually 8

Chinese Contemporary Ltd

21 Dering Street, London
W1S 1AL
T 020 74998898
F 020 74998852
E ccartuk@aol.com
W www.chinesecontemporary.com
Contact Julia Colman

Founded in London in 1996, specializing
exclusively in Chinese contemporary art from
artists living and working in mainland China,
both established and emerging. Sister gallery in
Beijing set up in 2004.
Submission policy Must be Chinese nationals
living and working in mainland China.
Price range US$1,000–$100,000
No of exhibitions annually 8–10 solo shows.

Clapham Art Gallery

61 Venn Street, London
SW4 0BD
T 020 77200955
E direct@claphamartgallery.com
W www.claphamartgallery.com
Established in 1998, the gallery discovers and
promotes emerging artists and runs a programme
of five-week curated and one-person exhibitions.
It also participates in selected art fairs and events.

Clarion Contemporary Art

387 King Street, Hammersmith, London
W6 9NJ
T 020 87483369
E info@clariongallery.co.uk
W www.clariongallery.co.uk
Opened in 2005. A small gallery that aims to
exhibit work that is 'interesting and sometimes
challenging without ambition to be "cutting edge" '.
Specializes in painting, representing both young
and better-established artists.
Submission policy Submissions welcome.
Painting only.
Price range £500–£3,500
No of exhibitions annually 10

Collins & Hastie Ltd

62 Tournay Road, London
SW6 7UF
T 020 73814957
E caroline@collinsandhastie.co.uk
W www.collinsandhastie.co.uk
Founded in 1993, dealing in contemporary (mainly
figurative) art. Specializes in the work of Paul
Maze, known as 'the lost British Impressionist'.
Gallery runs by appointment only. Also exhibits at
the Art on Paper Fair, the Affordable Art Fair and
the Chelsea Art Fair. Artists include Glen Preece,
Jenny Thompson, Michael Bennallack Hart,
Janet Tod, Caroline Chariot Dayez, Jim Bradford,
Alex Chamberlain, Rose Shawe-Taylor and
Jill Barthorpe.
Price range £500–£30,000

No of exhibitions annually 4 solo shows, not including London art fairs.

Contemporary Applied Arts

2 Percy Street, London
W1T 1DD
T 020 74362344
F 020 74362344
W www.caa.org.uk
Among Britain's largest galleries specializing in the exhibition and sale of contemporary crafts. Founded in 1948 as the Craft Centre of Great Britain, the double-level gallery shows leading makers of ceramic, glass, jewelry, textiles, metalwork, silver, wood and furniture.
Submission policy Professional craftpersons working in the British Isles can apply for membership of the society. Following selection, the subscription rate is £75 per year.
Price range £10–£10,000
No of exhibitions annually 7

Corvi-Mora

1a Kempsford Road, London
SE11 4NU
T 020 78409111
F 020 78409112
E tcm@corvi-mora.com
W www.corvi-mora.com
Specializes in international contemporary art. Exhibited artists include Liam Gillick, Brian Calvin, Monique Prieto, Rachel Feinstein, Richard Hawkins and Jason Meadows.

Cosa Gallery

7 Ledbury Mews North, London
W11 2AF
T 020 77270398
F 020 77929697
E info@cosalondon.com
W www.cosalondon.com
Contact Julie Pottle
Founded in 2002 to promote innovative and highly crafted work by artists working in a variety of media. Specializes in contemporary studio ceramics. Artists include James Evans, Vivienne Toley, Simon Carroll, Andy Shaw and Noel Hart.
Submission policy Contact by email. Check website first to determine whether work would complement existing artists' work. Especially interested in sculptural studio ceramics.
Price range £500–£4,000
No of exhibitions annually 6; also exhibits at Collect, the craft fair at the V&A.

Counter Gallery

44a Charlotte Road, London
EC2A 3PD
T 020 76848888
F 020 76848889
E info@countergallery.com
W www.countergallery.com
Contact Jo Stella-Sawicka
Established in 2003. Presents exhibitions by emerging international artists. Gallery artists include Armando Andrade Tudela, Michael Fullerton, Simon Martin, Rosalind Nashashibi, Peter Peri and Fergal Stapleton.
Submission policy Does not accept submissions.
Price range £300–£50,000
No of exhibitions annually 7

Cubitt Gallery and Studios

8 Angel Mews, London
N1 9HH
T 020 72788226
F 020 72782544
E info@cubittartists.org.uk
W www.cubittartists.org.uk
Contact Charlotte Nourse (Gallery Administrator)
An artist-run public art space with attached studios. The gallery is operated by an administrator and the programme devised by a curator on an eighteen-month bursary. Applications for studio space can be made via the website.

Cynthia Corbett Gallery

15 Claremont Lodge, 15 The Downs, Wimbledon
SW20 8UA
T 020 89476782
F 020 89476782
E info@thecynthiacorbettgallery.com
W www.thecynthiacorbettgallery.com
Contact Caro Foss or Odette Selva
International contemporary-art gallery founded in 2000 to showcase mid-career American, British and European artists. Art can be bought online through the website, and the gallery also provides an art-consulting service to corporate and private clients. corbettPROJECTS, launched in 2004, exhibits young, emerging and experimental artists in a variety of media including painting, sculpture, photography, video installation and performance art. corbettPROJECTS has an annual programme of exhibitions, both nationally and internationally, operating from innovative spaces and bringing art into unexpected environments.
Submission policy Contact via email.

Price range £100–£15,000
No of exhibitions annually 6, as well as a variety of UK and international art fairs.

Danielle Arnaud Contemporary Art

123 Kennington Road, London
SE11 6SF
T 020 77358292
F 020 77358292
E danielle@daniellearnaud.com
W www.daniellearnaud.com
Founded in 1995 and located in a large Georgian house. Encourages artists with strong individuality to explore freely and present work outside the constraints of market or trends. Also active in collaborations and temporary public art projects. Artists include David Cotterrell, Sophie Lascelles, Marie-France and Patricia Martin, Helen Maurer, Heather and Ivan Morison, and Sarah Woodfine.
Submission policy Artists should apply via email by sending images and short statement and/or proposals for themed exhibitions. It is highly recommended that artists visit the gallery and website before applying.
Price range £250–£10,000
No of exhibitions annually 6 curated for the gallery; 2–3 touring/off-site projects.

David Risley Gallery

Tannery Arts, Brunswick Wharf, 55 Laburnum Street, London
E2 8BD
T 020 76134006
F 020 77298008
E davidrisley@btconnect.com
W www.artnet.com/davidrisley.html
Contact David Risley or Poppy Sebire
Opened in 2003, presenting exhibitions of represented artists alongside curated group shows, mixing established and emerging artists. Artists include James Aldridge, Masakatsu Kondo, Henry Krokatsis, Helen Frik, Peter Jones, John Stezaker, Jonathan Allen, John Zurier, Matt Calderwood, James Hyde and Hurvin Anderson.

Dicksmith Gallery

74 Buttesland Street, Hoxton, London
N1 6BY
T 020 72530663
E dicksmithgallery@hotmail.com
W www.dicksmithgallery.co.uk
Contact Sam Porritt, Meiro Koizumi, Duncan Marquiss, Rupert Norfolk, Mauro Bonacina or Natsuki Uruma

Founded in 2003. Works with young artists to develop and present new work.
Submission policy Accepts application on CD only; images in jpeg only. Any other information also on CD.
No of exhibitions annually 6

Dominic Guerrini Fine Art

18 Redburn Street, London
SW3 4BX
T 020 75652333
F 020 75652444
E sales@dominicguerrini.com
W www.dominicguerrini.com
Stocks original watercolours, drawings, signed and unsigned limited editions, paintings and prints. Viewing is by appointment only.

domoBaal

3 John Street, London
WC1N 2ES
T 020 72429604
F 020 78310122
E domo@domobaal.com
W www.domobaal.com
Opened in 2000. Exhibits new work by artists engaged in contemporary fine-art practice. Solo shows by represented artists predominate, together with the occasional project-based exhibition. Artists shown include Christiane Baumgartner, Daniel Gustav Cramer, Sharon Kivland, Ansel Krut, Miho Sato, Martina Schmid and Rebecca Stevenson.
Submission policy Not open to submissions.
Price range Up to £20,000
No of exhibitions annually 7

Drawing Room

Brunswick Wharf, 55 Laburnum Street, London
E2 8BD
T 020 77295333
F 020 77298008
E mail@drawingroom.org.uk
W www.drawingroom.org.uk
Established in 2002 in association with Tannery Arts, an artists' studio group. Opened the first dedicated public space for drawing in the UK in 2003. The programme aims to investigate the language and diversity of drawing to include a range of ideas and media, from the traditional to the experimental, and reflect the practice of established and emerging artists in the UK and abroad. Exhibitions regularly tour to regional galleries and are interpreted and extended through

an education programme and in-house publications.
Submission policy Not able to deal with unsolicited submissions from artists.
Price range £100–£30,000
No of exhibitions annually 3

Duncan Campbell

15 Thackeray Street, London
W8 5ET
T 020 79378665
Contact Duncan Campbell
Specializes in contemporary and modern British art. Contemporary artists include Rowland Hilder OBE PPRI RSMA, Sandra Pepys and Harry Weinberger. Modern British artists include Heinz Koppel, Bernard Meninsky and the estate of Lucie Carrington Wertheim.
Submission policy Accepts watercolours only.
Price range £20–£25,000
No of exhibitions annually 12

Duncan R. Miller Fine Arts

6 Bury Street, St James's, London
SW1Y 6AB
T 020 78398806
F 020 78398806
E DMFineArts@aol.com
W www.duncanmiller.com
Contact Tanya R. Saunders
Founded in 1985. Dealers in nineteenth-century European and modern British works. Specialists in the Scottish Colourists. Artists include J.D. Fergusson, F.C.B. Cadell, S.J. Peploe and G.L. Hunter.
Submission policy Applications by email or post. No visits.
Price range From £500
No of exhibitions annually 4–6
Branches 17 Flask Walk, Hampstead, London, NW3 1HJ **T/F** 020 74355462.

E&R Cyzer

33 Davies Street, London
W1K 4LR
T 020 76290100
F 020 74993697
E info@cyzerart.com
W www.cyzerart.com
Opened renovated gallery space in Mayfair in 2002. Deals in twentieth-century modern masters and exhibits at several major international shows. Also acquires works for collectors and institutions both at home and internationally.

East West Gallery

8 Blenheim Crescent, London
W11 1NN
T 020 72297981
F 020 72210741
E david@eastwestgallery.co.uk
W www.eastwestgallery.co.uk
Contact David Solomon
Established in 1989. Art consultancy; valuations and commissions undertaken. Located in west London (Notting Hill), just off the Portobello Road. Contemporary art, paintings and drawings (some prints and sculpture), mainly figurative with a strong emphasis on drawing, design and colour.
Submission policy Submissions welcome. Send images either as CD, slides or photos plus CV and sae. Allow thirty days for return of material.
Price range £50–£30,000
No of exhibitions annually 10

ecArtspace

18 Temple Fortune Hill, London
NW11 7XN
T 020 84554548
F 020 84554548
E info@ecartspace.com
W www.ecartspace.com
Contact Angela Diamandidou
Founded in 1998 as a peripatetic or moving gallery. Aims to show contemporary artists in unused buildings and spaces – connecting the art with the architecture of the building. Organizes and curates exhibitions mainly in Clerkenwell, EC1, and in Mitte in Berlin. For the last two years, the gallery has used a more permanent space, the Old Slaughterhouse on St John Street, EC1. Artists represented include Basil Beattie, Frances Aviva Blane, Valerie Wiffen and Jo Schopfner.
Submission policy Interested in site-specific work and architectural projects, depending on type of work and possible building or space setting.
Price range £500–£15,000
No of exhibitions annually 1–2

Elastic Residence

22 Parfett Street, London
E1 1JR
T 020 72471375
E info@elastic.org.uk
W www.elastic.org.uk
Established in 2004. A gallery space for projects and durational performance. Run by artists, it aims to give artists direct access to exhibition opportunities.

Submission policy Does not accept unsolicited applications but occasional open-call events are advertised on the website.
No of exhibitions annually 10

Emily Tsingou Gallery

10 Charles II Street, London
SW1Y 4AA
T 020 78395320
F 020 78395321
E info@emilytsingougallery.com
W www.emilytsingougallery.com
Founded in 1998. Focuses on international contemporary art. Exhibition programme concentrates on artists represented by the gallery and includes off-site projects and publications. Artists represented include Michael Ashkin, Henry Bond, Kate Bright, Peter Callesen, Lukas Duwenhögger, Katy Grannan, Paula Kane, Karen Kilimnik, Justine Kurland, Dietmar Lutz, Won Ju Lim, Daniel Pflumm, Sophy Rickett, Jim Shaw, Georgina Starr, Marnie Weber and Mathew Weir.
No of exhibitions annually 6–7

Emma Hill

159 Farringdon Road, London
EC1R 3AL
T 020 78332674
F 020 76246597
E info@emmahilleagle.com
W www.emmahilleagle.com
Contact Andrea Harari
The gallery and its associated EMH Arts imprint were founded in 1991. Promotes contemporary British artists through exhibitions, installations and artists' books. Off-site projects include collaborations with Sadler's Wells and Almeida Opera. Artists include Basil Beattie, Jane Bustin, Tom Hammick and Terry Smith.
Submission policy Phone the gallery.
Price range £50–£30,000
No of exhibitions annually 8–10

The Empire

33a Wadeson Street, London
E2 9DR
T 020 89839310
E info@theempirestudios.co.uk
W www.theempirestudios.co.uk
Founded in 2004, aiming to build profile with high-quality group shows before beginning to represent individual artists in 2005. Artists represented include the Council.

Submission policy Accepts submissions from any area or medium. Specializes in painting.
Price range £1,000–£10,000
No of exhibitions annually 12

England & Co Gallery

216 Westbourne Grove, Notting Hill, London
W11 2RH
T 020 72210417
F 020 72214499
E england.gallery@virgin.net
Established in Notting Hill since 1987.
Hosts monthly shows of contemporary artists, together with exhibitions reappraising avant-garde twentieth-century art and artists. Also offers a corporate consultancy service.

f a projects

1–2 Bear Gardens, Bankside, London
SE1 9ED
T 020 79283228
F 020 79285123
E info@faprojects.com
W www.faprojects.com
Founded in 2001, the gallery represents artists from both the UK and abroad, working in a variety of media. Represented artists include John Wood and Paul Harrison, David Burrows, Grazia Toderi, Jason Salavon, Neal Rock and James Ireland.
Submission policy Submissions only considered after initial consultation with gallery directors.
Price range £500–£50,000
No of exhibitions annually 7

FarmiloFiumano

27 Connaught Street, London
W2 2AY
T 020 74046241
F 020 74026241
E info@farmilofiumano.com
W www.farmilofiumano.com
Specializes in contemporary European art, such as the Neapolitan Realismo Magico School. Constantly striving to find new artists.
Submission policy Artists should apply to the gallery by sending good-quality images and as much information as possible by post. Enclose sae if material is to be returned.
Price range £200–£25,000
No of exhibitions annually 6

Fine Art Commissions Ltd

79 Walton Street, London
SW3 2HP

T 020 75894111
F 020 75893888
E info@fineartcommissions.com
W www.fineartcommissions.com
Contact Sara Stewart
Founded in 1997, specializing in commissioned art (predominantly portraiture). Artists represented include Nick Bashall, Valery Gridnev, Marcus Hodge, Howard Morgan, Paul Benney and Tom Leveritt. Has recently opened a small contemporary exhibition space at the front of the gallery for clients to buy works by artists they have previously commissioned.
Submission policy Mainly interested in representing portrait painters. Artists wishing to apply must have worked on at least ten portrait commissions.
Price range £500–£40,000
No of exhibitions annually 10

Fine Art Society Plc
148 New Bond Street, London
W1S 2JT
T 020 76295116
F 020 74919454
E art@faslondon.com
W www.faslondon.com
Established in 1876, specializing in paintings, drawings, prints, sculpture, furniture and decorative arts of the nineteenth and twentieth centuries.
Submission policy Submissions in writing with photographs only.
Price range £1,000–£500,000
No of exhibitions annually 10

Flaca
69 Broadway Market, London
E8 4PH
T 020 72757473
E info@flaca.co.uk
W www.flaca.co.uk

Flowers East
82 Kingsland Road, London
E2 8DP
T 020 79207777
F 020 79207770
E gallery@flowerseast.com
W www.flowerseast.com
Founded over thirty years ago by Angela Flowers. Now has two London galleries (one on Kingsland Road, E2, and the other on Cork Street) and one on Madison Avenue in New York. Specializes in a variety of painting, sculpture, prints, photography, installation and also owns its own publishing company, Momentum. Artists represented include Tai-Shan Schierenberg, Glenys Barton, Glen Baxter, Peter Howson, Ken Currie and John Keane.
Submission policy Send photos, printouts or slides of work to Angela Flowers at the above address. Include CV, cover letter and sae for return of work.
No of exhibitions annually 12 per site.

Flying Colours Gallery
6 Burnsall Street, King's Road, London
SW3 3ST
T 020 73515558
F 020 73515548
E art@flyingcoloursgallery.com
W www.flyingcoloursgallery.com
Founded in Edinburgh in 1986 and moved to Chelsea in 1995. Still shows contemporary Scottish artists such as Shona Barr, Stephen Mangan, Jean B. Martin RSW, Anthony Scullion and Ethel Walker. Also John Cunningham RGI (1926–98).
Submission policy Scottish artists and sculptors may submit by email with jpegs or by post enclosing transparencies, photos or digital printouts.
Price range £500–£20,000
No of exhibitions annually 5

Fosterart
6 Willow Street, London
EC2A 4BH
T 020 77391743
E info@fosterart.net
W www.fosterart.net
Manages a collection of artist-owned work available for placement with individuals and institutions. All work selected by a panel of experts to ensure quality contemporary art.
Submission policy Ask for a copy of the agreement.
Price range £2,500–£20,000
No of exhibitions annually 10, focusing on artists in the collection.

Foyles Bookshop
113–119 Charing Cross Road, London
WC2H OEB
T 020 74375660
W www.foyles.co.uk
The bookshop has been in Charing Cross Road since 1906. The gallery space on the second floor

is available for hire. Recent exhibitions have included Lena Herzog and Carlos Reyes-Nanzo. Gallery also suitable for launch parties.

Frith Street Gallery
59–60 Frith Street, London
W1D 3JJ
T 020 74941550
F 020 72873733
E info@frithstreetgallery.com
W www.frithstreetgallery.com
Opened in 1989. Has developed a programme of exhibitions by international artists working in painting, photography, sculpture, film and video. Currently represents twenty artists from both Britain and abroad and also collaborates with other artists on specific projects. Artists represented include Chantal Akerman, Fiona Banner, Tacita Dean, Marlene Dumas, Craigie Horsfield, Callum Innes, Dayanita Singh, Annelies Strba and Daphne Wright.
No of exhibitions annually 6–7

Frivoli
7a Devonshire Road, London
W4 2EU
T 020 87423255
F 020 89947372
E frivoli@tiscali.co.uk
W www.DevonshireRoad.com
Contact Hazel Peiser
Founded by Hazel Peiser in 1991. Shows contemporary works in all media. Work by many artists displayed informally.
Submission policy Happy to view current work by professional artists in all permanent media.
Price range £150–£2,500
No of exhibitions annually Ongoing changing display; occasional exhibitions.

Gagosian Gallery
6–24 Britannia Street, London
WC1X 9JD
T 020 78419960
F 020 78419961
E info@gagosian.com
W www.gagosian.com
Has expanded from its space on Heddon Street in the West End into a 12,500 sq. ft space on Britannia Street, converted by architects Caruso St John in 2004. The gallery represents some of the world's most prestigious living artists and also has branches in New York, where it was founded, and Los Angeles.

Galerie Besson
15 Royal Arcade, 28 Old Bond Street, London
W1S 4SP
T 020 74911706
F 020 74953203
E enquiries@galeriebesson.co.uk
W www.galeriebesson.co.uk
Has won a worldwide reputation for exhibiting contemporary ceramics since opening in 1988. Runs mainly one-person shows and is the only London ceramic gallery showing international artists. Stock of classic artists includes Lucie Rie and Hans Coper.
Submission policy Although opportunities for new artists to exhibit at the gallery are rare, introductions and images from ceramic artists are welcomed.
No of exhibitions annually 10

Gallery in Cork Street Ltd and Gallery 27
28 Cork Street, London
W1S 3NG
T 020 72878408
F 020 72872018
E enquiries@galleryincorkstreet.com
W www.galleryincorkstreet.com
Contact Caroline Edwards (Manager)
One of London's leading suppliers of short-term gallery rental space. Operates two letting galleries in the centre of London's art trading area.
No of exhibitions annually 52; one per week.

Gallery Kaleidoscope
64–66 Willesden Lane, London
NW6 7SX
T 020 73285833
F 020 76242913
E info@gallerykaleidoscope.com
W www.gallerykaleidoscope.com
Established for over twenty-five years, with a policy of showing well-known names alongside promising newcomers. Artists represented include John Duffi, Elizabeth Tagart and Mark R. Hall.
Submission policy Welcomes enquiries from artists, sculptors and ceramicists but insists on seeing images first via email or post.
Price range £100–£10,000
No of exhibitions annually 6–8

Gallery N. von Bartha
Contemporary Art – London, 1st Floor,
136b Lancaster Road, London
W11 1QU
T 020 79850015

F 020 79850016
E info@vonbartha.com
W www.vonbartha.com
Contact N. or D. von Bartha
Founded in 2000, dealing in minimal, conceptual and new-media art. Represents Jill Baroff, Frank Gerritz, Herbert Hamak, Julia Mangold, Eline McGeorge and Winston Roeth.
Submission policy Does not guarantee to respond to every submission or return submitted material. Advises visiting the gallery or website prior to submitting.
Price range £80–£200,000
No of exhibitions annually 6

Gallery on the Green
33 Markham Street, London
SW3 3NR
T 020 73492917
E gallery@felixr.com
W www.galleryonthegreen.co.uk
Gallery grew from a company with 125 years' experience in the fine-art trade. Showcases contemporary decorative art for both the general public and the interior design market.
Submission policy Does not view original paintings for exhibitions, but is linked to an art-publishing company. Photographs or transparencies preferred. No originals.
Price range £250–£10,000
No of exhibitions annually 6

Gallery One
19 Station Road, London
SW13 0LF
T 020 84872144
E info@galleryone.ws
W www.galleryonelondon.com
Contact Teffany Tooke
Opened in 2001. Committed to sourcing and exhibiting the best of contemporary art. Includes emerging new talent and established names. Stocks and sources an extensive portfolio of original graphics, paintings and sculpture. Also provides a corporate-art consultancy service and a bespoke framing service.
Submission policy Welcomes submissions from all artists, by email or post in the first instance.
Price range £50–£10,000
No of exhibitions annually 4–8

Gillian Jason Modern & Contemporary Art
P.O. Box 35063, London
NW1 7XQ

E art@gillianjason.com
W www.gillianjason.com
In the 1980s and early 1990s the gallery in Camden Town was the focus for exhibitions by key artists of the modern British school and 1994 saw the creation of the Jason & Rhodes Gallery. In 1999 Gillian Jason began working as a private dealer, offering a personalized service to collectors and vendors, including sourcing and placing of works of art by British and European artists, consultancy and valuation. Artists represented include Trevor Bell, Michael Sandle, Paul Storey and John Plumb.

Gimpel Fils
30 Davies Street, London
W1K 4NB
T 0207 4932488
F 0207 6295732
E info@gimpelfils.com
W www.gimpelfils.com
Founded in 1946. Modern and contemporary art, project space for installations and video. Represents Alan Davie, Pamela Golden, Albert Irvin, Peter Kennard, Antoni Malinowski and the estate of Peter Lanyon.
No of exhibitions annually 8

Greengrassi
1a Kempsford Road, London
SE11 4NU
T 020 78409101
F 020 78409102
E info@greengrassi.com
W www.greengrassi.com
Has recently moved from central London to Kennington, south of the river. The stable of international artists includes Aleksandra Mir, Pae White, Lari Pittman and Margherita Manzelli.

Grosvenor Gallery (Fine Arts) Ltd
37 Albemarle Street, London
W1S 4JF
T 020 76290891
F 020 74914391
E art@grosvenorgallery.com
W www.grosvenorgallery.com
Specializes in twentieth-century European and British paintings and sculpture, and modern Indian painting. Limited to the representation of two contemporary artists, Mark Shields and Victor Newsome.
Submission policy Currently not looking to take on any more living artists.
No of exhibitions annually 3

Hales Gallery

7 Bethnal Green Road, London
E1 6LA
T 020 70331938
F 020 70331939
E info@halesgallery.com
W www.halesgallery.com
Founded 1991 in Deptford. Moved to the East End
in 2004. Represents Tomoko Takahashi, Hans Op
de Beeck, Spencer Tunick, Hew Locke, Adam
Dant, and Bob and Roberta Smith.
Submission policy Artists' submissions not
encouraged.
No of exhibitions annually 8

Hanina Fine Arts

180 Westbourne Grove, London
W11 2RH
T 020 72438877
F 020 72430132
E contact@haninafinearts.com
W www.haninafinearts.com
Contact Yuval Hanina
Specialists in twentieth-century European art,
particularly the post-war School of Paris.
Submission policy Contact from artists or their
representatives with relevance to European art
from 1900 to 1980 welcome. The gallery does not
deal in works on paper or in prints.
Price range £5,000–£250,000
No of exhibitions annually 4

Harlequin Gallery

68 Greenwich High Road, London
SE10 8LF
T 020 86927170
E jr@studio-pots.com
W www.studio-pots.com
Specializes in contemporary exhibitions of work
by leading British studio potters including Phil
Rogers, Alan Wallwork and Aki Moriuchi, together
with older work by Bernard Leach and associates.
Paintings and sculpture by artists such as Denis
Bowen are often shown in conjunction with the
above.
Submission policy Studio potters and artists may
apply, but telephone or email first.
Price range £25–£5,000
No of exhibitions annually 8

Haunch of Venison

6 Haunch of Venison Yard, off Brook Street,
London
W1K 5ES

T 020 74955050
F 020 74954050
E info@haunchofvenison.com
W www.haunchofvenison.com
Contact Stephanie Camu, Jade Awdry or Pernilla
Holmes
Founded in 2002. Artists include Thomas Joshua
Cooper, Bill Viola, Richard Long, Keith Tyson,
Mark Alexander and Jorge Pardo.
Submission policy Applications to Pernilla
Holmes, sending images and CV.
Price range £5,000–£1,000,000+
No of exhibitions annually 9

Hauser & Wirth

196A Piccadilly, London
W1J 9DY
T 020 72872300
F 020 72876600
E london@hauserwirth.com
W www.hauserwirth.com
Opened in 2000 just across the road from the
Royal Academy of Arts in a historic building
designed by Sir Edwin Lutyens in the 1920s.
Swiss gallerist–collectors Ursula Hauser and Iwan
Wirth, who represent important European and
American artists, also have branches of their
gallery in Zurich and a joint venture in New York.

Hazlitt Holland-Hibbert

38 Bury Street, St James's, London
SW1Y 6BB
T 020 78397600
F 020 78397255
E info@hh-h.com
W www.hh-h.com
Holds a selected stock of twentieth-century
art works with particular emphasis on modern
British painting, drawing and sculpture. Also
able to offer discreet advice on the purchase and
sale of modern paintings and sculpture and the
acquisition of new works either for stock or for sale
on a consignment basis.
Submission policy Does not represent living
artists.
No of exhibitions annually 1–2

Henry Boxer Gallery

98 Stuart Court, Richmond Hill, Richmond
TW10 6RJ
T 020 89481633
F 020 89481633
E henryboxer@aol.com
W www.henryboxergallery.com

Founded in 1980, specializing in modern British, visionary and outsider art. Artists represented include Joe Coleman, Donald Pass, Laurie Lipton, Dora Holzhandler, Scottie Wilson and Austin Spare. Henry Boxer is a director of *Raw Vision* magazine and curates exhibitions of Outsider art both in the UK and the USA.

Submission policy Submissions welcome, from self-taught, visionary and Outsider artists. Send sae and photographs or email images of work to be considered.

Price range £500–£10,000
No of exhibitions annually 4

Henry Peacock Gallery

38a Foley Street, London
W1P 7LB
T 020 73234033
E info@henrypeacock.com
W www.henrypeacock.com
Founded in 1999, specializing in contemporary art. Represents the Miller and McAfee Press, Gereon Krebber, Sadie Murdoch, Benedict Carpenter and Frenk Meeuwsen. The Henry Peacock Press is also located at the gallery.
No of exhibitions annually 8

Hicks Gallery

2–4 Leopold Road, Wimbledon
SW19 7BD
T 020 89447171
E galleryhicks@aol.com
W www.hicksgallery.co.uk
Contact Jeff or Ann Hicks
Founded in 1988. Handles the work of mainly contemporary artists with an emphasis on drawing skills. Exhibits both established and up-and-coming artists and currently particularly interested in artists from eastern Europe, especially Poland. Exhibited artists include Jeffrey Pratt, Andrea Byrne, Linda Meaney, Arkadiusz Wesolowski, John Gregson and Terry Whybrow.
Submission policy Submissions welcome either by email or, if possible, CD.
Price range £250–£15,000
No of exhibitions annually 6

Highgate Fine Art

26 Highgate High Street, Highgate Village, London
N6 5JG
T 020 83477010 / 83407564
F 020 83407564
E sales@oddyart.com
W www.oddyart.com
Contact Laurie MacLaren
Originally Phoenix Gallery Highgate; relaunched in 1997 as Highgate Fine Art. Twentieth-century artists represented include Frederick Gore CBE RA, Professor Sir Lawrence Gowing CBE RA, Anthony Green RA, Michael Quirke, Andrew Ingamells and Bruno Guaitamacchi.
Submission policy All submissions to site or exhibition programme are reviewed by committee (by appointment). The majority are living artists.
Price range £150–£20,000
No of exhibitions annually 15; new shows open every three weeks.

Honor Oak Gallery Ltd

52 Honor Oak Park, Forest Hill, London
SE23 1DY
T 020 82916094
Founded in 1986, the gallery specializes in original works of art on paper dating from the early twentieth century to the present day. Artists shown include Norman Ackroyd, June Berry, Elizabeth Blackadder, Margarete Berger-Hamerschlag, Sanchia Lewis and Karolina Larusdottir. A comprehensive framing and conservation service is also offered.
Submission policy Submissions welcome, provided they are within the area of specialization outlined above.
Price range From £25
No of exhibitions annually 1, plus 6 'features'.

Hotel

53a Old Bethnal Green Road, London
E2 6QA
T 020 77293122
E info@generalhotel.org
W www.generalhotel.org
Opened in 2003 with Vacancies, a specially commissioned neon sculpture by Peter Saville. Has since exhibited works by Carol Bove, Daria Martin, Alan Michael, Richard Kern, Hayley Tompkins, Luke Dowd and Scott Myles. Up-and-coming artists include Dustin Ericksen, Steve Claydon, David Noonan, Alexis Teplin and assume vivid astro focus. Artists not located in London are invited to stay at Hotel during the production period of their project.
Price range £20–£20,000
No of exhibitions annually 6

Hothouse Gallery

Hothouse, 274 Richmond Road, London Fields
E8 3QW

T 020 72493394
F 020 72498499
E contact@freeform.org.uk
W www.freeform.org.uk
Contact Joanne Milmoe
An artist-led gallery and workspace for visual and new media artists, urban designers and architects working in the public realm. Opened in 2003, a flexible white space 184m² (1,982 sq. ft) with mobile screens. Has all-round CAT 5 cabling for installations, digital and ICT media presentations, and external digital art space. Past exhibitors include RIBA London, Ash Sakula Architects and Maggie Ellenby. Hosts talks, seminars and events.
Submission policy Welcomes exhibition proposals from established and emerging visual artists, new-media artists, urban designers and architects working in the public realm.
No of exhibitions annually 3, in visual arts, photography, and architecture and urban design.

Houldsworth Gallery

33–34 Cork Street, London
W1S 3NQ
T 020 74342333
F 020 74343636
E gallery@houldsworth.co.uk
W www.houldsworth.co.uk
Contact Ben Cranfield
Opened in 1999, with a commitment to showing young, challenging and thought-provoking art in a central London location. Gallery artists were included in over fifty museum shows worldwide in 2003–4 alone. Seeks to instigate projects for its artists as well as working with museum curators and institutions all over the world.
Submission policy Submit email presentation or, ideally, a website link. Other documentation submitted cannot be returned or retained. Only successful applicants are contacted.
Price range £300–£65,000
No of exhibitions annually 10

House Gallery

70 Camberwell Church Street, London
SE5 8QZ
T 020 73584475
E info@housegallery.org
W www.housegallery.org
Contact Julia Alvarez
Neighbouring Camberwell College of Arts and the South London Gallery provide a varied and professional audience. The gallery has large front windows and is an airy space with high ceilings. Exhibitions tend to be experimental in nature, from installation to performance and video work. Aims to create an independent platform for artists to respond to contemporary stimuli in a professional environment.
Submission policy Exhibition proposals are accepted. Include a CV, short artist's statement, images and a written proposal for the exhibition. These can be sent or emailed. Group shows are also accepted.
No of exhibitions annually 20

IBID

Unit 4, 210 Cambridge Heath Road, London
E2 9NQ
T 020 89834355
F 020 89834355
E info@ibidprojects.com
W www.ibidprojects.com
Contact Vita Zaman Cookson
Founded in 2003, with a programme focused on a series of solo shows by emerging British and Baltic artists as well as curated shows, off-site mobile projects and publications. Artists include Carey Young, Christopher Orr, Janis Avotins, Milena Dragicevic, Arturas Raila, Anj Smith and Nedko Solakov. The gallery also has a space in Vilnius in Lithuania.
Submission policy Submissions not welcomed.
Price range £1,000–£100,000
No of exhibitions annually 10

Ieda Basualdo

8–9 Grosvenor Place, Belgravia, London
SW1X 7SH
T 020 72359522
F 020 72359577
E ieda@bottaccio.co.uk
W www.bottaccio.co.uk
Particularly suitable for large exhibitions, the Grand Gallery (300m²) has hosted exhibitions for, among others, Arturo Martini, Igor Mitoraj, Giorgio Morandi, Gio Pomodoro, Marino Marini and Damien Hirst. Exhibitions last a minimum of two weeks and a maximum of four weeks.
Price range £80–£50,000
No of exhibitions annually 12

Ingo Fincke Gallery and Framers

24 Battersea Rise, London
SW11 1EE
T 020 72287966

F 020 76527966
E kira@ingofincke.com
W www.ingofincke.com
Contact Kira Fincke
Founded in 1958, the gallery specializes in
contemporary paintings on canvas. Exhibits both
new and established artists and also offers a
framing service.

InsideSpace
34 Mortimer Street, London
W1W 7JS
T 020 72996680
F 020 72996690
E enquiries@insidespace.com
W www.insidespace.com
Founded in 2000, operating from a gallery in the
West End and from Selfridges on Oxford Street.
Specializes in affordable, striking, often humorous
art for the design-conscious buyer. Particular
focus on photography but does exhibit paintings,
drawings, original prints and multiples. Also
operates a corporate art consultancy service and
is active in the office, healthcare, hotel and leisure
markets.
Submission policy Email jpegs of work. The gallery
does not exhibit installations or video work.
Price range £50–£1,500
No of exhibitions annually 6

jaggedart
Studio 014 Westbourne Studios, 242 Acklam
Road, London
W10 5JJ
T 020 75753330
F 020 75753331
E info@jaggedart.com
W www.jaggedart.com
Contact Andrea Harari or Janeen Haythornthwaite
A relaxed, informal browsing space with a wide
selection of works including paintings, prints,
photographs and sculpture. Offers services
including advice, sourcing art works, and
assistance with framing and hanging. Also
organizes visits to galleries, exhibitions and
artists' studios.
Submission policy Phone the gallery.
Price range £50–£10,000

James Hyman Fine Art Ltd
6 Mason's Yard, Duke Street, St James's, London
SW1Y 6BU
T 020 78393906
F 020 78393907

E mail@jameshymanfineart.com
W www.jameshymanfineart.com

Jeffrey Charles Gallery
34 Settles Street, London
E1 1JP
T 07940 538607
E gallery@jeffreycharlesgallery.com
W www.jeffreycharlesgallery.com

Jerwood Space
171 Union Street, London
SE1 0LN
T 020 76540171
F 020 76540172
E space@jerwoodspace.co.uk
W www.jerwoodspace.co.uk
Contact Sarah Williams
A major initiative of the Jerwood Foundation.
As well as providing rehearsal facilities for
dance and theatre companies, the refurbished
Victorian building houses a contemporary-art
gallery. Free to visitors and offers a year-round
programme of work by young artists and
photographers, including awards and prizes
supported by the Jerwood Charity. Emerging
artists are shown in the café space and
courtyard.
Submission policy Visit website for information on
applying for Jerwood prizes.
No of exhibitions annually 8

Jill George Gallery
38 Lexington Street, London
W1F 0LL
T 020 74397319
F 020 72870478
E jill@jillgeorgegallery.co.uk
W www.jillgeorgegallery.co.uk
Established in 1974. Deals in paintings,
drawings, small sculpture, monoprints and
edition prints by contemporary British artists,
from established artists to recent graduates.
Participates in British and international art fairs.
Member of SLAD. Organizes commissions
and undertakes all ancilliary services. Artists
exhibited include Martyn Brewster, David
Leverett, Alison Lambert, David Mach, Chris Orr
and Tomas Watson.
Submission policy Media as above. Prefers to see
photographs initially.
Price range £200–£40,000
No of exhibitions annually 10

John Martin Gallery
38 Albemarle Street, London
W1S 4JG
T 020 74991314
F 020 74932842
E info@jmlondon.com
W www.jmlondon.com
Contact Tara Whelan
Two galleries in London showing the work of
contemporary British and Irish artists. Opened in
the West End in 1992 and exhibits at major British
and American art fairs.
Submission policy Exhibits both representational
and abstract painting and sculpture and artists
are always welcome to submit a selection
of photographs. Send sae, brief statement
and biography (no books or valuable items
should be sent). No responsibility is taken for
lost items.
Price range £200–£50,000
No of exhibitions annually 20

Kate MacGarry
95–97 Redchurch Street, London
E2 7DJ
T 020 76133909
F 202 76135405
E mail@katemacgarry.com
W www.katemacgarry.com
Opened in 2002 and hosts mainly solo shows with
one or two group shows. Artists exhibited include
Tasha Amini, Matt Bryans, Josh Blackwell, Stuart
Cumberland, Luke Gottelier, Dr Lakra, Goshka
Macuga, Peter McDonald, Stefan Saffer and
Francis Upritchard.
No of exhibitions annually 6

Keith Talent Gallery
2–4 Tudor Road, London
E9 7SN
T 020 89862181
F 020 85332060
E keithtalent@onetel.com
Established in 2001 in an industrial space
in London Fields by two graduates of the
Royal Academy Schools. Shows emerging
artists, collaborating and forming links with
a number of artist-run project spaces and
established commercial galleries both in
Britain and abroad.

Kenny Schachter ROVE
17 Britannia Street, London
WC1X 9JD

T 07979 408914
F 0207 2592335
E schachter@mindspring.com
W www.rovetv.net
Following the launch of Kenny Schachter
conTEMPorary space in New York in 2001,
Kenny Schachter ROVE opened in London in
2004. Showcases young and marginalized
artists alongside the more established. Artists
represented include Vito Acconci, Richard
Artschwager, Dennis Oppenheim, William Pope.L
and Kenny Scharf.
Submission policy Artist submissions are not
accepted.
No of exhibitions annually 6–8

Kings Road Galleries
436 Kings Road, Chelsea, London
SW10 0LJ
T 020 73511367
F 020 73517007
E admin@kingsroadgallery.com
W www.kingsroadartgallery.com
Represents contemporary painters and sculptors
(predominantly figurative but some strong
abstract artists such as Richard Allen), who
tend to be established on the international art-fair
circuit and museum front. Also has a corporate-
art consultancy division. Gallery owner Tanya
Baxter's ties to Hong Kong ensure a strong
reciprocal exhibition programme with galleries
in Hong Kong, Singapore and Shanghai.
Baxter opened the Ryder Street Gallery in
St James's in 2004, showcasing the same artists
and acting as a host to touring international
exhibitions.
Submission policy Represents artists whose
'fervour for painting and sculpting is markedly
different from the current trends, which favour
shock art and conceptual works'.
Price range £350–£65,000
No of exhibitions annually 10

Lawrence O'Hana Gallery
35–42 Charlotte Road, London
EC2A 3PD
T 020 77390245
E info@ohanagallery.com
W www.ohanagallery.com

Lena Boyle Fine Art
1 Earls Court Gardens, London
SW5 0TD
T 020 72592700

F 020 73707460
E lena.boyle@btinternet.com
W www.lenaboyle.com
Founded in 1986. A small gallery run from a private house and open by appointment only. The works shown are a selection of modern British and contemporary artists, ranging from established names to young unknown talent. Contemporary artists stocked include Sarah Coghill, Mary Fedden, Gregor Harvie, Padraig MacMiadhachain, Katty McMurray, Tessa Newcomb, Jonathan Clarke and Jane Muir. Attends several of the major art fairs in London.
Submission policy Does not have the scope to take on many new artists each year. Tends to specialize in contemporary figurative works with an abstract element.
Price range £200–£15,000
No of exhibitions annually 2–3

Lennox Gallery
77 Moore Park Road, London
SW6 2HH
T 01488 681379
F 01488 681379
E sally@poltimore.fsbusiness.co.uk
W www.lennoxgallery.co.uk
Founded in 1998, specializing in Scottish contemporary art. Artists include Pat Semple RSW, Leonie Gibbs, Elizabeth Cameron, Jim Neville, Allan MacDonald and Kate Slaven. Painting courses available and lectures held on past and present-day artists. Space also available for artists to put on their own exhibitions.
Submission policy Preferably living artists working in Scotland, using a strong sense of colour.
Price range £300–£5,000
No of exhibitions annually 4

lightgallery
5a Porchester Place, London
W2 2BS
T 020 77067033
E info@lightgallery.net
W www.lightgallery.net
New gallery for hire to artists and photographers. Specializes in contemporary art and offers exhibition organizing service. Particular focus on curation and representation of Latin American contemporary art.
No of exhibitions annually 30

Limited Edition Graphics
2 Winchester Road, London
N6 5HW
T 020 83481354
F 020 83481357
Contact Allan Wolman
Specializes in nineteenth- and twentieth-century and contemporary works.

Lisson Gallery
52–54 Bell Street, London
NW1 5DA
T 020 77242739
F 020 77247124
E contact@lisson.co.uk
W www.lisson.co.uk
Opened in 1967 and later moved into current premises (designed by Tony Fretton) near Baker Street, Marylebone, in London. Now one of the world's leading galleries for contemporary art. A new gallery at 29 Bell Street opened in 2002.

Llewellyn Alexander (Fine Paintings) Ltd
124–126 The Cut, opposite The Old Vic Theatre, Waterloo, London
SE1 8LN
T 020 76201322 / 76201324
F 020 7928 9469
E gallery@llewellynalexander.com
W www.llewellynalexander.com
Contact Diana Holdsworth
Founded in 1987, specializing in figurative paintings, oils, watercolours and pastels by British artists. Other subjects include the architecture and landscapes of Italy, France and London, still lifes and animals. Among the leading galleries in Europe for contemporary miniatures.
Submission policy Interested in figurative paintings in oils and watercolours. Submissions from living British artists welcome. Send photographs or CD with images (plus sae for return of items within the UK). Replies by post to UK only. Do not email images.
Price range £150–£6,000
No of exhibitions annually 9

London Picture Centre
723 Fulham Road, London
SW6 5HA
T 020 77314883
F 020 77367283
E info@thelondonpicturecentre.co.uk
W www.thelondonpicturecentre.co.uk
Contact Albert Williams

Established for over thirty years, with six sites.
Branches 709 Fulham Road, SW6; 18 Crawford
Street, W1 **T** 020 74872895; 75 Leather Lane,
EC1 **T** 020 74044110; 152 and 287 Hackney
Road, E2 **T** 020 74044110.

Long & Ryle
4 John Islip Street, London
SW1P 4PX
T 020 78341434
E longandryle@btconnect.com
W www.longandryle.com
Contact Tom Juneau
Established over fifteen years ago to promote the
work of emerging talents and mid-career artists
in the same space. Has a bias towards bold and
painterly work. Artists include Brian Sayers, John
Monks, Simon Casson, Simon Keenleyside, Balint
Bolygo and Ricardo Cinalli.
Submission policy Mostly painting, with an
emphasis on figuration. Looking for a certain
'edge' in an artist.
Price range £500–£30,000
No of exhibitions annually 10

Lounge Gallery and Studios
28 Shacklewell Lane, London
E8 2EZ
T 020 82110958
E monikabobinska@onetel.com
W www.lounge-gallery.com
Founded as a home gallery in 2000 and moved
into permanent commercial premises in 2004.
Specializes in conceptually based contemporary
art, with an emphasis on painting and
photography. Does not currently represent any
artists but does work regularly with a number
of individual artists.
Submission policy Welcomes submissions
from artists who are familiar with the gallery's
work and feel that their work suits its aims and
ethos.
Price range £200–£2,000
No of exhibitions annually 6

Lucy B. Campbell Fine Art
123 Kensington Church Street, London
W8 7LP
T 020 77272205
F 020 72294252
E lucy@lucybcampbell.com
W www.lucybcampbell.com
Contact Lucy B. Campbell
Founded in 1984. Represents British, European

and American artists and sculptors. Work includes
both figurative and abstract, contemporary, still
life, landscape, botanical and naive genres. Artists
exhibited include Anna Pugh, Sophie Coryndon,
Bernard McGuigan, Mia Tarney, Christine Pichette
and Patricia O'Brien.
Submission policy Still life, landscape,
contemporary.
Price range £1,000–£20,000

Lupe
7 Ezra Street, London
E2 7RH
T 020 76135576
F 020 76132287
E info@lupegallery.com
W www.lupegallery.com
Contact Nicky Sims
Launched in 2002. Represents the work of
some fifty of the UK's leading contemporary
photographers. Artists include David King,
Stuart Redler, Tim Flach, Perou, Morgan Silk and
George Kavanagh. Other services include fine-art
printing and scanning.
Submission policy Photography with an emphasis
on craft and innovation. Initial contact by email
preferred.
Price range £150–£2,000
No of exhibitions annually 3

M-Art
88 Bevington Road, London
W10 5TW
T 020 89690800
F 020 89690801
E m-artgallery@btconnect.com
W www.m-art.co.uk
Contact Martin Brock
Opened in 2004, specializing in contemporary
paintings, photography and sculpture by young,
up-and-coming artists.
Submission policy Welcomes submissions from
artists.
Price range £50–£3,000
No of exhibitions annually 9

Maas Gallery
15a Clifford Street, London
W1S 4JZ
T 020 77342302
F 020 72874836
E mail@maasgallery.com
W www.maasgallery.com
Founded in 1960 by the late Jeremy Maas.

Originally a 'revivalist' gallery, specializing in the then unfashionable field of Pre-Raphaelite paintings. Rupert Maas, his son, now owns and runs the gallery. Deals in major Victorian paintings and with myriad lesser-known artists of the period. Also deals in reproductive engravings and has a small stable of living artists.
Price range From £20
No of exhibitions annually 2

Manya Igel Fine Arts

21–22 Peters Court, Porchester Road, London
W2 5DR
T 020 72291669 / 72298249
F 020 72296770
E paintings@manyaigelfinearts.com
W www.manyaigelfinearts.com
Gallery meets clients by appointment only. Specializes in traditional, modern British oils by Royal Academicians, members of the New English Art Club and other well-known artists. Exhibited artists include Diana Armfield, Fred Cuming, Bernard Dunstan, Frederick Gore, Ken Howard, Geoffrey Humphries, Peter Kuhfeld and Susan Ryder.
Submission policy Generally has long-established relationships with artists and purchases their work outright.
Price range £350–£25,000
No of exhibitions annually 3–5 fine-art fairs, including solo shows in the Channel Islands.

Mark Jason Fine Art

First Floor, 71 New Bond Street, London
W1S 1DE
T 020 76294080
F 020 76295111
E info@jasonfinearts.com
W www.jasonfinearts.com
Contact Mark Jason or Kate Jason
Opened in 2001 and showcases young emerging talent from fresh new graduates to mid-career artists. Shows mainly paintings and photography. Artists are selected from most mainstream art schools including the Royal Academy, The Slade School of Art, Goldsmiths, Chelsea School of Art and others around the UK.
Submission policy For artist enquiries, send information in disc format to gallery address or jpeg images via email.
Price range £300–£10,000
No of exhibitions annually 8

Marlborough Fine Art

6 Albemarle Street, London
W1S 4BY
T 020 76295161
F 020 76296338
E info@marlboroughfineart.com
W www.marlboroughfineart.com
Founded in 1946. One of the world's leading contemporary art dealers. In addition to being a foremost dealer and publisher of fine-art prints, the gallery deals in paintings and sculpture by prominent international artists and has branches in New York, Madrid, Monte Carlo and Santiago.
No of exhibitions annually 6–8

Matt's Gallery

42–44 Copperfield Road, London
E3 4RR
T 020 89831771
F 020 89831435
E info@mattsgallery.org
W www.mattsgallery.org
Contact Rosalind Horne
Founded in 1979. Specializes in solo exhibitions of young and established artists, especially in installation, performance, video, sculpture and painting, and has a publishing programme. Arts Council-funded. Artists represented include Imogen Stidworthy, Willie Doherty, Mike Nelson, Lucy Gunning, Nathaniel Mellors and Hayley Newman.
Submission policy Seeks to support artists in the generation of new work, providing them with the time and space to experiment and engage audiences in a critical debate. Welcomes submissions from those familiar with the ethos of the gallery.
Price range £1,500–£100,000
No of exhibitions annually 5

Maureen Paley Interim Art

21 Herald Street, London
E2 6JT
T 020 77294112
F 020 77294113
E info@maureenpaley.com
Contact Dan Gunn or Maximilian Mugler
Established in 1984, showing art from the USA and continental Europe as well as launching new talent from Great Britain. Exhibited artists include Hannah Collins, Helen Chadwick, Susan Hiller, Angela Bulloch, Jenny Holzer and Richard Deacon.
No of exhibitions annually 8–10

Mayor Gallery

22a Cork Street, London
W1S 3NA
T 020 77343558
F 020 74941377
E mail@mayorgallery.com
W www.artnet.com/mayor.html
Founded by Fred Mayor in 1925; the first gallery to
open in Cork Street. Has exhibited many artists
for the first time in England including Bacon,
Ernst and Miró. James Mayor, Fred's son, took
over the gallery in 1973 and has since shown the
work of many leading American artists including
Lichtenstein, Oldenburg and Warhol. Continues to
show the works of leading American Pop artists
and remains London's foremost gallery for Dada
and Surrealism.
Submission policy Deals in most fields of the
visual arts but excludes prints. More inclined
towards established artists than new submissions.
No of exhibitions annually 5

Medici Gallery

5 Cork Street, London
W1S 3LQ
T 020 74952565
F 020 74952997
E info@medicigallery.co.uk
W www.medicigallery.co.uk
Contact Jenny Kerr
Established in Mayfair for the past ninety years and
recently moved to a new address at 5 Cork Street.
Known for contemporary figurative art and
exhibiting the work of leading British craftmakers.
Submission policy Images should be sent via post
with sae; include medium, size, artist's CV, etc.
Price range £1,000–£60,000
No of exhibitions annually 8

Michael Hoppen Gallery

3 Jubilee Place, London
SW3 3TD
T 020 73523649
F 020 73523669
E gallery@michaelhoppengallery.com
W www.michaelhoppengallery.com
Contact Genny Janvrin or Ingeborg Steckmest
(contemporary)
Founded in 1992. Holds various exhibitions across
three floors. Specializing in photographic art,
it has one of the widest selections of nineteenth-,
twentieth- and twenty-first-century works in
Europe. The gallery's remit is to present the
broadest spectrum of photography that is judged
not only on its market value, but also on the
quality and integrity of the artist's particular
vision. Champions new artists as well as
maintaining stock of the recognized masters.
Artists represented include Jacques-Henri
Lartigue, Desiree Dolron, Daido Moriyama,
Sarah Moon, Peter Beard and Bill Brandt.
Submission policy Works must be original and
photography-based, and the artist must have been
previously exhibited.
Price range £100–£100,000
No of exhibitions annually 6–7

Millinery Works Gallery

85–87 Southgate Road, London
N1 3JS
T 020 73592019
F 020 73595792
E jeff@millineryworks.co.uk
W www.millineryworks.co.uk
Contact Jeff Jackson
Founded in 1996 to exhibit, promote and sell
contemporary and modern British fine and applied
arts. Exhibited artists include Edward Wolfe RA,
John Bratby RA, Gordon House, Eric Rimmington,
Cecily Sash and Frances Newman. A leading
specialist in the British Arts & Crafts Movement.
Price range £150–£45,000
No of exhibitions annually 8

Modern Art

10 Vyner Street, London
E2 9DG
T 020 89807742
F 020 89807743
E info@modernartinc.com
W www.modernartinc.com
Formerly known as Modern Art Inc., the gallery
moved from Shoreditch to Bethnal Green in 2004.
Represents international and British contemporary
artists such as Juergen Teller, Nigel Cooke, Ricky
Swallow and Tim Noble & Sue Webster.

MOT

Unit 54, Regents Studios, 8 Andrews Road,
London
E8 4QN
T 020 79239561
F 020 79239561
E motlondon@yahoo.co.uk
Founded in 2002. Functions as both independent
space and curatorial project, exploring the
different roles within art production and
redefining their terms. Exhibitions have included

the work of curators and critics, and have showcased new talent and more established artists, including Kelley, Kippenberger, Graham, McCarthy, Gillick, Creed, Lucas, Wallinger, Jeremy Deller and Matthew Higgs.
Submission policy Will consider submissions from artists or curators. Material should be posted to the gallery on CD or DVD. Include full CV, supporting statement and sae for return.
Price range £500–£25,000
No of exhibitions annually 8

Multiple Store

Central St Martins College of Art & Design, 107–109 Charing Cross Road, London
WC2H 0DU
T 020 75147258
F 020 75148091
E info@themultiplestore.org
W www.themultiplestore.org
Founded in 1998. Commissions limited-edition multiples (mostly three-dimensional) by contemporary British artists, both emerging and established. Does not have a permanent exhibiting space but work can be shown to individual collectors at offices of Central St Martins.

Museum 52

52 Redchurch Street, London
E2 6HX
T 020 73665571
E info@museum52.com
W www.museum52.com
Founded in 2003, showing emerging international talent as well as working with established artists on one-off projects. Artists include Tom Gallant, Chris Landoni, John Issacs, Nick Waplington, Miguel Caldron and Benedetto Pietromarchi.
Submission policy All media accepted. Send jpegs or transparencies but not slides. Enclose a brief biography, CV and description of work.
Price range £500–£15,000
No of exhibitions annually 11

MWprojects

43b Mitchell Street, London
EC1V 3QD
T 020 72513194
E info@mwprojects.net
W www.mwprojects.net
Founded in 2002. Exhibits a programme of international artists and participates in international art fairs.
No of exhibitions annually 10

Nancy Victor

Basement, 36 Charlotte Street, London
W1T 2NA
T 020 78130373
E info@nancyvictor.com
W www.nancyvictor.com
Non-commercial underground space showing new and up-and-coming artists only. No services offered to artists.
Submission policy Artists sending applications should be proactive and display a quality of work and commitment.
Price range £20–£10,000
No of exhibitions annually 8

New Grafton Gallery

49 Church Road, Barnes, London
SW13 9HH
T 020 87488850
F 020 87489818
E art@newgrafton.com
W www.newgrafton.com
Founded in 1968, showing established and new British artists. Buys and sells pictures on behalf of clients and corporations. Exhibited artists include Mary Fedden, Ken Howard, Fred Cuming, Peter Brook, Ann Shrager and Richard Pikesley.
Submission policy Send digital images with CV and pricing via email in the first instance.
Price range £200–£10,000
No of exhibitions annually 14

Northcote Gallery Chelsea

253 King's Road, London
SW11 6QP
T 020 73510830
E info@northcotegallery.com
W www.northcotegallery.com
Contact Shaun Dolan
Founded in 1992 on Northcote Road in Battersea. Expanded into large additional site in Chelsea in 2002. Exhibits international contemporary and modern British paintings and sculpture. Artists include Daisy Cook, Ffiona Lewis, Robert McKellar, Carol Peace, Petrina Stroud and Richard Whadcock.
Submission policy Selection by committee. Artists are invited to submit portfolios to the committee, which meets every six weeks.
No of exhibitions annually 20, across the two sites.

October Gallery

24 Old Gloucester Street, London
WC1N 3AL
T 020 72426367

F 020 74051851
E gallery@octobergallery.co.uk
W www.octobergallery.co.uk
Contact Elisabeth Lalouschek
Founded in 1979. A charitable trust dedicated to
the advancement and appreciation of art from all
cultures. To this end, the gallery is actively engaged
in education and the promotion of intercultural
exchange. Exhibits and promotes artists of the
'transvangarde' – the trans-cultural avant-garde.
Artists represented include Aubrey Williams,
William Burroughs, Brion Gysin, Kenji Yoshida,
El Anatsui and Rachid Koraichi.
Submission policy Submissions from artists from
the cross-cultural exchange welcome.
Price range £250–£10,000
No of exhibitions annually 8

Offer Waterman & Co.

11 Langton Street, London
SW10 0JL
T 020 73510068
F 020 73512269
E info@waterman.co.uk
W www.waterman.co.uk
Aims to provide the best of twentieth-century
British painting, drawing and sculpture, with an
emphasis on the Camden Town Group, Euston
Road School, 7 and 5 Society, Unit One, School
of London, Neo-Romantics and St Ives Group.
Can source specific European and contemporary
work where required. Always looking to acquire
important pieces and will buy or consign directly
from private collectors. Additional services
include insurance and probate valuations,
research, conservation, framing and display
advice. Artists include Peter Dukes, Robert
Granger-Taylor, Nicolas Hegedus, Celia Kelley,
Diarmuid Logan, Johanna Nicholson, Rachel
Scrivener and Tony Yeoman.
Price range £2,000–£250,000

Old Truman Brewery

91 Brick Lane, London
E1 6QL
T 020 77706100
F 020 77706005
E events@trumanbrewery.com
W www.trumanbrewery.com
Contact Annabel Bowman, Marie Maduro, Rudi
Khalastchi or Sarah Jones
Since 1995 this eleven-acre site has combined both
commercial and event spaces, and is home to
many creative businesses and retail outlets in
London. Art projects have included Body Worlds,
Free Range, Julian Opie, Hussein Chalayan,
Inspired Art, Carnesky's Ghost Train, Hype
Gallery and Hidden Art.
Submission policy Galleries are available to hire by
day or by week. Each client creates their own show,
handling all aspects of their event. Further details
provided on application.
No of exhibitions annually 80

Oliver Contemporary

17 Bellevue Road, Wandsworth Common, London
SW17 7EG
T 020 87678822
F 020 87678822
E mail@oliverart.co.uk
W www.oliverart.co.uk
Founded in 2001. Brings together new and
established contemporary artists working within
the modern British tradition.
Submission policy Not looking for any new artists.
Price range £250–£5,000
No of exhibitions annually 6

One in the Other

4 Dingley Place, London
EC1V 8BP
T 020 72537882
F 020 72537882
E oneintheother@blueyonder.co.uk
W www.oneintheother.com
Works with an international stable of artists.
Occasionally allows other established artists the
freedom to experiment with different or new
works, and gives a platform to up-and-coming
artists defining emerging trends among
themselves and within an art framework.
Submission policy Does not invite submissions
but encourages artists to stage their own shows
and inform the gallery of them.
Price range £1,000–£20,000
No of exhibitions annually 6

Osborne Samuel

23a Bruton Street, London
W1J 6QG
T 020 74937939
F 020 74937798
E info@osbornesamuel.com
W www.osbornesamuel.com
Formed in 2004 as a new partnership
between Gordon Samuel (Scolar Fine Art)
and Peter Osborne (Berkeley Square Gallery).
Exhibition schedule includes established painters,

printmakers and sculptors. Known worldwide as a dealer in modern and contemporary sculpture, in particular the work of Moore and Chadwick. Substantial inventory of masterprints by major artists of the last century, specializing in graphics by Picasso and Miró, and 1930s linocuts by artists of the Grosvenor School of Modern Art. Contemporary artists represented include Sophie Ryder, Sean Henry and Graciela Sacco.
Submission policy Represents a number of contemporary artists and is therefore fully committed. Will look at submissions, but these will only be returned if an sae is included. Does not invite email submissions.
No of exhibitions annually 10–12

Panter & Hall

9 Shepherd Market, Mayfair, London
W1J 7PF
T 020 73999999
F 020 74994449
E enquiries@panterandhall.co.uk
W www.panterandhall.co.uk
Specialists in contemporary Scottish and modern British paintings.
Submission policy Only interested in looking at painters with established markets.
Price range £500–£20,000
No of exhibitions annually 12

Parasol Unit Foundation for Contemporary Art

14 Wharf Road, London
N1 7RW
T 020 74907373
F 020 74907775
E info@parasol-unit.com
W www.parasol-unit.com
Opened in 2004. A not-for-profit cultural space, including a gallery, reading space and artist-in-residence space.
Submission policy Gallery does not welcome submissions from artists but runs an education and artist-in-residence programme.
No of exhibitions annually 4–5

Paul Mason Gallery

149 Sloane Street, London
SW1X 9BZ
T 020 77303683
F 020 77307359
E Paulmasonart@aol.com
Founded in 1964. Specializes in eighteenth-century through to contemporary marine, sporting and decorative paintings and prints, ship models,

nautical artifacts, portfolio stands and picture easels.
Submission policy Top-quality marine oil paintings.
Price range From £2,000
No of exhibitions annually 3

Percy Miller

5 Vigo Street, London
W1S 3HB
T 020 77342100
E info@percymillergallery.com
W www.percymillergallery.com
First opened in 1999 at 39 Snowsfields Road and recently relocated to 5 Vigo Street, W1. Represents nine artists and works with a number of others on project-based exhibitions and events within the gallery space and in other venues. It is the gallery's intention to promote exchange with artists and other galleries alike in order to initiate exciting collaborative projects.

Photofusion

17a Electric Lane, London
SW9 8LA
T 020 77385774
F 020 77385509
E gallery@photofusion.org
W www.photofusion.org
Contact Catherine Williams
Started life in the early 1980s as a photographers' collective and now among London's most comprehensive photography and media centres. Situated in Brixton since 1991. Committed to promoting diversity within the photographic arts, encompassing both chemical and digital media. Presents a broad range of exhibitions, from showcasing emerging UK-based photographers to surveying more internationally recognized ones. Also runs artists' talks, professional-development workshops, and photography and digital training courses, as well as housing a picture library, studios, darkrooms, digital suites and a membership scheme.
Submission policy Accepts only photographic or digital-based work. Programming by committee. Send a comprehensive written description, CV and examples (not original prints).
Price range From £300
No of exhibitions annually 8

Piano Nobile Fine Paintings Ltd

129 Portland Road, London
W11 4LW

T 020 72291099
F 020 72291099
E art@piano-nobile.com
W www.piano-nobile.com
Contact Suzy Meek
Founded in 1985, specializing in fine-quality
twentieth-century international, modern British
and post-war paintings, drawings, watercolours
and sculpture for private, corporate and
museum collections. Period work exhibited
alongside shows by leading contemporary
painters and sculptors including Adam
Birtwistle, Dora Holzhandler, Barbara
van Hove, Leslie Marr, Kasey Sealy and
Nicolaus Widerberg.
Submission policy Painting and sculpture in all
media with a preference for figurative work.
Price range £150,000–£250,000
No of exhibitions annually 4–6

Pieroni Studios

1 Dickson House, 3 Grove Road, Richmond
TW10 6SP
T 020 89488066
E lark@pieronistudio.co.uk
Contact Lark Harrison
Represents several painters and sculptors.
Submission policy Does not want submissions
from other artists at present.
Price range £1,000–£4,000 for paintings;
£3,500–£7,500 for sculpture.
No of exhibitions annually 2 in-house; 6 off-site
(mainly London).

Plus One Plus Two Galleries

161–163 Seymour Place, London
W1H 4PJ
T 020 77247304
F 020 77245032
E info@plusonegallery.com
W www.plusonegallery.com
Contact Maggie Bollaert or Colin Pettit
Founded in 2001, specializing in an international
contemporary realist and photorealist art
programme. Deals exclusively in paintings and
sculptures. Artists represented include Andrew
Holmes, Cesar Santander, Gus Heinze, Carl
Laubin, Guillermo Munoz Vera and Malcolm
Poynter.
Submission policy Living artists represented but
within all aspects of the genre of contemporary
realism.
Price range £300–£100,000
No of exhibitions annually 9–10

Pond Gallery

26 The Pavement, Clapham Old Town, London
SW4 0JA
T 020 76224051
F 020 76224051
E info@pondgalleries.co.uk
W www.pondgalleries.co.uk
Contact Dee-Michael Hutchings
Founded in 2002, dealing in contemporary
paintings, ceramics and sculpture. Represented
artists include Rochelle Andrews, Samantha
Barnes, Henrie Haldane, Ilia Petrovic, Jess
Pearson and Jason Lilley.
Submission policy Submissions should be made
by sending CD of images or photographs by post
with sae.
Price range £500–£5,000
No of exhibitions annually 6–8, plus a summer
garden party in the sculpture garden.

Program

2 New Burlington Place, London
W1S 2HP
T 020 74391123
F 020 74393123
E info@pro-gram.net
W www.pro-gram.net
Contact Sotiris Kyriacou
Opened in 2004, with the aim to showcase
work by artists rarely or never seen in London.
Exhibits a wide range of international and
British contemporary artists, both emerging
and established, including Phyllida Barlow,
Pavel Buchler, Melanie Counsell, Clem Crosby,
Doug Fishbone, Tim Head, Alfredo Jaar, Simon
Moretti, Cathie Pilkington, Nike Savvas, Julia
Warr and Richard Wilson. Also curates group
exhibitions.
Submission policy Submissions by email.
Price range £500–£100,000
No of exhibitions annually 8

Purdy Hicks Gallery

65 Hopton Street, Bankside, London
SE1 9GZ
T 020 74019229
F 020 74019595
E purdyhicks@btconnect.com
W www.purdyhicks.com
Represents a number of pre-eminent British
and foreign artists including Hughie O'Donoghue,
Ralph Fleck and Alice Maher. Founded in 1993,
specializing in painting and photography and also
regularly publishes prints by gallery artists.

Price range From £300 for prints; from £1,000 for paintings and photographs.
No of exhibitions annually Approx. 10

Quantum Contemporary Art
The Old Imperial Laundry, 71–73 Warriner Gardens, London
SW11 4XW
T 020 74986868
F 020 74987878
E quantum.art@virgin.net
W www.quantumart.co.uk
Contact Johnny Gorman
Founded in 1996 in a design hub called the Old Imperial Laundry in Battersea. Represents about forty artists, mainly painters whose style is representational. Participates in art fairs in the UK and USA.
Submission policy Artists' submissions welcome, but conceptual, abstract, sculpture, photography, digital and performance art are not exhibited.
Price range £250–£10,000
No of exhibitions annually Approx. 10

Rachmaninoff's
Unit 106, Kings Wharf, 301 Kingsland Road, London
E8 4DS
T 020 72750757
E info@rachmaninoffs.com
W www.rachmaninoffs.com

Rafael Valls Ltd
6 Ryder Street, St James's, London
SW1Y 6QB
T 020 79300029
F 020 79762589
E lizzie@rafaelvalls.co.uk
W www.rafaelvalls.co.uk
Contact Caroline Valls or Lizzie Aubrey-Fletcher
Submission policy Artists wishing to be given an exhibition should email images or send a link to a website.
Price range £500–£25,000
No of exhibitions annually 4

Rebecca Hossack Gallery
35 Windmill Street, Fitzrovia, London
W1T 2JS
T 020 74364899
F 020 73233182
E rebecca@r-h-g.co.uk
W www.r-h-g.co.uk
Contact Maria Morrow

Opened in central London by Rebecca Hossack in March 1988. Programme combines non-Western art with work in the Western tradition. The first gallery in Europe to show Australian aboriginal art. In 2000 opened the Charlotte Street Gallery as an additional showcase for its artists.
Submission policy Artists wishing to apply to the gallery may send a copy of their CV along with images of recent works – jpegs if sent via email or slides with an sae if sent via post.
Price range £50–£50,000
No of exhibitions annually 24 (12 in each gallery).

Red Mansion Foundation
4th Floor, 12 Great Portland Street, London
W1W 8QN
T 020 73233700
E info@redmansion.co.uk
W www.redmansion.co.uk
Contact Amelie von Wedel
A not-for-profit organization that promotes artistic exchange between China and Great Britain. Its vision is to encourage mutual cultural understanding through contemporary art. Expert staff in both China and the UK provide advice to corporate and private clients on contemporary Chinese art. Has excellent relationships with artists and galleries; represents a cross-section of significant Chinese artists and exhibits their works in Britain. All proceeds from sales and consultancy services support the foundation's programmes. Works with Zhao Bandi, Cang Xin, Shi Jing, Zhan Wang, Liu Jianhua and Weng Fen, among others.
Submission policy Represents and welcomes submissions from contemporary Chinese artists.
Price range £500–£50,000
No of exhibitions annually 6

Redfern Gallery
20 Cork Street, London
W1S 3HL
T 020 77341732
F 020 74942908
E art@redfern-gallery.com
W www.redfern-gallery.com
Founded in 1923. One of London's oldest commercial galleries, dealing mainly in modern and contemporary British and European art. Artists represented include Paul Feiler, Eileen Agar, Patrick Procktor, David Tindle, Paul Jenkins and Linda Karshan.
Submission policy No unsolicited submissions.
Price range £500–£500,000
No of exhibitions annually 11

Richard Green

147 New Bond Street, London
W1S 2TS
T 020 74933939
F 020 76292609
W www.richard-green.com
Dealing in paintings for over forty years. Has
three galleries in London's West End, specializing
mainly in Old Master, Impressionist, marine and
sporting paintings, as well as twentieth-century
British art, with artists such as Sir Terry Frost RA
and Ken Howard RA.

Riflemaker

79 Beak Street, London
W1F 9SU
T 020 74390000
E info@riflemaker.org
W www.riflemaker.org
Focuses on contemporary visual art. Artists
represented include Jamie Shoulin, Francesca
Tove, Christopher Bucklow, Nicholas Hay and
Marta Marle.
Submission policy Does not welcome submissions
from artists.
Price range £1,000–£20,000
No of exhibitions annually 8

Ritter/Zamet

2 Bear Gardens, London
SE1 9ED
T 020 72619510
F 020 72619516
E info@ritterzamet.com
W www.ritterzamet.com
Founded in 2003 with a directive towards
presenting a cohesive programme of emerging
European and American contemporary artists.
Artists represented include Simon Bedwell (UK),
Nogah Engler (Israel), Nate Lowman (USA),
Moriceau and Mrzyk (France), Peter Stauss
(Germany) and Dolly Thompsett (UK).
Submission policy Does not normally work on an
artist-submission basis.
Price range £500–£30,000
No of exhibitions annually 5

Rivington Gallery

69 Rivington Street, London
EC2A 3AY
T 020 77397835
F 020 77397855
E rivingtongallery@aol.com
Founded in 1997. Shows painting, sculpture,
drawing, photography and crafts. Represented
artists include Tom Kemp, Michael Green, Nichollas
Hamper, Neave Brown and Julie Oakes.
Submission policy Has a very complete roster
of artists but will look at work by appointment.
Price range £200–£10,000
No of exhibitions annually 10–12

Robert Sandelson

5 Cork Street, London
W1S 3NY
T 020 74391001
F 020 74392299
E info@robertsandelson.com
W www.robertsandelson.com
Opened in Cork Street in 1999 and specializes
in modern and contemporary British and
international art. The gallery also presents
changing exhibitions of sculptures in the
grounds and premises of Narborough Hall
in Norfolk.

Rocket

13 Old Burlington Street, London
W1S 3AJ
T 020 74343043
F 020 74343384
E js.rocket@btinternet.com
W www.rocketgallery.com
Founded in 1995. Contemporary art with an
emphasis on minimalism and photography.
Artists include Martin Parr, Cedric Christie,
Michelle Grabner, Charles Christopher Hill,
Lars Wolter and the Estate of Jeremy Moon.
Price range £100–£30,000
No of exhibitions annually 7

Rockwell

Top Floor, 230 Dalston Lane, London
E8 1LA
T 07941 672101
E alex@therockwellproject.co.uk
W www.therockwellproject.co.uk
Until 2002, Rockwell was a derelict sweatshop and
warehouse but was transformed over a ten-month
period into an artist-run project space and studios.
Aiming to assess contemporary dilemmas and
questions raised by the very nature of art-making,
its in-house artists enlist the help of selected
contributors for curatorial assistance. Artists
include Chris Davies, Gavin Nolan, Alex Gene
Morrison, Reece Jones, Kiera Bennett, Sigrid
Holmwood, Isabel Young, Tim Parr, Will Turner,
James Jessop, Gavin Tremlett and Sam Dargan.

Rokeby

37 Store Street, London
WC1E 7BS
T 020 71689942
F 07813 144919
E rokeby@rokebygallery.com
W www.rokebygallery.com
Founded in 2005. One of London's newest
independent commercial galleries for
contemporary art. Exhibits work by emerging
and established artists from the UK and beyond,
in a wide range of media, from painting, drawing
and sculpture to sound, video and photography.
Presents solo shows or curated exhibitions
focusing on no more than two artists. Gallery
artists include Zoë Mendelson and Craig Fisher.
Other exhibited artists include Sam Dargan,
Graham Hudson, Samuel St Leger, Luke Oxley,
Claire Pestaille and Naglaa Walker.
Submission policy Welcomes submissions from
artists who should email the gallery with ten
low-resolution jpegs, a statement and biography.
Price range £10–£20,000
No of exhibitions annually 7

Rona Gallery

1–2 Weighhouse Street, London
W1K 5LR
T 020 74913718
F 020 74914171
E info@ronagallery.com
W www.ronagallery.com
Contact Stanley Harries
Founded in 1980. Shows figurative art mostly by
living artists. Particular focus on painting by
'one-off individualists'. Artists include Richard
Adams, Alfred Daniels RBA, Nicola Slattery,
Christopher Hall RBA, Martin Leman and
Michael Kidd.
Submission policy Paintings in oil or acrylic
(figurative only). Phone or email first.
Price range £2,000–£10,000
No of exhibitions annually 8–9

Rowley Gallery Contemporary Arts

115 Kensington Church Street, London
W8 7LN
T 020 72295561
F 020 72295561
E art@rowleygallery.com
W www.rowleygallery.com
Contact David Kitchin
Exhibits a continuous mixed exhibition, with an
average of fifteen to twenty artists at any one time.

Submission policy Submissions always welcome
from artists.
Price range £125–£4,500
No of exhibitions annually 2

Royal Exchange Art Gallery

7 Bury Street, St James's, London
SW1Y 6AL
T 020 78394477
F 020 78398085
E enquiries@marinepictures.com
W www.marinepictures.com
Contact Adrian Thomas
Founded in 1974. Specializes in fine marine oils,
watercolours and etchings from the eighteenth
century to the present day. Leading contemporary
marine artists represented include Steven Dews,
Martyn Mackrill and Paul Freeman. Other earlier
artists include A. Briscoe, T. Buttersworth,
N.M. Condy, G. Chambers, T. Luny, E. Seago,
N. Wilkinson and W.L. Wyllie.
Submission policy Always looking for fine-quality
marine pictures. Send photographs and size
details via email first.
Price range £650–£140,000
No of exhibitions annually 2 major shows, but a
regular change of stock.

Sadie Coles HQ

35 Heddon Street, London
W1B 4BP
T 020 74342227
F 020 74342228
E sadie@sadiecoles.com
W www.sadiecoles.com
Established in 1997. Represents around thirty
British and international artists working across all
media. Artists include Sarah Lucas, John Currin,
Wilhelm Sasnal, Urs Fischer, Elizabeth Peyton and
Richard Prince.
Price range £500–£400,000
No of exhibitions annually Approx. 10

Sartorial Contemporary Art

101a Kensington Church Street, London
W8 7LN
T 020 77925882
F 020 77925820
E art@sartorialart.com
W www.sartorialart.com
Founded in 2002 in an eighteenth-century
Georgian house in Kensington. Aims to bring
together a range of different work to expand
people's conceptions of contemporary art.

Shows both emerging and established artists, with an emphasis on supporting young artists and special projects. Exhibited artists include Jasper Joffe, Hugh Mendes, Peter Lamb, Stella Vine, James Jessop and Gavin Nolan.
Submission policy Gallery shows artists but does not represent them.
Price range £200–£8,000
No of exhibitions annually 8

Scout

1–3 Mundy Street, off Hoxton Square, London
N1 6QT
T 020 77490909
F 020 77396691
E mail@scoutgallery.com
W www.scoutgallery.com
Contact Simon Pearce
Founded in 2002 as an east London gallery dedicated to international contemporary photography and associated film or video work. Artists shown so far include Ben Watts, cinematographer Christopher Doyle, Steven Klein, Royal College of Art graduate Marc Wayland, Kyoichi Tsuzuki and Magnum photographer Susan Meiselas.
Submission policy Accepts photography proposals by email with a brief written statement accompanied by low-resolution jpegs or a website referral.
Price range £300–£10,000
No of exhibitions annually 6–7

Sculptastic

9 New Quebec Street, Marylebone, London
W1H 7RL
T 020 72248772
F 020 72249678
E kevin@sculptastic.co.uk
W www.sculptastic.co.uk
Specializes in contemporary sculpture, including hand-built figurative ceramics, bronze, bronze resin and other cast media, carvings in stone or wood, sculptural wall reliefs and hangings, and figurative jewelry. Deals in abstract and figurative forms (human and animal themes), encompassing colourful, humorous, witty and idiosyncratic styles, as well as more serious, traditional academic work.
Submission policy Sculptors and figurative jewelers can send images, discs or jpegs by email (preferred method) with a statement or CV. Artists should indicate sale amounts.
Price range £30–£5,000

Sesame Art

354 Upper Street, Islington, London
N1 0PD
T 020 72263300
E info@sesameart.com
W www.sesameart.com
Dedicated to exhibiting and promoting the work of emerging artists in the UK. Specializes mainly in painting. The focus is on distinctive and often unusual work, shown in a friendly, open and accessible environment.
Submission policy Send CV, six to eight images of work plus a brief statement giving insight into artist's approach. Professional artists only.
Price range £500–£5,000

Seven Seven Contemporary Art

75–77 Broadway Market, London Fields, London
E8 4PH
T 07808 166215
E abond@sevenseven.wanadoo.co.uk
W www.sevenseven.org.uk
Founded in 2002. A not-for-profit, artist-led organization showing emerging and established artists, representing the energy and diversity of contemporary practice. Runs a lively education programme and participates in a wide range of projects, both locally and internationally.
Submission policy Artists and curators should refer to website for application information and to see examples of recent shows.
No of exhibitions annually 16

Sheen Gallery

245 Upper Richmond Road West, London
SW14 8QS
T 0208 3921662
F 0208 8760422
E info@thesheengallery.com
W www.thesheengallery.co.uk
Specializes in modern British and leading contemporary artists. Prominent contemporary artists represented include Diana Armfield, Sonia Lawson, Mick Rooney, Charles Williams, Susan Ryder, Arthur Neal
Submission policy Paintings and drawings.
Price range £350–£12,000
No of exhibitions annually 8

The Ship

387 Cable Street, London
E1 0AH
T 020 77900409
E TheShip@Mail.com

A non-commercial project space in the East End of London, situated in a disused pub on Cable Street with a history of the sex industry and right-wing activism. All shows are curated projects focusing on contemporary art.
Submission policy Not currently handling any submissions.
No of exhibitions annually 7

The Showroom
44 Bonner Road, London
E2 9JS
T 020 89834115
F 020 89814112
E tellmemore@theshowroom.org
W www.theshowroom.org
Has existed as a publicly funded, not-for-profit contemporary-art gallery since 1989. It has offered many British artists their first solo show in London, including Mona Hatoum, Sam Taylor-Wood, Simon Starling, Jim Lambie, Claire Barclay and Eva Rothschild. Increasing focus on commissioning individual artists to make new work for the space.

Skylark Galleries
Unit 1.09, Oxo Tower Wharf, Barge House Street, London
SE1 9PH
T 020 74019666
E info@skylarkgallery.com
W www.skylarkgallery.com
Artist-run galleries in the Oxo Tower and Gabriel's Wharf on London's South Bank. Entirely staffed by exhibiting artists.
Submission policy Contact gallery (by email or post with sae) to request joining details.
Price range £20–£1,000

Space Station Sixty-Five
65 North Cross Road, London
SE22 9ET
T 020 86935995
E spacestationsixtyfive@btopenworld.com
W www.spacestationsixtyfive.com
Opened in 2002. An artist-run space that works closely with artists being shown. Does not currently represent artists. A shop-front gallery in a busy street, particularly interested in live art, sculpture, video, time-based/process work and installation. Hosts window exhibitions (viewed from the street) as well as exhibitions where the space is open to the public.
Submission policy Proposals should be a maximum of one side of A4. Also include a CV and visuals. Artists are strongly recommended to visit the gallery before sending proposals.
Price range Prices decided by artists and directors.
No of exhibitions annually 3–6

space-twotentwo
Unit 2, 210 Cambridge Heath Road, London
E2 9NQ
E info@space-twotentwo.com
W www.space-twotentwo.com
Founded in 2003 with a focus on new media, video and photography. Aims to support emerging artists through exhibitions and projects in conjunction with more established artists to encourage dialogue and the transfer of skills.
Submission policy Submissions for curatorial projects or exhibitions should be posted to the gallery.
No of exhibitions annually 7

Spectrum Fine Art
77 Great Titchfield Street, London
W1W 6RF
T 020 76377778
E anne@intelligent-pr.com
W www.spectrumlondon.co.uk
Opened in 2004, aiming to bring the work of a new generation of artists to the public and to provide a springboard for newly graduated talent. Artists include Craigie Aitchison, Marco Amura and Peter Howson.
Submission policy Excludes photography, installations and video. Only professional artists need apply. Submissions all year round.
Price range £150–£40,000
No of exhibitions annually 9

Spencer Coleman Fine Art
1 Cloisters Walk, St Katharine Docks, London
E1W 1LD
T 020 74811199
Contact Spencer Coleman
Established for over ten years, specializing in a selection of oils, watercolour and pastel paintings by British, Russian and Continental artists. These include Jorge Aguilar AEA APB FRSA, Andrew White, Crin Gale, Israel Zohar (Royal Portrait Artist), Douglas Gray, Juriy Ochremovich and Pippa Chapman.
Branches 8 Gordon Road, Lincoln LN1 3AJ; 5–9 The George Mews, The George Hotel, St Martins, Stamford, Lincolnshire PE9 2LB; 22a North Bar Without, Beverley, East Yorkshire HU17 7AB.

Submission policy New artists welcome (local and international) in all media, covering narrative, landscape, still life, seascape and equestrian topics.
Price range £300–£15,000
No of exhibitions annually 2, March and September.

Spitz Gallery
109 Commercial Street, Old Spitalfields Market, London
E1 6BG
T 020 72479747
F 020 73778915
E gallery@spitz.co.uk
W www.spitz.co.uk
Founded in 1996. Background in photography but displays other art forms including painting, graphic design, video art, sculpture, etc.
Submission policy Submissions accepted in June and November only. Email image(s) in body of email, or post on CD. Will contact if interested.
Price range £200–£3,000
No of exhibitions annually Approx. 20

Spruth Magers Lee
12 Berkeley Street, London
W1J 8DT
T 020 74910100
E info@spruethmagerslee.com
W www.spsruethmagerslee.com
Contact Lindsay Ramsay
Opened in 2003, showing work from prominent and influential artists beginning their careers in the late 1970s and early 1980s, including Stephen Shore, Jenny Holzer, Cindy Sherman, George Condo, Christopher Wool and Peter Fischli.
Submission policy The gallery is committed to its exhibition schedule for the next two years; artists are asked not to send proposals or portfolios.
No of exhibitions annually 6

SS Robin Gallery
SS Robin, West India Quay, Hertsmere Road, London
E14 4AE
T 020 75380652
F 0870 1316566
E info@ssrobin.com
W www.ssrobin.com
Contact David Kampfner
Documentary photography gallery based onboard SS *Robin*, the world's oldest complete steamship, moored at West India Quay in the heart of Canary Wharf in London. Founded by two photographers, David and Nishani Kampfner, in 2002. Shows a rolling programme of photography in the newly restored cargo hold, open from March to September.
Submission policy Visit the website to download the curation policy.
Price range £500–£5,000
No of exhibitions annually 6

Standpoint Gallery
45 Coronet Street, Hoxton, London
N1 6HD
T 020 77394921
F 020 77394921
E standpointgallery@btconnect.com
W www.standpointlondon.co.uk
Contact Rebecca Finney (Gallery Curator)
Opened in 1992. One of the first galleries in an area that has become a hub for the visual-art scene. Now the last surviving artist-run space in Shoreditch. Exhibits a range of media and reflects the diverse nature of contemporary artistic practice. Without commercial constraints, it focuses on quality of idea and execution over saleability and fashion. The gallery administers a bursary and exhibits new works for the annual Mark Tanner Sculpture Award.
Submission policy Application details for the gallery programme and the Mark Tanner Sculpture Award available on website.
Price range £50–£7,000
No of exhibitions annually 7

Stephen Friedman Gallery
25–28 Old Burlington Street, London
W1S 3AN
T 020 74941434
F 020 74941431
E info@stephenfriedman.com
W www.stephenfriedman.com
Founded in 1995. Specializes in contemporary art. Artists represented include Mamma Andersson (Sweden), Stephan Balkenhol (Germany), Tom Friedman (USA), Kendell Geers (South Africa), Dryden Goodwin (UK), Beatriz Milhazes (Brazil), Donald Moffett (USA), Yoshitomo Nara (Japan), Rivane Neuenschwander (Brazil), Yinka Shonibare (UK), Catherine Opie (USA) and David Shrigley (UK).
Submission policy Post CV and a maximum of ten slides demonstrating work. Enclose sae for return of material.
No of exhibitions annually 6

Store
92 Hoxton Street, London
N1 6LP

T 020 7729 8171
F 020 7729 8171
E info@storegallery.co.uk
W www.storegallery.co.uk
Opened in 2003. Presents new work by British and international emerging artists. Exhibitions have ranged from conceptual installation to provocative figurative painting. Artists represented include Marc Bauer, Ryan Gander, Tanya Fairey, Liz Neal, Claire Harvey and Andrew Rucklidge.
Submission policy Welcomes proposals from artists but gallery exhibitions are programmed up to a year in advance.
Price range £400–£10,000
No of exhibitions annually 6

Studio 1.1
57a Redchurch Street, London
E2 7DJ
T 07952 986696
E studio1-1.gallery@virgin.net
W www.studio1-1.co.uk
Contact M. Keenan
An artists' collective founded in 2003 to show contemporary work in any medium. No limitation on age, reputation or background of the artist. Artists shown include Cees Krijnen, Carrie Yamaoka, Terry Smith, John Dougill, Joy Episalla and Vanessa Jackson.
Submission policy Refer to website.
Price range £200–£10,000
No of exhibitions annually 6

Studio Glass Gallery
63 Connaught Street, Marble Arch, London
W2 2AE
T 020 7706 3013
E mail@studioglass.co.uk
W www.studioglass.co.uk
Contact Zaf Iqbal
Established in 1994. Represents leading English and European artists working in glass including Libensky/Brychtova, Cigler, Dany Lane, Colin Reid and Max Jacquard. Undertakes commissions for fabricating in glass both sculptural and architectural.
Price range £1,500–£75,000
No of exhibitions annually 4

Studio Voltaire
1a Nelson's Row, Clapham, London
SW4 8JS
T 020 7622 1294
F 020 7627 8008

E info@studiovoltaire.org
W www.studiovoltaire.org
Contact Joe Scotland
Founded in 1994. An artist-run gallery in south-west London promoting access and participation in contemporary art with its exhibition, education and studio programmes. Past exhibitors have included Liam Gillick, Rachel Whiteread, Lawerence Weiner, Joanne Tatham and Tom O'Sullivan.
Submission policy No areas excluded. Does not represent artists, but works in collaboration with artists to achieve ambitious projects and exhibitions.
Price range £2–£20,000
No of exhibitions annually 5

Sutton Lane
1 Sutton Lane, Entrance at 25–27 Great Sutton Street, London
EC1M 5PU
T 020 7253 8580
F 020 7253 8580
E info@suttonlane.com
W www.suttonlane.com
No of exhibitions annually 8

t1+2
t1+2 artspace, 4 Steward Street, London
E1 6AL
T 07903 876522
E info@t12artspace.com
W www.t12artspace.com
Independent, self-funded and run by artists. Can accommodate large-scale installations not usually possible outside the major commercial galleries.
Submission policy Artists should provide a CV and slides. By appointment only.
No of exhibitions annually 10

Terry Duffy – 340 Old Street
340 Old Street, Shoreditch, London
EC1V 9DS
E terryduffy@340oldstreet.co.uk
W www.340oldstreet.co.uk
Established in 1998 as an experimental art space to question and confront contemporary art, culture and society.
Submission policy Apply by email only with CV and jpegs of images. No media, method, sex, race, religion, nationality or beliefs excluded. No deadlines.
Price range £1,000–£25,000
No of exhibitions annually 10

Theresa McCullough Ltd

80 Riverview Gardens, Barnes, London
SW13 8RA
T 020 85631680
E info@theresamccullough.com
W www.theresamccullough.com
Opened in 2000 and moved to current riverside
location in 2004. Dealer specializing in Indian and
South-east Asian works of art (predominantly
stone and bronze sculpture) as well as South-east
Asian gold jewelry. Exhibits at the Asian Art in
London fair in November and in New York at the
International Asian Art Fair in March.
Submission policy Deals in antique South Asian
sculpture. Submissions welcome from
contemporary Indian artists.
No of exhibitions annually 2

Thomas Dane

11 Duke Street, St James's, London
SW1Y 6BN
T 020 79252505
F 020 79252506
E info@thomasdane.com
W www.thomasdane.com
Established in 2004 as the culmination of over a
decade of behind-the-scenes activity, including
supporting artists, hosting landmark exhibitions
and dealing privately. Closely associated from the
start with the generation of British artists whose
work grew in stature in the 1990s, the gallery
has now developed an expertise and reputation
in the international arena. Exhibitions of selected
international contemporary artists employing a
wide range of media. Artists include Paul Pfeiffer,
Michael Landy, Stefan Kürten, Anya Gallaccio,
Hurvin Anderson and Albert Oehlen.
Submission policy No unsolicited submissions.
No of exhibitions annually 5

Timothy Taylor Gallery

24 Dering Street, London
W1S 1TT
T 020 74093344
F 020 74091316
E mail@timothytaylorgallery.com
W www.timothytaylorgallery.com
Founded in 1996, specializing in contemporary
art. Artists include Craigie Aithchison,
J.M. Bustamante, Marcel Dzama, Susan Hiller,
Fiona Rae, Sean Scully, Alex Katz, Jonathan
Lasker, James Rielly and Richard Patterson.
Submission policy Submissions not welcome.
No of exhibitions annually 7–10

Tom Blau Gallery – Camera Press

21 Queen Elizabeth Street, London
SE1 2PD
T 020 73781300
F 020 72785126
E info@tomblaugallery.com
W www.tomblaugallery.com
Founded in 1993 and named after the founder
of the photographic agency Camera Press.
Specializes in vintage, modern and contemporary
photography. Exhibited artists have included
Jacques Lowe, Yousef Karsh, Jason Bell, Patrick
Lichfield, Chris Shaw, and Morten Nisson.
Also shows photographs from the Camera
Press Archives and hosts the annual Ian Parry
Scholarship Awards for young photojournalists.
Submission policy Submissions from artists
not welcome. Exhibitions by Camera Press-
represented photographers only.
Price range From £200
No of exhibitions annually 6–10

Transition

110a Lauriston Road, London
E9 7HA
T 020 85337843
E transition@huntergather.com
W www.transitiongallery.co.uk
An artist-run space founded in 2002, showing
cutting-edge contemporary art by emerging and
established artists. Particular focus on work that
crosses into other cultural fields such as music
and literature. Artists shown include Stella Vine,
Liz Neal, Paul Becker, Nicky Magliulo and
Esther Planas.
Submission policy Artists welcome to submit
images, statements and proposals by email
or post.
No of exhibitions annually 8

Trolley

73a Redchurch Street, London
E2 7DJ
T 020 77395948
E info@trolleynet.com
W www.trolleybooks.com
Specializes in art and photography books, Trolley
operates a gallery space primarily exhibiting work
linked to books projects but with exceptions.
Artists include Deirdre O'Callaghan, Adam
Broomberg and Oliver Chanarin, Chris Steele-
Perkins, Alex Majoli, Philip Jones Griffiths,
Werner Bischof, Vedovamazzei, Doris Vassmer,
Mia Enell and Stanley Greene.

Tryon Galleries

7 Bury Street, St James's, London
SW1Y 6AL
T 020 78398083
F 020 78398085
E info@tryon.co.uk
W www.tryon.co.uk
Contact Liz Thorold
Founded in 1959 with a strong reputation in the
fields of sporting, wildlife and Scottish paintings,
and bronzes. Deals in nineteenth- and twentieth-
century and contemporary artists, from Archibald
Thorburn, George Lodge and Lionel Edwards to
Rodger McPhail.
Price range £500–£50,000
No of exhibitions annually 6

Union

57 Ewer Street, London
SE1 0NR
T 020 79283388
F 020 79283389
E info@union-gallery.com
W www.union-gallery.com
Contact Jari Lager
Five minutes' walk from Tate Modern
and established at the start of 2003. Presents
group and solo shows by established and
emerging international contemporary artists,
many of whom are showing to a UK audience
for the first time. Has an mbitious programme
of exhibitions, effectively allowing museum
shows previously only seen overseas to be
brought to a London audience in the context
of a commercial space.
Submission policy Does not look at submissions
from artists.
No of exhibitions annually 4–5

Victoria Miro Gallery

16 Wharf Road, London
N1 7RW
T 020 73368109
F 020 72515596
E info@victoria-miro.com
W www.victoria-miro.com
Established in Cork Street in 1985 to show primarily
minimal and conceptual art. The programme
shifted emphasis in the 1990s towards young,
emerging artists from this country and abroad.
The gallery, one of the first to expand by moving to
the East End in 2000, has also had two Turner Prize
winners to date, Chris Ofili in 1998 and Grayson
Perry in 2003.

Vilma Gold

25b Vyner Street, London
E2 29G
T 020 89813344
F 020 89813355
E mail@vilmagold.com
W www.vilmagold.com
Represents international and young contemporary
artists such as Vladimir Dubossarsky and
Alexsander Vinogradov, Brian Griffiths and the
hobbypopMuseum collective.

W.H. Patterson Ltd

19 Albemarle Street, Mayfair, London
W1S 4BB
T 020 76294119
F 020 74990119
E info@whpatterson.com
W www.whpatterson.com
Founded in 1964. Deals in contemporary art
and has a nineteenth-century department.
Hosts an annual 'Venice in Peril' (VIP) exhibition;
ten per cent of proceeds donated to the VIP Fund.
Price range £450–£60,000
No of exhibitions annually 10

Waddington Galleries

11 Cork Street, London
W1S 3LT
T 020 78512200
F 020 78512200
E mail@waddington-galleries.com
W www.waddington-galleries.com
One of the most established art dealerships
in London. Exhibits paintings, sculpture and
works on paper by twentieth-century artists from
Great Britain, Europe and America, including
Patrick Caulfied, David Salle and Bill Woodrow.

White Cube

48 Hoxton Square, London
N1 6PB
T 020 79305373
F 020 77497480
E enquiries@whitecube.com
W www.whitecube.com
Contact Susannah Hyman
Founded in 1993. Has presented solo shows of
British artists such as Jake and Dinos Chapman,
Tracey Emin, Lucian Freud, Gilbert & George,
Antony Gormley and Damien Hirst. International
artists include Franz Ackermann, Chuck Close,
Ellsworth Kelly, Julie Mehretu, Doris Salcedo and
Hiroshi Sugimoto. Also frequent group shows.

Submission policy All works considered by any living artist.
Price range From £1,000
No of exhibitions annually 8–10

Whitechapel Project Space
20 Fordham Street, London
E1 1HS
T 020 73776289
F 020 73776289
E info@whitechapelprojectspace.org.uk
W www.whitechapelprojectspace.org.uk
Contact Maria Trimikliniotis or Richard Birkett
Founded in 2002. Aims to 'facilitate artists'
and curatorial practice that is in many senses
unfinished and unprescribed'. Artists at varying
stages of development are invited to consider how
the space can further their work and operate as a
catalyst to their practice. The gallery's organization
is sometimes reconstituted through exterior
curatorial input, manipulating previously fixed
assumptions of how it might operate. Has hosted
activities that both complement and contradict the
familiar notion of a contemporary-art gallery.
Submission policy Aims to show contemporary art
with the broad remit of presenting current cultural
production and provoking debate. Normally shows
invited artists but always ready to consider
proposals and submissions from artists.
No of exhibitions annually 6–10

Whitford Fine Art
6 Duke Street, St James's, London
SW1Y 6BN
T 020 79309332
F 020 79305577
E info@whitfordfineart.com
W www.whitfordfineart.com
Opened in 1973 as Whitford & Hughes and
changed its name to Whitford Fine Art in
1991. Stock spans the twentieth century, from
Modernism up to post-war abstraction and
Pop Art. Examples of 1960s and 1970s designer
furniture are a permanent feature of the gallery.
Price range £1,000–£500,000
No of exhibitions annually 4

Whitgift Galleries
77 South End, Croydon
CRO 1BF
T 020 86880990
F 020 87600522
E info@whitgiftgalleries.co.uk
W www.whitgiftgalleries.co.uk

Founded in 1945, showing fine-quality oil
paintings and watercolours. Artists include Brian
Davies, Ben Maile and David Smith. Limited
editions by Sir William Russsell Flint and others.
Also offers a framing and restoration service.
Price range £50–£10,000
No of exhibitions annually 2

Wilkinson Gallery
242 Cambridge Heath Road, London
E2 9DA
T 020 89802662
F 020 89800028
E info@wilkinsongallery.com
W www.wilkinsongallery.com
A principal gallery in the Hackney and
Bethnal Green area since 1998, showing a
mixture of international and British art by mostly
young and emerging artists including David
Batchelor and George Shaw.

William Thuillier
14 Old Bond Street, London
W15 4PP
T 020 74990106
F 020 72338965
E thuillart@aol.com
W www.thuillart.com
Established in 1982. European Old Master
paintings, British paintings and some works on
paper. All works date from between 1600 and 1850.
Submission policy Shows only one living artist,
Philip Chitting.
Price range £500–£250,000

Williams & Son
2 Grafton Street, London
W1S 4ED
T 020 74935751
F 020 74097363
E art@williamsandson.com
W williamsandson.com
Contact John R. Williams
Founded in 1932. Specializes in nineteenth-
and twentieth-century paintings. Handles the
work of a few contemporary artists who paint in
the academic and traditional styles and who can
hang with stock of nineteenth-century paintings.
Price range £1,000–£200,000
No of exhibitions annually 1

Wolseley Fine Arts Ltd
12 Needham Road, London
W11 2RP

T 020 77922788
F 020 77922988
E info@wolseleyfinearts.com
W www.wolseleyfinearts.com
Founded in 1990. Specializes in early twentieth-century works on paper, mainly by French Post-Impressionist and modern British artists. Also shows contemporary sculpture, carved lettering and still life painting.
Submission policy Although the gallery shows contemporary sculpture and carved lettering, the style is so specific that uninvited applications from artists are not encouraged.
Price range £150–£50,000
No of exhibitions annually 6

North-east

Art Café
18 Market Place, Corbridge
NE45 5AW
T 014334 634090
E info@theartcafe.uk.com
W www.theartcafe.uk.com
Contact Kay Allinson-Cooke
Opened in 2002. Exhibits original British contemporary art and design. Artists include Alexander Millar, Gavin Penn, Mary Ann Rogers, Jan Huntley-Peace, Kate Wilkinson and Cosmic Design.
Submission policy Viewing panel meets each Tuesday to select new work. All details (including contract and code of practice) on website.
Price range £5–£15,000
No of exhibitions annually 6

Barnard Gallery
2 Theatre Yard, Stockton-on-Tees
TS18 JZ
T 01642 616203

Biscuit Factory
Stoddart Street, Newcastle-upon-Tyne
NE2 1AN
T 0191 2611103
F 0191 2610057
E art@thebiscuitfactory.com
W www.thebiscuitfactory.com
Contact Karen Tait
One of Europe's largest commercial galleries, exhibiting a wide range of artists (national and international) and art forms including glass, ceramics, sculpture and paintings. Has shown

and sold work by over six hundred artists, including Damien Hirst and Andy Warhol.
Submission policy Artists who feel their work is suitable for the gallery should apply via criteria on the website.
Price range £20–£50,000
No of exhibitions annually A rolling programme, with four preview nights per year.

Centre Gallery
Deptford Terrace, Sunderland
SR4 6DD
T 0191 5658584

Chatton Gallery
Church House, New Road, Chatton, Alnwick
NE66 5PU
T 01668 215494

Colliers
Milburn House, Dean Street, Newcastle-upon-Tyne
NE1 1LF
T 0191 2322819
F 0191 2302026
E anne@colliers.wanadoo.co.uk
W www.colliersgallery.co.uk
Contact Anne Collier
Founded in 1975, initially specializing in framing. Now a contemporary gallery showing mainly local artists. Wall space available to rent. Some in-house publishing of mainly local images.
Submission policy 'Not interested in Turner Prize-type art – no installations, shockers, etc.' Well-executed art of a professional standard always welcome.
Price range £5–£5000
No of exhibitions annually Varies.

Corrymella Scott Gallery
5 Tankerville Terrace, Jesmond, Newcastle-upon-Tyne
NE8 4EL
T 0191 2818284
E corrymella@corrymella.co.uk

Crown Fine Arts
25 Selbrigg Lane, Ingleby Barwick, Stockton-on-Tees
TS17 0XT
T 01642 761883

Crown Studio Gallery
The Village Green, Elsdon
NE19 1AA

T 01830 520144
E info@crownstudio.co.uk
W www.crownstudio.co.uk
Founded 2001, specializing in painting, prints, sculpture and ceramics. Exhibits professional (mostly regional) artists, both emerging and established. Space is domestic in scale but carefully arranged to show work to its best advantage. Shows high-quality contemporary art in a rural setting.
Submission policy Exhibition proposals welcome. Send photographs, prints, slides or jpegs, CV and statement. Enclose sae for return of material.
Price range £20–£2,000
No of exhibitions annually Up to 6

Customs House
Mill Dam, South Shields, Tyne & Wear
NE33 1ES
T 0191 4541234
F 0191 4565979
E mail@customshouse.co.uk
W www.customshouse.co.uk
Contact Kathryn Wakeman (Visual Arts Officer)
With a riverside location, the exhibition programme incorporates a diversity of art forms by artists of regional, national and international standing.
Submission policy Contact Kathryn Wakeman on 0191 4278191.
No of exhibitions annually 12

Dale Gallery
Castle Gardens, Durham Dale Centre Stanhope, Bishop Auckland
DL13 2UT
T 01388 526151

Dial Gallery
5 Dial Place, Warkworth
NE05 0WR
T 01665 710822

Evergreen Gallery
3 Grainger Street, Newcastle-upon-Tyne
NE1 5DQ
T 0191 2321011

Fenwick Gallery
21 Castle Street, Warkworth, Morpeth
NE65 0UW
T 01665 711136
E enquiry@fenwickgallery.co.uk
W www.fenwickgallery.co.uk

Established in 1990, offering a range of paintings and prints, ceramics, studio glass, wood pieces and jewelry.

fifiefofum
Westside Farm, Newton Hall, Stocksfield
NE43 7TW
T 01661 843778
E info@fifiefofum.com
W www.fifiefofum.com
Contact Sue Moffitt
Established in 2003. A rural contemporary gallery specializing in original fine art from established, emerging and graduate north-eastern artists. Artist-led, with a specific focus on supporting the artist. Also offers art-related workshops and courses.
Submission policy All artists' work is considered on an individual basis but it is expected that artists have some formal relevant qualifications or have been working as artists for many years. Aims to support and show work from graduates from BA, MA and PhD programmes.
Price range £65–£4,000. From £3.50 for original hand-printed cards.
No of exhibitions annually 6

Gallagher & Turner
St Thomas Workshops, St Thomas Street, Newcastle-upon-Tyne
NE1 4LE
T 0191 2614465
F 0191 2614465
E gallery@gallagher-turner.co.uk
W www.gallagher-turner.co.uk
Contact Clare Turner
A small, established gallery with eclectic tastes, showing local and national artists. Mostly solo shows but some mixed. Exhibitions include Ray Richardson, Albert Irvin and Norman Ackroyd. Also interested in printmakers and sells Japanese woodblock prints. A specialist conservation framer – will take exhibitions unframed.
Submission policy Does not currently display craft or jewelry. Welcomes submissions by email with images or post containing slides, with CV attached. All submissions by post will be returned safely.
Price range £40–£5,000
No of exhibitions annually Approx. 5

Gate Gallery
12 Bondgate Within, Alnwick
NE66 1TD
T 01665 602165

Glass and Art Gallery
194 Medomsley Road, Consett
DH8 5HX
T 01207 583353
F 01207 500218
E ron@glassdesign.co.uk
W www.glassdesign.co.uk
Founded in 1999, specializing in north-eastern
artists. Exhibits and sells across various media
including glass, ceramics, wood, metal sculpture,
paintings and textiles. Has over 160 artists
including Sheila Mackie, Bill Hindmarsh, Annette
McKinnon and Maralyn O'Keefe.
Submission policy Interested in original and
unique work (framed paintings), preferably from
north-eastern artists. Work must be different from
what is already exhibited.
Price range £10–£5,000
No of exhibitions annually 12

Lime Tree Gallery
6 The Butts, Stanhope, Bishop Auckland
DL13 2UF
T 01388 526110

Macdonalds Fine Art
6 Ashburton Road, Gosforth, Newcastle-upon-Tyne
NE3 4XN
T 0191 2844214

Newgate Gallery
6a The Bank, Barnard Castle
DL12 8PQ
T 01833 695201
E info@newgate-gallery.co.uk

Norslands Gallery
The Old School, Warenford, Belford
NE70 7HY
T 01668 213465

Serendipity
10 Market Place, Wolsingham
DL13 3AF
T 01388 526800
Founded in 2003, specializing in north-eastern art
and especially Weardale artists.
Submission policy Interested in original and
unique work (framed paintings) by north-eastern
artists. Work must be different from what is
already exhibited.
Price range £10–£5,000
No of exhibitions annually 12

Side Gallery
5 & 9 Side, Newcastle-upon-Tyne
NE1 3JE
T 0191 2322000
W www.amber-online.com
Specializes in photography.

Space
20 Pink Lane, Newcastle-upon-Tyne
NE1 5DW
T 0191 2330222
E Karentstone@hotmail.com
Contact Karen Stone
Founded in 2003 as a venue for selling
contemporary home accessories, art and design
books, and art work. Art work ranges from
ceramics to fashion bags to paintings. The
gallery prides itself on its affordability. Artists
include Hazel Stone, Francesca Hudson and
Duncan Lloyd.
Submission policy Art work is chosen to
complement each season's homewares; includes
paintings, sculpture, ceramics and textiles.
Price range £10–£250
No of exhibitions annually 4

T.B. & R. Jordan
Aslak Eaglescliffe, Stockton-on-Tees
TS16 0QN
T 01642 782599
F 01642 780473
W www.tbrj.cwc.net

Northern Ireland

Annexe Gallery
15 Main Street, Eglinton
BT47 3AA
T 028 71810389
E aml.davidson@talk21.com
W www.annexegallery.co.uk
Stocks original paintings, many by local artists,
and a wide selection of prints and limited editions.
Also offers framing service.

Ballance House
118a Lisburn Road, Glenavy, Crumlin
BT29 4NY
T 028 92648492

Bell Gallery
13 Adelaide Park, Lisburn Road, Belfast
BT9 6FX

T 028 90662998
F 028 90381524
E bellgallery@btinternet.com
W www.bellgallery.com
Contact Pauline McLarnon
Founded in 1964, dealing in work by Irish artists
of all periods and providing exhibition space
throughout the Troubles. Specializes in modern
British paintings, drawings and sculpture, and also
nineteenth- and twentieth-century Irish sculpture.
The gallery consists of three rooms.
Submission policy Lack of space precludes very
large exhibitions or excessively large individual
video or installation work.
Price range £500–£10,000
No of exhibitions annually Approx. 6, over spring
and autumn. Gallery closed in July.

Collett Art Gallery

73 Dublin Road, Belfast
BT2 7HF
T 028 90319589
E marion@collettartgallery.com
W www.collettartgallery.com
Established in 1990 and moved to its current
premises in 1995. Displays and sells paintings by
Irish artists to buyers all over the world.

Context Gallery

5–7 Artillery Street, Derry
BT48 6RG
T 028 71373538
E info@contextgallery.com

Eakin Gallery Armagh

3 Cloughan Road, Portadown Road, Armagh
BT61 8RF
T 028 38872013
E info@eakingalleryarmagh.co.uk
W eakingalleryarmagh.co.uk
Opened in 2004 by Harry and Carol Eakin,
who have over twenty-five years' experience in the
Irish art market. Artists include Tom Carr, Maurice
C. Wilks, J.B. Vallely, William Cunningham, Joe
Hynes, Gavin Fitzsimmons, Tom Kerr, David Jess,
Tanya Smith, Denis Orme Shaw, William Conor,
Frank McKelvey, Paul Henry, Hamilton Sloan,
Basil Blackshaw, Sam McLarnon, J.W. Carey
and Liam Reilly.
Submission policy Leading Irish artists are
welcome to show work on acceptance by the
gallery.
Price range £150–£10,000
No of exhibitions annually 4

Emer Gallery

467 Antrim Road, Belfast
BT15 3BJ
T 028 90778777
F 028 90779444
E info@emergallery.com
W www.emergallery.com
Displays and sells Irish art of the nineteenth
and twentieth centuries alongside contemporary
artists. Has a particular interest in naive and
primitive painting. Artists include Jimmy
Bingham, Comhghall Casey, Sasha Harding,
John McCart, Noel Murphy, Rhonda Paisley,
J.B. Valley and Ross Wilson.

Gallery 148

148 High Street, Holywood
County Down
E mail@gallery148.com
W www.gallery148.com
Shows established and emerging contemporary
Irish artists.

Gallery One

1 Brewery Lane, Cookstown
BT80 8LL
T 028 86765438
F 028 86765438
E info@galleryone.co.uk
W www.galleryone.co.uk
Stocks traditional and contemporary fine art by
European, UK and Irish artists in media including
oils, watercolours and acrylics and mixed media.

Manor Fine Arts

18 Rathfriland Street, Banbridge
BT32 3LA
T 028 40623434
F 028 40623434
W www.manorfinearts.co.uk
Exhibits both emerging and established artists and
offers a framing service.

Ormeau Baths Gallery

18a Ormeau Avenue, Belfast
BT2 8HS
T 028 90321402
F 028 90312232
E admin@obgonline.net
W www.ormeaubathsgallery.co.uk
Opened in 1995. An innovative exhibition and
education programme features nationally and
internationally recognized artists working across
a broad range of contemporary visual-art practice.

Stables Gallery

Ballywindland House, 27 Ballywindelland Road,
Ballymoney
BT53 6QT
T 028 27665919
E stewart-moore@btconnect.com
W www.stablesgallery.co.uk
Founded in 1980. Deals in twentieth-century and
contemporary paintings. Specializes primarily in
Irish art but also represents the work of several
French, Spanish and English artists.
Submission policy The gallery is happy to look
objectively at submissions by artists of quality.
Price range £500–£30,000
No of exhibitions annually 9

TailorMadeArt

2 Brookmount Road, Omagh
BT78 5HZ
T 028 82246613
F 028 82252097
E info@tailormadeart.com
W www.tailormadeart.com
A team of artists and art specialists produce
paintings and digitally created images on canvas,
board, card or premium-quality art paper to order.

Taylor Gallery

471 Lisburn Road, Belfast
BT9 7EZ
T 028 90687687
E taylorgallery@btinternet.com
W www.taylorgallery.co.uk
Contact Stephen Donnelly
Established in 1998. Generally features works by
leading Irish and contemporary artists such as
Michael Gemmell, Patsy Dan Rodgers (King of
Tory Island), Gladys Maccabe, Dennis Orme Shaw
and Joop Smits. Also specializes in original
screenprints by Andy Warhol and keeps an
extensive range of these in stock. Offers a
professional appraisal and valuation service.
Submission policy Usually Irish artists.
Price range £195–£100,000
No of exhibitions annually 5

Tom Caldwell Gallery

429 Lisburn Road, Belfast
BT9 7EY
T 028 90661890
F 028 90681890
E info@tomcaldwellgallery.com
W www.tomcaldwellgallery.com
Contact Chris Caldwell

Founded in 1969. A two-floor gallery specializing
predominantly in Irish living art (primarily
painting but also sculpture and ceramics).
Exhibited artists include Colin Middleton, George
Campbell, Gerard Dillon, Paddy Collins, Tom Carr
and Basil Blackshaw. Currently represents fifteen
to twenty artists including Christine Bowen, Colin
Davidson, Carol Graham PRUA, Barbara Rae RA,
Neil Shawcross and Ronnie Wood.
Price range £300–£50,000
No of exhibitions annually 9

Townhouse Gallery Portrush

6 Bath Street, Portrush
BT56 8AW
T 028 70822826
F frankie@townhousegalleryportrush.com
W www.townhousegalleryportrush.com
Opened in 2003, exhibiting photographs,
paintings and prints by leading contemporary
artists as well as ceramics, textiles and jewelry.
Artists include Jonathan Aiken, Frankie Creith
Hill, Naomi Horner, John Johnson, Martin Lloyd,
Brian Magee, Anne Michael, Peter McCausland,
Patricia McCormack-French, Vincent McDonnell,
James McNulty, Ross Wilson, Simon Craig,
Stephen Duke, Andrew Hill and Alastair McCook.

WhiteImage.com

34 Lisburn Street, Hillsborough
BT26 6AB
T 028 92689896
F 028 92688433
E info@whiteimage.com
W www.whiteimage.com
Contact Bill Morrison
Founded in 1994. Specializes in contemporary
Irish art. Aims to bring affordable Irish art to
the widest possible audience. Gallery artists
currently represented include J.P. Rooney,
Sue Howells, Marie Carroll, Colin Middleton,
Louis Le Brocquy and Darren Paul.
Submission policy Interested artists should submit
at least six works. See website for details.
Price range £75–£14,000
No of exhibitions annually 6

North-west

5+ **Contemporary Ceramics**

Unit A, Dixons Court, 101 Lake Road, Ambleside
LA22 0DB
T 015394 33821

E fiveplus@onetel.com
W www.fiveplus.org.uk
Contact Abigail Jacobs or Roger Bell
Founded in 2003 and run by the makers of
the work on show. Established to promote
contemporary ceramics in the north and provide a
fresh and friendly atmosphere in which to discuss
and view contemporary crafts. Artists represented
include Michael and Vicky Eden, Philamena
Pretsell, Vivid Ceramics, Jonathan Garratt and
Fiona Thompson.
Submission policy Artists interested in exhibiting
should send an up-to-date CV with good-quality
images of work.
Price range £5–£500
No of exhibitions annually 2

Ainscough Gallery
9–11 Falkner Street, Liverpool
L8 7PD
T 0151 7099633

Arena Gallery
82–84 Duke Street, Liverpool
L1 5AA
T 0151 7079879
F 0151 7071667
E arenastudios@clara.co.uk
W www.arena.uk.com
Contact James Buso or Paul Luckraft
Artist-led space within walking distance of all
of Liverpool's major public galleries. Aims to show
the work of emerging talent and to build dialogue
and exchange with other artist-led organizations,
both nationally and internationally. The 9m × 9m
gallery is suitable for one-person and small group
exhibitions.
Submission policy Send written proposal and CV.
No of exhibitions annually 6

Artizana
The Village, Prestbury
SK10 4DG
T 01625 827582
F 01625 827582
E art@artizana.co.uk
W www.artizana.co.uk
Founded in 1984 as a private gallery. Aims to
promote contemporary British crafts, with a
particular emphasis on one-off furniture designs.
Exhibited artists include Rachel Woodman
(studio glass), Magdalene Odundo (ceramics),
Ahmed Moustafa (calligraphy), Alan Peters OBE
(furniture), Stephen Broadbent (sculpture),

Tim Stead MBE (furniture), Kevin O'Dwyer
(silver), Verina Warren (embroidery) and Charles
Bray (glass sculpture). Commissions undertaken
for private clients and public institutions.
Submission policy Most craft disciplines
considered. Primary requirement is that work is
contemporary, original and of the highest quality.
Price range £50–£15,000
No of exhibitions annually 2

Benny Browne & Co. Ltd
63 Lawton Street, Congleton
CW12 1RU
T 07765 047598
E bennybrowne@yahoo.com
W www.bennybrowne.com
Contact Vanessa Browne or William Kemp
Exclusive art boutique offering original paintings
and limited-edition giclée prints by living artists
and designers. Offers bespoke commissioning
through on-site artists that combine traditional
principles of colour, harmony and proportion with
modern trends and design flair.
Submission policy Work must display traditional
principles of colour, harmony and proportion.
Price range £50–£1,000
No of exhibitions annually Regularly changing
works and quarterly events.

Blyth Gallery
Amazon House, Brazil Street, Manchester
M1 3PJ
T 0161 2361004
F 0161 2880633
E gallery@artmanchester.com
W www.artmanchester.com
Contact Denise Thornton (Gallery Director)
Established in 1997 and located in the Canal Street
area of central Manchester. Catering for corporate
and private clients, it exhibits contemporary
paintings, sculpture, ceramics and glass works
by both northern-based and international artists.
Has an eclectic selection policy, with an associated
art shop on the premises.
Submission policy Professional/established artists
and sculptors should submit a CV, statement and
captioned images with an sae. No photography,
installations or video.
Price range £80–£1,800
No of exhibitions annually 12

Castlefield Gallery
2 Hewitt Street, Knott Mill, Manchester
M15 4GB

T 0161 8328034
F 0161 8192295
E info@castlefieldgallery.co.uk
W www.castlefieldgallery.co.uk
Contact Sophia Crilly (Programme Coordinator)
Initiated by artists in 1984. Now one of the most
established artist-run galleries in the UK. Curates
exhibitions by both emerging and high profile
national and international contemporary artists.
Runs a creative and professional-development
programme for artists and curators, including
residencies, seminars, debates, e-newsletters, a
resource directory and assistance in new artist-led
projects. Artists represented include Gordon
Cheung, Elaine Constantine, Tom Hackney,
Chris Jones, Mark Leckey and Olivia Plender.
Submission policy One annual deadline. All media
considered. Artists should provide exhibition
proposal, statement, CV, professional reference
and five to ten images. See website for full details.
Price range £80–£50,000. Operates Arts Council
England's Own Art interest-free loan scheme.
No of exhibitions annually 6 exhibitions in main
gallery; 6 in project space.

Colin Jellicoe Gallery
82 Portland Street, Manchester
M1 4QX
T 0161 2362716
W www.colinjellicoe.co.uk
Opened in 1963 by Colin Jellicoe, a painter
since the late 1950s. Specializes in figurative
and modern drawings, paintings, graphics and
sculpture. Gallery artists include B.E. Cole,
Granville, Colin Gilbert, Debbie Hill, Jellicoe
and John Picking. Acts as agent for several art
competitions (Royal Academy Summer
Exhibition, Singer Friedland Watercolour,
Discerning Eye).
Submission policy Only shows living artists.
Send a CV and up to ten good colour prints.
Price range £50–£500
No of exhibitions annually 2–4

Comme Ca Art Gallery
24 Worsley Street, Castlefield, Manchester
M15 4LD
T 0161 8397187
E info@commecaart.com
W www.commecaart.com

De Lacey Fine Art
15 The Colonnades, Albert Dock, Liverpool
L3 4AA

T 0151 7076020
E info@delaceyfineart.co.uk
W www.delaceyfineart.co.uk
Contact Gordon or Martin Farmer
Founded in 2001, specializing in modern British
and contemporary art. Deals in original works and
original printed works of established artists.
Submission policy Approachable, but does not
usually welcome submissions from artists.
Price range £200–£200,000
No of exhibitions annually 6

Domino Gallery
11 Upper Newington, Liverpool
L1 2SR
T 0151 7070764 / 07775 605326
E felicity.wren@fsbdial.co.uk
Founded in 1989. Shows local, national and
international artists (established and new) such
as John Bratby, Adrian Henri, George Jardine and
Nicholas Horsfield. Has a wide range of work
including painting, photography, prints, drawings,
jewelry and small-scale ceramics.
Submission policy Director chooses exhibitors
according to fairly strict criteria but approaches
welcomed. Advice given to new graduates
regarding portfolios and presentation, etc.
Price range £75–£2,000
No of exhibitions annually Approx. 6

dot-art
4 Princes Park Mansions, Croxteth Road, Liverpool
L8 3SA
T 07976 723796
E lucy.byrne@dot-art.co.uk
W www.dot-art.co.uk
Aims to give individuals and businesses the
opportunity to buy and commission contemporary
art at realistic prices. Provides artists in the north-
west with a vehicle through which to exhibit and
sell their work without prohibitive costs. Art is sold
through the website and at local venues.
Submission policy Artists are welcome to submit
work for consideration at any time, either by email
or post. All media considered.
Price range £30–£8,000
No of exhibitions annually 6

Egg Café
2nd Floor, 16–18 Newington, Liverpool
L1 4ED
T 0151 7072755
E egg_cafe@hotmail.com
W www.cocoon.u-net.com

floating ip

8 Loom Street, Ancoats, Manchester
M4 6AN
T 07979 363698
E info@floatingip.com
W www.floatingip.com
An artist-run space committed to innovative, independent and collaborative projects since 2002.
Submission policy Programme does not include submissions but always glad to engage in discussions with artists and curators.
Price range Does not usually sell art.
No of exhibitions annually 6

Fold Gallery

3 Walton's Yard, Market Square, Kirkby Stephen
CA17 4QT
T 017683 71561
E newart@foldgallery.co.uk
W www.foldgallery.co.uk
An artist-run space in a rural market town. Established in 2001 with the aim of providing and promoting access to cutting-edge contemporary art in rural areas. Also aims to promote the work of innovative artists who live and work in rural communities and to change the perceptions of art produced in rural areas. The exhibition space is a four-metre cube, after the original White Cube in London, only 'it isn't white, nor does it have any right angles.'
Submission policy Work must meet the exhibition criteria, available from the website. Work does not need to be commercially viable.
Price range £2–£10,000. Most work is not for sale.
No of exhibitions annually 6

The Gallery – Manchester's Art House

131 Portland Street, Manchester
M1 4PY
T 0161 2373551
F 0161 2283621
E enquiries@manchestersarthouse.com
W www.manchestersarthouse.com

Gallery 2000

Windle Court, Clayhill Industrial Park, Neston
CH64 3UH
T 0151 3531522

Henry Donn Gallery

138–142 Bury New Road, Whitefield, Manchester
M45 6TD
T 0161 7668819
F 0161 7668819
E donn@netline.uk.net
W www.henrydonngallery.com

Howarth Gallery

134–138 St James Street, Burnley
BB11 1NR
T 01282 416079
E richard@howarth-gallery.co.uk
W www.howarth-gallery.co.uk
Established for over twenty years. Deals in both antique and contemporary art and prints. Also offers framing and valuation services. Contemporary artists include McKenzie Thorpe, Sandra Blow RA, Sir Terry Frost RA, Alex Millar, Stephen Ormerod, Sir Peter Blake RA and Roy Fairchild-Woodard.
Submission policy Always willing to look at new work.
Price range £20–£30,000
No of exhibitions annually 6

International 3

8 Fairfield Street, Manchester
M1 3GF
T 0161 2373336
F 0161 2373336
E info@international3.com
W www.international3.com
A non-profit gallery founded in 2000 to provide space for two organizations, Work & Leisure International and the Annual Programme. Exhibits and commissions new work by contemporary artists, both initiating projects and working with invited curators. Artists commissioned include Andrew McDonald, Bob and Roberta Smith, Ryan Gander, Rachel Goodyear, Harrison and Hughes, and Hayley Newman. Also the base for i3 Publications, whose recent titles include books by Brass Art, Pavel Buchler and Oliver East.
Submission policy Artists wishing to exhibit should visit the gallery and be familiar with its programme. Most exhibitions are initiated by the gallery rather than as a result of unsolicited applications.
Price range £100–£10,000
No of exhibitions annually 8

The Kif

23a Parr Street, Liverpool
L1 4JN
T 0151 7060008
E kif@livingbrain.co.uk
W www.livingbrain.co.uk

Founded in 2003 as an exhibition, workshop, recording and rehearsal space in a disused warehouse in Liverpool city centre. There is also a pottery on site. Aims to assist artists young and old within the city to become established and move forward into self-sustainability.
Submission policy Artists should phone or visit the space to assess suitability.
Price range £25–£500
No of exhibitions annually 10

L.issue Gallery @ Urban Coffee
349 Smithdown Road, Liverpool
L15 3JJ
T 0151 7342624
E lisedgar@iclway.co.uk
Contact Lis Edgar
Founded in 2003. Aims to give a voice to local artists. Includes a sculpture garden. Has a biennial show of work by seventeen artists including Adrian Henri and Richard Young. A catalogue, website and print service are under development.
Submission policy Views artists' work by appointment and plans shows accordingly.
Price range £10–£5,000
No of exhibitions annually 8

Liverpool History Shop
5 The Colonnades, Albert Dock, Liverpool
L3 4AA
T 0151 7093566
E norma@liverpoolpictures.co.uk
W www.liverpoolpictures.co.uk
Contact Norma Lyons
Founded in 1991, specializing in photographs, prints and paintings of Liverpool and surrounding areas. Showcases many Liverpool artists.
Submission policy Must be of local interest. Laser prints not accepted.
Price range £120–£1,500 for original paintings; £20–£200 for original photographs; £24.50–£125 for unframed art prints.

Lowes Court Gallery
12 Main Street, Egremont
CA22 2DW
T 01946 820693
E email@egremont-tic.fsnet.co.uk
W www.lowescourtgallery.co.uk
Contact Gallery Manager or Exhibition Organizer
Established in 1972 to promote appreciation of visual arts in Cumbria. Aims to show a high standard of contemporary and traditional arts and crafts by emerging and established artists.

Exhibitions are in the main gallery; members work in the back gallery.
Submission policy Submissions welcome; hard copy preferred. Limited space available. Work from Cumbria or bordering counties only.
Price range Up to £500
No of exhibitions annually 8, at least two of which are reserved for specific local features.

Manchester Craft & Design Centre
17 Oak Street, Northern Quarter, Manchester
M4 5JD
T 0161 8324274
F 0161 8323416
E info@craftanddesign.com
W www.craftanddesign.com
Sited in the heart of Manchester's Northern Quarter, the hub of the city's artistic and innovative community. Occupying the old Smithfield fish market, it provides studio and retail space for a wide range of contemporary applied artists producing ceramics, jewelry, furniture and interiors, textiles and fashion, photography and visual arts, in workshops over two floors. Also has a year-round programme of exhibitions; the exhibition space can be hired when not in use. Open to the public throughout the year. Admission free. All work is for sale and commissions are welcome.
Submission policy Focuses on contemporary crafts, both for tenant artists and temporary exhibitions.
Price range £3–£3,000
No of exhibitions annually 5

Mathew Street Gallery
31 Mathew Street, Liverpool
L2 6RE
T 0151 2350009
E lennonart@mathewstgallery.co.uk
W www.lennonart.co.uk

Mill House Gallery
The Old Windmill, Mill Lane, Parbold
WN8 7NW
T 01257 462333
E jb.millhousegallery@virgin.net
W www.jamesbartholomew.co.uk
Founded in 1997, specializing in work by James Bartholomew. Also sells work of other artists including Neville Fleetwood ROI, David Stanley NAPA and Lawrence Isherwood. Offers a full framing service ('Space Framing') in adjoined premises.

Submission policy All media considered. Apply in the first instance by photos, slides, etc.
Price range £100–£2,000
No of exhibitions annually 4

Northern Lights Gallery

22 St John Street, Keswick
CA12 5AS
T 01768 775402
E info@northernlightsgallery.co.uk
W www.northernlightsgallery.co.uk
Founded in 1999, specializing in contemporary art and crafts from the north of England and Scotland. Artists represented include Jonathan Trotman, Alison Critchlow, Matt Jardine and Joe Dias.
Submission policy Artists must be resident in Cumbria or neighbouring counties.
Price range £10–£2,000
No of exhibitions annually 4–6

Percy House Gallery

38–42 Market Place, Cockermouth
CA13 9NG
T 01900 829667
W www.percyhouse.co.uk
Established in 2002 as an outlet for work by Cumbrian artists. Artists featured include Jenny Coweru (feltwork), Sue Lawson (oils), Geoff Marsters (pastels) and David Herrod (photographs).
Submission policy Photographs of work must be submitted and an appointment made. Prefers local work for exhibitions.
Price range £50–£2,000
No of exhibitions annually 8 solo; 2 mixed.

Philips Contemporary Art

Studio 10, 10a Little Lever Street, Manchester
M1 1HR
T 0161 9414197
E philipsgallery@supanet.com
W www.philipscontemporaryart.com

Platform Gallery

Station Road, Clitheroe
BB7 2JT
T 01200 443071
F 01200 414556
E platform.gallery@ribblevalley.gov.uk
W www.ribblevalley.gov.uk
Contact Grace Whowell
The showcase for contemporary craft in Lancashire, run by Ribble Valley Borough Council. Specializes in textiles, ceramics, glass, jewelry and wood by local and national makers. There is also a craft shop and education space for workshops and talks.
Submission policy Work must be craft-based, rather than painting or photography. Send images, CV and artist's statement.
Price range £3–£3,000
No of exhibitions annually 8

Richard Goodall Gallery

59 Thomas Street, Northern Quarter, Manchester
M4 1NA
T 0161 8323435
F 0161 8323266
E richard@richardgoodallgallery.com
W www.richardgoodallgallery.com

Ruhm Gallery

15 Victoria Road, Penrith
CA11 8HN
T 01768 867453
F 01768 866621
E info@ruhmgallery.plus.com
W www.ruhmgallery.plus.com
Contact Pauline or Helen
Exhibits both local and national artists working in glass, textiles, pottery, mixed media, paintings, prints and photography. The spacious exhibition room is connected by double doors to the Ruhm Café, encouraging large numbers of browsers.
Submission policy If liked, work is shown for a six-week trial. Artists must have their own insurance. Semi-abstract art welcome.
Price range £20–£5,000

Thornthwaite Galleries

Thornthwaite, Keswick
CA12 5SA
T 01768 778248
E enquiries@thornthwaite.net
W www.thornthwaite.net
Contact Ron Monk
Now in its thirty-fifth year, displaying over one hundred artists. Work includes paintings (oil, pastel, watercolour, etc.), wood-turning, wood sculpture, metal sculpture, pottery, ceramics, jewelry, photography and furniture.
Price range £5–£2,000

Tib Lane Gallery

14A Tib Lane, Manchester
M2 4JA
T 0161 8346928
Contact J.M. Green

Founded in 1959, dealing primarily in British (mainly figurative) twentieth-century works. Established and less widely known artists are shown in both solo and mixed exhibitions from October to June. Exhibited artists include Frink, Herman, Valette and Vaughan.
Submission policy Gallery exhibits oil paintings, watercolours, drawings and pastels. No ceramics.
Price range From £100
No of exhibitions annually 6

Unicorn Gallery
1 Kings Court, Water Lane, Wilmslow
SK9 5AR
T 01625 525276
E originalpaintings@btconnect.com
W www.originalpaintings.com
Established in 1950, dealing in traditional and contemporary original works of art. Specialists in northern artists including L.S. Lowry, Arthur Delany and Braag. Others include portrait artist Robert Lenkiewicz, teddy-bear artist Deborah Jones and landscape artist Gerhard Neswadba. Large studio space may be available for use by artists.
Submission policy Always looking for talented new artists. Both painters and sculptors are welcome to submit work.
Price range £175–£40,000
No of exhibitions annually 2–3

Victorian Gallery
40 St John's Hill, Shrewsbury
SY1 1JQ
T 01743 356351
F 01743 356351
E victoriangallery@xln.co.uk
Founded in 1987. A specialist in antique maps and prints. Also stocks etchings, aquatints, etc. by contemporary artists, including Piers Browne and other British and Latvian etchers.
Price range £50–£300

View Two Gallery
23 Mathew Street, Liverpool
L2 6RE
T 0151 2369555

Watergate Street Gallery
60 Watergate Street, Chester
CH1 2LA
T 01244 345698
F 01244 3458837
W www.watergatestreetgallery.co.uk

Opened in 1992, offering original paintings, etchings and screenprints. Artists include Bernhard Vogel, Roy Fairchild Woodard, Willi Kissmer, Jurgen Gorg and Ian Fennelly.
Price range £250–£4,000
No of exhibitions annually 3

Wendy J. Levy Contemporary Art
17 Warburton Street, Didsbury, Manchester
M20 6WA
T 0161 4464880
E wendy@wendyjlevy-art.com
W www.wendyjlevy-art.com

Scotland

Amber Roome Contemporary Art
75–79 Cumberland Street, Edinburgh
EH3 6RD
T 0131 5583352
E mail@amberroome.co.uk
W www.amberroome.co.uk
Based in the heart of Edinburgh's New Town. Exhibits a changing programme of contemporary art by established and emerging artists from Scotland and beyond.
Submission policy Accepts submissions from artists in painting, photography, printmaking and drawing.
Price range £150–£5,000
No of exhibitions annually 10, including painting and photography.

Anthony Woodd Gallery
4 Dundas Street, Edinburgh
EH3 6HZ
T 0131 5589544 / 5589545
F 0131 5589525
E sales@anthonywoodd.com
W www.anthonywoodd.com
Formally called the Malcolm Innes Gallery. Specialist in Scottish, sporting, military, landscape and contemporary works. Framing, restoration, valuation and commission services undertaken.
No of exhibitions annually 4

Bourne Fine Art
6 Dundas Street, Edinburgh
EH3 6HZ
T 0131 5574050
F 0131 5578382
E art@bournefineart.com
W www.bournefineart.com

Founded in 1978, specializing in paintings and sculpture from the seventeenth century to the present day. Artists represented include Allan Ramsay, Sir Henry Raeburn and Sir David Wilkie, as well as contemporary artists including John Boyd, John Bryne and Jilly Sutton.
Submission policy Not currently taking on any new artists.
Price range £200–£650,000
No of exhibitions annually 8

Castle Gallery

43 Castle Street, Inverness
IV2 3DU
T 01463 729512
E info@castlegallery.co.uk
W www.castlegallery.co.uk
Contact Denise Collins
Founded in 2001. A leading contemporary-art gallery in Scotland. Exhibitions feature paintings, sculpture, handmade prints, crafts and designer jewelry. Represents established artists and emerging talent including Karolina Larusdottir, Shazia Mahmood, Jonathan Shearer, Vega, Blandine Anderson and Dorothy Stirling.
Submission policy Artists should send by post the following: ten recent images as photos, slides or jpegs; details of the images with titles, sizes and artist's prices; biographical information; an sae.
Price range £100–£5,000
No of exhibitions annually 5 solo or joint shows. Also a constantly changing mixed display throughout the year.

Cat's Moustache Gallery

54 St John's Street, Creetown, nr Newton Stewart
DG8 7JT
T 01671 820577 / 01659 50680
F 01671 820577
E rtrevanion@hotmail.com
W www.thecatsmoustachegallery.co.uk
Contact Penelope Nye
Offers original unique handmade arts and crafts from Scotland, the UK and beyond. Stocks a wide range of paintings in oils, acrylics and watercolours, silk painting, calligraphy and lettercutting, ceramics, jewelry, wood, glass, textiles and other handmade gifts. Runs a regular series of exhibitions and demonstrations throughout the year, all of which are free. Open Saturdays and Sundays from 11 a.m. to 5 p.m., or by appointment.
Price range £1–£500
No of exhibitions annually 12

Centre for Contemporary Arts (CCA)

350 Sauchiehall Street, Glasgow
G2 3JD
T 0141 3327521
F 0141 3323226
E gen@cca-glasgow.com
W www.cca-glasgow.com
Scotland's Centre for Contemporary Arts is made up of six flexible arts spaces presenting the very best in contemporary visual art, film, music, performance, club nights and more.
No of exhibitions annually 6

Collective Gallery

22–28 Cockburn Street, Edinburgh
EH1 1NY
T 0131 2201260
E mail@collectivegallery.org
W www.collectivegallery.org
Originally established as an artist-run space in 1984; has now developed into an independent, publicly funded exhibition, commissioning and development agency. Aims to support emergent Scottish contemporary art and artists within the context of an international programme. Committed to creating access to the contemporary visual arts through a range of innovative projects and structures. Ongoing exhibition programme in the two galleries and project room. Increasingly interested in inviting artists to design specific projects operating within the framework of the city's contemporary social, economic, political and physical spheres.
Submission policy Has extensive membership scheme, costing £5 for Scottish-based artists and £15 for all other artists. Members are entitled to submit exhibition applications twice a year (deadlines are in March and September).
No of exhibitions annually 8 in main gallery; 8 in project room.

Compass Gallery

178 West Regent Street, Glasgow
G2 4RL
T 0141 2216370
F 0141 2481322
E compass@gerberfineart.co.uk
W www.compassgallery.co.uk
Contact Jill Gerber
In its thirty-sixth year, promoting young, emerging Scottish-based artists and established contemporary artists throughout the UK.
A registered charity and non-profit-making company.

Submission policy By email or post (CD preferred).
Price range £50–£10,000
No of exhibitions annually 6–8

Custom House Art Gallery and Studios

Custom House, 19 High Street, Kirkcudbright
DG6 4JZ
T 01557 330585
E customhouse@btinternet.com
W www.customhousegallery.co.uk
Contact Suzanne Davies
Shows contemporary art in the traditional setting
of Kirkcudbright, an attractive coastal town in
south-west Scotland with strong links to the
Glasgow Boys and the Scottish Colourists. Painter
Suzanne Davies and printmaker–illustrator
Malcolm Davies live and work here, showing their
own work and work by other professional artists
and makers, mostly from Dumfries and Galloway.
Non-residential drawing and painting courses are
held all year.
Submission policy CV and recent images welcome
from professional artists and makers in southern
Scotland, northern England and Northern Ireland.
Price range £20–£1,000
No of exhibitions annually 5–6

Cyril Gerber Fine Art

148 West Regent Street, Glasgow
G2 2RQ
T 0141 2213095
F 0141 2481322
E cyril@gerberfineart.co.uk
W www.gerberfineart.co.uk
Contact Jill Gerber
Established in 1983, the gallery's large stock
includes prominent nineteenth- and twentieth-
century British artists (including the Glasgow
School, Scottish Colourists and twentieth-century
Scottish masters) as well as contemporary work.
Submission policy Apply by email or post (CDs
preferred).
Price range £100–£95,000
No of exhibitions annually 4–6

doggerfisher

11 Gayfield Square, Edinburgh
EH1 3NT
T 0131 5587110
F 0131 5587179
E mail@doggerfisher.com
W www.doggerfisher.com
Established in May 2001. Exhibits and promotes
new-generation and established artists from

Scotland and beyond. The 100m² gallery in a
former tyre garage was designed by architect
Oliver Chapman. Has so far been selected to
participate in over ten international art fairs
including the Armory in New York, Liste in
Basel and Frieze in London. In addition to the
programmed exhibitions, it also holds an archive
of represented artists' work, available to view in the
gallery. Represented artists include Claire Barclay,
Graham Fagen, Moyna Flannigan, Louise
Hopkins, Sally Osborn, Hanneline Visnes.
Submission policy The gallery is programmed by
the director, showing exhibitions by represented
and invited artists. It does not accept proposals for
exhibitions. Non-returnable invites and details of
exhibitions welcomed.
Price range £200–£20,000
No of exhibitions annually 4

Dundas Street Gallery

6a Dundas Street, Edinburgh
EH3 6HZ
T 0131 5589363
E carolyn@bournefineart.com
W www.bournefineart.com
Contact Carolyn Henderson
A recently refurbished gallery offering 700 sq. ft
of exhibition space available for hire.

Edinburgh Printmakers

23 Union Street, Edinburgh
EH1 3LR
T 0131 5572479
F 0131 5588418
E info@edinburgh-printmakers.co.uk
W www.edinburgh-printmakers.co.uk
Contact David Watt
Established in 1967. Dedicated to promoting
contemporary printmaking practice. It achieves
this by providing, maintaining and staffing an
entrance-free gallery and open -ccess print studio,
where artists and members of the public can use
equipment and source technical expertise to
develop their printmaking skills.
Submission policy Annually selects a set number
of exhibitions from artists' proposals.
Price range £30–£3,000
No of exhibitions annually 6

English-Speaking Union Scotland

23 Atholl Crescent, Edinburgh
EH3 8HQ
T 0131 2291528
F 0131 2298620

E director@esuscotland.org.uk
W www.esuscotland.org.uk
Contact John A. Duncan
A charity founded in 1918 to promote international understanding through English. The Edinburgh gallery has provided high-quality exhibition space in the heart of the city for the last forty years.
Submission policy No restrictions.
Price range Depends on exhibitors.
No of exhibitions annually 5–6

Glasgow Print Studio
22 & 25 King Street, Merchant City, Glasgow
G1 5QP
T 01415 520704
F 01415 522919
E gallery@gpsart.co.uk
W www.gpsart.co.uk
Active since 1972 in encouraging and promoting the art of printmaking through practice, exhibition, education and sales. One of the largest publishers of original prints in the UK. A member-led organization offering artist members open-access facilities in etching, lithography, relief print, screenprint and digital print production. Also offers introductory classes in printmaking.
Submission policy Exhibition submissions welcome from artists specializing in printmaking.
Price range £100–£5,000
No of exhibitions annually 20

Infrared Gallery
18a Meadow Road, Glasgow Harbour, Glasgow
G11 6HX
T 0141 3371283
E infraredgallery@btconnect.com
Contact James Russell
Founded in 2003, specializing in contemporary Scottish art. Artists represented include Rick Ulman, Leila Smith, Evan Sutherland, Simon Laurie, Michelle Dawn Hannah and James Russell.
Submission policy All contemporary living artists considered. Work viewed preferably on slides or as digital photos on CD.
Price range £50–£10,000
No of exhibitions annually 12

Ingleby Gallery
6 Carlton Terrace, Edinburgh
EH7 5DD
T 0131 5564441
F 0131 5564454
E info@inglebygallery.com
W www.inglebygallery.com

Contact Caroline Broadhurst (Gallery Manager)
Founded in 1998, aiming to show some of the best in international contemporary painting, photography and sculpture. Exhibited artists include Susan Derges, Ian Hamilton Finlay, Howard Hodgkin, Callum Innes, Sean Scully and Garry Fabian Miller.
Submission policy Welcomes serious submissions from artists but recommends artists consider the gallery programme and the specific kinds of work exhibited before making a proposal. Prefers an initial submission of a CV and a small number of images by email.
Price range From £10 for prints; from £500 for original works.
No of exhibitions annually 6

The Jerdan Gallery
42 Marketgate South, Crail, Fife
KY10 3TL
T 01333 450797
E david@thejerdangallery.com
W www.thejerdangallery.com
Founded in 2002, the gallery specializes in Scottish contemporary art, woodwork, sculpture, glass and jewelry. Works regularly in stock by Duncan Macleod, Joe McIntyre, Lin Pattullo, Derek Sanderson, Pat Kramek and Tom Scott.
Price range £100–£10,000
No of exhibitions annually 8

John Green Fine Art
182 Bath Street, Glasgow
G2 4HG
T 0141 3331991
E mail@johngreenfineart.co.uk
W www.johngreenfineart.co.uk
Contact Phyllis Malcolm
Founded in 1984. Dealers in nineteenth- and twentieth-century and contemporary oils and watercolours, mostly by Scottish artists but also including British and continental artists. Current stock includes works by the Glasgow Boys and Girls, the Scottish Colourists, post-war artists Sir Robin Philipson and William Gear, and contemporary artists Blair Thompson, Jonathan Robertson and Norman Edgar. Also offers specialist framing and restoration services.
Submission policy Welcomes submissions from artists. Initial contact should be made via email or telephone.
Price range From £100
No of exhibitions annually 4

Lloyd Jerome Gallery

200 Bath Street, Glasgow
G2 4HG
T 0141 3310722
F 0141 3310733
E lj@dentalpractice.com
W www.dentalpractice.com
Opened in 1994 with the aim of creating a space
that would show work that might not otherwise be
seen in Glasgow.
Price range Up to £50,000
No of exhibitions annually 10

Marchmont Gallery and Picture Framer

56 Warrender Park Road, corner with Marchmont
Road, Edinburgh
EH9 1EX
T 0131 2288228
F 0131 2288228
E enquiries@marchmontgallery.com
W www.marchmontgallery.com
Contact James Sutherland
Founded in 2004. Shows mainly new and up-
and-coming artists including Claudia Massie,
Nicola Moir and Peter Gorrie. Professional
in-house picture-framing service (including
canvas-stretching).
Submission policy Happy to view any works of art.
Contact the gallery to arrange a date and time.
Price range £5–£1,500

Modern Institute

Suite 6, 73 Robertson Street, Glasgow
G2 8QD
T 0141 2483711
F 0141 2483280
E mail@themoderninstitute.com
W www.themoderninstitute.com
Contact Toby Webster
Founded in 1998. Represents thirty artists,
including Jim Lambie, Cathy Wilkes, Victoria
Morton, Simon Starling, Richard Wright, Martin
Boyce, Urs Fischer, Mark Handforth and Monika
Soswsnowska.
No of exhibitions annually 10

Open Eye Gallery and i2 Gallery

34 Abercromby Place, Edinburgh
EH3 6RD
T 0131 5571020 / 5589872
F 0131 5571020
E open.eye@virgin.net
W www.openeyegallery.co.uk
Contact Michelle Norman

Established in 1982 and situated in Edinburgh's
historic New Town, the Open Eye Gallery is
equidistant between the Scottish National
Gallery and the Portrait Gallery. Deals with both
established and young contemporary artists.
Exhibitors include Alan Davie, John Bellany,
Calum Colvin and Adrian Wiszniewski. In
addition to paintings, the gallery exhibits applied
arts. i2 focuses on British and international
printmaking, exhibiting Picasso, Miró, Albers,
Warhol, Lucian Freud, William Scott and
David Hockney.
Price range £100–£50,000
No of exhibitions annually 16

Peacock Visual Arts

21 Castle Street, off the Castlegate, Aberdeen
AB11 5BQ
T 01224 639539
F 01224 627094
E info@peacockvisualarts.co.uk
W www.peacockvisualarts.co.uk
Contact Monika Vykoukal (Assistant Curator)
Founded in 1974. An educational charity funded
by Aberdeen City Council and the Scottish Arts
Council. It exists to bring artists and public
together to share and explore ideas and to make
and present art in innovative ways. Has developed
a wide range of production facilities and skills (in
design, digital imaging, photography, printmaking
and video) and promotes numerous artists'
participatory and exhibition projects each year.
Submission policy Artists are invited to submit
exhibition or project proposals, focusing on
participatory, socially engaged practice. No areas
or media are excluded.
Price range From £25
No of exhibitions annually Exhibition programme
changes regularly throughout the year.

scotlandart.com

2 St Stephen's Place, Stockbridge, Edinburgh
EH3 5AJ
T 0131 2256257
E www.edinburgh@scotlandart.com
W www.scotlandart.com
Contact Marion Ferguson
Established in 1999. Carries Scotland's largest
stock of original art work (over 1,400 paintings).
Has a number of top Scottish artists, including
Blair Thomson, Patsy Macarthur, Lesley Banks,
Barry Mcglashan, Kirsty Whiten and Ian King.
The website has a page for each artist where
purchases can be made. Offers gift vouchers,

wedding lists, free art consultancy to homes or offices and a leasing service. Takes artists' work to art fairs all over the UK, arranges commissions, ships work to customers in the UK and abroad. Holds exhibitions every month of selected artists. Can also arrange framing for artists and reframes for customers.
Submission policy Only accepts original paintings, sculptures and jewelry from living artists. Applications welcome all year round, preferably jpegs or photos.
Price range £80–£6,000
No of exhibitions annually 12 in each gallery (total of 24).
Branches 6 Burnfield Road, Giffnock, Glasgow G46 7QB **T** 0141 6381200.

Scottish Gallery
16 Dundas Street, Edinburgh
EH3 6HZ
T 0131 5581200
F 0131 5583900
E mail@scottish-gallery.co.uk
W www.scottish-gallery.co.uk
Established by Aitken Dott in 1842. Deals in contemporary and twentieth-century Scottish painting and contemporary objects by established figures and talented newcomers. A craft department was established in 1986. Work by gallery artists and makers always available. Also exhibits at major art fairs and holds an annual exhibition in London.
Submission policy Specializes in the work of Scottish artists, artists with a strong Scottish connection through training, etc. or artists living and working in Scotland.
Price range £20–£20,000

Shoreline Studio
2 Shore Road, Aberdour
KY3 0TR
T 01383 860705
F 01383 860705
E ianmcc@shoreline.demon.co.uk
W www.shoreline.sco.fm
Contact Ian McCrorie
Founded in 1997. A compact gallery aiming to promote quality works of art primarily from artists living and/or working in Scotland. Adjacent listed buildings are intended to become nine workspaces for artists, and an exhibition and workshop space.
Submission policy For display purposes, all art work should be signed and appropriately presented and labelled.

Price range £1–£1,000+
No of exhibitions annually 6

Sorcha Dallas
5 St Margaret's Place, Glasgow
G1 5JY
T 07812 605745
F 0141 5532662
E info@sorchadallas.com
W www.sorchadallas.com

Street Level Photoworks
26 King Street, Glasgow
G1 5QP
T 0141 5522151
F 0141 5522323
E sl-photoworks@btconnect.com
W www.sl-photoworks.demon.co.uk
Contact Malcolm Dickson
Founded in 1989, promoting the creative use of photomedia. Recognized for its integrated practice, the organization presents an ongoing series of exhibitions, and an education and open-access programme. The gallery facilitates photography and media art from both emerging and established artists, whether invited or selected from open submission. Artists represented include Daniel Reeves, Louise Crawford and Stephan Gueneau, Sandy Sharpe, Beverley Hood, Peter Kennard and Virtual Migrants.
Submission policy Accepts open submissions in photography and media art. Send six slides or video/CD, a CV and statement or proposal.
Price range £15–£4,000
No of exhibitions annually 8

Torrance Gallery
36 Dundas Street, Edinburgh
EH3 6JN
T 0131 5566366
F 0131 5566366
E enquiries@torrancegallery.co.uk
W www.torrancegallery.co.uk
Founded in 1970. The first contemporary-art gallery in Dundas Street, the accepted Scottish centre for contemporary art.
Price range £100–£8,000
No of exhibitions annually 15

Tracey McNee Fine Art
47 Parnie Street, Merchant City, Glasgow
G1 5LU
T 0141 5525627
F 0141 5528207

E info@traceymcnee.com
W www.traceymcnee.com
Contact Tracey McNee
Seeks to exhibit the best in contemporary art
from Scotland and beyond. Promotes artists
in the gallery and at the major art fairs throughout
the UK. Artists represented include Gerard M.
Burns, Francis Boag, Sandra Bell and James
Hawkins.
Submission policy Artists from all media
welcomed. Preferably send CV, statement and
images by email.
Price range £200–£40,000
No of exhibitions annually 8

Westgate Gallery

39–41 Westgate, North Berwick
EH39 4AG
T 0160 894976
F 01620 890452
E admin@westgate-gallery.co.uk
W www.westgate-gallery.co.uk
A gallery and gift shop selling original and limited-
edition works by local, Scottish and UK artists.
Includes jewelry, glass and ceramics.
Submission policy All submissions, from both
new and established artists, considered.
Price range Up to £1,000
No of exhibitions annually 2

South-east

Alan Kluckow Fine Art

65 Chobham Road, Sunningdale
SL5 ODT
T 01344 875296
E alan@kluckow.com
W www.kluckow.com
Contact Alan Kluckow
Founded in 1999. Promotes contemporary
British and international painters, sculptors and
photographers. Shows styles from traditional
representational through abstract and new
media. Artists include Ian Rank-Broadley,
Claire Gavronsky, John Meyer and Alistair
Morrison. Other services offered include arts
management, career advice for artists and
portfolio analysis.
Submission policy Preferably send a CD with a
minimum of six images, including a CV and artist
statement (with sae if returns necessary).
Price range £250–£30,000
No of exhibitions annually 10

Albion

Albion House, North Street, Turners Hill, Worth
RH10 4NS
T 01342 715670
E albion@fsmail.net
Contact Paul Avery
Founded in 1965. Specializes in international,
modern and contemporary art. Undertakes
research for private collectors and public
institutions. Art works researched for authenticity,
publication, condition reports and valuation.
Works also purchased and sold via private treaty.
Submission policy Submissions welcomed from
established international artists only.
Price range £500–£5,000,000
No of exhibitions annually None; strictly by
appointment only.

Alexander-Morgan Gallery

7b Station Road, Epping
CM16 4HA
T 01992 571639
F 01992 571639
Contact Dee Alexander-Morgan
Opened in 1997. Sells original paintings,
handmade prints such as etchings and silkscreens,
a few sculptures, ceramics and one-off glass
pieces. Mostly abstract and humorous pieces.
Submission policy Always happy to look at new
work. Usually asks to see photos or flysheets first.
Price range £10–£3,000
No of exhibitions annually 3

Alexandra Wettstein Fine Art

52 Wendover Way, Welling
DA16 2BN
T 020 83047920
E alexandra.wettstein@virgin.net
Deals in paintings, sculpture, prints and ceramics.
Exhibited artists include John Piper, Charles
Newington, Dale Devereux Barker and Sandy
Sykes. Has arranged exhibitions of twentieth-
century and contemporary British artists at
museums and galleries around the country,
including three major retrospectives of John
Piper's work.
Price range From £100

Animal Arts

20 Orange Street, Canterbury
CT1 2JA
T 01227 451145
E info@AnimalArts.co.uk
W www.AnimalArts.co.uk

Contact Keith Williams
Founded in 2001. An independent publisher of wildlife art producing giclée prints from artists' original work. The gallery is situated in the shadow of Canterbury Cathedral and sells throughout the world and to the fine-art trade.
Submission policy Only sells prints (not originals). All media are accepted.
Price range £45–£300

Art Connection Eton

100 High Street, Eton, Windsor
SL4 6AF
T 01753 865265
F 01753 865265
E info@theartconnectioneton.co.uk
W www.theartconnectioneton.co.uk
Contact Jon Barker, Soozy Barker
Founded 1999. Specializes in contemporary landscape, abstract and figurative work in oils and mixed media. Light and spacious gallery offers a relaxed environment to view high-quality, affordable art. Main artists include Jon Barker, John Lawrence, George Thomas, Peter Collins, Soozy Barker and Ian Elliot.
Submission policy Email applications preferred.
Price range £300–£7,500
No of exhibitions annually 4

Art in Action Gallery

Waterperry Gardens, Waterperry, nr Wheatley
OX33 1JZ
T 01844 338085
E art_in_action.gallery@virgin.net
Contact Wendy Farha
Founded in 1994 as a spin-off from 'Art in Action' and a haven for highly crafted decorative and fine arts. Emphasis is on excellence and originality, with work by John Leach, T. Millway, Jennie Gilbert and Laurence McGowan.
Submission policy Highly trained and exhibited artists from all media welcome.
Price range £10–£16,500
No of exhibitions annually 4

Art@94

94 London Road, Apsley, Hemel Hempstead
HP3 9SD
T 01442 234123
F 01442 239761
E info@art4interiors.co.uk
W www.art4interiors.co.uk
Retail and trade (wholesale) outlet for abstract, contemporary, mixed media and traditional paintings on canvas. Most media are catered for. Artists include Kriss Keer, Lizzie Gregory, D. Zealey, S Ringer, Saiqa, Edward Clarke and John Greenwell. Suppliers of blank canvases (single- and double-stretched). Trade and contract framing also undertaken. Specializes in art for homes, interior designers and businesses.
Submission policy Requires mature artists painting contemporary seascapes and abstracts in oils on canvas (not panels). Apply by sending in photos of work or email high-resolution jpegs.
Price range £35–£7,500
No of exhibitions annually 3–4

Arthouse Gallery

10 Western Road, Brighton
BN3 1AE
T 01273 770083
E info@brightonarthouse.com
W www.brightonarthouse.com
Opened in 2005. One of the largest commercial contemporary-art galleries in Brighton and Hove. Provides a retail outlet for a diverse range of artists producing paintings, prints, sculptures, ceramics, jewelry and furniture. The integrated skylight café ensures a high level of traffic. Aims to provide a friendly, calm, non-pressured environment for people from all walks of life to enjoy and purchase art.
Submission policy Constantly looking for new, exciting artists. Offers highly competitive commission rates and hard-working representation.
Price range £50–£5,000
No of exhibitions annually Private views every month.

artrepublic

13 Bond Street, Brighton
BN1 1RD
T 01273 724829
F 01273 746016
E info@artrepublic.com
W www.artrepublic.com
Contact Lawrence Alkin
Features thousands of art prints from hundreds of famous artists including Dalí, Warhol, Lichtenstein, de Lempicka, Klee and Hockney. Also offers a high-quality mounting and framing service.
Submission policy Although most prints are by famous artists, it occasionally features prints by local artists.
Price range £10–£2,500

Artwork Sculpture Gallery

3 The Shambles, Sevenoaks
TN13 1LJ
T 01732 450960
E info@artworksgallery.co.uk
W www.artworksgallery.co.uk
Founded in 1990. Specializes in sculptures in bronze, bronze resin, steel and stone. Artists represented include Tom Greenshields, Kate Denton, Everard Meynell, Gill Brown, Angela Bishop and Martin Roberts.
Price range £200–£15,000

Barn Galleries

Aston, Henley-on-Thames
RG9 3DX
T 01491 577786
F 01491 577786
E info@barngalleries.com
W www.barngalleries.com
Established in 1990. Hosts Artspace, an annual contemporary art extravaganza where seventy-five invited artists show in eighteenth-century timbered barns and gardens.
Submission policy Applications invited from September to December for the following summer season.
Price range £20–£5,000. Most paintings under £1,000.
No of exhibitions annually 2–3

Barry Keene Gallery

12 Thameside, Henley-on-Thames
RG9 1BH
T 01491 577119
E barrykeene@fsbdial.co.uk
W www.barrykeenegallery.co.uk
Opened in 1971. Shows antique, modern and contemporary art including paintings, watercolours, etchings, prints, drawings and sculpture. Master frame-maker, picture restorer and conservator. Artists represented include Ronald Ossary Dunlop, RA RBA NEAC, L.G. Samuel Palmer RWS, John Martin RBA, Helen Hale ROI NS SWA FPS, David Eustace RBA and Richard Pikesley RWS NEAC.
Submission policy Details and photos by post or email.
Price range From £50
No of exhibitions annually 2

Bell Fine Art Ltd

67b Parchment Street, Winchester
SO23 8AT

T 01962 860439
F 01962 860439
E bellfineart@btclick.com
W www.bellfineart.co.uk
Founded in 1977, specializing in original art from 1800 to the present day. Also sells sculpture, ceramics and glass, and offers a full picture-framing service. Exhibits at ten art and antique fairs annually.
Submission policy No video or installations.
Price range £5–£5,000
No of exhibitions annually 1

Bluemoon Gallery

18 Camden Road, Tunbridge Wells
TN1 2PT
T 01892 540100
E iaysha@iaysha.com
W www.bluemoongallery.co.uk, www.iaysha.com
Originally opened as a base for owner Iaysha Salih to show her paintings. Now also exhibits work by other artists including paintings, sculptures, vases, textiles, scarves, bags, jewelry and more. Items exhibited must be individually handmade. The gallery's primary focus is to raise awareness of healing with art.
Submission policy Original art only (no prints). Artists wishing to exhibit should send in a CD of their work.

Brian Sinfield Gallery Ltd

150 High Street, Burford
OX18 4QU
T 01993 824464
E gallery@briansinfield.com
W www.briansinfield.com
Established in 1972. Specializes in contemporary and twentieth-century painters including Fred Cuming, P.J. Crook, Peter Kuhfeld, L.S. Lowry and Alan Lowndes. Up to eight exhibitions a year with catalogues. Also art brokers (selling higher priced paintings on behalf of clients).
Submission policy Will consider the work of new artists in any medium, though not pure abstract or 'cutting-edge'.
Price range £500–£100,000+. Most paintings sell between £1,500 and £12,000.
No of exhibitions annually 8

Brighton Artists' Gallery of Contemporary Art

108a Dyke Road, Brighton
BN1 3TE
T 01273 711016
E alicia.murphy@baggallery.co.uk

W www.baggallery.co.uk
Established in 2001 and one of the largest commercial galleries in East Sussex. Exhibited artists include Man Ray and Damien Hirst as well as local artists. Gallery restructured in 2005 to include the Bank café–bar. Solo-show, print and photographic galleries available. Framing service offered.
Submission policy Artists looking for solo shows should send jpegs at 300 pixels high and no more than 72 dpi, plus short biography and statement. Only contemporary artists will be considered.
Price range From £50 for limited-edition prints. Up to £2,500 for paintings.
No of exhibitions annually 12 in each gallery space.

Canon Gallery

New Street, Petworth
GU28 0AS
T 01798 344422
F 01798 344422
E enquiries@canongallery.co.uk
W www.thecanongallery.co.uk
Founded in 1985, specializing in eighteenth-, nineteenth- and twentieth-century oils and watercolours. Also sells work by contemporary artists.
Submission policy 'Any artist who can paint!'
Price range £400–£50,000
No of exhibitions annually 3

Chameleon Gallery

13a Prince Albert Street, Brighton
BN1 1HE
T 01273 324432
F 01273 324432
E info@chameleongallery.org
W www.chameleongallery.org
Contact Mark Francis
Positioned at the heart of Brighton in the Lanes, the gallery displays work on two floors, holding over one hundred pieces. As well as showing local artists, the owner travels extensively across the country looking for new talent. The gallery's philosophy is to show art of the highest quality at affordable prices.
Submission policy Considers all contemporary art. Artists should send examples of work via email.
Price range £100–£1,000
No of exhibitions annually 6

Chichester Gallery

8 The Hornet, Chichester
PO19 7JG

T 01243 779821
F 01243 773345
Founded to sponsor the sale of good-quality fine art (contemporary and period). Cleaning and restoration of oils and watercolours also undertaken.
Price range £75–£7,000
No of exhibitions annually 2

Cottage Gallery

4 Eastcliff Road, Shanklin Old Village, Isle of Wight
PO37 6AA
T 01983 868373
F 01983 531447
W www.afton-gallery.co.uk
Founded in 1988, exhibiting an extensive range of Isle of Wight paintings and prints, limited and signed editions of Anne Cotterill (floral) and Tim Thompson (marine), and handpainted bone china. Also offers picture-framing service.
Submission policy No further submissions wanted.
Price range Framed prints up to £200. Framed originals up to £1,500.

Craftsmen's Gallery

1 Market Street, Woodstock
OX20 1SU
T 01993 811995
F 01993 811995
E richard.marriott@btclick.com
W www.craftsmensgallery.co.uk
Under present ownership since 1984. Specializes in work by British artists and craftsmen. Artists include Andrea Bates (pastels), Ken Messer (watercolours), Valerie Petts (watercolours and prints), Colin Tuffrey (watercolours and oils) and David Langford (watercolours and acrylics). The art materials department provides a wide range of materials for students and professional artists. Complete picture-framing service available. Ten per cent discount offered to students.
Price range £50–£1,200
No of exhibitions annually 1–2

Cranbrook Gallery

Stone Street, Cranbrook
TN17 3HF
T 01580 720720
E info@cranbrookgallery.com
W www.cranbrookgallery.com
Contact Paul Rodgers
Founded in 1977, specializing in watercolours by British artists working from the eighteenth to early

twentieth centuries. Also UK sales agents for award-winning equestrian artist Alison Guest. Publishers of fine-art prints.
Submission policy Submissions from living artists working in watercolour are welcome.
Price range £100–£16,000
No of exhibitions annually 2

Daniel Laurence Fine Artworks
226 and 246 Kings Road Arches, Brighton
BN1 1NB
T 01273 739694 / 07780 616223
F 01273 739694
E info@daniellaurence.co.uk
W www.daniellaurence.co.uk
A seafront studio and gallery set within Brighton's artists' quarter. Displays a range of works including limited-edition prints, original paintings, sculpture and furniture.
Submission policy Open to applications by painters, sculptors and craftspeople.
Price range £65–£255 for limited-edition works. £250–£1,000 for original works (oil paintings).

East Meets West Gallery
50 High Street, Oxford
OX1 4AS

Fairfax Gallery
23 The Pantiles, Tunbridge Wells
TN2 5TD
T 01892 525525
E andrew@fairfaxgallery.com
W www.fairfaxgallery.com
Founded in 1995. Exhibits established, award-winning and emerging contemporary artists including Fred Cuming RA, David Atkins, Shaun Ferguson, Mark Johnston and Ross Loveday.
Submission policy Work may be submitted on slides, prints or CD with CV and sae. May also be submitted by email.
Price range £100–£10,000
No of exhibitions annually 9

Farnham Maltings East Wing Gallery
Bridge Square, Farnham
GU9 7QR
T 01252 726234
F 01252 718177
E info@farnhammaltings.com
W www.farnhammaltings.com
Contact Kate Martin (Visual Arts Officer)
Set in one of the old kilns. Hosts a variety of exhibitions throughout the year, ranging from

graduate shows to national touring exhibitions. Exhibited artists include David Hockney, Matisse and Andy Goldsworthy.
Submission policy Space is for rental to individuals and art groups. All artists are asked to present work for selection. All media considered.
No of exhibitions annually 15–20

Fourwalls
9 Foundry Street, Brighton
BN1 4AT
T 01273 694405
E info@four-walls.co.uk
W www.four-walls.co.uk
Contact Lara Bowen
An art agency with an eclectic portfolio of quality contemporary work from artists in Brighton and the surrounding area. From portraiture to landscapes, oils to photography, there is no house style. Manages, promotes and publishes work by artsits including Sophie Abbott, Becky Blair, Simon Dixon, Chris Kettle, Shyama Ruffell and Adrian Talbot. Also curates group and solo shows in a range of spaces including non-gallery settings.
Submission policy Artists should initially send five images, a CV and statement by email or post. Does not curently work with sculptors.
Price range £100–£2,500
No of exhibitions annually 50, many rotated around various spaces.

Fovea Gallery
140 Vaughan Road, Harrow
HA1 4EB
T 020 83572924
E fovea@freeuk.com
W www.foveagallery.co.uk
Contact Debbie de Beer
Founded in 2002 in an old butcher's shop, aiming to give solo shows in a small dedicated space. Occasional mixed shows. Peer critique sessions for artists. Opportunities to run workshops.
Submission policy Any medium considered. Artists should visit to view the space. Solo shows usually scheduled at least eighteen months in advance.
Price range Up to £1,000
No of exhibitions annually 10

Francis Iles
Rutland House, 103 High Street, Rochester
ME1 1LX
T 01634 843081
F 01634 846681

E nettie@francis-iles.com
W www.artycat.com
Contact Nettie Iles-North
Established in 1962. Exhibited living artists work mainly in a representative vein but there is some contemporary work as well. Handles the estates of Rowland Hilder OBE PPRI RSMA and Roland Batchelor RWS. Shows over seven hundred works at any one time.
Price range £60–£20,000
No of exhibitions annually 4 in-house; 4 art fairs.

Gallery 99

25 High Street, Knaphill, Woking
GU21 2PP
T 01483 797884
F 01483 797884
W www.gallery-99.co.uk
Sells mainly original paintings. Also offers a picture-framing service and sells artists' materials.
Submission policy Applications welcome in person, by prior arrangement. All works sold on commission (thirty per cent to the gallery, seventy per cent to the artist). Flat art work only; no room for sculpture.
Price range £50–£500

Gallery Beckenham

71A High Street, Beckenham
BR3 1AW
T 020 86503040
E enquiries@gallerybeckenham.com
W www.gallerybeckenham.com
Family-owned gallery specializing in contemporary art from noteworthy young artists and those more established. Specializations include original canvases, sculpture, glass and art photography. Artists include Yuri Gorbachev, Sandro Negri, Anna Bocek, Susan Caines, Mark Leach, Enver Gursev, Manuel Quintanilla, Ev Meynell and Danny Green.
Submission policy All types of art considered. Email contact details with six images of work.
Price range £200–£40,000
No of exhibitions annually 6

George Street Gallery

4 George Street, Brighton
BN2 1RH
T 01273 681852
E gsg@onetel.com
Established in 1898. For hire to established artists only. Also offers bespoke picture-framing service.

Submission policy Artists should submit images of work and CV by post or email. All types of art considered. Established artists only.
Price range £50–£2,000
No of exhibitions annually 5

Grace Barrand Design Centre

19 High Street, Nutfield
RH1 4HH
T 01737 822865
F 01737 822617
E info@gbdc.co.uk
W www.gracebarrand.co.uk
Contact Aileen Hamilton
Founded in 1996. Committed to promoting and selling the best in contemporary art and design by established and new makers. Regular exhibitors include Bob Crooks, Peter Layton, Sharon Ting, Janet Bolton and Sandra Eastwood. There is a café where wall space is rented out to artists.
Submission policy Artists need to contact the centre initially and then submit their work, which is put before a selection committee.
Price range £25–£17,000
No of exhibitions annually 6

Greengage Gallery

21 High Street, Chalfont St Giles
HP8 4QH
T 01494 875855
Established in 2002 and located in the heart of a Chilterns village in a seventeenth-century listed building. Shows a variety of contemporary works by living artists from the south-east and Lakeland.
Submission policy Will consider original paintings only, plus ceramics, sculptures and wrought iron designs.
No of exhibitions annually 10

Hannah Peschar Sculpture Garden

Black & White Cottage, Standon Lane, Ockley
RH5 5QR
T 01306 627269
F 01306 627662
E hpeschar@easynet.co.uk
W www.hannahpescharsculpture.com
Contact Hannah Peschar
Has developed over the last twenty-five years and shows over one hundred different national and international sculptors, including Peter Randall Page, Stephen Cox, Charlotte Mayer, Neil Wilkin and Bert Frijns.

Submission policy Good-quality images and CV in the first instance. All work must be durable for the outdoors, i.e. frost- and storm-proof.
Price range £200–£70,000
No of exhibitions annually 1

Inspires Art Gallery
27 Little Clarendon Street, Oxford
OX1 2HU
T 01865 556555
F 01865 556555
E artgallery@inspires.co.uk
W www.inspires.co.uk
Opened in 2000. Stocks a wide range of original limited-edition prints, original canvases, ceramics, sculpture and glassware. Artists include Heidi Konig, Terry Frost, Carol Peace and Peter Layton. Also offers a framing service with full conservation framing if needed.
Submission policy The gallery requests images on slides or transparencies or by email for the owner's consideration. Does not accept jewelry or embroidery.
Price range £20–£6,500
No of exhibitions annually 10, including 5 solo exhibitions.

Island Fine Arts Ltd
53 High Street, Bembridge
PO35 5S
T 01983 875133
E gallery@islandfinearts.com
W www.islandfinearts.com
Contact Nick Fletcher or Polly Zanardi
Founded in 1997 and based in the seaside village of Bembridge, the gallery is split into four rooms and deals in works by twentieth- and twenty-first-century modern British painters. Artists include Ken Howard RA, LS Lowry RA, Mary Fedden RA, Rod Pearce and Edward Seago RBA RWS. Exhibits throughout the year both on the Isle of Wight and in London. Has a corporate arm specifically aimed at working with companies.
Submission policy Always interested in meeting and viewing the work of new painters.
Price range £150–£30,000
No of exhibitions annually 11

Jointure Studios
11 South Street, Ditchling
BN6 8UQ
T 01273 841244
F 01273 841244
E gallery@jointurestudios.co.uk

W www.jointurestudios.co.uk
Contact Shirley Crowther
Spacious gallery for rental created from the late Sir Frank Brangwyn's studios. Good natural daylight, modern lighting and hanging systems, high-ceilinged main hall plus balcony area.

Kent Potters' Gallery
22 Union Street, Maidstone
ME14 1ED
T 01622 681962
W www.kentpotters.co.uk
Contact Janet Jackson
Opened in 1994. Promotes original, exclusive and innovative work. The centre of excellence for the Kent Potters' Association (KPA) and over twelve members represented at any one time. Includes a resource centre on courses, etc. and is stewarded by members. Work is for sale and/or commission.
Submission policy Entry is by being a member of the KPA. Applications from non-members are not accepted.
Price range £4–£400

Legra Gallery
8 The Broadway, Leigh-on-Sea
SS9 1AW
T 01702 713572
Contact Peter Vinten
Founded in 1973, specializing in marine paintings (traditional and contemporary). Also offers conservation-framing service to artists and public. Oil-painting-restoration service available. Resident artists include Colin Moore, Peter Vinten, Eric Pead, John Dawkins and Rod Brown. The gallery has also shown work by the late Vic Ellis in recent years.
Submission policy No specific entry requirements. Preference given to local artists.
Price range £20–£500. £200–£2,000 for Vic Ellis works, when available.

Lincoln Joyce Fine Art
40 Church Road, Great Bookham
KT23 3PW
T 01372 458481
F 01372 458481
E rosemarylincolnjoyce@hotmail.com
W www.artgalleries.uk.com
Contact Rosemary Pearson
Gallery since 1987, aiming to present fine-quality paintings in a relaxed and friendly atmosphere. Focuses on watercolours and oil paintings. Subject matter (mostly representational) includes

landscapes, marine scenes, figures, still lifes and genre paintings. Artists represented include Paul Banning, Rod Baxter, Richard Bolto, Derek Brown, Simon Cannacott and Bob Eckersley. Valuation and framing services also offered.
Price range £50–£20,000
No of exhibitions annually 11

Linda Blackstone Gallery
The Old Slaughterhouse, R/O 13 High Street, Pinner
HA5 5QQ
T 020 88685765
F 020 88684465
E linda@lindablackstone.com
W www.lindablackstone.com
Founded in 1985 to exhibit contemporary British artists whose work is classed as representational. Artists include Mike Bernard RI, Leo McDowell RI, Janet Ledger, Colin Kent RI, Mat Barber Kennedy RI, Ken Paine PS SPF. Shows paintings, sculpture, ceramics and studio glass. Offers a bespoke framing service. Artists' work is exposed at many national and international art fairs as well as in-house exhibitions.
Submission policy No print, photography, abstract or installation work. Apply by email or post with examples of work and full CV. Seen by appointment only.
Price range £150–£8,000
No of exhibitions annually 3–6 set exhibitions and ongoing exhibition of works.

Magic Flute Gallery
231 Swanwick Lane, Lower Swanwick, Southampton
SO31 7GT
T 01489 570283
E art@magicfluteartworks.co.uk
W www.magicfluteartworks.co.uk
Contact Bryan Dunleavy
At current location since the late 1990s. Exhibits paintings, original prints and small sculpture. Features south-coast and national artists including Russell Baker, Dorothy Brook, Bryan Dunleavy, John Horsewell, Michael Morgan and Stan Rosenthal.
Submission policy Applications should be made in the first instance by email with low-resolution jpeg images.
Price range Up to £3,000; most under £1,000.
No of exhibitions annually 6

Modern Artists' Gallery
High Street, Whitchurch-on-Thames, nr Pangbourne, Reading
RG88 7EX
T 0118 9845893
E info@modernartistsgallery.com
W www.modernartistsgallery.com
Contact Peggy Gibson
Founded in 2000. Aims to support independent artists, including sculptors, ceramicists, furniture makers and painters. Specializes in contemporary abstract and figurative work. Artists include Paul Kessling, Kathryn Thomas, Anita Austwick, Lucy Orchard, Paul Wright and Stuart Buchanan.
Submission policy Artists should submit by email or telephone, sending jpegs or directions to own website.
Price range £50–£5,000
No of exhibitions annually 9

Neville Pundole Gallery
8a-9 The Friars, Canterbury
CT1 2AS
T 01227 453471
F 01227 453471
E neville@pundole.co.uk
W www.pundole.co.uk
Contact Neville Pundole
Established in 1980 and moved to current premises in 1996. Artists represented include Sally Tuffin, Siddy Langley, Peter Layton, Roger Cockram, Martin Evans and the Moorcroft family. Specializes in art pottery and studio glass with pictures, textiles and sculpture. Gallery space for self-promoting artists.
Submission policy The owner 'must like the work'.
Price range £50–£5,000
No of exhibitions annually 8

Nicholas Bowlby
Owl House, Poundgate
TN22 4DE
T 01892 667809
F 01892 667809
E info@nicholasbowlby.co.uk
W www.nicholasbowlby.co.uk
Contact Nicholas Bowlby
A direct descendant of Sir Henry Tate, Nicholas Bowlby started to deal in early English watercolours in 1976, and since then has extended his interests to include modern British paintings from the first half of the twentieth century, as well as representing a number of contemporary painters and sculptors.

Submission policy Enquiries welcome. Send photographs in the first instance, preferably by email. All submissions answered.
Price range £100–£55,000
No of exhibitions annually 6

Nick Whistler

5 High Street, Battle
TN33 OAE
T 01424 772458
E nickwhistler@btinternet.com
W www.nickwhistler.com
Contact Nick Whistler
Established in 2000, showing contemporary paintings by British artists including Andrew James, Alan Rankle, Heather Stuart, John Holdcroft, Tim Pryke and Paul Jackson.
Price range £50–£5,000
No of exhibitions annually Rotating exhibitions in three locations.

North Laine Photography Gallery

Snoopers Paradise, Kensington Gardens, Brighton
BN1 8AR
T 01273 628794
E studio@northlainephotography.co.uk
W www.northlainephotography.co.uk
Contact Nicola Holloway
Founded 2003. Uses sales of popular Brighton photographic images by N.K. Swallow to fund free space for new photographers. A competition exhibition (see below) is held in September and October in a 900 sq. ft space.
Submission policy Interested in all art forms based on photography. Contact Nicole Holloway regarding arts relevance. Photographers are found through a £2,000-prize competition; four finalists each get one-month 'free choice' exhibition of their work, free studio work, etc.
Price range From £2.50 for greetings cards. £5–£150 for reproductions. £120–£2,000 for individual framed prints.
No of exhibitions annually 8–10

Omell Galleries

The Corner House, Course Road, Ascot
SL5 7HL
T 01344 873443
F 01344 873467
E aomell@aol.com
W www.omellgalleries.co.uk
Founded in 1947, offering fine-quality paintings at realistic prices. Specializes in traditional oil paintings. Artists include Antoine Blanchard,

Pierre Bittar, David Dipnall, Raymond Campbell, John Donaldson and Ivars Jansons.
Submission policy Traditional works by professional artists.
Price range £300–£15,000
No of exhibitions annually 6

Oxmarket Centre of Arts

St Andrew's Court, East Street, Chichester
PO19 1YH
T 01243 779103
F 01243 779103
E info@oxmarket.com
W www.oxmarket.com
Contact Ben Davis (Senior Administrator)
Founded in 1971 with the aim of promoting the arts in the community. Works with music and the arts generally but has a concentration on visual arts. Exhibits paintings and drawings, sculpture and ceramics. Mainly used by artists from West Sussex and Home Counties but hosts national figures too.
Submission policy All two- and three-dimensional work welcomed. Selection is by a panel of professional artists.
Price range Varies from exhibition to exhibition. No artist represented permanently.
No of exhibitions annually 150, in six gallery spaces.

Paddon & Paddon

113 South Street, Eastbourne
BN21 4LU
T 01323 411887
E paddon@uk2.net
W www.paddonandpaddon.co.uk
Contact Henry Paddon
Established in 1992. Offers a diverse range of two- and three-dimensional work by leading studio makers based in the UK and Europe. Media offered include ceramics, glass, metalwork, jewelry, wood, sculpture, printmaking and furniture. A commissioning service is available. Selected by Arts Council England for participation in the Own Art scheme, which facilitates interest-free purchases of contemporary art and craft by members of the public.
Submission policy Welcomes enquiries from makers and artists in writing, by email or telephone.
Price range £10–£3,750
No of exhibitions annually Up to 4

Penn Barn

By the Pond, Elm Road, Penn
HP10 8LB

T 01494 816535

Established in 1968 as Export Galleries and moved to present premises in 1979. Specializes in traditional bird and wildlife pictures (mainly watercolours but some oils). Artists exhibited include Neil Cox, Peter Hayman, Rodger McPhail, Janet Pridoux SWA, Ingrid Weiversbye and Owen Williams.

Submission policy Only sells traditional pictures. Interested in seeing good wildlife pictures by living artists.

Price range £200–£2,000

No of exhibitions annually 2

Permanent Gallery

20 Bedford Place, Brighton

BN1 2PT

T 01273 710771

E info@permanentgallery.com

W www.permanentgallery.com

A not-for-profit space, opened in 2003. Dedicated to bringing challenging and innovative contemporary art to the public. Programme includes local, national and international artists exhibiting work of all disciplines. Houses an independent art bookshop selling artist-made books, small-press publications, magazines and multiples sourced both locally and internationally. The gallery runs a varied events programme, which has featured group drawing on the beach, live drawing in the gallery, readings, discussion forums and artists talks.

Submission policy Accepts submissions by email or post all year round from artists creating contemporary work in any medium.

No of exhibitions annually 12

Pierrepont Fine Art

1 Folly Bridge, Oxford

OX1 4LB

T 01865 798833

F 01865 798833

E kate@pierrepontfineart.co.uk

Planet Janet

86 Church Road, Hove

BN3 2EB

T 01273 738230

E richard@onehappymother.co.uk

W www.planet-janet.com

Founded in 2002. A healthy vegetarian café and therapy centre specializing in alternative therapies, complete with a changing collection of art work on display.

Submission policy Artists' work must be shown to one of the managers.

Price range £40–£500

No of exhibitions annually 6

Red Gallery

54 North Street, Thame

OX9 3BH

T 01844 217622

F 01844 260776

E micky@redgallery.co.uk

W www.redgallery.co.uk

Founded in 1998 to showcase renowned artists and promote fresh graduates through solo gallery exhibitions and representation at international art fairs. Artists represented include Olivia Brown, Stanley Dove, Robin Eckardt, Garry Raymond-Peirera, Trevor Price and Kathryn Thomas.

Submission policy Submissions must be hard copy only. Include photos or CD, CV and biography, plus sae for reply.

Price range £100–£12,000

No of exhibitions annually 2 gallery solo shows; up to 6 art fairs.

Roche Gallery

93 High Street, Rye

TN31 7JN

T 01797 222259

E timroche@onetel.com

W www.rochegallery.com

Contact Timothy Roche

Showcases the work of Marina Kim, a painter and printmaker from Tashkent, Uzbekistan. Also regularly exhibits paintings from other leading contemporary artists from the former Soviet Union including Lena Lee, Alexander Kim and Gairat Baimatov.

Submission policy Interested in original paintings, drawings, prints and sculpture in any medium. Overseas artists preferred. No crafts or photography.

Price range £55–£1,500

No of exhibitions annually 6

Room for Art Gallery

15a Church Street, Cobham

KT11 3EG

T 01932 865825

F 01932 865825 (phone first)

E john@roomforart.co.uk

W www.roomforart.co.uk

Contact Hilary Donnelly

Opened in 2004, specializing in contemporary original British and South African art. Also specializes in Zimbabwean stone sculpture (also known as Shona sculpture), with one of the widest ongoing selections of this genre in the UK.
Submission policy Preference for contemporary oils and acrylic work, mainly figurative or landscape.
Price range £250–£5,000
No of exhibitions annually 4–6, each of 4–5 weeks' duration. Mixed shows in between.

Royall Fine Art
52 The Pantiles, Tunbridge Wells
TN2 5TN
T 01892 536534
F 01892 536534
E royallfineart@tiscali.co.uk
W www.royallfineart.co.uk
Established in 1983. Specializes in fine-quality paintings, sculpture and studio glass by established and emerging artists. Regular exhibitors include Matthew Alexander, Raymond Campbell, Jonathan Pike, Paddy Burrow and Ronald Cameron.
Submission policy Applications should be made by photograph, email or appointment.
Price range £300–£20,000
No of exhibitions annually 4

Saltgrass Gallery
1 Angel Courtyard, Lymington
SO41 9AP
T 01590 678148 / 07976 830569
F 01590 678148
E info@saltgrassgallery.co.uk
W www.saltgrassgallery.co.uk
Owned and run by practising painter Jenny Sutton. Alongside her own work in oil, watercolour and acrylic, she exhibits a varied selection of paintings, prints, ceramics and glass by chosen contemporaries. The work is largely representational and mostly under £1,000.
Submission policy Telephone in the first instance to see whether submission is advisable.
Price range £10–£1,000
No of exhibitions annually 4

Simon Fairless
27 Balmoral Gardens, Windsor
SL4 3SG
T 01753 841216
E simon@simonsgallery.com

W www.simonsgallery.com
Contact Simon Fairless
Specializes in abstract, landscape and Pop Art works using acrylic on canvas. Exhibits owner's own work as well as work of other artists.

Star Gallery
Castle Ditch Lane, Lewes
BN7 1YJ
T 01273 480218
F 01273 488241
E info@stargallery.co.uk
W www.stargallery.co.uk
Contact Hayley Brown
Established in 1989 and now a centre where artists of local, national and international reputation sell their work. As well as the contemporary gallery in the old brewery building, it also features a series of creative workshops and studios for hire.
Submission policy Welcomes artists' submissions. Work can be emailed as jpegs or posted as slides or on CD with an sae.
Price range Prices vary according to artist being shown.
No of exhibitions annually Approx. 12

Start Contemporary Gallery
8 Church Street, Brighton
BN1 1US
T 01273 233984
E email@startgallery.co.uk
W www.startgallery.co.uk
Contact Edward Milbourn
Opened in 2000. Shows and sells new ceramics, glassware and jewelry by living makers from all over the UK. Specializes in showing work by recent graduates and new makers although regularly shows work by more established names such as Sarah Perry, Helen Rondell and Ian Stallard.
Submission policy Decorative and functional ceramics, glassware and jewelry in any medium. No deadlines. Send images and idea of prices.
Price range £10–£500

Sundridge Gallery
9 Church Road, Sundridge, Sevenoaks
TN14 6DT
T 01959 564104
Founded in 1986. Sells well-draughted watercolours, oil paintings and drawings in good condition. Mostly nineteenth- and twentieth-century but does sell some twenty-first-century modern and traditional work.

Artists include Robert Thone Waite, David Cox Jr, F.J. Aldridge, Frank Henry Mason and Edward Wesson. Restoration service also offered.
Submission policy Will show modern artists but traditional fine art only.
Price range £100–£5,000
No of exhibitions annually 1–2

Sussex Arts Club Ltd

7 Ship, The Laines, Brighton
BN1 1AD
T 01273 778020
E info@sussexarts.com
W www.sussexarts.com
Contact Michael Fowdrey (Events Manager)
Submission policy Ring to arrange appointment and viewing of portfolio.
No of exhibitions annually Monthly for individuals; bimonthly for joint shows.

Taurus Gallery

16 North Parade, off Banbury Road, Oxford
OX2 6LX
T 01865 514870

Upstairs at the Halcyon

The Halcyon Bookshop, 11 The Broadway, Haywards Heath
RH16 3AQ
T 01444 412785
F 01444 443509
E halcyonbookshop@aol.com
W www.halcyonbookshop.com
Contact Kay O'Regan
Opened in 2003, specializing in works by Sussex artists.
Submission policy Chooses exhibitors from samples of their work. Encourages new talent.
Price range £50–£10,000
No of exhibitions annually 15

Verandah

13 North Parade, Oxford
OX2 6LX
T 01865 310123
Small gallery opened in 1999 by five designers and makers. Offers jewelry, ceramics, glass, textiles, metal and paper work and some paintings. Contributors include James C. Cochrane, Sara Drake, Sara Glass and Prue Cooper.
Submission policy Welcomes submissions from craftspeople and artists at the lower end of the size and price scale, as the gallery is small.

Price range £8–£800
No of exhibitions annually 2, plus featured artists.

Webb Fine Arts

The Gallery, 38 Jewry Street, Winchester
SO23 8RY
T 01962 842273
F 01962 880602
E davieswebb@hotmail.com
W www.webbfinearts.co.uk
A gallery established by Davies Webb, an international art dealer for over forty years. Holds a large stock of nineteenth- and twentieth-century oil paintings.
Price range £350–£10,000

Webster Gallery

13 Pevensey Road, Eastbourne
BN21 3HH
T 01323 735753
Founded in 1984, dealing in twentieth-century paintings (mainly French). Offers full restoration and valuation service. Artists include Frank Wootton, Pierre de Clausade, Gabriel Deschamps, Erwin Eicheiger, Rene His and James Noble.
Submission policy Only original works on paper or canvas. No prints, etchings, photos, SLE prints, etc.
Price range £500–£3,000
No of exhibitions annually 2

Whittington Fine Art

26 Hart Street, Henley-on-Thames
RG9 2AU
T 01491 410787
F 01491 410787
E barry@whittingtonfineart.com
W www.whittingtonfineart.com
Contact Barry Whittington
Opened in 1992 and relocated to Henley-on-Thames in 2001. Specializes in contemporary paintings and bronze sculpture. Has a large stock of traditional watercolours and oil paintings dating from 1796 to 1940, as well as works by approximately thirty contemporary artists including Peter Graham VPROI, Jeremy Barlow ROI, Jacqueline Rizvi RBA RWS NEAC, Nick Hebditch and Aldo Balding. Other artists include Mary Fedden RA, Donald Hamilton Fraser RA, Ceri Richards, Sir William Russell Flint RA, Jonathan Wylder, Adrian Sorrell, Anne Smith and Peter Knapton.
Submission policy Portfolios welcomed for viewing. Time and advice will always be given, although wall space is limited.

Price range £400–£52,000
No of exhibitions annually 6

Wiseman Gallery

40–41 South Parade, Summertown, Oxford
OX2 7JL
T 01865 515123
E sarahjane@wisegal.com
W www.wisegal.com

Wren Gallery

Bear Court, 34 Lower High Street, Burford
OX18 4RR
T 01993 823495
F 01993 823247
E enquiries@wrenfineart.com
W www.wrenfineart.com
Specializes in contemporary British and Irish art.
Price range £500–£10,000
No of exhibitions annually 11

Zimmer Stewart Gallery

29 Tarrant Street, Arundel
BN18 9DG
T 01903 885867
E james@zimmerstewart.co.uk
W www.zimmerstewart.co.uk
Contact James Stewart
Founded in 2003, specializing in contemporary art
in all media by living artists. Represented artists
include Ann Sutton MBE, Duggie Fields and
Andrew Logan. Works directly with artists and
aims to show work to both buyers and as many
other visitors to the gallery as possible.
Price range £100–£7,000
No of exhibitions annually 11

South-west

Alexander Gallery

122 Whiteladies Road, Bristol
BS8 2RP
T 0117 9734692
F 0117 9466991

Anthony Hepworth Fine Art Dealers Ltd

3 Margarets Buildings, Brock Street, Bath
BA1 2LP
T 01225 447480
F 01225 442917
E anthony.hepworth@btinternet.com
Founded 1989. Dealers in twentieth-century

and contemporary British painting, sculpture and
drawings, specializing in post-war British pictures.
Artists represented include Peter Lanyon, Keith
Vaughan, Christopher Wood, Roger Hilton, Ben
Nicholson, Barbara Hepworth. Offers services to
executors of deceased estates regarding the
dispersal of collections on their behalf.
Submission policy Artists are invited to send slides
of their work for consideration if they feel their
work would fit in with the gallery's ethos.
Price range £500–£400,000
No of exhibitions annually 2

Art Space Gallery

The Wharf, St Ives
TR26 1PU
T 01736 797062
E lesley@artspace-cornwall.co.uk
W www.artspace-cornwall.co.uk
Contact Lesley Ninnes
A seven-member cooperative gallery established in
2000. And offshoot of Taking Space, a local group
of women artists formed ten years ago to find
venues for regular exhibitions. Founding members
took the next logical step and acquired permanent
exhibiting space.
Submission policy Artists can submit contact
details for when a vacancy arises. Members pay a
share of rent/rates, spend one day per week in the
gallery and attend a monthly meeting/rehanging.
Price range £45–£750
No of exhibitions annually Monthly rotation of
work, with an optional monthly theme.

ArtFrame Galleries

61 Cornwall Street, Plymouth
PL1 1NS
T 01752 227127
F 01752 672235
E artframegallery@supanet.com
W www.artframegallery.co.uk
Contact Harry or Sally Eves
Founded in 1984. Exhibits 'special and different'
art and craft work. With an emphasis on quality
and affordability, the gallery stocks a wide
selection of artists and makers working in
diverse media. Bespoke picture-framers, with
discounts to exhibiting artists. Painters include
Ben Maile, Lee Woods and James Martin.
Makers include Rudge Ceramics, Jennie Hale
and Suzie Marsh.
Branches 17 Duke Street, Tavistock, Devon PL19
0BA **T** 01822 611091 **F** 01822 611092.
Submission policy Any medium considered,

providing it is professional, commercial, 'special and different'. Send images or call to discuss suitability for gallery.
Price range £20–£2,000; up to £8,000 for artists of repute.
No of exhibitions annually 12

Astley House Contemporary
Astley House, London Road, Moreton-in-Marsh
GL560LL
T 01608 650601 / 652896
F 01608 651777
E astart333@aol.com
W www.contemporaryart-uk.com
Family business opened in 1973. Contemporary gallery opened in 1997. Artists include Charles Neal, Daniel Van der Putten, Chris Bruce, Michael Kitchen-Hurle, Helen Haywood and Kay Elliott. Ceramics by Peter Beard and Ashraf and Sue Hanna. Jewelry by Guen Palmer and Gordon Yates.
Submission policy Happy to look at artists' original work to decide if it is suitable.
Price range £250–£12,000.
No of exhibitions annually 3

Atishoo Designs
71 Charlestown Road, Charlestown, St Austell
PL25 3NL
T 01726 65900
E enquiries@atishoodesigns.co.uk
W www.atishoodesigns.co.uk
Established in 2003. Contemporary gallery mainly featuring West Country artists including David Wheeler, Paul Clark, Lamorna Penrose, Alan Arthurs, Keith Bunt and Karrie Fox. Picture-framing workshop on site.
Submission policy Mainly West Country artists. Common theme is 'Vibrant'.
Price range £100–£1,000
No of exhibitions annually 3

Atrium Gallery
Units 2 & 3, The Podium, Northgate Street, Bath
BA1 5AL
T 01225 443446
F 01225 422910
E framing@theframingworkshop.com
W www.theframingworkshop.com
Recently expanded, having been established for five years selling both limited-edition prints and originals by artists including Doug Hyde, David Cobley, Jonathan Shaw, Fletcher Sibthorpe and Michael Austin. Also sources poster prints.

A specialist framing service is available from the workshop at 80 Walcot Street in Bath, which stocks a selection of art work by local artists depicting local scenes.

Baytree Gallery
48 St Margaret's Street, Bradford on Avon
BA15 1DE
T 01225 864918
E jane.gibson@ukonline.co.uk
Situated in the centre of town, has exhibitions of two or three complementary artists' work lasting for about three weeks. Artists showing include David Cox, Diana Heeks, Jackie Morins, Estienne Sheppard, Lizzie Macrae and Amanda Backhouse.
Submission policy Work taken on a sale-or-return basis. Cards and prints sold only with original work.
Price range £5–£5,000
No of exhibitions annually 8

Beaux Arts
12–13 York Street, Bath
BA1 1NG
T 01225 464850
F 01225 422256
E info@beauxartsbath.co.uk
W www.beauxartsbath.co.uk
Contact Aidan Quinn
Has exhibited the work of contemporary and modern British painters, sculptors and ceramicists since 1980 including Dame Elisabeth Frink, the post-war St Ives School and Lynn Chadwick. Current exhibitors include Nicholas Archer, Nathan Ford and Roxana Halls and other young British artists working in a mainly figurative style.
Submission policy Does not accept email applications from artists. Slides, photos or CDs with sae will be returned after viewing.
Price range £60–£30,000
No of exhibitions annually 8 exhibitions, including a selected summer exhibition of painting, sculpture and ceramics.

Bettles Gallery
80 Christchurch Road, Ringwood
BH224 1DR
T 01425 470410
W www.bettles.net
Founded in 1989, specializing in original contemporary paintings and studio ceramics by British artists and makers. Work in stock from leading established potters and painters, plus some from promising newcomers. Painters include Brian Graham, Peter Joyce and Martyn

Brewster. Ceramicists include David Leach, Peter Hayes and William Marshall.
Submission policy Original paintings, prints and individual one-off ceramics considered. First approach should be photographs (not slides or CD) accompanied by CV.
Price range Up to £2,500
No of exhibitions annually 8

Bi-Hand

121 St George's Road, Hotwells, Bristol
BS1 5UW
T 0117 9210053
E joandsimon@bihand.co.uk
W www.bihand.co.uk

Black Swan Arts

2 Bridge Street, Frome
BA11 1BB
T 01373 473980
F 01373 473980
E office@blackswan.org.uk
W www.blackswan.org.uk
Set up in 1986. Has three exhibition spaces, Gallery One, Gallery Two in the Round Tower, and the Arts Café. Shows a variety of both two- and three-dimensional visual art and holds an open competition biannually (next scheduled for February 2006).
Submission policy Submissions accepted.
No of exhibitions annually 8–10

Blue Dot Gallery

14 Regent Street, Clifton, Bristol
BS8 4HG
T 0117 9467777
E lee.purvis@bluedotgallery.com
W www.bluedotgallery.com

Blue Lias Gallery

47 Coombe Street, Lyme Regis
DT7 3PY
T 01297 444919
E office@bluelias.co.uk
W www.bluelias.co.uk
Contact Jennie Pearson
Founded in 1996 and under present ownership since 2002. Specializes in contemporary art and craft works celebrating especially the Jurassic Coast (sea, cliffs, beaches, fish, etc). Particular emphasis on artists from the locality and south-west region. Commissioning actively undertaken. Artists include Robert Freame, Cath Read, Rebecca Stidson, Joy White, Rachel Jennings and Albert Duplock.

Submission policy All artists considered whose work is compatible with the ambience of the gallery.
Price range Up to £2,000. Works of higher value considered.
No of exhibitions annually 6

Bluestone Gallery

8 Old Swan Yard, Devizes
SN10 1AT
T 01380 729589
E gp@bluestonegallery.com
W www.bluestonegallery.com
Contact Guy Perkins
Started in 2000 to showcase the best of British contemporary crafts by both established and emerging makers. Displays jewelry, ceramics, glass, textiles, wood, sculpture, automata and prints.
Submission policy Submissions welcomed, preferably by email with images of work (stating sizes, prices, etc.) plus information about the maker.
Price range £5–£5,000
No of exhibitions annually 2

Bristol Guild

68–70 Park Street, Bristol
BS1 5JY
T 0117 9265548
F 0117 9255659
E info@bristolguild.co.uk
W www.bristolguild.co.uk
Contact Simone Andre (Manager)
The gallery is on the second floor of the Bristol Guild shop, which was founded in 1908 as a guild of craftsmen.
Submission policy Exhibitors are selected for the high standard of their work. Paintings, prints, ceramics and glass are the main exhibits.
Price range Up to £2,000
No of exhibitions annually 12

Chagford Galleries

20 The Square, Chagford
TQ13 8AB
T 01647 433287
F 01647 433287
E sales@chagfordgalleries.fsnet.co.uk
Contact Jenny Hole
In existence for over thirty-five years and under present ownership for fifteen years. Specializes in West Country artists and craftspeople, with Dartmoor providing a lot of inspiration. Sells

original paintings, prints, ceramics, jewelry, glass
and woodwork.
Submission policy West Country artists only,
preferably from Devon or Cornwall.
No of exhibitions annually 2

Chapel Gallery
Saltram House, Plympton, Plymouth
PL7 1UH
T 01752 347852
F 01752 347852
E kirsty.eales@nationaltrust.org.uk
Contact Kirsty Eales
Shows local arts and crafts from Devon and
Cornwall. Work on display includes pottery,
ceramics, original paintings, prints, jewelry, glass
and woodturning. Holds three large art-and-craft
fairs every year.
Submission policy Artists need to live in Devon or
Cornwall.
Price range £1–£4,000
No of exhibitions annually 6 solo exhibitions
in the upper gallery; 4 exhibitions in the lower
gallery.

Church House Designs
Church House, Broad Street, Congresbury
BS49 5DG
T 01934 833660
F 01934 833660
E robert-coles@btconnect.com
W www.churchhousedesigns.co.uk
Established for over twenty years. Specializes in
quality handmade British crafts (ceramics, glass,
textiles, jewelry and woodware). Artists include
Lucy Willis (prints), John Leach (ceramics), Peter
Layton (glass), Nick Rees (ceramics), Richard
Dewar (ceramics) and Clive Bowen (ceramics).

Clifton Gallery
18 Princess Victoria Street, Clifton, Bristol
BS8 4BP
T 0117 9706650
E info@cliftonart.co.uk
W www.cliftonart.co.uk
Opened twelve years ago in an exclusive area of
Clifton Village. Specializing in original-only,
contemporary fine art, mainly paintings with
some sculpture. Showing artists from all
around the world. Represented artists include
Shen Ming Cun, Les Matthews, Stephen Brown
and Hennie De Korte.
Submission policy Only original work will be
considered. Does not show abstract and conceptual

work. Artists must have minimum of ten years'
experience.
Price range £500–£25,000
No of exhibitions annually 6

Contemporary Art
1 John Street, Stroud
GL5 2HA
T 01453 758829
Contact Wendy Drake
Founded in 2002, specializing in contemporary
art, including paintings, prints, ceramics, glass,
sculpture, textiles and jewelry. Artists include
Lawson Rudge, Paul Jenkins, Ralph Bayer, Dorothy
Brooks and Alister Malcolm.
Submission policy All areas and media covered.
Send images in the first instance, together with
statement and CV.
Price range £1–£1,500
No of exhibitions annually 5

Contemporary Studio Pottery
6 Mill Street, Chagford
TQ13 8AW
T 01647 432900
W www.contemporarystudiopottery.co.uk
Founded in 1999, specializing in studio ceramics.
Artists include Svend Bayer, Clive Bowen, Bruce
Chivers, Nic Collins, Penny Simpson and Ross
Emerson.
Submission policy National and international
potters invited.
Price range £10–£3,000
No of exhibitions annually 4 masterclass
exhibitions.

Coombe Gallery
20 Foss Street, Dartmouth
TQ6 9DR
T 01803 722352
F 01803 722275
E mark@coombegallery.com
W www.coombegallery.com
Contact Mark Riley
Opened in 2004 as an extension of Coombe Farm
Gallery, which was established in 1989. Exhibits
fine and applied arts from predominantly UK-
based artists. Exhibitors include Mary Stork, David
Leach OBE, Gerry Dudgeon, Paul Riley, Tom
Rickman and Diane Nevitt. Displays work from
recent graduates alongside artists and makers with
international reputations.
Submission policy Living artists whose work
displays skill, integrity and imagination.

Price range £100–£10,000
No of exhibitions annually 4

Cornwall Galleries

4, Bank Street, Newquay
TR7 1JF
T 01637 873678
F 01637 873868
E enquiries@cornwallgalleries.co.uk
W www.cornwallgalleries.co.uk
Founded in 1960 by Leonard Charles Rollason and
run as a family business since the early 1990s.
Aims to provide quality oil paintings that anybody
can afford. Exhibited artists include Josephine
Wall, Deborah Jones, Joel Kirk, Graham Petley and
John Bampfield.
Price range £16–£6,000

Courtenays Fine Art

11 Westbourne Arcade, Bournemouth
BH4 9AY
T 01202 764884
E info@courtenaysfineart.com
W www.courtenaysfineart.com
Gallery opened in 1998. Shows originals, limited
editions and prints. Over fifty artists, including
Josephine Wall, Bill Tolley and David Danbey-
Wood.
Submission policy Initial contact by photographs
then, if interested, four originals required.
Price range £50–£5,000

Cowdy Gallery

31 Culver Street, Newent
GL18 1DB
T 01531 821173
F 01531 821173
E info@cowdygallery.co.uk
W www.cowdygallery.co.uk
Contact Harry Cowdy
Established in 1990. Aa 125m² private glass gallery
showing leading established artists alongside
notable emerging makers. Selection is based on
quality, integrity and craftsmanship. A permanent
collection is displayed between exhibitions.
Exhibited artists include Keith Cummings, Sally
Fawkes, Ronald Pennell, Pauline Solven, Colin
Reid and Rachael Woodman.
Submission policy Applicants should have an art
or craft degree. Submissions should include CV
and illustrations (CD, slides or prints). Interested
in glass only.
Price range £100–£3,000
No of exhibitions annually 2

Crescent Galleries Ltd

9 Bath Place, Taunton
TA1 4ER
T 01823 335050
F 01278 663317
E ian@crescentgallery.co.uk
W www.crescentgallery.co.uk
Under current ownership since 2001. Two
galleries in Somerset actively supporting local
artists with shows and free hangings. Open policy,
with work encompassing the traditional to
contemporary abstract.
Submission policy Only considers artists from the
West Country.
Price range £150–£2,500
No of exhibitions annually 6

Croft Gallery

22 Devizes Road, Old Town, Swindon
SN21 4BH
T 01793 615821
F 01793 615821
E info@thecroftgallery.co.uk
W www.thecroftgallery.co.uk
Opened in 2000. Promotes up-and-coming and
established artists, and sells variety of original art
work (oils, acrylics, pastel, watercolours, limited
editions). Specialist framing service available.
Artists include Carl Scanes, Ken White,
Henderson Cisz, Victoria Stewart, William Tolley
and Alex Jawdokimov. Offers to sell art work
(featured on website) on commission basis.
Submission policy Submissions from artists
always welcome.
Price range £100–£2,500
No of exhibitions annually Approx. 2

Crown Gallery

7 Winchcombe Street, Cheltenham
GL52 2LZ
T 01242 515716
E paul-bott@tiscali.co.uk
W www.crowngallery.co.uk
Contact Paul or Donald Bott
Opened in 1984. Offers a framing service and
discount plans for artists and repeat clients.
Price range £30–£2,500
No of exhibitions annually 2–3

Cube Gallery

17 Perry Road, Bristol
BS1 5BG
T 0117 3771470
W www.cube-gallery.co.uk

Delamore Arts

Delamore, Cornwood, Ivybridge
PL21 9QT
T 01752 837711
F 01752 837888
E enquiries@delamore.com
W www.delamore-arts.co.uk
Contact Gavin Dollard or Alison Bean
An art and sculpture park, promoting the work
of painters and sculptors (mainly in the West
Country) through several shows including an
annual art and sculpture exhibition each May.
Also represents artists at other exhibitions and
has interests in publishing.

Dolphin House Gallery

Dolphin House, Dolphin Street, Colyton
EX24 6NA
T 01297 553805
E art@dolphinhousegallery.co.uk
W www.dolphinhousegallery.co.uk
Founded in 1990, specializing in the works of
etcher Roger St Barbe, with guest exhibitions
several times a year (e.g. the late Mary Shields).
Ceramics by Nicholas Hillyard. Framing service
offered.
Submission policy Original works or handmade
original prints only (no reproductions or
photographs exhibited). Small works preferred
due to limited space.
Price range £50–£800
No of exhibitions annually 5

Elliott Gallery

Hillsview, Braunton
EX33 2LA
T 01271 812100 / 863539
W www.elliottartgallery.co.uk
Contact Walter A. Elliott
Founded in 1984. Aims to encourage local and
West Country arts (especially painting and
sculpture) and crafts.
Submission policy Artists are invited to send
photographs of their paintings, craft works or
sculpture and, if considered suitable, to submit
art work for exhibition.
No of exhibitions annually 2–8 one-person
exhibitions in the two smaller halls. Continuously
changing displays in the two large galleries.

Exmouth Gallery

46 Exeter Road, Exmouth
EX8 1PY
T 01395 273155
E info@exmouthgallery.co.uk
W www.exmouthgallery.co.uk
The main room shows changing exhibitions;
a second room shows prints and illustrated books;
a third shows botanical illustrations by Royal
Horticultural Society Medallists; and a fourth
shows gallery artists including Bob Clement,
Alan Richards, Michael Buckland, Jean Esther
Brook, Rob Ritchie, Pat Johnn, Mark Abdey, John
Stone and Tim Hogben.
Submission policy No pottery or jewelry, but
outdoor sculpture can be displayed in the enclosed
garden.
Price range £50–£2,000
No of exhibitions annually 8

Farrington Gallery

Bristol Road, Farrington Gurney
BS39 6TG
T 01761 453880
E email@farringtongallery.freeserve.co.uk
W www.farringtongallery.freeserve.co.uk

Frances Roden Fine Art Ltd

Beacon House, New Street, Painswick
GL6 6UN
T 01452 814877
E info@francesrodenfineart.com
W www.francesrodenfineart.com
Founded in 2004. Specializes in contemporary art.
Artists represented include Stephen Goddard,
Sally Trueman, Alan Thornhill and Jon Edgar.
Price range £1,000–£40,000
No of exhibitions annually 2

Gallerie Marin

31 Market Street, Appledore, nr Bideford
EX39 1PP
T 01237 473679
F 01237 421655
E galleriemarine@btopenworld.com
Established in 1972, specializing in contemporary
marine art. Artists include Mark E. Myers PP
RSMA, Michael Les, David Brackman, Tim
Thompson, Steven Thor Johanneson RSMA and
Jenny Morgan.
Price range £200–£6,000
No of exhibitions annually 1

The Gallery

Silver Street House, South Cerney, Cirencester
GL7 5TP
T 01285 869469
E gallery.cirencester@virgin.net

W www.cirencester-galleries.com
Founded in 1997, specializing in colourful
watercolours. Expanded to display themed
exhibitions and group exhibitors. Now specializing
in renting art works to businesses that need to
impress both staff and sales prospects.
Submission policy Shows works that are
representational, colourful and peaceful.
Price range £500–£2,500

The Gallery

Fisherton Mill, 108 Fisherton Street, Salisbury
SP2 7QY
T 01722 415121
F 01722 415121
E thegallery@fishertonmill.co.uk
W www.fishertonmill.co.uk
Opened in 1995 in a converted nineteenth-
century grain mill. One of the region's largest
independent galleries. Work exhibited is
predominantly from artists in the south-west.
Artists include Nick Andrew (painting), Michael
Peckitt (jewelry), Stephanie Wooster (textiles),
Stuart Akroyd (glass), Eric French (furniture) and
Mark Sanger (wood). Studio spaces are available to
rent within the complex.
Submission policy Applications should be made
with photographs of the work in the first instance.
No specific entry requirements or restrictions.
Price range £3–£4,000

Glass House Gallery

Kenwyn Street, Truro
TR1 3DJ
T 01872 262376
E theteam@glasshousegallery.co.uk
W www.glasshousegallery.co.uk
Founded in 1995 in Truro to represent the work of
established and rising Cornish artists, sculptors,
ceramicists, jewelers and printmakers. Exhibitions
have included the first solo shows of artists such as
Naomi Frears and Sasha Harding. Other artists
represented include David Briggs, Jason Lilley,
John Middlemiss and Colin Orchard. The gallery
undertakes commissions.
Price range £100–£2,000
No of exhibitions annually 2

Goldfish Contemporary Fine Art

56 Chapel Street, Penzance
TR18 4AE
T 01736 360573
E mail@goldfishfineart.co.uk
W www.goldfishfineart.co.uk

Contact Joseph Clarke
Founded in 2000 in St Ives and relocated to the
current multiple-floor space in 2003. Specializes
in the best of Cornish contemporary painting
and sculpture, from figurative to abstract with
an emphasis on originality and personal
expression. Gallery artists include Kenneth
Spooner, Nicola Bealing, Zoe Cameron,
David Briggs, Andrew Litten, Nicola Bealing,
Tim Shaw, Simon Allen and Joy Wolfenden
Brown.
Price range £300–£30,000
No of exhibitions annually 9 solo shows alongside
mixed exhibitions.

Great Atlantic Map Works Gallery

St Just, Penzance
TR19 7JB
T 01736 788911 / 786016
F 01736 786005
E gallery@greatatlantic.co.uk
W www.greatatlantic.co.uk
Contact Sarah Brittain
Founded in 1995, the Great Atlantic Group
specializes in painting, sculpture, printmaking
and ceramics from both Cornwall and Wales
where its galleries are situated. Travelling
exhibitions are staged annually around the UK
and also in Canada and America.
Submission policy Submissions welcome
(no textiles, jewelry or photography). In the
first instance approach in writing to Sarah
Brittain.
Price range £100–£10,000
No of exhibitions annually Exhibitions change
fortnightly.

Grimes House Fine Art

Grimes House, High Street, Moreton-in-Marsh
GL56 0AT
T 01608 651029
E grimes_house@cix.co.uk
W www.grimeshouse.co.uk
Contact Steve or Val Farnsworth
Founded in 1978, representing many nationally
known living artists with a traditional rather than
contemporary style. Artists featured include
Edward Hersey, Gordon King, Brian Jull and John
Trickett.
Submission policy Gallery owners must
'personally like the artist and their work'.
Price range £100–£7,000
No of exhibitions annually 1 ongoing exhibition; 2
additional specialist exhibitions.

Hartworks Contemporary Art

12 Foss Street, Dartmouth
TQ6 9DR
T 01803 839000
F 01803 839000
E art@hartworks.co.uk
W www.hartworks.co.uk
Contact Theresa or Simon Hart
Established in 1999 and features work by many
renowned contemporary artists from the West
Country, as well as prominent British artists,
printmakers and ceramicists. Artists include
Simon Hart, Sue McDonald, Gerry Plumb,
Louise Braithwaite, Michael Turner and Glyn
Macey.
Submission policy Submissions by slide,
photographs or email invited from contemporary
makers and artists (excluding photography, jewelry
and watercolour).
Price range £20–£2,000
No of exhibitions annually 4

Hind Street Gallery and Frame Makers

Hind Street, Ottery St Mary
EX11 1BW
T 01404 815641
E info@therealart.co.uk
W www.therealart.co.uk
Established in 1978, showing original art works
from local and international atists. Bespoke
frame-making service offered.
Price range £50–£5,000
No of exhibitions annually 4

Innocent Fine Art

7A Boyces Avenue, Bristol
BS20 6AZ
T 0117 9732614
F 0117 9741425
E enquiries@innocentfineart.co.uk
W www.innocentfineart.co.uk
Founded in 1997, specializing in contemporary
West Country art with particular emphasis on
Cornish artists. Has a large collection of
twentieth-century Cornish artists including
Sir Terry Frost, Barbara Hepworth and Patrick
Heron. Contemporary artists include Paul Lewis,
Mary Stork, Gerry Plumb, Neil Pinkett and
Elaine Jones.
Submission policy Prints and paintings only. Send
slides or photos, or email first.
Price range £250–£4,000
No of exhibitions annually 3

John Davies Gallery

Church Street, Stow-on-the-Wold
GL54 1BB
T 01451 831698
F 01451 832477
E daviesart@aol.com
W www.the-john-davies-gallery.co.uk
Established in 1977, showing European Post-
Impressionist paintings (1890–1950), nineteenth-
and twentieth-century British art, and a wide
range of contemporary painting and sculptures.
Artists include David Prentice, John Kingsley,
Sandy Murphy, Peter Evans, John Brown and
Nicola Toms.
Submission policy Email details of website or send
a CV plus photos/transparencies/CD of images.
The gallery will make contact if considered suitable.
Price range £250–£100,000
No of exhibitions annually 8

Jonathan Poole Gallery

Compton Cassey House, nr Withington,
Cheltenham
GL54 4DE
T 01242 890224
F 01242 890479
Established for over thirty years, specializing in
contemporary sculpture and exhibition-organizing
throughout the world. Represents the art estates of
John Lennon and Miles Davis. Exhibited artists
include Lucy Kinsella, Jonathan Poole, Bobby
Plisnier, Vicky Wallis, Dennis Westwood, Jill
Sanders and Ronnie Wood.

Jordan & Chard Fine Art

c/o Bridge House, Truro
TR1 1ER
T 01872 262202
F 01872 260566
E taraphysick@jordanchard.com
W www.jordanchard.com
Contact Tara Physick
Specializes in the *plein air* painting of the
Newlyn and early St Ives Schools (1880–1940).
Based in Cornwall, the gallery presents an ever-
changing selection of these paintings, many
sourced from private local collections. Works
are offered by the leading and lesser names
from the schools, including Stanhope Forbes,
Walter Langley, Harold Harvey, Henry Scott Tuke,
Lamorna Birch, Laura Knight, Dorothea Sharp
and Newlyn Copper. Viewing is by appointment.
Telephone or visit the website to view paintings,
reference material and artists' biographies.

Submission policy Interested in contemporary impressionist and realist painters, particularly those working in Cornwall. Subjects of interest include figurative, seascape, marine/nautical subjects and local landscape.
Price range £450–£60,000
No of exhibitions annually 3–4

Lander Gallery
Lemon Street Market, Truro
TR1 2PN
T 01872 275578
F 01872 275578
E landergallery@btconnect.com
W www.landergallery.co.uk
Housed in an award-winning new building, making the gallery one of the largest in the south-west. Offers fine art from four centuries, with a rich Cornish flavour. Newly discovered artists welcomed alongside works from celebrated artists from all periods and styles.
Submission policy Particularly interested in work with a Cornish connection. New and established artists shown; new artists are welcome to make an appointment.
Price range From £100–£45,000
No of exhibitions annually 10 featured exhibitions (solo or mixed) and a large permanent show of artists working today.

Maggie Miller Gallery
67b Fore Street, Bovey Tracey, Newton Abbot
TQ13 9AB
T 01626 835961
E maggie.miller@tesco.net
W www.themaggiemillergallery.co.uk
Founded in 2002, principally to promote Maggie Miller's fine art paintings of the Devon countryside and wildlife scenes. Other artists include Alan Young, Andrew Lennon and Peter Rogers.
Submission policy Artists represented are complementary to the areas of specialization within the gallery. The gallery reserves the right to accept or reject any submissions.
Price range £25–£2,000

Market House Gallery
Market House, Marazion
TR17 0AR
T 01736 710252
Specializes in post-war West Country artists such as Sir Terry Frost, Alfred Wallis and Ben Nicholson, and potters such as Leach and Troike.

Submission policy Applications welcome from living local artists in any media.
Price range £120–£20,000
No of exhibitions annually 8

Martin's Gallery
Imperial House, Montpellier Parade, Cheltenham
GL50 1UA
T 01242 526044
E ian@martinsgallery.co.uk
W www.martinsgallery.co.uk
Started in 1987 to present art in the home environment. Concentration on Victorian watercolours, modern British, Vietnamese contemporary and west European. Also shows modern and traditional sculpture. Exhibited artists include W.L. Wyllie and Thomas Bush Hardy (Victorian watercolours), Sir William Russell Flint (modern British), Dan Llewelyn Hall, Inge Clayton and Sophie Raine (contemporary), and Dinh Quan, Ng Dieu Thuy and Van Ngoc (Vietnamese).
Submission policy Artists should submit a CV and some photos of their work initially (preferably by email and including contact details). If the gallery is interested, artists will then be contacted.
Price range £300–£20,000
No of exhibitions annually 12–15

Mayfield Gallery
907 Wimborne Road, Moordown, Bournemouth
BH92BJ
E mayfield.gallery@tiscali.co.uk
W www.juliestooksart.com
Contact Julie Stooks
Opened 1987. Attracts well-known artists who exhibit regularly, both contemporary (Simon Stooks, James Preston) and traditional (David Dipnall, Josephine Wall, Sally Winter). Solo and group exhibitions held. Commissions accepted for portrait and animal studies.
Submission policy Always interested in seeing new artists.
Price range £100–£5,000; gallery commission applies.
No of exhibitions annually 4

Michael Wood Fine Art
The Gallery, 1 Southside Ope, The Barbican, Plymouth
PL1 2LL
T 01752 225533
F 01752 225770
E michael@michaelwoodfineart.com

W www.michaelwoodfineart.com
Contact Michael Wood
Established in 1967, offering an eclectic selection of work from 1800 to the present day. Over two thousand works in stock at any time including paintings, watercolours, original prints, sculptures, ceramics and studio glass. Exhibited artists include local, national and international artists of the Newlyn School, St Ives Society of Artists and Royal Academicians.
Price range £150–£100,000
No of exhibitions annually 1

Mid Cornwall Galleries
St Blazey Gate, Par
PL24 2EG
T 01726 812131
F 01726 814943
E info@midcornwallgalleries.co.uk
W www.midcornwallgalleries.co.uk
Opened in 1980 and housed in a Victorian school east of St Austell. Regularly shows new collections of contemporary arts and crafts.
Submission policy New submissions welcome either on CD by post (with return postage) or via email.
Price range £100–£2,500
No of exhibitions annually 6

New Art Centre Sculpture Park & Gallery
Roche Court, East Winterslow, Salisbury
SP5 1BG
T 01980 862244
F 01980 862447
E nac@globalnet.co.uk
W www.sculpture.uk.com
Contact Helen Waters (Curator)
Founded in 1957 in London and relocated to Roche Court in Wiltshire in 1993. Represents the Estates of Barbara Hepworth and Kenneth Armitage and shows sculpture from 1950 to the present day in an art-historical context, including works by Antony Gormley, Richard Long, Gavin Turk and Rachel Whiteread. In two contemporary buildings there is a changing exhibition programme and there is an active education programme. All works are for sale.
Submission policy Sculptors are welcome to send CVs and images of their work, although space is limited.
Price range From £100
No of exhibitions annually 6–8

New Craftsman
24 Fore Street, St Ives
TR26 1HE
T 01736 795652
E stella.redgrave@btinternet.com
Contact Stella Redgrave
The oldest established craft shop in St Ives, established in the 1960s. Stocks paintings and prints, mostly modern and contemporary. Artists represented include Peter Lanyon, Tony O'Malley, Bryan Pearce, John Miller and John Piper.
Submission policy Artists must be living and working in Cornwall.
Price range £10–£10,000

New Gallery
Portscatho, nr Truro
TR2 5HW
T 01872 580445
E a.insoll@virgin.net
Contact Lynn Golden
Founded in 1984. An artist-run gallery, showroom and studio. Artists include Chris Insoll, Lynn Golden, Trevor Felcey, Eric Ward, Endel White and Grace Gardner.
Submission policy Submissions from painters welcome. New artists would be required to help existing cooperative in some way. The gallery is an established 'society of artists'.
Price range £60–£6,000
No of exhibitions annually 12

New Millennium Gallery
Street-an-Pol, St Ives
TR26 2DS
T 01736 793121
F 01736 793121
E stives@newmillenniumgallery.co.uk
W www.newmillenniumgallery.co.uk
Contact Beatrice Brandt
Established in 1996, showing contemporary painting (abstract and figurative) in a well-lit uncluttered environment. A three-storey building in St Ives town centre provides three large exhibition spaces.
Price range £160–£10,000
No of exhibitions annually 5

Off-Centre Gallery
13 Cotswold Road, Windmill Hill, Bedminster
BS3 4NX
T 0117 9872647
E offcentre@lineone.net

Organised Gallery

Churchill House, Olveston, Bristol
BS35 4DP
T 01454 613788
F 01454 202606
E gallery@organised.com
W www.organisedgallery.co.uk

Plackitt Gallery

St Michael's Barn, Rodden, Frome
BA11 5LD
T 01373 832156
F 01373 832156
E plackittcaro@hotmail.com
W www.plackittgallery.co.uk
Opened in 2002 to show quality glass art from
Seattle. Paintings and furniture added in 2003
but specialization remains glass. Glass artists
exhibited include Mel Munsen, Sabine Lintzen,
Yosuke Otsuki and James Minson. Painters
exhibited include Richard Howell and Anne Mieke
Van Ogtrop.
Submission policy Will look at submissions.
Price range £200–£3,000
No of exhibitions annually 2

Rainyday Gallery

116 Market Jew Street, Penzance
TR18 2LD
T 01736 366077
E rainyday@macunlimited.net
W www.rainydaygallery.co.uk
Started in 1992 and shows mostly Cornwall-based
artists. Abstract, landscape, seascape and naive.
Monthly exhibition is complemented by about one
hundred other works. Artists include Matthew
Lanyon, Chris Hankey, Phil Whiting, Anthony
Frost, Jo March and Nick Williams.
Submission policy Paintings only. Send photos
(and sae) or indicate website if useful.
Price range £100–£5,000
No of exhibitions annually 12

Red Rag Gallery

Church Street, Stow-on-the-Wold, Cotswolds
GL54 1BB
T 01451 832563
E mail@redraggallery.co.uk
W www.redraggallery.co.uk
Contact Carole Teagle
Originally the studio of influential British artist
John Blockley, the building has operated as a
gallery for twenty years. Specializes in the original
art works of present-day British artists, including
Davy Brown, Gerard Burns, Romeo di Girolamo,
Charles Hardaker, Joe Hargan, Louis McNally and
Dawn Sidoli.
Price range £300–£10,000
No of exhibitions annually 10

Rooksmoor Gallery

31 Brock Street, Bath
BA1 2LN
T 01225 420495
E info@rooksmoorgallery.com
Contact Verity James (Manager)
Founded in 1985, specializing in traditional
contemporary paintings, sculpture and ceramics.
Permanent artists include Colin Vincent,
Allan Morgan, Walter Awlson and the
Rudge family.
Submission policy Artists' work must show
traditional skills, quality of execution and
composition.
Price range £100–£2,000
No of exhibitions annually 6

Ropestore

The Shambles, Stroud
GL5 1AS
T 01453 753799
F 01453 753799
E lizzi@ropestoregallery.co.uk
W www.ropestoregallery.co.uk
Shows contemporary fine and applied arts from
national and local designers and makers.
Submission policy The gallery prefers to source its
own work.
Price range £10–£5,000
No of exhibitions annually 4

Rostra Gallery

5 George Street, Bath
BA1 2EH
T 01225 448121
F 01225 447421
E info@rostragallery.co.uk
W www.rostragallery.co.uk
Contact Julie Bennett
Opened in 1997. Has developed a reputation for
showcasing a diverse range of sculpture, ceramics,
paintings, jewelry, glass and giftware. Specialists
in limited-edition prints. Exhibited artists include
Sir Terry Frost, Sonia Rollo, Caroline Pedler,
Joe Cooke and Anna Danielle.
Submission policy Contact the gallery for specific
dates and requirements. Maximum of four
submission dates throughout the year.

Price range £2.75–£5,000
No of exhibitions annually 12+

Sadler Street Gallery

23 Market Place, Wells
BA5 2RF
T 01749 670220
E jillswale@thesadlerstreetgallery.co.uk
W www.thesadlerstreetgallery.co.uk
Contact Jill Swale
Founded in 1993 and moved to present location
in 2003 (one minute from Wells Cathedral).
Specializes in watercolours and etchings from
1750 to 1950, some oils, small bronzes and
contemporary work in all media. Particular focus
on work by West Country artists. Artists include
John Yardley RI and David Sawyer RI.
Submission policy Landscape, marines, figure
studies, etc.
Price range £50–£10,000
No of exhibitions annually 8

Salar Gallery

20 Bridge Street, Hatherleigh
EX20 3HY
T 01837 810940
F 01837 810940
W www.salargallery.co.uk
Founded in 1991. Exhibits paintings,
sculpture, photography and multimedia work
in contemporary and traditional styles by living
West Country artists. Subject matter includes
domestic animals and horses, markets, landscape
and railways. Featured artists include Helen Allin,
Hermione Dunn, Paul Hardy, Bernard Jones,
Ron MacKnight and Leila Winslade.
Submission policy Send photos of work, details of
work and career history to the gallery. Chosen work
is usually taken on consignment.
Price range Up to £1,000
No of exhibitions annually 6

Salisbury Playhouse Gallery

Malthouse Lane, Salisbury
SP2 7RA
T 01722 320117 / 320333
F 01722 421991
E marketing2@salisburyplayhouse.com
W www.salisburyplayhouse.com
Contact Jane Wilkinson (Gallery Officer)
Founded in 1977. A large space within a well-
attended theatre, with room for sixty to eighty
paintings or photographs from new and established
artists. Design and distribution of preview

invitations, preview organization, and all sales,
publicity, etc. catered for by the gallery. Exhibiting
artists include Elisabeth Frink, Bill Toop, Hugh
Casson, Mary Feddon and Julian Barrow.
Submission policy Selection by gallery committee
based on suitability to venue. No fee; thirty-five
per cent commission plus VAT. No facility for
three-dimensional work.
Price range £95–£2,500
No of exhibitions annually 10, approximately three
weeks each (January to June and September to
December).

Six Chapel Row Contemporary Art

6 Chapel Row, Bath
BA1 1HN
T 01225 337900
F 01225 336577
E sixchapelrow@btinternet.com
W www.sixchapelrow.com
Opened in 1995, specializing in contemporary fine
and applied art, from painting, sculpture and
installation to contemporary design, jewelry,
furniture, ceramics and glass.

Somerville Gallery

25 Mayflower Street, Plymouth
PL1 1QJ
T 01752 221600
E lenkiewicz@btconnect.com
W www.somervillegallery.com
Contact Ben Somerville
Established in 1995 to represent the best of
West Country painters. Specialists in Robert
Lemkiewicz, Sir Terry Frost, Anthony Frost, Luke
Frost, Henrietta Dybrey and Bob Crossley.
Submission policy Local established artists
welcome. Gifted newcomers need to work their
passage through established means.
Price range Up to £50,000
No of exhibitions annually 5

St Ives Society of Artists Gallery

Norway Quare, St Ives
TR26 1NA
T 01736 795582
E gallery@stisa.co.uk
W www.stisa.co.uk
Contact Judy Joel
Founded in 1927. Aims to provide an
independent exhibition space for the visual arts
in St Ives for members and other groups and
individuals. Judges work on artistic worth,
regardless of commercial appeal. Prominent

members include Ken Howard RA, Lionel
Aggett, Nicholas St John Rosse, Ken Symonds,
Raymund M. Rogers and Sonia Robinson.
The Mariners Gallery in the former crypt of the
old Church (which houses the society) is also
available for artists to hire for individual
separate exhibitions.
Submission policy Membership is currently
about fifty living artists and applications are
welcomed from all good artists in any medium.
Price range £120–£20,000 for framed work and
sculptures. Unframed etchings, prints and cards
also available.
No of exhibitions annually 3 members'
exhibitions and 2 invited exhibitions in the main
gallery; 20 exhibitions in the Mariners Gallery.

Steam Pottery

Pendeen, Penzance
TR19 7DN
T 01736 788070
E patrick@steampottery.co.uk
W www.steampottery.co.uk
Established in the late 1990s, showing high-
quality ceramics in stoneware and porcelain by
Patrick Lester. Has now broadened its range to
include work by a number of known and emerging
potters including Walter Keeler, Emma Johnstone,
Daniel Boyle, Richard Henham, Simon Rich and
Georgina Dunkley.
Price range £10–£800

Steps Gallery

15 Christmas Steps, City Centre, Bristol
BS1 5BG
T 0117 9304137
E enquiries@stepsgallery.co.uk
W www.stepsgallery.co.uk
Contact Davinia Bulford-Cooper
Founded in 2004, aiming to provide a platform for
both unknowns (including recent graduates) and
those more established but unshown in the south-
west. Specializes in cutting-edge contemporary
and modern work (in terms of style and new
techniques). Exhibited artists include Klori Reis,
Mandy Wilkinson, Juliet Rose, David Stanley and
Robert Belderson.
Submission policy Interested in modern
contemporary work, including paintings and
sculptures and excluding digital work/computer
generated images, etc. Exhibitions can be arranged
in spaces outside the gallery.
Price range £1–£10,000
No of exhibitions annually 5

Strand Art Gallery

2 The Strand, Brixham Harbourside, Brixham
TQ5 8EH
T 01803 854762
E strandartgallerybrixham@hotmail.com
W www.strandartgallery.com
A specialist marine gallery with a strong
West Country flavour, founded in 1972. Artists-in-
residence paint in front of the public. Finished
paintings for sale around the gallery. Artists
include Gordon Allen, Bill Stockman, Terry Burke,
David Deakins and Bob Tucker.
Submission policy Submissions considered from
local (South Devon area) professional artists only.
Acrylics, oils or watercolours preferred.
Price range £25–£2000
No of exhibitions annually Ever-changing
exhibitions run for fifty weeks per year. As work
is sold, new work is put up to take its place.

Street Gallery

1 The Bayliss Centre, 147 High Street, Street
BA16 0EX
T 01458 447722
E andrew@street-gallery.co.uk
W www.street-gallery.co.uk
Specialists of Edward Wesson, Archibald
Thorburn and Rolf Harris. Stockists of signed
prints by Sir Peter Scott, L.S. Lowry, David
Shepherd, Robert Taylor, Alan Fearnley, Nick Eatts,
Govinder, Mackenzie Thorpe and E.R. Sturgeon.
Originals by Richard Thorn, Cecil Rice and
Edward Wesson.
Price range £100–£10,000
No of exhibitions annually Annual Edward Wesson
and Rolf Harris exhibitions.

Stroud House Gallery

Station Road, Stroud
GL5 3AP
T 01453 750575
E info@stroudhousegallery.co.uk
W www.stroudhousegallery.co.uk
Founded in 1997, specializing in conceptual,
contemporary works of art (including fine art,
installation, performance and film). Work is
curated around a theme from artists selected
throughout the UK.
No of exhibitions annually 8–10

Summerleaze Gallery

East Knoyle, Salisbury
SP3 6BY
T 01747 830790

F 01747 830790
E kelly@summerleazegallery.co.uk
W www.summerleazegallery.co.uk
Contact Kelly Ross
Founded in 1991, exhibiting the work of contemporary and modern British painters and sculptors. Exhibited artists include Charlie Baird, Ursula Leach, Paul Macdermot, Tobit Roche, Tim Scott Bolton and Henrietta Young.
Price range £150–£20,000
No of exhibitions annually 4

Susan Megson Gallery

Digbeth Street, Stow-on-the-Wold
GL54 1BN
T 01451 870484
F 01451 831051
E SueMegsonGallery@aol.com
Founded in 2000, showing unique examples of creative glass art from around the world. Exhibited artists include Bob Crooks, Peter Layton, Amanda Brisbane, Cohn-Stone, Wandermark-Merrit and Loumani.
Submission policy Pieces must be unique and handblown.
Price range £50–£2,000
No of exhibitions annually 4

Swan Gallery

51 Cheap Street, Sherborne
DT9 3AX
T 01935 814465
F 01308 8868195
E L4949@aol.com
W www.swangallery.co.uk
Founded in 1982. Specializations include fine eighteenth-, nineteenth- and twentieth-century watercolours and oil paintings, and antique maps and prints. Artists represented include Myles Birkett-Foster, Harry Sutton Palmer, John Varley, W. Tatton Winter, Henry Alken and T.B. Hardy. Other services offered include restoration, framing and valuation.
Submission policy Occasional exhibitions by living artists only.
Price range £15–£10,000
No of exhibitions annually 2

Toll House Gallery

Clevedon Pier, The Beach, Clevedon
BS21 YQU
T 01275 373346
F 01275 790077
Contact Mrs Mikhael Comerford

Gallery hired by local artists on a monthly basis, exhibiting anything from driftwood sculpture and ceramics to photography and paintings. Also hired for promotional exhibitions.
Price range £25–£450
No of exhibitions annually 12

Tregony Gallery

58 Fore Street, Tregony, Truro
TR2 5RW
T 01872 530505
F 01872 530505
W www.tregonygallery.co.uk
Established in 1998, selling fine contemporary Cornish art. All original work, predominantly seascapes. Hosts a constantly changing display of paintings, sculpture, ceramics, jewelry and glassware. Artists represented include John Brenton, David Rust, Josep Pla, John Piper, Paul Lewin and Robert Jones.
Price range £100–£6,000
No of exhibitions annually 1

Turn of the Tide Gallery

7 The Triangle, Teignmouth
TQ14 8AU
T 01626 777455
E sal@andersons5.fsnet.co.uk
W www.turnofthetide.net
Opened in 2000, showing mainly Cornish and Devon painters. Most work has connections to the sea. Artists include Robert Jones, Michael Praed, Judy Hempstead, Andrea Stokes, and Norman and Lesley Stuart Clarke. Shows etchings, collographs, ceramics, handmade jewelry and open prints.
Submission policy Existing work includes boats, beaches and the Devon countryside painted on board, canvas and driftwood. Gallery looking for work with vibrant colours and a 'slightly quirky and naive style'.
Price range £1.50–£1,500
No of exhibitions annually 1, mixed.

Turner Gallery

88 Queen Street, Exeter
EX4 3RP
T 01392 273673
E turnergallery@yahoo.com
W www.thebarnardturnergallery.co.uk
Founded in 1997 with the aim of showing paintings of quality by artists dedicated to the traditions of painting (landscape, figurative, abstract and idiosyncratic, in acrylic, oil and watercolour). Artists include Brian J. Turner,

Philip James AROI, Richard Slater RI and Ken Symonds. Tutorial scheme with artists offered.
Submission policy Applications welcome but from professional artists only. Send hard-copy examples of work with CV, letter of introduction and sae.
Price range £150–£5,000
No of exhibitions annually Continually changing with occasional keynote exhibitions.

Vitreous Contemporary Art
7 Mitchell Hill, Truro
TR1 1ED
T 01872 274288
E info@vitreous.biz
W www.vitreous.biz
Contact Jake Bose
Founded in 2004. Specializes in contemporary living artists and aims to represent both established and up-and-coming artists. Exhibitions change every month. All media and styles shown, including sculpture, ceramics and fine art.
Solo and joint shows, and small themed group exhibitions.
Submission policy Always looking to introduce new artists to the exhibition programme and is committed to considering all applications. Initially provide at least four images either by email or on CD, slides or hard copy.
Price range £300–£2,000
No of exhibitions annually 10

Wharf Gallery
The Wharf Arts Centre, Canal Road, Tavistock
PL19 8AT
T 01822 611166 (box office) / 613928 (office)
F 01822 613974
E enquiries@tavistockwharf.com
W www.stavistockwharf.com
Contact Chris Burchell
Founded in 1996. One of West Devon's leading arts and entertainment centres. Aims to promote local artists, arts groups, schools and photographers.
Submission policy Interested in well-presented work in any medium (limited sculpture).
West Country artists welcome.
Price range From £25
No of exhibitions annually 12

Widcombe Studios Gallery
The Old Malthouse, Comfortable Place, Upper Bristol Road, Bath
BA1 3AJ
T 01225 482480
E admin@widcombestudios.co.uk

W www.widcombestudios.co.uk
Founded in 1996 to provide studio accommodation, gallery and exhibition space and a programme of courses and talks. Moved to new premises in 2004.
Submission policy Applications for hiring the gallery should be made to the studios' administrator. There is a selection process.

Wales

Art 2 By Ltd
Harbour Lights Gallery, Porthgain, Haverfordwest
SA62 5BW
T 01348 831549
F 01348 831549 (phone first)
E info@art2by.com
W www.art2by.com
Founded in 1995 to promote the art of Pembrokeshire and Welsh artists. Artists include Bernard Green, Sheils Knapp Fisher, Wendy Yeo, Gillian McDonald, Cherry Pickles and Graham Hurd-Wood.
Submission policy Artists' work is viewed strictly by appointment.
Price range £19.50–£20,000
No of exhibitions annually 4

Art Matters Gallery
South Parade, Tenby
SA70 7DG
T 01834 843375
E Info@artmatters.org.uk
W www.artmatters.org.uk
Contact John Faulkner or Margaret Welsh
Established in 2001. A large gallery with an eclectic and changing mix of work. More than fifty current artists including Sue McDonagh, Elizabeth Haines, Hilary Paynter, Derek Williams and Barry Herniman. Mostly paintings but also shows sculpture, ceramics, wood (carved and turned) and wood engravings.
Submission policy Application by post or email with CV and images, prior to possible appointment for viewing.
Price range £100–£2,000
No of exhibitions annually 15, plus continuously changing exhibition in other parts of the gallery.

Attic Gallery
14 Cambrian Place, Swansea
SA1 1RG
T 01792 653387

E roe@atticgallery.co.uk
W www.atticgallery.co.uk
Contact David Roe
Founded in 1962 and among Wales's longest established private galleries. Aims to highlight the work of contemporary artists working in Wales. A full exhibition programme of solo and mixed shows with a changing display of new paintings, graphics and sculpture.
Submission policy Initial approach by post (include sae) with photos and CV, or by email.
Price range £50–£10,000
No of exhibitions annually 8

Black Mountain Gallery

The Square, Cwmllynfell, Swansea
SA9 2FJ
T 01639 830920
E mark@blackmountaingallery.com
W www.blackmountaingallery.com

Bowie & Hulbert

5 Market Street, Hay-on-Wye
HR3 5AF
T 01497 821026
F 01497 821801
E info@hayclay.co.uk
W www.hayclay.co.uk
Partner gallery to Brook Street Pottery (also in Hay-on-Wye), founded in 1994. Specializes in applied arts (ceramics and jewelry) and some fine-art prints. Artists include Walter Keeler, Jane Hamlyn, Peter Beard and Catherine Mannheim. Only shows UK artists and makers.
Submission policy Apply only by letter with slides or photographs and other relevant information.
Price range £50–£2,000
No of exhibitions annually 3–4

Brooklyn Art Gallery

52 Birchgrove Road, Birchgrove, Cardiff
CF14 1RS
T 029 20529950
E info@brooklynartgallery.co.uk
W www.brooklynartgallery.co.uk
Founded in 1999 by artist Nasir Shiraz. Continuously exhibits new works by resident artists including Nasir Shiraz, Rob Lee, Babette Edwards, Huw Walters and Victoria Stewart. Art works are presented on large canvas to suit the modern interior.
Submission policy Artists should send a CV and photos of work by email.

Price range £100–£5,000
No of exhibitions annually 8

Capsule

Charles Street, Cardiff
CF10 2GF
T 029 20382882
E info@acidcasuals.com
W www.acidcasuals.com
Contact Calcio
Owned and run by Acid Casuals.
Submission policy All applications welcome.
Price range £36–£2,000
No of exhibitions annually 8–10

Celf Gallery

85 Newton Road, Mumbles, Swansea
SA3 4BN
T 01792 366800
E info@celfgallery.co.uk
W www.celfgallery.co.uk

Chapel of Art – Capel Celfyddyd

8 Marine Crescent, Criccieth
LL52 0EA
T 01766 523570
E mail@the-coa.org.uk
W www.the-coa.org.uk
Contact Eckhard or Janet Kaiser
Established in 1995. Exhibits contemporary fine art and selected crafts by local, regional and international artists and makers. A specialist ceramic gallery and home of the International Potters' Path, made by potters and ceramic artists from around the world.
Submission policy Artists are required to submit work appropriate to the exhibition titles as published on the website and are advised to contact Janet Kaiser about size and weight restrictions. Textiles and jewelry are only accepted in exceptional circumstances.
Price range £25–£2,000
No of exhibitions annually 6

Coed Hills Rural Artspace

St Hilary, Cowbridge
CF71 7DP
T 01446 774084
E mail@coedhills.co.uk
W www.coedhills.co.uk
An arts venue based on a philosophy of positive living in environmental and social contexts. Has workshops, galleries and a woodland sculpture trail, among other facilities.

Submission policy Welcomes proposals of all types.

Craftsman Gallery
58 St Helen Road, Swansea
SA1 4BE
T 01792 642043
F 01792 642043
E bowden@craftsmangallery.co.uk
W www.craftsmangallery.co.uk

GPF Gallery
18 George Street, Newport
NP20 1EN
T 01633 264581
E gpfgallery@aol.com
Contact Janet Martin
Gwent Picture Framing has been established for over twenty-five years, and the associated GPF Gallery opened in the late 1990s. Artists represented include Philip Muirden, John Selway, Sarah Ball and Michael Organ. Opened Robbins Lane Studios in 2004, housing eight studios and an artist's studio–flat, as well as providing exhibition space and meeting-room hire.
Submission policy Any living artist is welcome to contact the gallery to make an appointment to show work.
Price range £100–£3,000
No of exhibitions annually 6

Green Gallery
The Green, Rhossili, Swansea
SA3 1PL
T 01792 391190
E GreenGalRhossili@aol.com
W www.thegreengallery.co.uk
Contact Fiona Ryall
Founded in 2001. Specializes in fine art, mainly traditional twentieth-century paintings. Also stocks a broad spectrum of modern work including sculptures in bronze and stone. Artists represented include Helen Sinclair, Kevin Ryall, Stuart Mulligan, James Selway and Janet Bligh.
Submission policy Welcomes applications and keen to represent new talent.
Price range £60–£3,000
No of exhibitions annually 2

Kilvert Gallery
Ashbrook House, Clyro, nr Hay-on-Wye
HR3 5RZ
T 01497 820831
F 01497 820831
E art@clyro.co.uk
W www.kilvertgallery.co.uk, www.clyro.co.uk
Founded in 1986 by the painter Elizabeth Organ to promote recent graduates in fine art and specialist crafts. The gallery's artist-in-residence is portrait painter Eugene Fisk. Other artists represented include Peter Bishop, Roger Cecil, Sally Matthews, Kate Milsom Hawkins, Betty Pennell, Ronald Pennell, Charles Shearer and Alfred Stockham.
Submission policy Not currently taking any more artists.
Price range £50–£5,000
No of exhibitions annually 2

La Mostra Gallery
Mermaid Quay, Cardiff Bay, Cardiff
CF10 5BZ
T 029 20492225
F 029 20492226
E enquiries@lamostragallery.com
W www.lamostragallery.com
Cardiff's first commercial art gallery to exhibit international paintings, sculpture and *objets d'art* exclusively. Periodically holds group and personal exhibitions, with special evening openings and private viewings. International artists represented include Julian Murphy (UK), Andrew Buryah (Belarus), Sandro Soravia (Italy) and Rebecca Adams (UK).
Submission policy Send CV, exhibition history and images of work, plus sae if you wish images to be returned.
Price range From £150

Makers' Guild in Wales
Craft in the Bay, The Flourish, Lloyd George Avenue, Cardiff Bay, Cardiff
CF10 4QH
T 029 20484611
F 029 20491136
E mgw@craftinwales.com
W www.makersguildinwales.org.uk
Contact Exhibitions Officer
Founded in 1984, with a permanent exhibition venue at Craft in the Bay in Cardiff; all work is for sale. There are fifty-six members of the guild and the work exhibited includes ceramics, jewelry, textiles, woodwork and metalwork. Also shows temporary exhibitions of contemporary designs created by artists throughout the UK and abroad. A comprehensive education programme provides opportunities for young people and adults to participate in practical courses, demonstrations and talks.

Submission policy Artists living and working in Wales wishing to apply for membership should contact the manager at Craft in the Bay for further details. Artists interested in showing work in the temporary exhibitions area should contact the exhibitions officer at Craft in the Bay.
Price range A wide range of prices.
No of exhibitions annually 7, temporary. Guild members have permanent displays of their work.

manorhaus

10 Well Street, Ruthin
LL15 1AH
T 01824 704830
F 01824 707333
E post@manorhaus.com
W www.manorhaus.com
Contact Christopher Frost
Founded in 2001 and housed within a listed Georgian townhouse hotel and restaurant. Artists include Ann Bridges RCA, Ian Williams, Dave Merrills RCA, Meurig Watkins, Tim Pugh RCA and Alan Baynes.
Submission policy Preference for contemporary works and wall-hung pieces; no space for sculpture or display cabinets. Solo exhibitions require approximately twenty to forty pieces, depending on size.
Price range £100–£1000
No of exhibitions annually 6

Martin Tinney Gallery

18 St Andrew's Crescent, Cardiff
CF10 3DD
T 029 20641411
E mtg@artwales.com
W www.artwales.com
Contact Myfanwy Shorey
Founded 1990, promoting the best of twentieth-century and contemporary Welsh art in Cardiff, London and abroad. Clients include Tate Gallery and National Museum of Wales. Artists represented include Ceri Richards, Shani Rhys James, Kevin Sinnott, Harry Holland, Gwilym Prichard and Sally Moore.
Submission policy Welsh or Welsh-based artists. Submit a portfolio of images (digital, photograph or slide format) and current CV with sae.
Price range £100–£100,000
No of exhibitions annually 12

Mission Gallery

Gloucester Place, Maritime Quarter, Swansea
SA1 1TY
T 01792 652016
F 01792 652016
E missiongallery@btconnect.com
Founded in 1977. Hosts a changing exhibition programme of contemporary visual art photography, film, installation, painting and craft. The gallery's Craft Space shows work by established and emerging makers and designers.
Submission policy Contact the gallery for application form.
No of exhibitions annually 8

Oriel

2 Tyn-Y-Coed Buildings, High Street, Barmouth, Gwynedd
LL42 1DS
T 01341 280285
E info@orielgallery.com
W www.orielgallery.com
Founded in 1992. Offers a broad selection of contemporary work, as well as more traditional work. Apart from work by Valerie McArdell and Sue Moore (both working full-time at the gallery), also promotes the work of Keith Davis, Alex McArdell and Janet Bell. Offers giclée printing services in-house, as well as bespoke framing.
Submission policy Considers other artists' work. However, it has to fit in well with other work being exhibited at that time. If the gallery rejects, it may well reconsider at a later date.
Price range £50–£1500

Oriel Canfas Gallery

44a Glamorgan Street, Cardiff
CF5 1QS
T 029 20666455
F 029 20666455
E info@olacanfas.co.uk
W www.olacanfas.co.uk
Contact Old Library Artists Ltd
Old Library Artists Ltd is an artists' cooperative formed in 1994. In 1996, with the help of Lottery funding, it secured the present building, Oriel Canfas gallery, studios and education space. Exhibits a wide variety of visual art including painting, sculpture and photography, as well as mixed and multimedia.
Price range £50–£5,000
No of exhibitions annually 10

Phillip Davies Fine Art
130 Overland Road, Mumbles, Swansea
SA3 4EU
T 01792 361766

Signature Gallery
59 Newton Road, Mumbles, Swansea
SA3 4BL
T 01792 366360
E robert@thesignaturegallery.co.uk
W www.wleshartsarchive.org.uk/
signature-gallery.htm

St Anthony Fine Art
30A St Anthony Road, Heath, Cardiff
CF11 6JZ
T 029 20400160
E keith@stanthonyfineart.co.uk
W www.stanthonyfineart.co.uk
Founded in 2004, representing established and
emerging artists. Previous exhibitors include Jack
Crabtree, Peter Nicholas and John Selway.
Price range From £50
No of exhibitions annually 8

Washington Gallery
1–3 Washington Buildings, Stanwell Road, Penarth
CF64 2AD
T 029 20712100
F 029 20708047
E info@washgallery.co.uk
W www.washingtongallery.co.uk
Founded in 1998, specializing in Welsh
contemporary art. Artists include Neale Howells,
Iwan Lewis, Laurie Williams, Arthur Giardelli,
Aneurin Jones and James Charlton.
Submission policy Entry open to contemporary
artists in all media (but restricted for video or
photographic artists). Send examples of work.
Enquiries welcome from Welsh artists (based in
Wales or working elsewhere).
Price range £100–£6,000
No of exhibitions annually 30, over two levels.

West Wales Arts Centre
16 West Street, Fishguard
SA65 9AE
T 01348 873867
E westwalesarts@btconnect.com
W www.btconnect.com/WEST-WALES-ARTS/
Contact Rosemary Holcroft or Myles Pepper
Established for over twenty years, exhibiting
contemporary paintings, sculpture and ceramics.
Gallery artists include David Tress, James

MacKeown, Ross Loveday, Brendon Stuart Burns
and Sonya Dawn Flewitt.
Price range £100–£5,000
No of exhibitions annually 4

Workshop Gallery Chepstow
13 Lower Church Street, Chepstow
NP16 5HJ
T 01291 624836
F 01291 624836
E nedheywood@aol.com
W www.nedheywood.com
Founded in 1982, specializing in studio ceramics.
Exhibited artists include Walter Keeler, Lawson
Rudge, Julia Land and Ned Heywood.
Submission policy Ceramics only.
Price range £20–£1,000
No of exhibitions annually 6

Workshop Wales Gallery
Manorowen, Fishguard
SA65 9QA
T 01348 891619
F 01348 891619
E alicecleal@hotmail.com
Contact Alice Cleal
Founded in 1970. Currently exhibits about forty
contemporary artists, including Daniel Backhouse,
Mitchell Cleal, Jack Crabtree, David Humphreys,
Barbara Stewart and Alice Tennant.
Submission policy Only original works accepted.
No prints, photography, jewelry or craft items.
Price range £100–£5,000
No of exhibitions annually 2

West Midlands

Acanthus Gallery
326 Kenilworth Road, Balsall Common,
Warwickshire
CV7 7ER
T 01676 535792
F 01676 535792
E acanthusart@btconnect.com
W www.acanthusart.co.uk
Contact Sandra Tattersall
Founded in 1976 as trade framer (artists'
exhibitions and retail). Artists include Ian
Warwick-King, Laurence Hayfield, Nancy Wood
SFP, Geoff Birks YWS, Stuart Ellis and Roger
Cockram (ceramics).
Submission policy Gallery area available for artists'
exhibitions free of charge, subject to conditions.

Price range £50–£5,000
No of exhibitions annually 4, but none for the past two years.

Artist's Gallery
373 Bearwood Road, Smethwick, Birmingham
B66 4DL
T 0121 4292298
E support@artistsgallery.co.uk
W www.artistsgallery.co.uk
Founded in 1990, specializing in Italian oil paintings and contemporary art. Artists represented include Sue Canonico, Mario Sanzone, Franco Casalloni and Nino D'Amore.
Submission policy All artists welcome to exhibit work after prior agreement.
Price range £100–£2,000
No of exhibitions annually 1, permanent.

Birties of Worcester
46 Friar Street, Worcester
WR1 2NA
T 01905 28836
F 01905 339418
E linda.birtwhistle@birties.fsnet.co.uk
W www.birtiesofworcester.com
Contact Linda Birtwhistle
Founded in 1979 to promote contemporary fine art by local and nationally known artists. Artists include David Birtwhistle (watercolours), Graham Clarke (etchings), John Harris (watercolours), Tom Greenshields (sculpture), Howard Coles (pastels) and Paul Powis (acrylics and oils).
Submission policy By appointment only. Gallery requires to see at least six original recent works. Decisions cannot be made based solely on slides or photographs. Work exhibited must be framed to conservation standard.
Price range £100–£3,000
No of exhibitions annually 6

Bond Gallery
180–182 Fazeley Street, Digbeth, Birmingham
B5 5SE
T 0121 7532065

Broadway Modern
10 The Green, Broadway
WR12 7AA
T 01386 859338
E modern@john-noott.com
W www.john-noott.com
Contact Amanda Noott
Founded in 1999, showing contemporary painting, sculpture, ceramics and furniture.
Price range £50–£5,000
No of exhibitions annually 6

Castle Galleries
Bards Walk, Stratford-upon-Avon
CV37 6EY
T 01789 262031
F 01789 262480
E stratford@castlegalleries.com
W www.castlegalleries.co.uk
Artists include Mackenzie Thorpe, Paul Horton, Alex Miller and Rolf Harris.
Price range £100–£20,000
No of exhibitions annually 4

Cowleigh Gallery
14 Cowleigh Road, Malvern
WR14 1QD
T 01684 560646
F 01684 560646
E cowgall@tiscali.co.uk
Contact William E. Nicholls or Caroline A. Nicholls
Has hosted six exhibitions per year for the last six years, including the Society of Wildlife, the ROI, the RWA and the Bath Society.
Submission policy Encourages emerging painters, but has a large list of gallery artists who are professional and established.
Price range £100–£5,000
No of exhibitions annually 2–3 special solo shows, in addition to continual display.

Custard Factory
Gibbs Square, Birmingham
B9 4AA
T 0121 6047777
F 0121 6048888
E info@custardfactory.com
W www.custardfactory.com
A new arts and media quarter for Birmingham, in development since 1990 and covering over five acres of riverside factories built a hundred years ago by Sir Alfred Bird, the inventor of custard. Houses over five hundred artists and small creative enterprises, offering not only exhibition spaces but also affordable studio workshops and examples of large-scale public art.

Driffold Gallery
78 Birmingham Road, Sutton Coldfield
B72 1QR
T 0121 3555433
Established in 1983, specializing in British and

European paintings by valued artists from 1840 to the present. Living artists include members of British academies and societies.
Price range £300–£25,000
No of exhibitions annually 4–5

England's Gallery
Ball Haye House, 1 Ball Haye Terrace, Leek
ST13 6AP
T 01538 373451
F 01538 373451
Founded in 1967, showing mainly nineteenth- and twentieth-century oils and watercolours. Holds specialist exhibitions of lithography, etching, engraving and woodcuts. Offers framing, restoration, conservation and valuation services.
Submission policy Only original works (oil, acrylic and watercolour preferred). Any print must be limited and produced by the artists concerned.
Price range £45–£8,000
No of exhibitions annually 5 named exhibitions; gallery stock on show when no featured exhibition. Open from 2 p.m. to 5 p.m. daily (except Sunday and Monday) throughout the year.

Eyestorm-Britart Gallery
Radio House, Swan Street, Warwick
CV34 4BJ
T 01926 495506
E alan@aeart.co.uk
W www.eyestorm.com
Founded in 1989, now specializing in modern art. Artists exhibited include Damien Hirst, Sir Terry Frost, Helmut Newton, Willi Kissmer and Bob Carlos Clarke.
Submission policy Submissions from new artists should be sent to head office at 18 Maddox Street, London W1S 1PL.
Price range £200–£20,000
No of exhibitions annually 6–8

Friswell's Picture Gallery Ltd
223 Albany Road, Earlsdon, Coventry
CV5 6NF
T 024 76674883
E patrick@friswells.com
W www.friswells.com
Contact Patrick Kelly
Established 1870. Offers artists the opportunity to exhibit their work in a prominent location (subject to approval). Holds work by artists including Govinder, Lawrence Coulson, Mark Spain, Russell Baker and David Morgan. A full bespoke framing

service is also available.
Submission policy A portfolio of works needs to be submitted by artists wishing to exhibit. If approved, details are then discussed.
Price range From £2.50
No of exhibitions annually 10

Gallery Upstairs Ltd
Torquil, 81 High Street, Henley-in-Arden
B95 5AT
T 01564 792174
E galleryupstairs@aol.com
Shows work of contemporary artists in ceramics and fine art. Deals with leading artists in their fields but also likes to promote those starting out. Has run two large group exhibitions a year (November to December and May to June) since 1985.
Price range £50–£5,000
No of exhibitions annually 2

The Gallery
17A Broad Street, Leek
ST13 5NR
T 01538 372961
F 01538 399696
E info@leekbooks.co.uk
Contact Lisa Salt
Established in 2001, specializing in paintings, art work and crafts by local artists. Artists exhibited include Leslie Gilbert RI, Tom Mountford and Ivan Taylor. Framing service also offered.
Submission policy Artists welcome to leave work at the gallery for inspection. All work must be framed for hanging to a reasonable standard.
Price range £50–£600
No of exhibitions annually 3, including a Christmas exhibition in November and December.

Halcyon Gallery
The International Convention Centre, Broad Street, Birmingham
B1 2EA
T 0121 2488484
E icc@halcyongallery.com
W www.halcyon.co.uk

Helios Gallery
25 Valentine Road, Birmingham
B14 7AN
T 0121 4441585

John Noott Galleries
14 Cotswold Court, Broadway
WR12 7AA

T 01386 858969
E aj@john-noott.com
W www.john-noott.com
Contact Amanda Noott
Founded in 1972, showing contemporary
paintings and sculpture.
Price range £50–£5,000
No of exhibitions annually 10

Manser Fine Art

Coleham Head, Shrewsbury
SY3 7BJ
T 01743 240328
F 01743 270066
E info@fineartdealers.co.uk
W www.fineartdealers.co.uk
Contact Charlotte Cash
Founded in 1994 and owned and managed by
the third generation of the Manser family. Sells
eighteenth-, nineteenth- and twentieth-century
works of art, including sculpture and works with a
Russian or maritime theme. Artists include Anton
Bouvard, Alfred de Breanski, Oliver Clare, Paul
Gribble, Richard Hilder and Edgar Hunt. Also
offers restoration, valuation and framing services.
Submission policy Contact the gallery by phone,
post or email. Send slides or jpegs of works.
Price range £500–£150,000
No of exhibitions annually 3

Montpellier Gallery

8 Chapel Street, Stratford-upon-Avon
CV37 6EP
T 01789 261161
F 01789 261161
W www.montpelliergallery.com
Contact Peter Burridge
Established in 1991, specializing in contemporary
paintings, printmaking, sculpture, studio
ceramics, glass and designer jewelry by established
and emerging artists. Annual exhibition
programmes feature group and solo shows.
Exhibited artists include John Hammond, Brenda
Hartill, Anita Klein and Peter Eugine Ball.
Submission policy Artists should be semi-
professional or professional, showing a
consistency of style and technique.
Price range £25–£5,000
No of exhibitions annually 4

Moya Bucknall Fine Art

Barn End, Park Avenue, Solihull
B91 3EJ
T 0121 7056215

F 0121 7051699
E moya@moyabucknall.co.uk
W www.moyabucknall.co.uk
Formed over thirty years ago. Specializes in sourcing
and commissioning original works of art for both
companies and private individuals. Represents a
wide range of established artists, including James
Butler, Iestyn Davies, Peter Evans, Pam Hawkes
and Terence Millington. Always on the lookout for
new artists. Works with all types of media, from
paintings, drawings and etchings to ceramics,
glassware, fabric installations and three-dimensional
sculpture in bronze, wood and other materials.
Submission policy Requires digital images,
photographs or samples of actual work prior to a
meeting to view the artist's portfolio.
Price range £100–£40,000
No of exhibitions annually 2

New Gallery

St Paul's Square, Birmingham
B3 1RL
T 0121 2330800
E info@thenewgallery.co.uk
W www.thenewgallery.co.uk
Specializes in British twentieth-century greats
(John Piper, Graham Sutherland et al.), living
UK-based artists of international renown (Royal
Academicians, etc.) and other professional UK-
based artists in all styles (Roger Oakes, John
Hodgett, Sara Hayward, David John Robinson).
Limited-edition prints and photographic prints,
monoprints and originals available. Caters to
private and corporate collectors. Offers interest-
free Arts Council England Own Art loans.
Submission policy By email with CV, images and
exhibition history.
Price range £100–£5,000
No of exhibitions annually 8

Number Nine the Gallery

9 Brindley Place, Birmingham
B1 2JA
T 0121 6439099
F 0121 6439199
E noninethegallery@btclick.com
W www.numberninethegallery.com
Established in 1999, selling a diverse range of
Midlands-linked international artists in painting,
glass, ceramics and sculptures, original prints
and rock art. Linked to Arts Council England's
Own Art scheme. Artists include Ralph Brown RA,
Mila Judge Furstova RCA, Glenn Badham, Kevin
Pearsh, Kosta Boda and Bertil Valien.

Submission policy Does not take published commercial artists. Sells mainly original works of art.
Price range £100–£35,000
No of exhibitions annually 6

Owen Taylor Art
The Hunting Lodge, Castle Park, Warwick
CV34 6SZ
T 01926 400058
F 01926 402898
E cyril@owentaylorart.com
W www.owentaylorart.com
Contact Cyril Taylor
Founded in 2002. Stocks British contemporary painting and graphics. Work is varied in style and content. Artists range from Royal Academicians and London Group to recent art-school graduates. Operates Arts Council England's Own Art purchase scheme.
Submission policy Artists should review the gallery website to establish suitability of their work.
Price range £50–£3,000
No of exhibitions annually 4, plus a mixed stock.

Park View Gallery
70 Vicarage Road, Kings Heath, Birmingham
B14 7QL
T 0121 4444851

Priory Gallery Broadway
34 The High Street, Broadway, Worcestershire
WR12 7DT
T 01386 853783
F 01386 853783
E info@priorybroadway.com
W www.info@priorybroadway.com
Deals in twenty-first-century artists and sculptors including Dianne Flynn, Paul Hedley, Paul Gribble, Tony Sheath, Bruce Hardley and Tina Morgan.
Price range £200–£5,000
No of exhibitions annually 4–6

Retrospectives Gallery
The Minories, Rother Street, Stratford-upon-Avon
CV37 6NE
T 01789 297706
E info@retrospectives.co.uk
W www.retrospectives.co.uk
Contact Noric Dorn
In Stratford for nearly twenty years and taken over by present management in 2003. Offers modern and contemporary art, specializing in originals and some limited editions. Local artists include David

Collins, Tom Ashridge FRSA and Geoffrey Kroll. International artists supplying originals include Starlie Sokol-Hohne (USA), Pinto (Portugal) and Wilfred (USA).
Submission policy Only looking for contemporary and mainly abstract art in oils, acrylic and mixed media.
Price range £100–£800
No of exhibitions annually 1

Shell House Gallery
36 The Homend, Ledbury
HR8 1BT
T 01531 632557
E padireland@aol.com
W www.shellhousegallery.co.uk
Contact Pat Ireland
Founded in 1979, specializing in original watercolours and mixed media by living artists. Main exhibitions are by the Royal Institute of Painters in Watercolours and the Royal Institute of Oil Painters. Also offers a framing and restoration service and publishes limited-edition prints.
Price range £50–£3,000
No of exhibitions annually 10

St Paul's Gallery
94–108 Northwood Street, Birmingham
B3 1TH
T 0121 2365800
F 0121 2360098
E info@stpaulsgallery.com
W www.stpaulsgallery.com

Valentyne Dawes Gallery
Church Street, Ludlow
SY8 1AP
T 01584 874160
E sales@gallery.wyenet.co.uk
W www.maritime-paintings.com
Founded in mid-1980s, specializing in coastal and maritime paintings. Mainly nineteenth and early twentieth century. Artists include E.W. Cooke RA, David James and John Brett. Modern British artists are also represented, in particular Terrick Williams RA. Contemporary painters include Ian Cryer.
Price range £80–£80,000
No of exhibitions annually 1 – the December Maritime Exhibition continues until Christmas.

Warstone & Turner
67 Warstone Lane, Hockley, Birmingham
B18 6NG
T 0121 6936968

Warwick Gallery

14 Smith Street, Warwick
CV34 4HH
T 01926 495880
E wg@artisatart.fsnet.co.uk
W www.art-is-a-tart.com
Contact Peter Forde
Founded in 1976, specializing in contemporary
work by established and emerging craftspeople
mainly from the UK. Artists include David
Dodsworth, Deborah Scaldwell, Liz Cox, Christine
Cummings, Suzie Marsh and Jenny Hale.
Submission policy Chooses work that appeals to it.
Branches 82 Regent Street, Warwick CV32 4NS
T 01926 422833.
Price range £1–£3,000
No of exhibitions annually 2

Wenlock Fine Art

3 The Square, Much Wenlock
TF13 6LX
T 01952 728232
Opened in 1991, dealing in twentieth and twenty-
first-century artists. Artists represented include
William Gear RA, John Piper, Mich Rooney RA,
Henry Inlander, John Christopherson and
Adrian Ryan.
Price range £100–£15,000
No of exhibitions annually 3

Wildside Books and Gallery

Rectory House, 26 Priory Road, Great Malvern
WR14 3DR
T 01684 562818
F 01684 566491
E enquire@wildsidebooks.co.uk
W www.wildsidegallery.co.uk
Founded in 1999, specializing in wildlife and
botanical art with a particular interest in artists'
prints. Exhibits work by David Koster, Robert
Gillmor, Keith Shackleton, Charles Tunnicliffe,
Winifred Austen and R. Talbot Kelly. Also handles
book launches for wildlife artists.
Submission policy Initially submit CV by email.
Price range £25–£15,000
No of exhibitions annually 1–2 major exhibitions at
Nature in Art in Gloucester.

Yorkshire and Humberside

108 Fine Art

108 West End Avenue, Harrogate
HG2 9BT
T 01423 819108 / 709108
F 01423 525847
E andrew@108fineart.com
W www.108fineart.com
Established in 1997 to promote the work of
emerging Scottish artists. Although it continues to
work primarily with Scottish and northern artists,
also shows other work the owners consider
challenging and exciting. Artists shown include
Joash Woodrow, George Rowlett, Alan Davie,
Peter Sedgley, Christopher P. Wood, Paul Reid
and Robert MacMillan. Also stocks work by
numerous modern British artists. Offers a fully
comprehensive paintings conservation service to
collectors, museums and galleries.
Submission policy Welcomes work by artists in all
media.
Price range £500–£20,000
No of exhibitions annually 4

Archipelago Art Gallery and Studio

742 Ecclesall Road, Sheffield
S11 8TB
T 0114 2686885
F 0114 2682272
E info@archipelago-art.co.uk
W www.archipelago-art.co.uk
Contact Rupert Wood
Opened in 2002, featuring contemporary
painters, printmakers and photographers. Also
incorporates Archipelago digital printmaking
and giclée services, and a framing and making
workshop. Exhibitions in 2005 included work by
Heidi Konig, Charlotte Cornish, Ian Wilkinson
and flyeronthewall.com, an Internet showcase
for graphic artists and illustrators producing club
and music industry designs, made available as
art objects.
Submission policy Submissions welcome from
active painters, printmakers or designers.
Price range £250–£2,500
No of exhibitions annually 6

Artco

1 Meanwood Close, Leeds
LS7 2JF
T 0113 2620056
F 0113 2628388
E info@artco.co.uk
W www.artco.co.uk
Contact Leah Hester-Brown
Established for over twenty years. Exhibits work
from both well-established artists and emerging
talent, maintaining a strong presence at selected

art fairs throughout the UK. The gallery covers 2,000 sq. ft, exhibiting a diverse selection of styles of art work. Bespoke and commercial framing service offered.
Submission policy Submissions from artists welcome. No installation or video art.
Price range £75–£5,000
No of exhibitions annually 4

Artolicana
25 Church Street, Ilkley
LS29 9DR
T 01943 603866
E info@artolicana.org
W www.artolicana.org
Established over ten years ago, selling local artists' work. Deals in original paintings only. Artists exhibited include Giuliana Lazzerini, David Greenwood, Tamara Lawson, Judith Levin, Jane Fielder and Brian Irving.
Submission policy Established artists with proven mailing lists considered for inclusion in the gallery's programme of exhibitions.
Price range £100–£5,500
No of exhibitions annually Every three weeks for established artists; unsold work held in stock after three weeks for further month.

Blake Gallery
18 Blake Street, York
YO1 8QH
T 01904 733666
E info@blakegallery.com
W www.blakegallery.com
Shows contemporary art including a permanent collection of sculpture by Sally Arnup and an extensive range of works by Piers Browne. Other artists include Mamdoh Badran, Lesley Fotherby, Roy Hammond, Tom Wanless and Walter Holmes.
Price range £50–£20,000
No of exhibitions annually 6

Bohemia Galleries
7 Gillygate, York
YO31 7EA
T 01904 466488
E info@a-r-t.co.uk
W www.a-r-t.co.uk
Contact Sheana Eccles
Opened in the mid-1990s. Has developed a reputation for innovative stock, which includes contemporary works of art, ceramics and glass of the last two centuries. Artists represented include

Mark Halsey, Frank Bentley, David Baumforth, Ludmila Curilova, Giluliana Lazzerini and Emilija Pasagic.
Submission policy Submissions welcome.

Braithwaite Gallery
42 Low Petergate, York
YO1 7HZ
T 01904 655707
F 01904 655707
E artist@yorkartist.com
W www.yorkartist.com
Contact Victoria Peake
Located a few yards from the South Transept of York Minster in a historic, beamed, listed building belonging to York Minster. Owned by the Braithwaite family. Resident artist M.J. Braithwaite has a constant display, and there are prints and originals of many other artists including Kay Boyce, John Silver, David Shepherd, Christine Comyn and Warwick Higgs. Offers an in-house giclée printing service for artists.
Submission policy Most originals are purchased from leading publishers. Self-publishing artists can contact via email or phone (no cold-calling; contact Vicky for an informal chat).
Price range £1–£10,000
No of exhibitions annually Permanent selling exhibition.

Browns Gallery
Wesley Street Chambers, Wesley Street, Otley
LS21 1AZ
T 01943 464656 / 850404
F 01943 464328
E sales@brownsgallery.co.uk
W www.brownsgallery.co.uk
Contact Peter Brown Snr
Established over fifteen years ago and situated in a building occupying the site of Chippendale's birthplace. A family company representing well-known artists such as Shepherd, Flint, Rolf Harris, Mackenzie Thorpe, Doug Hyde and Kay Boyce, in addition to established and emerging local artists.
Price range £25–£4,000
No of exhibitions annually 4

Bruton Gallery
P.O. Box 145, Holmfirth
HD9 1YU
T 0870 7471800
E art@brutongallery.co.uk
W www.brutongallery.co.uk

Crescent Arts

The Crescent, Scarborough
YO11 2PW
T 01723 351461
E info@crescentarts.co.uk
W www.crescentarts.co.uk
Contact Rachel Massey (Temporary Manager)
Established in 1979, providing: studio space for
up to eight resident artists; support and resources
for artists across the Borough of Scarborough; a
programme of contemporary exhibitions; related
education workshops; open-access facilities
including darkroom, kiln and printmaking
facilities. Resident artists pay subsidized rent
in return for their time administering the
exhibition/education programme. They are
expected to undertake a personal, tailormade
programme of professional training, supported
by the management committee.
Submission policy Look at website or phone
for details of exhibition opportunities, studio
vacancies, workshops or open-access bookings.
No of exhibitions annually 6

Cupola Contemporary Art Ltd

178a Middlewood Road, Hillsborough, Sheffield
S6 1TD
T 0114 2852665 / 2812154
F 0114 285 2665
E info@cupolagallery.com
W www.cupolagallery.com
Contact Helen Inckle
Established in 1991, now one of the most
successful privately run contemporary galleries
in the north. Exhibits a broad range of work from
both new, emerging talent and more established
artists. Painting, sculpture, photography (chemical
print and lens-based digital), original printmaking
(etching, lino cuts, mezzotint, collograph,
etc.), ceramics, glass, textiles and jewelry are
represented. Installations, film, video and new
media work are occasionally exhibited. Also
offers a comprehensive bespoke framing service.
Artists represented include Lyn Hodnett, Derek
McQueen, John Brokenshire, Anne Penman
Sweet, Anita Klein and Corinna Button.
Submission policy Entry requirements are
available from the gallery on request; contact by
phone or by email. Submissions are welcomed
throughout the year. Applications for
representation are preferred. Applications
for solo exhibitions are rarely considered prior
to an artist being represented by the gallery
on a regular basis.

Price range £10–£5,000
No of exhibitions annually 8–10

Eyecandy

118 Trafalgar Street, Devonshire Quarter,
Sheffield
S1 4JT
T 0114 2787979
F 0114 2787979
E info@eyecandyimagesuk.com
W www.eyecandyimagesuk.com
Opened in 2004, Eyecandy merges gallery,
retail outlet and workshop in a loft-style setting.
Offers contemporary and fine-art prints, limited
editions, originals, quality greeting cards and
ceramics. There is also an in-house framing
service. Exhibited artists include Caroline Wood,
Sheryl Lee, Alistaire Scarlett, Elvis Davis and
Ben Sutcliffe.
Submission policy Accepts submissions at any
time. All works considered.
Price range £25–£600
No of exhibitions annually 4

Forge Gallery

New Road, Robin Hood's Bay
YO22 4SF
T 01947 881049
E dave@forgegallery.co.uk
W www.forgegallery.co.uk
Contact Dave Jeffery
Opened in 1998. Sells original works of art
including paintings, ceramics and sculpture.
Specializes in work produced in Yorkshire
and in particular the north Yorkshire coast
area. Artists include Dave Jeffery, Janet
R. Moodie ARCA, Philip Stuttard and
David Beven.
Submission policy Contact Dave Jeffery by letter,
phone or email. Alternatively, call in at the gallery
for further information.
Price range £10–£1,500

Gallery 42

42 St Joseph's Street, Tadcaster
LS24 9HA
T 01937 530465
F 01937 530465
E art@gallery42.com
W www.gallery42.com
Aims to take modern art into the local community
and encourage local artists. Artists exhibited
include Nel Whatmore, Graham Illingworth,
Malcolm Cowerd and John Wilson.

Submission policy Work taken on a commission basis.
Price range £20–£15,000
No of exhibitions annually 2–3

The Gallery
24 Market Place, Masham
HG4 4EB
T 01765 689554
E enquiries@mashamgallery.co.uk
W www.mashamgallery.co.uk
Contact Josie Beszant
Founded in 1994. Exhibits high-quality contemporary art and craft.
Submission policy Work should be clearly labelled and include an sae if posted. Do not send original pieces. Submissions are welcomed by email but the gallery should be contacted before sending images. Restrictions include no installations, photography or video art. Artists must be living and working in the UK.
Price range £5–£2,000
No of exhibitions annually 4

Gascoigne Gallery
Royal Parade, Harrogate
HG1 2JN
T 01423 525000
F 01423 525000
E info@thegascoignegallery.com
W www.thegascoignegallery.com
Founded in 1998, showing original contemporary work that is semi-abstract and marginally representational. Landscape predominates, with the aim of conveying the essence and atmosphere of a subject rather than describing each minute detail.
Price range £200–£4,000
No of exhibitions annually 12–18

Glenrhydding Gallery
38 Bondgate, Otley
LS21 1AD
T 01943 466323
E howardgcf@tiscali.co.uk
W www.glenrhydding.com
Contact www.glenrhydding.com
Established in 1985 and under present ownership for the last nine years. Artists include John Sibson, Graham Carver, Neil Simone, Keith Melling, Patricia Jones and Sue Howells. Framing service also offered.
Price range £20–£1,000
No of exhibitions annually 2

Godfrey & Watt
7–8 Westminster Arcade, Parliament Street, Harrogate
HG1 2RN
T 01423 525300
E mail@godfreyandwatt.co.uk
W www.godfreyandwatt.co.uk
Contact Alex Godfrey
Founded in 1985 by Alex and Mary Godfrey to show work that 'we personally love by the best artists and makers that we can find.' Constantly changing range of ceramics, jewelry, studio glass, sculpture, paintings and original prints. In addition to this, a series of exhibitions is mounted each year, usually focusing on the work of an individual artist. Artists and makers exhibited include John Maltby, Morgen Hall, Lucy Casson, Guy Taplin, Piers Browne and Elaine Pamphilon.
Submission policy Submissions welcome from artists by post or email. Should include photos, biography and prices.
Price range £50–£2,000
No of exhibitions annually 5

Grosmont Gallery
Front Street, Grosmont, Whitby
YO22 5QE
T 01947 895007
E info@grosmontgallery.com
W www.grosmontgallery.com
Relaunched by new owners in 2004. Aims to promote and sell fine art and quality crafts. Most artists currently on show are reasonably local but not exclusively. Among current artists exhibiting are David Baumforth, Sally Gatie, Chris Geall, Janet Moodie, Wendy Tate and April Young.
Submission policy All artists are welcome to make contact, especially those with new and challenging work.
Price range £5–£5,000
No of exhibitions annually 4

Headrow Gallery
588 Harrogate Road, Alwoodley, Leeds
LS17 8DP
T 0113 2694244
F 0113 2694244
E maxwellroberts@btconnect.com
Founded in 1900. Specializes in contemporary northern European art work.
Submission policy Artists' submissions always welcome.
Price range £150–£5,000
No of exhibitions annually 2–3

Jim Robison and Booth House
Gallery and Pottery
3 Booth House Lane, Holmfirth, Huddersfield
HD9 2QT
T 01484 685270
E jim.robison@virgin.net
W www.jimrobison.co.uk,
www.boothhousegallery.co.uk
Contact Jim or Liz Robison
Began in 1975 as a studio for Jim Robison and
exhibition space for invited artists. Specializes
in ceramics with continuous displays of both
established and emerging talent. Paintings and
prints also exhibited.
Submission policy Exhibition by invitation only.
Price range £5–£500
No of exhibitions annually Continuous
displays and two major annual shows,
the Christmas show in November and the
summer exhibition in July.

Massarella Fine Art and Darren Baker Gallery
14 Victoria Road, Saltaire, Shipley
BD18 3LQ
T 01274 580129
E admin@dbfinearts.co.uk
Founded in 1998 to promote and raise awareness
of the local art scene as well as to represent
national artists. Artists include Darren Baker,
Joe Scarborough, Stuart Hirst, Jeremy Taylor,
Chris Wade and Steve Capper.
Submission policy Artists should submit CV and
five examples of work (photos or CD). All media
considered.
Price range £100–£6,000
No of exhibitions annually 4

McTague of Harrogate
17–19 Cheltenham Mount, Harrogate
HG1 1DW
T 01423 567086
E paul@mctague.co.uk
W www.mctague.co.uk
A traditional art gallery established in 1974,
dealing in old watercolours, antique prints, maps
and oil paintings. Specialities include Yorkshire
and northern artists, and sporting and rural
subjects.
Price range £50–£1,500
No of exhibitions annually 1

Michael Pybus Fine Arts
127 Church Street, Whitby
YO22 4DE
T 01947 820028
E enquiries@mpybusfinearts.co.uk
W www.mpybusfinearts.co.uk
Founded 1997, selling modern and antique works
including early twentieth-century works by the
Staithes group of artists. Contemporary artists
include David Curtis, Trevor Chamberlain,
David Allen, Peter Hicks, Howard Bedford and
Michael Pybus.
Submission policy Solo shows of loosely realist
works, mainly by artists with an established track
record.
Price range £200–£6,000
No of exhibitions annually 4

Phoenix Fine Arts Ltd
11 Finkle Street, Richmond
DL10 4QA
T 01748 822400
Founded in 2002, exhibiting mostly local
original art. Has shown over 250 different
artists including Piers Browne, Chris Mounay,
Peter Bailey, John Degnan and Barbara Lamb.
Commissions undertaken and an art purchase
plan offered.
Submission policy New artists welcome. Work
shown on a commission basis for five weeks.
Price range £25–£3,000
No of exhibitions annually 12

Reubens Gallery
83 Great Goerge Street, Leeds
LS1 3BR
T 0113 2457771
E enquiries@reubensgallery.co.uk
W www.reubensgallery.co.uk

Sanderson, George and Peach
Contemporary Gallery
39 Station Road, Holmfirth
HD9 1AB
T 01484 684485
Contact Debbie George
Founded in 1996. Represents over fifty artists at
any one time. Seeks to show quality work by both
known and unknown artists. Works exhibited
include painting, sculpture, photography, jewelry
and ceramics.
Submission policy Submissions should be
in writing to the gallery, with good images
(preferably photographs) accompanied
by a CV.
Price range £5–£5,000
No of exhibitions annually 4

Sculpture Lounge

11 Upperbridge Street, Huddersfield Road,
Holmfirth
HD9 2JR
T 01484 687425
F 01484 687425
E sculpture.lounge@virgin.net
W www.sculpturelounge.com
Founded in 2002, specializing in ceramics,
ceramic scupture, sculpture, paintings and jewelry.
Prominent artists represented include Brendon
Hesmondhalgh, Elizabeth Price, Mari-Ruth-Oda,
Annie Peaker, Christine Cummings and Melanie
Adkins.
Submission policy Artist applications by post,
including photographs of works, artist statement
and CV.
Price range £20–£5,000
No of exhibitions annually 8

Smart Gallery

Redbrick Mill, 218 Bradford Road, Batley
WF17 6JF
T 01924 455445
F 01924 455425
E info@smartgallery.co.uk
W www.smartgallery.co.uk
Contact Gillian Cohen
Founded in 2002 at Redbrick Mill, followed by a
second at Christopher Pratts in Leeds. Sells
Washington Green limited-edition and original
prints and has a craft and design centre based in
Batley. Encourages local artists to exhibit.
Branches 9 Regent Street, Leeds LS2 7QN
T 0113 2444545 **F** 0113 2443636.
Submission policy Encourages work from a wide
range of artists in a variety of media.
Price range £100–£5,000
No of exhibitions annually 8

Talents Fine Arts

7 Market Place, Malton
YO17 7LP
T 01653 600020
F 01653 600020
E talentsfinearts@hotmail.com
Contact Clive Vaughan
Established for over eighteen years. Contemporary
artists include David Howel, John Gibson, Neil
Spelman, Barry Peckham, Susan Bower, Steven

Lingham. Shows glass and ceramics. Framing and
restoration services offered.
Submission policy Submissions by prior notice
only.
Price range £100–£3,000
No of exhibitions annually 2

Taylor-Pick Fine Art

7 North Bar Within, Beverley
HU17 8AP
T 01482 881169
E andrew@taylor-pick.com
W www.taylor-pick.com
Contact Andrew Pick
Founded in 1996 with the aim of presenting
quality contemporary fine art by either established
artists or up-and-coming young artists. The gallery
has an established and growing regular client
base. Represents artists from the UK, Spain,
Ireland and the Czech Republic, including George
Hainsworth, Beltran Bofill, Gordon King, Fraser
King and Jan Vich.
Submission policy Submissions should be of a
professional manner by artists of a high standard.
All media considered. Photographs or CD
preferred.
Price range £400–£25,000
No of exhibitions annually 5

Walker Galleries Ltd

13 Montpellier Parade, Harrogate
H91 2TJ
T 01423 526366
F 01423 525975
E walkercontemp@aol.com
W www.walkerfineart.co.uk
Contact Angela Noble
Founded in 1971, presenting a wide array of styles
from photographic to semi abstract. Gallery artists
include Jeremy Barlow Roi, John Mackie, John
Lowrie Morrison, Peter Graham, Caroline Bailey
and Mike Bernard.
Branches 104 High Street, Honiton, Devon.
Submission policy Only handles living artists.
Submissions welcome from established artists but
will consider other artists if photographs supplied.
Price range £250–£10,000 for paintings;
£200–£4,500 for bronzes; £40–£400 for
ceramics.
No of exhibitions annually 10

02

Public museums and galleries

Culture clashes:
Are museums where artists go to die?

Iwona Blazwick

*Museums: cemeteries! ... Identical, surely in
the sinister promiscuity of so many bodies
unknown to one another. Museums: public
dormitories where one lies forever beside hated
or unknown beings. Museums: absurd abattoirs
of painters and sculptors ferociously slaughtering
each other...(cemeteries of empty exertion.
Calvaries of crucified dreams, registries of aborted
beginnings!). ... Smash them...pitilessly.*
– F.T. Marinetti, Futurist Manifesto, *Le Figaro*,
20 February 1909

A hundred years on from the Futurists' demand
for their destruction, museums of art are more
ubiquitous and powerful than ever before.
Ranked as one of the most successful brands in
the world, Tate joins the Guggenheim in Bilbao,
the Centre Georges Pompidou in Paris and
MoMA in New York, as not only a repository of
art but also an urban spectacle, a destination for
mass entertainment and a source of cultural
capital. Museums are platforms for corporate
promotions and political ambitions. They not
only bestow value on art; they also generate
revenues from it. Why should artists have
anything to do with them?

Artists' love–hate relationship with the
institution stems as much from being left
out of the 'absurd abattoir' as being made
part of it. The modern museum collects art
and arranges it into a narrative sequence –
often chronological, sometimes thematic.
It also presents high-profile temporary
exhibitions, increasingly of living artists.
And so it makes history, as much by its
exclusions as its inclusions. Until the end
of the twentieth century, many artists who
happened to be female, of colour, living
outside the West, or just not making objects,
were absented from the 'cemeteries of empty

exertion' and consequently found themselves
also absent from art history and from the
art market.

But museums and public galleries haven't
stood still. Fired by the assaults of the avant-
garde they have grown ever more dynamic and
central to the life of art. So what makes them
important for artists?

Inspiration and influence

To enter the modern art museum is to
move across time and space, to revel in
aesthetic, phenomenological and even erotic
sensations that are encapsulated both in
individual works of art and the spaces between
them. A museum's collection also immerses
us in historical, political and mythic narratives.
These might generate intense stimulation
but also provocation, even revulsion. Critical
judgments, assessments of technique and
wrestling with meaning must all surely be
part of the work of the artist immeasurably
enhanced by an encounter with the
history of art.

Finding love

We rarely encounter works of art in isolation.
Rather, they are experienced in relation to each
other in a series of juxtapositions. These can
be very contentious – why is this work hung
next to that work and what do they say about
each other? The display of a collection or
the installation of a show is like arranging
words in a sentence: curators create meta-
narratives that may enhance – or distort –
the meaning of works of art. Often these
arrangements reveal completely unexpected
qualities in works of art by different
practitioners.

These juxtapositions also include the
architecture of the museum – its windows,
doorways, corridors and stairwells, each of
which impact on our experience of the work.
Finally, we see works of art in juxtaposition with
other people. Museums are great places to look
at each other, which is why they are popular

cruising destinations and great places to pick people up.

Being loved and understood

To have your work acquired by a museum is perhaps the most powerful endorsement of its value, not just in monetary but also in symbolic terms. Entering a collection marks entry into a grand narrative.

Museums are also scientific institutions, dedicated to the conservation and study of the objects of art. Conservators analyze the effects of environment, movement and time on the art object and will go to extraordinary lengths to guarantee its preservation for posterity and to restore it lovingly to perfection in the face of damage or old age.

To have a work in a museum collection is also to offer it to art-historical appraisal through indexes and catalogue entries. Curators are often scholars who use expert art-historical and technical knowledge to investigate the origin, technique and provenance of a work. Artists can describe their creative processes, motivations and intentions through exhibition guides and publications. Conversely, these interpretive tools offer invaluable research materials to artists investigating individuals, themes and movements across time.

Having room to breathe

Since the founding of what some would call the first museum of modern art, the Louvre, museum architecture has mutated from palace to pavilion, from architect's signature piece to factory conversion. Throughout the twentieth century there has also been a shift in art from offering a picture of the world to creating a world in its own right. Sculpture has expanded into environment, picture-making has mutated into projection. Just as works of art have become bigger, so have public museums and galleries. They are often the only kind of buildings that can physically accommodate works of art that defy domestic space.

It is as a platform for an encounter with the public that is the most vital aspect of the museum or public gallery. When a work of art makes its debut into the exhibition space, it begins a dynamic and ever-changing encounter with the viewer. Arguably the point where a work of art comes to life, it can communicate with an audience far wider than could ever be reached in a studio, private collection or commercial gallery.

Changing the world

The great works of art we can encounter in the museum can move us and inspire profound philosophical meditations on the nature of being and the world around us. Museums are also full of representations. However, the life experience and aesthetic sensibilities of entire sections of society may never surface in their parades of movements and masterpieces. The inclusion of art by those historically left out, by virtue of gender or geography, also offers a moment of recognition to those communities that feel disenfranchised. Not only may they encounter their own view of the world, but they might also find public recognition for an artist from their community.

Making money

A popular misconception about artists is that they don't need to eat. The media and the public are often outraged that an artist has exchanged a work of art for money, in a way that they seldom do in relation to sports, pop or film stars. Nonetheless, most artists struggle to survive through their art. Museums are beneficial in two ways: they both buy works of art and also provide employment.

The most skilled and sensitive handlers of art are artists themselves; most technical teams in museums and galleries are made up of artists. The growth of education departments has also seen artists become educators, working with a range of audiences – from schoolchildren to senior citizens – on interpreting art and using their experience of an exhibition to tap into their own creativity.

Artists also make the best curators. For many, curating, writing and promoting the work of other artists is a way of making art.

The operation of a museum or even a small municipal gallery involves many people; not just curators and education staff, but also registrars, technicians, guards, reception staff, accountants, press officers, fund-raisers, editors, designers, archivists and librarians. These positions offer opportunities for being involved in art and enjoying your job, while making a bit of money.

The downside
Even if you are lucky enough to have your work acquired by a museum, there is no guarantee that it might not just languish in its crate, unseen for decades. An artist's oeuvre might be reduced to representing a fleeting moment in the parade of movements – now past – or 'isms' – now unfashionable. Worse still, artists might find their work on display with art they despise. Some may shudder at the interpretations a curator imposes on their art through labels and catalogues, establishing misconceptions for posterity. Others may feel discomfort as they find the art they created to be part of the flux of people and places being suspended in the timeless, placeless vacuum of the white cube – or reduced to a trophy for a multinational marketing campaign. The worst of all is being 'de-accessioned' – the fancy euphemism for having your work sold by a museum.

Visitors, too, can experience the downside of museums: they might feel uncomfortable with the increasingly corporate style of museum architecture or overwhelmed by the throngs who might be just as happy in a shopping mall.

Hope on the horizon
None of this can detract from the fact that museums and public galleries are playing an ever more central role in providing a platform for art in society. In Britain, where museums are free, audiences are expanding exponentially every year. The media are increasingly recognizing that readers and viewers want engaged, knowledgeable criticism and guidance, and not just sensationalism. Politicians are waking up to the fact that there is a substantial economy generated by artists and art institutions, and that ordinary people derive enormous satisfaction from their encounters with contemporary as well as historical art.

Rather than being mausoleums, these spaces can be playgrounds, cruising destinations, laboratories, political platforms, temples of worship, black boxes or white cubes – it's up to you.

Iwona Blazwick is the Director of the Whitechapel Gallery and an independent curator and critic.

Public museums and galleries

East Anglia

Boxfield Gallery

Stevenage Arts and Leisure Centre, Lytton Way, Stevenage
SG1 1RZ
T 01438 242644
F 01438 242342 / 242679
E william.barnard@stevenage-leisure.co.uk
W www.stevenage-leisure/gordoncraig/arts_crafts.htm
Part of the Gordon Craig Theatre situated within the Stevenage Leisure Centre complex and opened in 1975. Hosts ten exhibitions per year (suitable for large-scale works and group shows). The smaller Foxer Gallery puts on twelve exhibitions per year (suitable for water-colourists, printmakers and photographers).
Submission policy Application by portfolio and interview with the Visual Arts Officer. Will show artists of national and local standing, and both retrospective or topical shows.
Talks/Events/Education Outreach to all local schools. Workshop and classes run in studio facilities for all age and skill groups. Also competitions.

Broughton House Gallery

98 King Street, Cambridge
CB1 1LN
T 01223 314960
E bhg@dircon.co.uk
W www.broughtonhousegallery.co.uk
Founded in 1987. Hosts nine exhibitions (solo, duo, theme) a year. Home of the Gwen Raverat Archive of wood engravings (over four hundred for sale).
Submission policy Applications with images and CV, etc.
Talks/Events/Education Occasional talks by artists.

Bury St Edmunds Art Gallery

The Market Cross, Bury St Edmunds
IP33 1BT
T 01284 762081
F 01284 750774
E enquiries@burystedmundsartgallery.org
W www.burystedmundsartgallery.org
Talks/Events/Education Holds events, talks and workshops related to current exhibition. Prices vary.

Cecil Higgins Art Gallery

Castle Lane, Bedford
MK40 3RP
T 01234 211222
F 01234 327149
E chag@bedford.gov.uk
A recreated Victorian mansion and adjoining modern gallery housing an important collection of watercolours, prints and drawings, ceramics, glass and lace.

Fitzwilliam Museum

Trumpington Street, Cambridge
CB2 1RB
T 01223 332900
F 01223 332923
E fitzmuseum-enquiries@lists.cam.ac.uk
W www.fitzmuseum.cam.ac.uk
Founded in 1816 by the bequest of the Seventh Viscount Fitzwilliam to the University of Cambridge. Houses collections of art and antiquities spanning centuries and civilizations, displayed in twenty-seven galleries. Highlights include antiquities from the Ancient Near East, Greece, Rome and Cyprus; English and European pottery and glass; sculpture; Oriental art; Korean ceramics; masterpieces by Domenico Veneziano, Leonardo da Vinci, Titian, Rembrandt, Tubens and Van Dyck; outstanding works by British artists including Gainsborough, Reynolds, Stubbs and Constable; and a collection of twentieth-century art. Runs programme of temporary exhibitions, events, courses and activities for all ages.

Focal Point Gallery

Southend Central Library, Victoria Avenue, Southend-on-Sea
SS2 6EX
T 01702 612621 ext. 207
F 01702 469241
E focalpointgallery@southend.gov.uk
W www.focalpoint.org.uk
Established in 1991 as the result of an Essex County Council arts initiative to establish a photographic centre for Essex. Housed on the second floor of Southend Central Library, it specializes in photography and media arts.
Submission policy The exhibitions programme is usually planned up to eighteen months in advance. Those wishing their work to be considered for exhibition should submit a written proposal with supporting visual material to the Gallery Director. It is advised that artists and curators visit the gallery, or at least consider the

physical nature of the exhibition area and past programme before submitting proposals. Exhibition proposals are submitted on the understanding that programming meetings to view unsolicited proposals take place once every six months.

Talks/Events/Education Runs a regular programme of events for adults, children and family groups to accompany exhibitions. These include artists' talks and workshops, film screenings and drop-in events. Free exhibition tours can be arranged by gallery staff for school, college and community groups who book in advance.

Gainsborough's House

46 Gainsborough Street, Sudbury
CO10 2EU
T 01787 372958
F 01787 376991
E mail@gainsborough.org
W www.gainsborough.org
The museum and art gallery at the birthplace of Thomas Gainsborough.

Kettle's Yard

Castle Street, Cambridge
CB3 0AQ
T 01223 352124
F 01223 324377
E mail@kettlesyard.cam.ac.uk
W www.kettlesyard.co.uk
Once the home of Jime Ede, a curator at the Tate Gallery. The house displays Ede's collection, including works by Ben and Winifred Nicholson, Alfred Wallis, Christopher Wood, David Jones, Joan Miró, Henri Gaudier-Brzeska, Constantin Brancusi, Henry Moore and Barbara Hepworth. Holds regular exhibitions, including an annual exhibition deriving from the Artist's Fellowship and exhibitions of artists working in the east arts region.
Submission policy In addition to a library and archive, there are education programmes for children and adults.

King's Lynn Arts Centre

27–29 King Street, King's Lynn
PE30 1HA
T 01553 779095
E lfalconbridge@west-norfolk.gov.uk
W www.kingslynnarts.co.uk
The gallery holds exhibitions, and runs workshops and a Saturday art club.

Letchworth Museum and Art Gallery

Broadway, Letchworth Garden City
SG6 3PF
T 01462 685647
F 01462 481879
E letchworth.museum@north-herts.gov.uk
W www.north-herts.gov.uk
Founded in 1914 by the Letchworth Naturalists' Society. Main permanent displays are on archaeology, particularly Iron Age and Roman, and natural history. Has regular temporary displays of works from the museum's fine- and decorative-art collections, and its social history collection. Art collections include the largest holding of works by Camden Town artist William Ratcliffe. Also has a good collection of oils by Margaret Thomas. Decorative art includes glass and ceramics.
Submission policy Exhibits work in all media except digital and film.

Minories Art Gallery

High Street, Colchester
CO1 1UE
T 01206 577067
F 01206 577161
Shows contemporary art and sculpture.

Norwich Castle Museum and Art Gallery

Shirehall, Market Avenue, Norwich
NR1 3JQ
T 01603 493625
F 01603 493623
E museums@norfolk.gov.uk
W www.museums.norfolk.gov.uk
One of the city's most famous landmarks, Norwich Castle was built by the Normans as a Royal Palace nine hundred years ago. The gallery houses an important collection of fine art.
Talks/Events/Education Holds regular talks and events connected to exhibitions, some of which are free.

Norwich Gallery

Norwich School of Art & Design, St George Street, Norwich
NR3 1BB
T 01603 610561
E info@norwichgallery.co.uk
W www.norwichgallery.co.uk
Shows temporary exhibitions of contemporary art all year round. Forty national and international artists go to Norwich each year to show painting, sculpture, photography, video and new media.

Submission policy Artists should send a CV, a maximum of ten slides or CD and a written proposal/supporting statement.
Talks/Events/Education Conferences are organized to support specific exhibitions (approximately eight per year). Open to artists and the public, free of charge.

Saffron Walden Museum

Museum Street, Saffron Walden
CB10 1JL
T 01799 510333
F 01799 510333
E museum@uttlesford.gov.uk
Founded in 1835. Collections include decorative arts (ceramics and glass), textiles, woodwork, prints, photos and drawings. Limited amount of fine art.
Submission policy Small special exhibition space is programmed two to three years ahead. Art exhibitions tend to have local connections or relevance to collections.
Talks/Events/Education Events held but infrequently; some free (e.g. ceramics workshop).

Sainsbury Centre for Visual Arts

University of East Anglia, Norwich
NR4 7TJ
T 01603 593199
F 01603 259401
E scva@uea.ac.uk
W www.scva.ac.uk
Designed by Sir Norman Foster and opened in 1978, the building is home to three permanent collections of international importance and also affords space for special exhibitions and the delivery of a wide range of educational and public programmes. Some exhibitions are developed by the Sainsbury Centre, some in partnership with other galleries and others by external curators or institutions.
Talks/Events/Education Organizes over one hundred and twenty events a year (some free).

Sir Alfred Munnings Art Museum

Castle House, Castle Hill, Dedham
CO7 6AZ
T 01206 322127
F 01206 322127
W www.siralfredmunnings.co.uk
Sir Alfred Munnings KCVO PRA lived and worked at Castle House from 1919 until his death in 1959. The house has a comprehensive collection of Munnings's work, some of which is housed in his studio.

University of Essex Collection of Latin American Art (UECLAA)

Department of Art History and Theory, University of Essex, Wivenhoe Park, Colchester
CO4 3SQ
T 01206 873971
F 01206 873702
E gsalgaa@essex.ac.uk
W www.essex.ac.uk/ueclaa/ueclaaWelcome.htm
Founded in 1993, the only public collection in Europe dedicated exclusively to modern and contemporary Latin American art. The collection comprises over six hundred works by modern and contemporary artists including Carlos Cruz-Diez, Guillermo Kuitca, Roberto Matta, Cildo Meireles, Ana Maria Pacheco, Nadin Ospina, Fernando de Szyszlo, Rufino Tamayo and Mariana Yampolsky. UECLAA Online is a fully-searchable catalogue available to Internet users worldwide.

University of Hertfordshire (UH) Galleries

Art & Design Gallery, College Lane, Hatfield
AL10 9AB
T 01707 285376
F 01707 285376
E m.b.shaul@herts.ac.uk
W www.herts.ac.uk/artdes/galleries
Founded in 1996, aiming to offer exhibition and publishing opportunities to artists, designers and makers in the early stages of their careers. Collection based on acquisitions from past programming.
Submission policy Submissions from professional artists and groups welcome after May 2007. Short text and some images sufficient in the first instance.
Talks/Events/Education Currently establishing an education programme.

Watford Museum

194 Lower High Street, Watford
WD17 2DT
T 01923 232297
F 01923 224772
E info@watfordmuseum.org.uk
W www.watfordmuseum.org.uk
Housed in the former Benskins Brewery Mansion and includes the Cassiobury Collection of fine art. A changing programme of exhibitions gives opportunities for local artists to display their work.
Submission policy Opportunities are available for local artists to display and be employed to deliver

art workshops and projects.
Talks/Events/Education Active programme
includes workshops for children and adults, and
talks on local art and history.

Wolsey Art Gallery (WAG) – Visual Arts Ipswich
Christchurch Mansion, Christchurch Park,
Ipswich
IP4 2BE
T 01473 433554
E wolseyartgallery@ipswich.gov.uk
W www.wolseyartgallery.org.uk
Opened in 1932, presenting a programme of
contemporary art and related historical works
from the region and beyond. The Room Upstairs
exhibits works by professional and emerging
artists with regional links. The gallery programme
also takes projects away from Christchurch
Mansion to other places in and around Ipswich.

East Midlands

20–21 Visual Arts Centre
St John's Church, Church Square, Scunthorpe
DN15 6TB
T 01724 297070
F 01724 297080
E 20-21.epd@northlincs.gov.uk
W www.northlinkcs.gov.uk/20-21
Founded in 2001 and housed in a converted
church. An exhibition centre focusing on
contemporary fine art and crafts. Has six
exhibition spaces including an outdoor sculpture
courtyard. The centre also houses a contemporary
art and craft shop and holds artist-led workshops
for all age ranges.
Submission policy Welcomes submissions from
contemporary artists working in all media.
An exhibition request form is available online or
from 20–21.
Talks/Events/Education Continuous programme
of events and courses (prices vary).

Alfred East Art Gallery
c/o Coach House, Sheep Street, Kettering
NN16 0AN
T 01536 534274
F 01536 534370
E museum@kettering.gov.uk
W www.kettering.gov.uk
Opened in 1913 with an initial donation of seventy
works by Sir Alfred East. Has subsequently
expanded its collections to nine hundred works
including major collections of East and Thomas

Cooper Gotch alongside other local artists, and
contemporary art collected between the 1950s and
1980s.
Submission policy Programmes a year in advance.
For terms and conditions, phone or see website.
Talks/Events/Education Monthly talks
programme – £2 (£1 concessions) – and occasional
workshops.

Angel Row Gallery
Central Library Building, 3 Angel Row,
Nottingham
NG1 6HP
T 0115 9152869
F 0115 9152860
E angelrow.info@nottinghamcity.gov.uk
W www.angelrowgallery.com
A leading venue for contemporary art. The scope
of the programme is broad, reflecting the diversity
of trends within contemporary visual-art practice.
Submission policy Contact the gallery to check if it
is accepting submissions.
Talks/Events/Education The gallery provides a
programme of workshops, short courses, talks and
live events.

Brewhouse Gallery
The Old Malthouse, Springfield Road, Grantham
NG31 7BG
T 01476 576703
F 01476 576703
E lmtbrady@aol.com
W www.grantham-online.co.uk/pp/business/
detail.asp?id=20619
A public gallery of painting, sculpture, prints and
furniture, as well as commissioned work. Runs art
workshops, and community projects in schools,
businesses and organizations. Participates in
public art including mosaics, mapmaking, textiles,
murals and temporary installations. Also offers
framing, antique restoration and consultation
services.

Burghley
Burghley House, Stamford
PE9 3JY
T 01780 752451
F 01780 480125
E burghley@burghley.co.uk
W www.burghley.co.uk
One of the grandest houses of the Elizabethan age.
Includes imposing painted ceilings by Antonio
Verrio, over four hundred paintings and an
important collection of Japanese porcelain.

Submission policy Burghley's sculpture garden features new exhibitions annually to showcase work from new artists. Burghley also hosts several exhibitions throughout the year for artists working in a variety of media.

Talks/Events/Education Twice a year Lady Victoria Leatham presents a talk on the 'Hidden Treasures of Burghley', which focuses on items from the collection not usually on display (tickets £10). Throughout the summer season a programme of art-based workshops for both adults and children are held in the sculpture garden (prices vary).

Derby Museum and Art Gallery
The Strand, Derby
DE1 1BS
T 01332 716659
F 01332 716670
E exhibitions@derby.gov.uk
W www.visitderby.co.uk
Shows contemporary artists of international, national and regional importance. Work includes digital media, photography, painting, decorative and applied art, together with the museum's reserve collection.

Talks/Events/Education Exhibitions are accompanied by talks and lectures for the public, other artists and students. Holds workshops and related activities for both children and adults.

Djanogly Art Gallery
Lakeside Arts Centre, University Park, Nottingham
NG7 2RD
T 0115 9513138
F 0115 9513194
W www.lakesidearts.org.uk
The exhibition programme ranges from major historical shows to groundbreaking contemporary installations.

Future Factory
Nottingham Trent University, Dryden Street, Nottingham
NG1 4GG
T 0115 8486131
F 0115 8486132
E sam.rose@ntu.ac.uk
W www2.ntu.ac.uk/ntsad/bonington/
Houses the Bonington and 1851 art galleries, as well as the performance venue Powerhouse. The venues present work of multidisciplinary art forms, with emphasis on new media, performance, live art and installation work.

Talks/Events/Education Active education programme. Contact sam.rose@ntu.ac.uk or annette.foster@ntu.ac.uk.

Harley Gallery
Welbeck, Worksop
S80 3LW
T 01909 501700
F 01909 488747
E info@harley-welbeck.co.uk
W www.harleygallery.co.uk
Built in 1994 on the site of the original nineteenth-century gasworks for Welbeck Estate. Includes three gallery spaces, displaying a changing programme of contemporary art and craft, and a museum with select displays of objects from the Portland Collection.

Submission policy Artists should apply in writing to Lisa Gee (Director).

Talks/Events/Education For a programme of current events contact Jen Gray (Education Officer).

Leicester City Art Gallery
90 Granby Street, Leicester
LE1 1DJ
W www.leicester.gov.uk/citygallery
Three exhibition spaces, including fine art and crafts. Changing exhibitions programme (twelve shows per year). Programme is balanced to include all art and craft disciplines and aims to show local, regional, national and international work.

Northampton Museum and Art Gallery
Guildhall Road, Northampton
NN1 1DP
T 01604 838111
F 01604 838720
E museums@northampton.gov.uk
W www.northampton.gov.uk/museums
Founded in 1865. Collections include fifteenth- and eighteenth-century Italian and British art, and Oriental and British ceramics.

Submission policy Any application welcome (only criterion being the enrichment of visitors' experience), but currently oversubscribed.

Talks/Events/Education Talks and educational events frequently held and often free, although not specifically aimed at artists. Opportunities for artists and practitioners to lead and/or devise workshops, etc.

Picture House Centre for Photography
3rd Floor, International House, 125 Granby Street, Leicester
LE1 6FD

T 0116 2555282
F 0116 2555282
E photo@pichouse.demon.co.uk
W www.pichouse.org.uk
In its thirteenth year as a cooperative, focusing on the art of traditional and digital photography. Exhibitions, reference collection and coffee bar are open to all. Existing users range from newcomers to professionals, attracted by the extensive facilities. Subscription scheme offered for access to practical facilities.
Talks/Events/Education Various talks, workshops, courses and events are held throughout the year.

Q Arts Gallery

35–36 Queen Street, Derby
DE1 3DU
T 01332 295858
F 01332 295859
E create@q-arts.co.uk
W www.q-arts.co.uk
Built on the foundations of Derby Community Arts (DCA), an organization that has collaborated with artists and thousands of local people to create art work over the last twenty years. Has a strong focus on digital arts. Offers a wide array of training opportunities to artists and arts workers.
Submission policy The curated programme is booked eighteen months to two years in advance. Artists wishing to submit for exhibition should send or bring in a proposal and samples of their work in any format. Do not bring in the work itself unless under prior arrangement.
Talks/Events/Education Each exhibition is accompanied by an artist talk ('Feedback') and a musical or performance response to the art work ('Playback'). These events are free and open to all.

Usher Gallery

Lindum Road, Lincoln
LN2 1NN
T 01522 527980
F 01522 560165
E usher.gallery@lincolnshire.gov.uk
Founded in 1926 to house the collection of James Ward Usher and set in the grounds of the Temple Gardens. Includes paintings by J.M.W. Turner, Thomas Girtin, John Piper, L.S. Lowry and Duncan Grant, as well as works by Lincolnshire artists. Since 1999 the Usher Gallery has commissioned annual residencies.

London

Architectural Association

36 Bedford Square, London
WC1B 3ES
T 020 78874000
F 020 74140782
E press@aaschool.ac.uk
W www.aaschool.ac.uk
Annually hosts five main gallery exhibitions, ten smaller exhibitions in its other exhibition spaces, and an end-of-year show, 'Projects Review' in July. Exhibitions primarily focus on current debate within the architectural and design world and themes relating to projects being undertaken at the school. All exhibitions are open to the public and there is no admission fee.
Submission policy Artists should have an architectural direction or concern. Applications in writing only. Do not include original material.
Talks/Events/Education Each exhibition has related lectures and events, which are free to attend and publicized online.

Arts Gallery

University of the Arts, 65 Davies Street, London
W1K 5DA
T 020 75148083
F 020 75146131
E gallery@arts.ac.uk
W www.arts.ac.uk
Exists to promote the work of alumni of University of the Arts London. Primary emphasis on those who have been practising for at least two years since graduation. Aims to reflect the diversity of practice across the colleges of the university and to remain at the cutting edge of art and design. Opened in 1993 as the London Institute Gallery, becoming the Arts Gallery in 2004.
Submission policy To make an application to exhibit please contact the gallery for a proposal application form.
Talks/Events/Education Artists' and curators' talks for the public are regularly held. See the website for details of events. Practical workshops for schools are also organized to coincide with exhibitions.

Austrian Cultural Forum London

28 Rutland Gate, London
SW7 1PQ
T 020 75848653
F 020 72250470
E culture@austria.org.uk
W www.austria.org.uk/culture

Founded in 1956, the Austrian Cultural Forum in London promotes cultural contacts between the UK and Austria by organizing events and supporting artists and projects in the fields of the visual arts, music, performing arts, literature and film. Also runs academic symposia and public discussions.
Talks/Events/Education If not stated otherwise, events at the Austrian Cultural Forum London are free.

Bankside Gallery
48 Hopton Street, London
SE1 9JH
T 020 79287521
F 020 79282820
E info@banksidegallery.com
W www.banksidegallery.com
The gallery of the Royal Watercolour Society and the Royal Society of Painter-Printmakers. Runs changing exhibitions featuring contemporary watercolours and prints by members of both societies, as well as work by invited guests in a variety of media, including video installation, photography and oil painting.
Submission policy Representation is only by invitation or through membership in one of the two Royal Societies. The gallery is available for hire.
Talks/Events/Education Holds occasional workshops, talks, lectures and demonstrations. These are free to Friends of the gallery.

Barbican Art Gallery
Silk Street, London
EC2Y 8DS
T 0845 1216828
E artinfo@barbican.org.uk
W www.barbican.org.uk/gallery/index.htm
Europe's largest multi-arts and conference venue, with a regularly changing exhibitions programme backed by talks and workshops.
Talks/Events/Education There is a regular programme of Wednesday-evening talks. To book, call the box office on the number above.

Beaconsfield
22 Newport Street, London
SE11 6AY
T 020 75826465
F 020 75826486
E mail@beaconsfield.ltd.uk
W www.beaconsfield.ltd.uk
Founded in 1995 to provide a laboratory and

presentation space for artists. Runs an annual range of exhibitions and an evening membership club.
Submission policy Two galleries available for hire. Contact Julie Clark.
Talks/Events/Education Provides talks and events and maintains links with higher education and schools. For further information or to book a visit contact Naomi Siderfin or Julie Clark.

Bloomberg SPACE
50 Finsbury Square, London
EC2A 1HD
T 020 73307959
E gallery@bloomberg.net
W www.bloomberg.com
Founded in 2002. Not a conventional corporate art collection, but rather a dynamic space dedicated to commissioning and exhibiting contemporary art.
Submission policy Programmed by four freelance curators. Does not accept open submissions.
Talks/Events/Education Every exhibition is accompanied by an events programme, free and open to all.

Bow Arts Trust and Nunnery Gallery
181–183 Bow Road, London
E3 2SJ
T 020 89807774
F 020 89807770
E info@bowarts.com
W www.bowarts.com
Bow Arts Trust was founded in 1995 as an Educational Arts Charity. The Nunnery Gallery is a contemporary project space that initiates and develops projects that reflect and address issues in contemporary art, and in doing so works with a range of artists, curators, writers and arts organizations. Holds approximately five exhibitions per year including an in-house summer show, which is guest-curated to help support the profile of the trust as a whole. Previous curators include Mo Mowlam, David Dimbleby and Graham Norton. It is available for hire for a variety of functions.
Submission policy Gallery proposals and applications are required eight to twelve months before the projected start date. Include images, biographies, a clear outline of show and a clear and realistic budget structure.
Talks/Events/Education Free educational events, seminars and talks usually accompany each show in the gallery. Occasional skills-sharing workshops for local artists.

British Museum

Great Russell Street, London
WC1H 8DG
T 020 73238000
E information@thebritishmuseum.ac.uk
W www.thebritishmuseum.ac.uk
Founded in 1753; the first national public museum in the world. From the outset its collection was made available to every citizen, to all 'studious and curious' people regardless of rank or status, free of charge. Its role is to display the world's great civilizations and cultures, and to tell the story of human achievement throughout its ages. Its collections include archaeological and ethnographic material, prints and drawings and coins and medals.
Submission policy The museum does show and collect work by living artists through the Department of Prints and Drawings and Africa, Oceania and the Americas. It does not welcome submissions direct from artists, however.
Talks/Events/Education Runs a full education programme that covers all aspects of its collections. Many events are free.

Brunei Gallery

School of Oriental and African Studies, Thornhaugh Street, London
WC1H 0XG
T 020 78984046
F 020 78984259
E gallery@soas.ac.uk
W www.soas.ac.uk/gallery
Founded in 1995 and run as a non-commercial gallery. As part of the School of Oriental and African Studies (University of London), Europe's leading centre for the study of Asia and Africa, the gallery is dedicated to showing work of and from Asia and Africa, of both a historical and contemporary nature, through a programme of changing exhibitions.
Submission policy When submitting an initial proposal, artists should consider academic content as well as artistic merit and interest. Exhibitions that focus on the work of a single artist are not normally exhibited within the main galleries.

Café Gallery Projects London

Southwark Park, London
SE16 2UA
T 020 72371230
E cgp.mail@virgin.net
W www.cafegalleryprojects.org

One of south-east London's foremost exhibition spaces, administered by Bermondsey Artists' Group (an educational charity) founded in 1984. Funded by Arts Council England and Southwark Council. A policy of access to art for all encourages a varied programme and a diverse audience.
Submission policy There are set application times and a form that needs to accompany any application.

Camden Arts Centre

Arkwright Road, London
NW3 6DG
T 020 74725500
F 020 74725501
E info@camdenartscentre.org
W www.camdenartscentre.org
A centre for contemporary visual arts and art education, comprising three gallery spaces and three studios, where visitors are invited to actively engage with art, artists and ideas through a frequently changing programme of exhibitions and education. The centre is housed in a grade II-listed building that began life in 1898 as a library and was converted into an arts centre in 1964.
Submission policy Proposals from artists are welcome although majority of exhibitions and residencies arise from direct invitations to artists and curators.
Talks/Events/Education Full programme of courses, talks and events. For more information see website or contact by phone.

CHELSEA Space

Chelsea College of Art & Design, Millbank, London
SW1P 4RJ
T 020 75146000 ext. 3710
E d.s.smith@chelsea.arts.ac.uk
W www.chelsea.arts.ac.uk
Opened in 2005 and set within Chelsea College of Art & Design's campus next to Tate Britain, CHELSEA Space is a research development centre of invited contemporary art and design professionals. Some shows draw specifically on Chelsea's special collections of artists' books, ephemera, multiples, etc.
Submission policy Does not accept submissions from artists.
Talks/Events/Education Regular public events including talks and conferences are held.

Chisenhale Gallery

64 Chisenhale Road, London
E3 5QZ

T 020 89814518
F 020 89807169
E mail@chisenhale.org.uk
W www.chisenhale.org.uk
Founded in 1986. One of London's most important public spaces for contemporary art, in a converted factory offering 2,500 sq. ft of space with a dedicated education studio. The gallery is a charitable organization whose mission is to encourage and promote innovation and experimentation in contemporary visual arts and art education. Organizes five solo exhibitions each year from British and international artists.
Submission policy Unsolicited proposals are very rarely taken up as part of the Director's gallery programme.
Talks/Events/Education Organizes free talks, events and conferences alongside each exhibition and education project.

Courtauld Institute of Art Gallery
Somerset House, Strand, London
WC2R 0RN
T 020 78482526
F 020 78482589
E galleryinfo@courtauld.ac.uk
W www.courtauld.ac.uk
Founded in 1932 and housed at Somerset House, one of the finest eighteenth-century buildings in London. Among the most important small collections in Britain, including world-famous Impressionist and Post-Impressionist paintings, as well as Old Master paintings, sculpture and decorative arts from the fourteenth to twentieth centuries.
Submission policy Does not show living artists' work apart from well-known or successful comtemporary artists.
Talks/Events/Education Regular talks, lectures, and activities are often free on purchasing an admission ticket.

Croydon Clocktower
Katharine Street, Croydon
CR9 1ET
T 020 82531022
F 020 82531003
E museum@croydon.gov.uk
W www.croydon.gov.uk/clocktower
A multipurpose cultural centre with three galleries, including the Fiesco Gallery of Chinese Pottery and Porcelain and a gallery for programmed temporary exhibitions. The Croydon Museum Service also manages a programme of changing exhibitions by local artists in the café–gallery.
Submission policy Submissions welcomed from artists living and/or working in Croydon, for exhibition in the café–gallery. Two-dimensional hung work only.

Czech Centre London
13 Harley Street, London
W1G 9QG
T 020 73075180
F 020 73233709
E info@czechcentre.org.uk
W www.czechcentres.cz/london
Organizes frequent exhibitions of Czech art.

Design Museum
Shad Thames, London
SE1 2YD
T 0870 8339955
F 0870 9091909
E info@designmuseum.org
W www.designmuseum.org
A leading museum of modern and contemporary design, founded in 1989. A cultural champion of UK design, with a strong reputation for exhibitions of modern design history and contemporary design innovation, as well as for an international programme of touring exhibitions.
Talks/Events/Education Hosts talks by some of the world's leading designers and architects, from Jonathan Ive to Zaha Hadid.

Dilston Grove
Clare College Mission Church, South-west corner of Southwark Park, London
SE16 2UA
W www.cafegalleryprojects.com
Opened in 1999 and run by Café Gallery Projects. Aims to provide a venue for large-scale installations, experimental work, performance and video events.

Dulwich Picture Gallery
Gallery Road, London
SE21 7AD
T 020 86935254
F 020 82998700
E info@dulwichpicturegallery.org.uk
W www.dulwichpicturegallery.org.uk
Founded in 1811. Houses a collection of seventeenth- and eighteenth-century Old Masters, including Rembrandt, Poussin, Claude, Rubens, Murillo, Van Dyck, Watteau and Gainsborough,

collected by the King of Poland in the 1790s. When Poland was partitioned, Dulwich Picture Gallery was designed for the collection by the famed Regency architect Sir John Soane. The gallery houses loan exhibitions as well as the permanent collection.

Submission policy Has occasional exhibitions of living artists (Lucian Freud, Paula Rego, Howard Hodgkin and Antony Gormley for example). From time to time also has an artist-in-residence, who reinterprets the collection and teaches.

Talks/Events/Education Holds lunchtime lectures, art-history lecture series and education events for both adults and children, as well as courses for unemployed people. Some are free.

Estorick Collection of Modern Italian Art

39a Canonbury Square, London
N1 2AN
T 020 77049522
F 020 77049531
E curator@estorickcollection.com
W www.estorickcollection.com

Formed by Eric and Salome Estorick during the 1950s and housed in a converted Georgian villa, the collection has been open to the public since 1998. Known internationally for its core of Futurist works, as well as figurative painting and sculpture from 1895 to the 1950s. Artists include Balla, Boccioni, Carrà, Russolo, Severini, de Chirico, Modigliani and Morandi. Also runs a programme of temporary exhibitions, all connected to the permanent collection.

Submission policy Does not accept applications from contemporary artists.

Fashion Space Gallery

20 John Princes Street, London
W1G 0BJ
T 020 75142998 / 75147701
F 020 75148388
E pr@fashion.arts.ac.uk
W www.fashion.arts.ac.uk

A contemporary exhibition space located in the heart of London's West End. Based within London College of Fashion, the gallery runs a programme of exhibitions by students, staff and visiting artists. Displays of fashion, photography and fine art can be visited for free all year round.

Submission policy Artists' exhibition proposals are judged upon individual merit and should be submitted to the Events Office for consideration.

Fleming Collection

13 Berkeley Street, London
W1J 8DU
T 020 74095730
F 020 74095601
E flemingcollection@ffandp.com
W www.flemingcollection.co.uk

Opened to the public in 2002, consisting of works by Scottish artists from 1770 to the present day. Includes works by early nineteenth-century artists, the Glasgow Boys, the Scottish Colourists, the Edinburgh School and many contemporary Scottish names. Holds four exhibitions a year drawn from the collection as well as loans from public and private collections.

Talks/Events/Education Regular public lectures and events. There is also a Friends Association.

Foundling Museum

40 Brunswick Square, London
WC1N 1AZ
T 020 78413600
F 020 78413601
E enquiries@foundlingmuseum.org.uk
W www.foundlingmuseum.org.uk

London's first public art gallery, created by William Hogarth in William Coram's Foundlings' Hospital in the eighteenth century. There are permanent and temporary exhibitions. The collection contains works by Hogarth, Reynolds, Gainsborough, Wilson, Hayman, Highmore, Roubiliac and Rysbrack, displayed as they would have been seen by visitors to the hospital in the 1700s.

Geffrye Museum

136 Kingsland Road, Shoreditch, London
E2 8EA
T 020 77399893
F 020 77295647
E info@geffrye-museum.org.uk
W www.geffrye-museum.org.uk

Established in 1914, the museum's specialist area of research is middle-class domestic interiors and gardens. It presents the history of English interiors from 1600 to the present day through a chronological sequence of period rooms containing furniture, paintings and decorative arts. Also has a series of period gardens.

Gilbert Collection

Somerset House, Strand, London
WC2R 1LA
T 020 74209400
F 020 74209440

W www.gilbert-collection.org.uk
Opened in 2000. Comprises gifts given to the
nation by the late Sir Arthur Gilbert, including fine
examples of Italian mosaics. Also holds related
temporary exhibitions.
Talks/Events/Education Gallery talks held
each Thursday from 1.15 p.m. to 1.35 p.m. (free
with admission). For information on other
educational events, call 020 74209406 or email
education@somerset-house.org.uk.

Goethe-Institut London
50 Princes Gate, Exhibition Road, London
SW7 2PH
T 020 75964000
F 020 75940240
E arts@london.goethe.org
W www.goethe.de/london
The Goethe-Institut is the cultural institute of the
Federal Republic of Germany with a global reach.
Promotes knowledge of the German language
abroad and fosters international cultural
cooperation. The gallery at Hugo's Restaurant
focuses on young German photography. Also
displays films and video installations on the
in-house cinema screen.
Submission policy Focus on photographic works
with a strong German element. A clear link to the
institute's key themes is necessary.
Talks/Events/Education Frequently invites artists
for panel discussions and artist talks. Admission is
usually £3.

Guildhall Art Gallery
Guildhall Yard, London
EC2P 2EJ
T 020 73323700
F 020 73323342
E guildhall.artgallery@corpoflondon.gov.uk
W www.guildhall-art-gallery.org.uk
Originally founded in 1885 to house the
Corporation of London's art collection. A new
gallery opened in 1999. Holds collections of Pre-
Raphaelite works and images of London and its
people from the sixteenth century to the present.
Now specializes in London-related material.
Talks/Events/Education For education information
phone 020 73321632.

Hayward Gallery
Belvedere Road, London
SE1 8XX
T 020 79605226
E hginfo@hayward.org.uk

W www.hayward.org.uk
Opened in 1968. An icon of 1960s brutalist
architecture. Has a programme of four to five
temporary exhibitions each year. The Waterloo
Sunset was opened in 2004, designed by Dan
Graham in association with Howarth Tompkins
Architects, to provide the gallery with a new space.
Talks/Events/Education A creative programme of
talks and events runs alongside each exhibition.

Hermitage Rooms at Somerset House
Somerset House, Strand, London
WC2R 1LA
T 020 78452630
F 020 78454637
W www.hermitagerooms.org.uk
Opened in 2000. The first exhibition space to be
created in the West to show rotating exhibitions of
works from the collections of the State Hermitage
Museum in St Petersburg.
Talks/Events/Education Gallery talks each Friday
from 1.15 p.m to 1.35 p.m. (free with admission).
For further information, call 020 74209406 or
email education@somerset-house.org.uk.

Imperial War Museum
Lambeth Road, London
SE1 6HZ
T 020 74165211
F 020 74165409
E art@iwm.org.uk
W www.iwm.org.uk
The national museum of twentieth-century conflict
involving Britain and the Commonwealth. Founded
in 1917, the museum seeks to provide for, and to
encourage, the study and understanding of the
history of modern war. The collections include one
hundred and twenty million feet of cine film, thirty
thousand posters and some of the nation's best-
known twentieth-century paintings.
Submission policy The Artists Records Committee
commissions work on specific projects.
Talks/Events/Education Hosts a varied
programme of talks and events. For details visit
website or call 020 74165320.

Institute of Contemporary Arts (ICA)
The Mall, London
SW1Y 5AH
T 020 79300493
E exhibit@ica.org.uk
W www.ica.org.uk
Events include exhibitions of contemporary art
in many media, performing arts, film and new

media. The ICA is a membership organization and also provides opportunities for networking. Its newmediacentre.com is a developing resource for online artists and audiences.

Talks/Events/Education Runs an innovative PhD programme, digital training for the socially excluded and courses, especially in the digital domain, for secondary and tertiary education. There are also programmes of talks.

Institute of International Visual Arts (inIVA)

6–8 Standard Place, Rivington Street, London
EC2A 3BE
T 020 77299616
F 020 77299509
E institute@iniva.org
W www.iniva.org

Since it was established in 1994, inIVA has developed and produced a diverse portfolio of projects that have engaged audiences throughout the UK and worldwide in a creative dialogue with contemporary art. Creates exhibitions and publications, as well as multimedia, education and research projects designed to bring the work of artists from culturally diverse backgrounds to the attention of the widest possible public.

Submission policy Proposals for education or research projects should be submitted to Indie Choudhury (Projects Curator) at indie@iniva.org. Proposals should include details of the nature of the proposed project (e.g. talk, learning activity, research) and a brief synopsis (no more than one page). If applicable, also include a statement on artist's practice (no more than one page), potential or identified collaborators, participants and audience, biographical information (no more than one page) and any supporting material (text, image, audio and/or visual).

Iveagh Bequest

Kenwood House, Hampstead Lane, London
NW3 7JR
T 020 84381286
W www.english-heritage.org.uk

Founded in 1827. The gift of Arthur Cecil Guinness to the nation. The grade I-listed Adam building contains Guinness's collection of masters, including works by Rembrandt, Vermeer, Gainsborough, Turner, Constable, Van Dyck and Reynolds.

Jerwood Space

171 Union Street, London
SE1 0LN
T 020 76540171
F 020 76540172
E space@jerwoodspace.co.uk
W www.jerwoodspace.co.uk

Opened in 1998. A public gallery that predominantly holds shows focusing on the Jerwood Prizes and initiatives (including the painting, sculpture and drawing prizes, and the photographic awards).

Jewish Museum

Raymond Burton House, 129–131 Albert Street, London
NW1 7NB
T 020 72841997
F 020 72679008
E admin@jmus.org.uk
W www.jewishmuseum.org.uk

Founded in 1932 and moved to Camden Town location in 1995. The art collection includes Jewish ceremonial art and a collection of paintings, prints and drawings.

Leighton House Museum

12 Holland Park Road, London
W14 8LZ
T 020 76023316
F 020 73712467
E museums@rbkc.gov.uk
W www.rbkc.gov.uk/leightonhousemuseum

Former home of the eminent Victorian artist and president of the Royal Academy, Frederic, Lord Leighton. House includes a substantial collection of Leighton's work as well as important examples by his contemporaries including G.F. Watts, Edward Burne-Jones and Waterhouse. A temporary exhibition gallery is used for a programme of exhibitions exploring Victorian painting, design and architecture and Leighton's interest in the art of the Middle East. Work by contemporary artists is also shown.

Submission policy Work exhibited by living artists exploring themes of 'East meets West' or by artists from the Middle East.

London Jewish Cultural Centre

The Old House, c/o Kings College, Kidderpore Avenue, London
NW3 7SZ
T 020 74310345
F 020 74310361
E admin@ljcc.org.uk
W www.ljcc.org.uk

Hosts exhibitions as part of cultural and educational programmes aimed at a broad

audience of Jews and non-Jews, encouraging inter-faith and inter-cultural dialogue and activities. (NB From November 2005 the London Jewish Cultural Centre will move to Ivy House, North End Road, London NW11.)
Talks/Events/Education Holds events on most Tuesdays and Thursdays (usually cost £5). Also runs mid-week courses.

London Print Studio Gallery
425 Harrow Road, London
W10 4RE
T 020 89693247
W www.londonprintstudio.org.uk
Promotes the graphic arts in both traditional and innovative media. Presents programmes of projects and exhibitions that reflect the cultural diversity of London.

Museum of Installation
175 Deptford High Street, London
SE8
T 020 86928778
E moi@dircon.co.uk
Provides a venue for the making, appraisal and discussion of major installation works (usually of a site-specific, time-based nature). Around four to five exhibitions per year at main venue.

National Gallery
Trafalgar Square, London
WC2N 5DN
T 020 77472885
F 020 77472423
E information@ng-london.org.uk
W www.nationalgallery.org.uk
In April 1824 the House of Commons agreed to pay £57,000 for the picture collection of the banker John Julius Angerstein and in 1831 decided to build a permanent home for the gallery in Trafalgar Square. The permanent collection spans the period from about 1250 to 1900 and consists of western European paintings. The entire permanent collection and long-term loans are illustrated and described in the collection online. Also hosts many exhibitions.
Talks/Events/Education Runs a substantial education programme. For further details see www.nationalgallery.org.uk/education/default.htm.

National Maritime Museum
Park Row, Greenwich, London
SE10 9NF

T 020 83126565
F 020 83126632
W www.nmm.ac.uk
Opened in 1937. A museum celebrating Britain's seagoing history. Includes an extensive collection of maritime art works.

National Portrait Gallery
St Martin's Place, London
WC2H 0HE
T 020 73122463
F 020 73060056
E jrowbotham@npg.org.uk
W www.npg.org.uk
Founded in 1856. The primary collection consists of over 10,500 portraits and constitutes a unique record of the people who have shaped the history and culture of the UK. Admission to the gallery is free, although an entry fee is charged for some special exhibitions.
Talks/Events/Education Every month the gallery offers a wide variety of talks and events. Most activities are free with no need to book.

The Orangery and Ice House Galleries
Holland Park, London
W8 6LU
T 020 76031123
F 020 737122467
E sally.dobinson@rbkc.gov.uk
W www.rbkc.gov.uk/theorangery
www.rbkc.gov.uk/theicehouse
Available for hire for public exhibitions of the visual and applied arts. The galleries are situated in the grounds of Holland Park.
Submission policy Artists should submit six slides of work with a CV and details of any previous exhibitions. The gallery welcomes works from every discipline. Artists' work is approved by a selection panel, which sits annually during November. The Orangery Gallery costs about £550 for thirteen days and the Ice House Gallery roughly £650 for twenty days. Artists set up and take down their own exhibitions.

Percival David Foundation of Chinese Art
53 Gordon Square, London
WC1H 0PD
T 020 73873909
F 020 73835163
E ej4@soas.ac.uk
W www.pdfmuseum.org.uk
The foundation was presented with the finest

collection of Chinese ceramics outside China in 1950. Exists to promote the appreciation, study and teaching of the art and culture of China.
Talks/Events/Education Evening lectures are held approximately every two months. Lectures are open to the public and there is a small charge.

Photofusion
17a Electric Lane, Brixton, London
SW9 8LA
T 020 77385774
F 020 77385509
E info@photofusion.org
W www.photofusion.org
Founded in 1981. Aims to encourage all members of the community to use and enjoy its hpotographic facilities and to raise the profile of the photographic arts in London and the UK. Provides access to a full range of facilities including a contemporary gallery space, studio, digital imaging training, picture library, agency, darkrooms, and an ongoing photo-art education programme for professional, student and amateur photographers.
Submission policy The gallery programme promotes diversity within the photographic arts reflecting on current cultural and political issues that have widespread relevance.
Talks/Events/Education The education programme includes basic to advanced technical courses on darkroom and digital practices including camera, studio and digital photography skills.

Photographers' Gallery
5 and 8 Great Newport Street, London
WC2H 7HY
T 020 78311772
F 020 78369704
E info@photonet.org.uk
W www.photonet.org.uk
Founded in 1971. The first independent gallery in Britain devoted to photography. Has developed a reputation as the UK's primary venue for contemporary photography and was first in the country to show key names in world photography such as André Kertész, Jacques-Henri Lartigue and Irving Penn. Runs an integrated programme of exhibitions and educational events.
Submission policy For exhibition submissions, visit the gallery website to download an application form and receive further information.
Talks/Events/Education Presents an ongoing programme of talks and events, which offers

access to ideas about photography to non-specialist and specialist audiences. Some events are free and others charged for.

PM Gallery and House
Walpole Park, Mattock Lane, Ealing, London
W5 5EQ
T 020 85671227
E pmgalleryandhouse@ealing.gov.uk
Comprises Pitshanger Manor (owned and designed by Sir John Soane) and an extension to the house, built in 1940. The largest art gallery in west London, hosting exhibitions of professional contemporary art, in all media. Includes a large collection of ceramics by the Martin Brothers produced between 1873 and 1923.

Pump House Gallery
Battersea Park, London
SW11 4NJ
T 020 73500523
F 020 7228 9062
E pumphouse@wandsworth.gov.uk
W www.wandsworth.gov.uk/gallery
A public contemporary-art space located in a Victorian listed building in Battersea Park. Offers a diverse and innovative year-round exhibition programme in four gallery spaces.

The Queen's Gallery
Buckingham Palace, London
SW1A 1AA
T 020 77667301
F 020 79309625
E press@royalcollection.org.uk
W www.royal.gov.uk
Reopened in 2002 to celebrate the Queen's Golden Jubilee, the gallery hosts a series of changing exhibitions of works of art from the Royal Collection.
Talks/Events/Education Private evening tours available for pre-booked groups (admission charged).

Royal Academy of Arts
Burlington House, Piccadilly, London
W1J 0BD
T 020 73008000
W www.royalacademy.org.uk
Founded in 1768. An independent fine arts institution that supports contemporary artists and promotes interest in the arts through a comprehensive exhibition programme.
Submission policy Details of the application

procedure for the Summer Exhibition are available from February each year on the website or via the gallery.
Talks/Events/Education Designs events to help stimulate understanding and provide a focus for the interests of artists and art-lovers.

Royal College of Art

Kensington Gore, London
SW7 2EU
T 020 75904444
F 020 75904500
E info@rca.ac.uk
W www.rca.ac.uk
The world's only wholly postgraduate university of art and design. Displays a changing programme of student exhibitions and hosts external events, such as art fairs and prizes.
Talks/Events/Education Regular series of talks, lectures and symposia, regularly featuring leading figures from the art and design world. All events are free.

Royal Institute of British Architects (RIBA) Gallery

66 Portland Place, London
W1B 1AD
T 020 75805533
F 020 73073703
E gallery@inst.riba.org
W www.riba-gallery.com
Promotes excellence in architecture through a programme of exhibitions, lectures, debates and outreach activities. Houses the RIBA collections of drawings and manuscripts and collections of paintings, models and photographs.
Submission policy Work must be related to architecture. Submissions in writing.
Talks/Events/Education Three seasons per year of talks by architects and conferences, etc. All open to members of the public.

Saatchi Gallery

County Hall, Southbank, London
SE1 7PB
T 020 79288195
W www.saatchi-gallery.co.uk
Based around the collection of Charles Saatchi, one of the UK's leading arts patrons. Aims to provide a forum for contemporary art, presenting work by largely unseen young artists or by established international artists whose work has rarely or never been exhibited in the UK.

Serpentine Gallery

Kensington Gardens, London
W2 3XA
T 020 74026075
F 020 74024103
E information@serpentinegallery.org
W www.serpentinegallery.org
A publicly funded modern- and contemporary-art gallery located in Kensington Gardens, in the heart of central London. The gallery has gained an international reputation for its exhibition, architecture and education programmes, and showcases both established artists and artists in the early stages of their career. Free admission.
Submission policy Accepts exhibition proposals from artists and curators. Programming is decided by the Gallery Director and Chief Curator.
Talks/Events/Education Education programme consists of free public gallery talks, events, seminars, artist residencies and workshops that welcome artist participation.

Sir John Soane's Museum

13 Lincoln's Inn Fields, London
WC2A 3BP
T 020 74052107
F 020 78313957
E jbrock@soane.org.uk
W www.soane.org
Sir John Soane's (1753–1837) house, which became a museum after his death. The collection includes paintings by Hogarth, Canaletto, Turner and Reynolds, antique sculpture, plaster casts, architectural models, and the sarcophagus of Pharaoh Seti I.
Talks/Events/Education Regular talks and courses throughout the year.

South London Gallery

65 Peckham Road, London
SE5 8UH
T 020 77036120
F 020 72524730
E mail@southlondongallery.org
W www.southlondongallery.org
Founded in 1891, showing fine and applied arts.

Tate Britain

Millbank, London
SW1P 4RG
T 020 78878008
E information@tate.org.uk
W www.tate.org.uk

Tells the story of British art from 1500 to the present day, through the largest collection of it in the world. Includes masterpieces from the Pre-Raphaelites, Turner, Gainsborough, Blake, Constable, Bacon, Hepworth and Gormley. Also holds six temporary exhibitions annually, focusing on the work of well-known British artists or movements.
Talks/Events/Education A wide range of events, courses, seminars and workshops, many of which are free.

Tate Modern
Bankside, London
SE1 9TG
T 020 78878000
W www.tate.org.uk
National museum of modern art, opened in the restored Bankside power station in 2000.

University College London (UCL) Art Collections
Strang Print Room, University College London, Gower Street, London
WC1E 6BT
T 020 76792540
F 020 78132803
E college.art@ucl.ac.uk
W www.art.museum.ucl.ac.uk
Founded in 1847 with the gift of John Flaxman's sculpture models to UCL, the collection includes sixteenth- to eighteenth-century Old Master prints and drawings from northern Europe, English watercolours, Japanese Ukiyo-E Prints and the Slade Collection of student prize works, which illustrates the history of the Slade School of Fine Art and includes works by Augustus John, William Orpen, Gwen John, Stanley Spencer, David Bomberg, Dora Carrington and Paula Rego.
Submission policy Work by living artists is limited to works by artists who attended the Slade School of Fine Art.
Talks/Events/Education Two to four gallery talks and workshops per term, all free. Open to all groups or individuals wishing to work from the collection. Appointments may be booked.

Victoria & Albert Museum
Cromwell Road, London
SW7 2RL
T 020 79422000
E vanda@vam.ac.uk
W www.vam.ac.uk
One of the world's leading museums of art and design, with collections of great scope and diversity covering three thousand years of civilization.

Talks/Events/Education A wide range of events and activities for families, adults, older learners, students, teachers and young professionals complement the exhibitions and collections.

Wallace Collection
Hertford House, Manchester Square, London
W1U 3BN
T 020 75639500
F 020 72242155
W www.wallacecollection.org
A national museum based around one of the finest private collections of art ever assembled by one family. It was bequeathed to the nation by Lady Wallace, widow of Sir Richard Wallace, in 1897, and opened to the public in 1900. Among its holdings are an important collection of French eighteenth-century pictures, porcelain and furniture, and an extensive range of seventeenth-century paintings.
Talks/Events/Education Holds gallery lectures and runs a postgraduate diploma in the History and Business of Art and Collecting in London, Paris, Brussels and Florence (organized by the Institut d'Etudes Supérieures des Arts in conjunction with the Wallace Collection).

Wapping Project
Wapping Hydraulic Power Station, Wapping Wall, London
E1W 3ST
T 020 76802080
Opened in 2004, a centre for the arts in east London, located in the historic Wapping Hydraulic Power Station. A multipurpose exhibition and performance space, featuring newly commissioned works by visual artists, choreographers, composers, writers, poets, designers and film-makers.

Wellcome Trust
215 Euston Road, London
NW1 2BE
T 020 76118888
F 020 76118545
E contact@wellcome.ac.uk
W www.wellcome.ac.uk
Organizes exhibitions on science and art in a range of exhibition initiatives including shows at the Science Museum, British Museum and TwoTen Gallery. A suite of permanent and temporary exhibition spaces will be a major feature of the trust's new public facility planned for opening in 2006.

▶ **Talks/Events/Education** Has collaborated with
the Institute of Contemporary Arts on a series of
public debates on science and its applications in
broad contexts.

Whitechapel Gallery
80–82 Whitechapel High Street, London
E1 7QX
T 020 75227888
F 020 75227887
E info@whitechapel.org
W www.whitechapel.org
In the heart of east London for over a century.
Has provided a platform for many of Britain's most
significant artists, from Gilbert & George to Lucian
Freud, Peter Doig to Mark Wallinger, as well as
premiering key international artists such as Pablo
Picasso, Frida Kahlo, Jackson Pollock, Mark
Rothko and Nan Goldin. In addition to exhibitions,
the gallery provides a platform for leading art
practitioners, commentators and thinkers through
talks, debates and events. Also offers an education
programme to cultivate a deeper appreciation of
the creative process and of the work of modern
and contemporary artists. With every exhibition,
catalogues are produced and artists donate limited
editions; proceeds go towards supporting the
programmes.
Submission policy Runs a yearly submission
exhibition called the East End Academy,
showcasing new work from emerging artists living
and working in east London.

North-east

Ad Hoc Gallery
Buddle Arts Centre, 258b Station Road, Wallsend
NE28 8RG
T 0191 2007132
F 0191 2007142
E the.buddle@northtyneside.gov.uk
W www.northtynesidearts.org.uk
Located within the Buddle Arts Centre and
managed by North Tyneside Arts. The gallery's key
objective is to promote and maintain a balanced
programme that is accessible to audiences,
supportive of artists, and provides opportunities
for schools, community groups and the voluntary
arts sector to exhibit in a dedicated contemporary
gallery space.
Submission policy Approximately six to ten
exhibitions per year. Proposals are welcome from
artists, curators and artists' groups at any time.

BALTIC Centre for Contemporary Art
South Shore Road, Gateshead
NE8 3BA
T 0191 4781810
E info@balticmill.com
W www.balticmill.com
Opened in 2002. A major international centre
for contemporary art. The landmark building
is situated on the south bank of the River Tyne
in Gateshead. With no permanent collection,
it provides a programme that places a heavy
emphasis on commissions, invitations to artists
and the work of artists-in-residence.
Submission policy Programmed two years
in advance. The majority of exhibitions and
residencies arise from direct invitations to
artists and curators. Rarely able to accommodate
unsolicited submissions for exhibitions.
Talks/Events/Education Runs education and
public programmes, and artists' workshops, talks
and seminars. Most are free.

Berwick Gymnasium Art Gallery
Berwick Barracks, Berwick-upon-Tweed
TD15 1DG
T 01289 304493
Opened in 1993, the gallery has established itself
as a leading venue for contemporary art and artists
in the region. Details of current exhibitions are
available from English Heritage

Billingham Art Gallery
Queensway, Billingham Town Centre, Billingham,
Stockton-on-Tees
TS23 2LN
T 01642 397590
F 01642 397594
E billinghamartgallery@stockton.gov.uk
W www.stockton.gov.uk/citizenservices/
leisureandents/artandculture/artscentres/
Exhibits work by local artists.
Talks/Events/Education Runs art classes and
workshops for adults.

Bowes Museum
Barnard Castle, Barnard Castle
DL12 8NP
T 01833 690606
F 01833 637163
E info@bowesmuseum.org.uk
W www.bowesmuseum.org.uk
Based on an extensive collection of European
fine and decorative arts of the period between
1400 and 1875, originally collected by John and

Josephine Bowes in the nineteenth century.
Submission policy A limited number of artists'
works are represented in the museum's exhibition
programme. Applications can be made by post.
Talks/Events/Education Some events are free.

Customs House

Mill Dam, South Shields
NE33 1ES
T 0191 4541234
F 0191 4565979
E mail@customshouse.co.uk
W www.customshouse.co.uk
Shows contemporary visual art by local, regional,
national and international artists working in a
variety of art forms and styles, and working from
differing theoretical backgrounds. Artists are at
varying stages of their careers.
Submission policy Submission guidelines are
available on the website.
Talks/Events/Education Free lectures, talks,
activities and workshops relating to artist's
exhibitions and projects currently shown. Events
held in gallery and as part of outreach programme.

Durham Light Infantry Museum and Durham Art Gallery

Aykley Heads, Durham
DH1 5TU
T 0191 3842214
F 0191 3861770
E dli@durham.gov.uk
W www.durham.gov.uk/dli
Founded in 1968, the museum features displays
covering the history of the County Regiment,
the Durham Light Infantry. The art gallery
provides a changing programme of exhibitions
related to all aspects of the visual arts, linked to
an ongoing series of workshops, concerts and
other events.
Submission policy Applications are welcomed
from all fields of artistic activity.
Talks/Events/Education Most activities are aimed
at general and family audiences. More specific
events may be held depending on the current
exhibition.

Green Dragon Museum and Focus Photography Gallery

Theatre Yard, Calverts Lane, Stockton-on-Tees
TS18 1JZ
T 01642 527982
E greendragon@stockton.gov.uk
W www.stockton.gov.uk/museums

Located in the historic Georgian area of Stockton,
the building houses a local history and archive
photography gallery on the upper floor and the
Focus Gallery on the ground floor. The Focus
Gallery has a varied programme of photographic
displays throughout the year.
Submission policy Artists may submit
photography or digital-art exhibition proposals at
any time. Contact the Exhibitions Coordinator for
details.
Talks/Events/Education Occasional free
photography-based events or talks.

Hatton Gallery

The Quadrangle, University of Newcastle-upon-
Tyne, Newcastle-upon-Tyne
NE1 7RU
T 0191 2226059
F 0191 2223454
E hatton-gallery@ncl.ac.uk
Shows a changing programme of historical and
contemporary art alongside exhibitions of work
from its permanent collection. On permanent
display is Kurt Schwitters *Merzbarn* and the
Uhlman Collection of African art.
Submission policy Unsolicited exhibition
proposals will be considered by the programming
team. However, the gallery normally initiates
contact with artists.
Talks/Events/Education Regularly holds talks and
educational events for individuals, community
groups and schools. Contact the gallery for details.

Laing Art Gallery

Blandford Square, Newcastle-upon-Tyne
NE1 4JA
W www.twmuseums.org.uk/laing/
Founded in 1901. Houses an extensive collection
of British oil paintings, watercolours, ceramics,
silver and glassware. There is also an active
temporary exhibition programme.

Myles Meehan Gallery

Darlington Arts Centre, Vane Terrace, Darlington
DL3 7AX
T 01325 348845
F 01325 365794
E wendy.scott@darlington.gov.uk
W www.darlingtonarts.co.uk
Founded in 1983, supporting new and emerging
innovative artists. Provides visitors with a
balanced programme of media including
installation and film, sculpture, painting, textiles
and photography.

Submission policy Welcomes innovative and contemporary exhibition applications with a focus on collaboration and experimentation.

Newcastle Arts Centre
67 Westgate Road, Newcastle-upon-Tyne
NE1 1SG
E venue@newcastle-arts-centre.co.uk
W www.newcastle-arts-centre.co.uk
Opened in 1988, the centre is only 100m from Newcastle Central Station and Metro. Underwent an extensive upgrade in 2000 to include a full-time gallery and art materials store. The gallery holds frequent exhibitions.

Northern Gallery for Contemporary Art
City Library and Arts Centre, Fawcett Street, Sunderland
SR1 1RE
T 0191 5141235
F 0191 5148444
E ngca@sunderland.gov.uk
W www.ngca.co.uk
Opened in 1995 as part of the Sunderland City Library and Arts Centre. Presents changing exhibitions of new work by emerging and established artists from the UK and abroad.
Submission policy Artists wishing to apply should send six images, CV and artist's statement addressed to the Programme Director.
Talks/Events/Education Gallery talks accompany major exhibitions.

Shipley Art Gallery
Prince Consort Road, Gateshead
NE8 4JB
T 0191 4771495
W www.twmuseums.org.uk/shipley
Permanent collection includes studio ceramics, glass, metalwork, jewelry, textiles and furniture. Collection of historical paintings has examples of Dutch and Flemish Old Masters. Temporary programme of mainly craft-based exhibitions.
Talks/Events/Education Hosts a wide range of regular events and activities.

South Shields Museum and Art Gallery
Ocean Road, South Shields
NE33 2JA
T 0191 4568740
F 0191 4567850
W www.twmuseums.org.uk/southshields
Includes extensive collections of fine and applied art.

Sunderland Museum and Winter Gardens
Burdon Road, Sunderland
SR1 1PP
T 0191 5532323
F 0191 5537828
W www.twmuseums.org.uk/sunderland
Gallery houses works by by L.S. Lowry alongside an important collection of Victorian masterpieces.

Northern Ireland

Ards Arts Centre
Ards Town Hall, Conway Square, Newtownards
BT23 4NP
T 028 91810803
F 028 91823131
Presents varied monthly programme of visual arts, primarily in two galleries in the town arts centre. Covers range of media and styles, by local, national and international artists.

Armagh County Museum
The Mall East, Armagh
BT61 9BE
T 028 37523070
F 028 37522631
E acm.um@nics.gov.uk
W www.armaghcountymuseum.org.uk
Two exhibition spaces regularly display the museum's collection. Featured artists include James Black, Tom Carr, William Conor, James Humbert Craig, T.P. Flanagan, Charles Lamb, John Luke, J.B. Vallely and G.W. Russell.

Belfast Exposed Photography
The Exchange Place, 23 Donegall Street, Belfast
BT1 2FF
T 028 90230965
F 028 90314343
E info@belfastexposed.org
Northern Ireland's only dedicated photography gallery. Has traditionally focused on the development and exhibition of community photography.

Catalyst Arts
5 College Court, Belfast
BT1 6BS
T 028 90313303
F 028 90312737
E info@catalystarts.org
W www.catalystarts.org

A non-commercial artist-run gallery and resource centre based in Belfast, which celebrated its tenth anniversary in 2003. Aims to maintain, to the highest possible standard, a Northern Irish centre for contemporary arts. The organization is run by a volunteer committee of artists who work there for a two-year period on a rolling committee basis.

Fenderesky Gallery
2–4 University Road, Belfast
BT7 1NH
T 028 90235245
Occupies three areas of the Crescent Arts Centre, with exhibitions of contemporary Irish artists. Shows last up to four weeks.

Golden Thread Gallery
Brookfield Mill, 333 Crumlin Road, Belfast
BT14 7EA
T 028 90352333
E info@gtgallery.fsnet.co.uk
W www.gtgallery.fsnet.co.uk
A publicly funded gallery presenting contemporary visual arts and touring exhibitions by local, national and international artists.

Island Arts Centre
Lisburn
BT27 4RL
T 028 92509250
F 028 92509288
E enquiries@lisburn.gov.uk
An arts centre that includes an artist-in-residence studio, artists' studios and exhibition galleries.

Naughton Gallery at Queens
Lanyon Building, Queens University, Belfast
BT7 1NN
T 028 90273580
E s.mcanena@qub.ac.uk
W www.qub.ac.uk/visarts/page2.htm
Holds Queens's fine-art collection, compiled since the mid-nineteenth century. Includes an extensive selection of landscapes, genre paintings and portraits. Irish artists include Sir John Lavery, William Conor, James Humbert Craig, Louis le Brocquy, Paul Henry, John Luke and Frank McKelvey.

Old Museum Arts Centre
7 College Square North, Belfast
BT1 6AR
T 028 90235053
F 028 90233332

W www.oldmuseumartscentre.org
Established in 1990, with a visual arts programme committed to presenting new and emerging as well as established visual artists from the UK, Ireland and beyond. Work is exhibited in a small white-box gallery space and exhibitions change on a six-weekly basis.
Submission policy Exhibition is by invitation only. Proposals are welcome from interested artists.

Ormeau Baths Gallery
18a Ormeau Avenue, Belfast
BT2 8HS
T 028 90321402
F 028 90312232
E admin@obgonline.net
W www.obgonline.net
Opened in 1995, showing major exhibitions of work by contemporary artists of national and international standing.

Safehouse
25 Lower Donegall Street, Belfast
BT1 2FF
T 028 90314499
F 028 90319950
E info@safehouseartsspace.org
W www.safehousearts.org
Has a varied programme of contemporary paintings, traditional paintings, drawings, sculpture and ceramics.

Ulster Museum
Botanic Gardens, Belfast
BT9 5AB
T 028 90383000
W www.ulstermuseum.org.uk
Home to the most important public holdings of art in Northern Ireland, collected since the 1880s. Includes collections of continental Old Masters and icons, seventeenth-, eighteenth-, and nineteenth-century British masters, twentieth-century British, European and American paintings, and Irish painting from the seventeenth century to the present. Also has sculpture by the likes of Henry Moore, Barbara Hepworth, F.E. McWilliam, Kenneth Armitage, Anthony Caro, Philip King, Barry Flanagan and Isamo Noguchi.

Waterfront Hall
2 Lanyon Place, Belfast
BT1 3WH
T 028 90334400
F 028 90249862

W www.waterfront.co.uk
A major arts and entertainment centre, with a
regularly changing programme of exhibitions.

North-west

Abbot Hall Art Gallery
Kendal, Kendal
LA9 5AL
T 01539 722464
F 01539 722494
E info@abbothall.org.uk
W www.abbothall.org.uk
A small independent gallery with a reputation for
showing important exhibitions of British artists.
The permanent collection includes eighteenth-
century portraits by George Romney and
watercolours by Turner and Ruskin. The modern
collection includes works by Ben Nicholson,
Lucian Freud, Bridget Riley and Paula Rego.
Submission policy Main gallery shows British art
and artists. All media considered. Coffee shop has
a focus on printmaking. Exhibition proposals
considered by a curatorial panel.
Talks/Events/Education Hosts lectures, 'meet the
artist' events and walking tours associated with
the exhibitions programme (ticketed; admission
charge applies).

Astley Hall Museum and Art Gallery
Astley Park, off Hallgate, Chorley
PR71NP
T 01257 515555
E astley.hall@chorley.gov.uk
W www.chorley.gov.uk
A grade - listed, refashioned Elizabethan mansion
with a Renaissance-style great hall. The art gallery
hosts four temporary exhibitions each year.
Submission policy Exhibition proposals welcome
from established and up-and-coming artists.
Talks/Events/Education Talks and courses held
throughout the year and educational visits (all
levels) welcomed.

Beacon Harbour Gallery Whitehaven
West Strand, Whitehaven
CA28 7LY
T 01946 592302
F 01946 598150
E thebeacon@copelandbc.gov.uk
W www.thebeacon-whitehaven.co.uk
Founded in 1996 on Whitehaven's harbourside,
home to the town's museum collection and art
gallery. Admission is free.

Submission policy Artists in any medium
are welcome to submit exhibition propo
sals for consideration by exhibition panel
each autumn.
Talks/Events/Education School activity sessions
available and young people's craft workshops
held every school holiday.

Blackwell Arts & Crafts House
Bowness-on-Windermere
LA23 3JR
T 01539 446139
F 01539 488486
E info@blackwell.org.uk
W www.blackwell.org.uk
An Arts and Crafts Movement house dating
from 1900. Blackwell was restored by the Lakeland
Arts Trust and opened to the public in 2001 as a
showcase for important Arts and Crafts furniture
and objects, and a platform for contemporary
craft. The growing collection includes important
examples of the arts and crafts, twentieth-century
and contemporary applied arts.
Submission policy Send a CV and details,
including images, to Harvey Wilkinson (Curator).
Exhibitions are planned at least a year ahead.
The shop and selling exhibitions concentrate
on contemporary craft (e.g. jewelry, ceramics,
glass, textiles).
Talks/Events/Education Evening lectures and
occasional workshops, which artists are welcome
to attend. 2005 lecture prices: £5 for students and
Friends, patrons and benefactors of the Lakeland
Arts Trust; £7.50 for non-members. Prices of
courses may vary.

Bluecoat Display Centre
Bluecoat Chambers, College Lane, Liverpool
L1 3BX
T 0151 7094014
F 0151 7078106
E crafts@bluecoatdisplaycentre.com
W www.bluecoatdisplaycentre.com
Founded in 1959 as a not-for-profit organization to
exhibit and retail the finest contemporary applied
art, including jewelry, ceramics and glass.
Submission policy Artists working in
contemporary craft media should apply to
Maureen Bampton (Director) with images,
CV, supporting statement and price guide to
the work illustrated. A selection committee
meets regularly to consider new work.
Talks/Events/Education Occasional events;
details via mailing list or website.

Bolton Museum, Art Gallery and Aquarium

Le Mans Crescent, Bolton
BL1 1SE
T 01204 332211
F 01204 332241
E museum.customerservices@bolton.gov.uk
W www.boltonmuseums.org.uk
Bolton Museum has collections ranging from fine art to Egyptian archaeology. Among its holdings is the Mass Observation Archive, consisting of over nine hundred photographs taken in 1937 by photo-journalist Humphrey Spender.
Talks/Events/Education For information on education programmes, email Educational Services at museum@bolton.gov.uk or phone 01204 332245.

Bury Art Gallery, Museum and Archives

Moss Street, Bury
BL9 9HT
T 0161 2535878
F 0161 2535915
E artgallery@bury.gov.uk
W www.bury.gov.uk/arts
Opened in 1901, the art gallery houses an internationally important collection of Victorian paintings, including works by Turner, Constable and Landseer. The temporary exhibition programme is driven by contemporary-art exhibitions exploring challenging issues, showcasing both international and up-and-coming artists.
Submission policy Artists' applications for exhibitions to be addressed to the curator.
Talks/Events/Education Hosts talks, events, schools workshops, and family-friendly and adult learning activities relating to the building, exhibitions and collections.

Castlefield Gallery

2 Hewitt Street, Manchester
M15 4GB
T 0161 8328034
F 0161 8192295
E info@castlefieldgallery.co.uk
W www.castlefieldgallery.co.uk
Founded by Manchester's Artists Studio Association in 1984. The gallery presents six main exhibitions per year, focusing on new and commissioned work. Supports emergent practice through 'Project Space' residency, and artists' film and video through 'Purescreen' events consisting of an annual 'open call'-curated screening programme.
Submission policy Welcomes exhibition proposals in any art form by artists and curators. Deadline is the last day of February each year, for programming twelve months in advance.
Talks/Events/Education Presents interpretive exhibition and professional-development talks and events. All events are free unless otherwise stated and require booking.

Chinese Arts Centre

Market Buildings, 7 Thomas Street, Manchester
M4 1EU
T 0161 8327271
F 0161 8327513
E info@chinese-arts-centre.org
W www.chinese-arts-centre.org
Founded in 1986, the centre is the UK flagship for the promotion and interpretation of Chinese arts and culture. Initiatives include exhibitions of contemporary art by artists of Chinese descent, an education programme, an artist-in-residence scheme and surgeries offering advice on subjects ranging from 'How to write an exhibition proposal' to 'How to apply for funding'. The building houses a large main gallery, the smaller Breathe Gallery and a fully equipped education and conference suite.
Submission policy To submit work for consideration for future exhibitions or residencies, contact the Exhibitions Coordinator or Curator for details and an application. Artists specializing in traditional Chinese arts who would like to be involved in the education programme should contact the Learning Coordinator.
Talks/Events/Education Runs an extensive education programme ranging from artist-led workshops in traditional Chinese arts to exhibition tours for groups (up to twenty) and artist- and curator-led exhibition discussions aimed at arts students and practitioners. Programme caters for all ages.

Cornerhouse

70 Oxford Street, Manchester
M1 5NH
T 0161 2001500
E exhibitions@cornerhouse.org
W www.cornerhouse.org
Opened in 1985 as Manchester's centre for international contemporary art and film. Exhibitions and events bring together artists, critics, curators, filmmakers, educators and audiences to discuss contemporary culture. The programme of visual art, film and moving image aims to question currently accepted art and cultural practice.

Submission policy Submissions from artists are considered for various projects. Send to Exhibitions at the above address.

Talks/Events/Education Runs a programme of events examining relevant issues within contemporary art including curators' talks, Q&As, discussions and live perfomances. Specifically curated events for artists, students and the public are regular and often free.

Dock Museum

North Road, Barrow-in-Furness
LA14 2PW
T 01229 894444
E dockmuseum@barrowbc.gov.uk
W www.dockmuseum.org.uk
Has a small fine-art gallery displaying a selection of works collected over the past hundred years. The gallery includes work by local artists William McDowell, Edward Beckett and John Duffin.

Folly

26 Castle Park, Lancaster
LA1 1YQ
T 01524 388550
F 01524 388550
E director@folly.co.uk
W www.folly.co.uk
Founded in 1982. A non-profit media arts organization that promotes photographic, video and new-media work. There is an annual members' exhibition.

Talks/Events/Education Events include summer courses, webstreaming, live events, video, audio and purescreen showings.

Foundation for Art and Creative Technology (FACT)

88 Wood Street, Liverpool
L1 4DQ
T 0151 7074450
F 0151 7074445
E info@fact.co.uk
W www.fact.co.uk
Opened in 2003 and dedicated to inspiring and promoting creativity through film, video and new and emerging media forms. It was the first cultural building to be purpose-built in Liverpool for sixty years. Combines state-of-the-art cinemas, galleries and flexible exhibition spaces.

Submission policy Presents exisiting work and commissions new pieces from artists working in the field of new media. The exhibitions are programmed by the Exhibitions Department, which can be contacted on 0151 7074444.

Talks/Events/Education Regular talks and events open to the public linked to exhibitions and films at FACT.

Gallery Oldham

Greaves Street, Oldham
OL1 1AL
T 0161 9114653
F 0161 9114669
E ecs.galleryoldham@oldham.gov.uk
W www.galleryoldham.org.uk
Opened in 2002. Incorporates Oldham's extensive art, social and natural-history collections alongside touring work, newly commissioned and contemporary art, international art and work produced with local communities.

Talks/Events/Education A programme of talks and events.

Grizedale Sculpture Park

Grizedale, Ambleside
LA22 0QJ
T 01229 860291
F 01229 860050
W www.grizedale.org
A major sculpture park, set in a dramatic Cumbrian setting.

Grosvenor Museum

27 Grosvenor Street, Chester
CH1 2DD
T 01244 402024
F 01244 347587
E p.boughton@chester.gov.uk
W www.grosvenormuseum.co.uk
Opened in 1886, with archaeology, natural history and social history collections plus exhibitions of fine and decorative arts (including Chester silver). Art shown is related to Cheshire or North Wales, illuminating artistic practice and patronage in the region since the sixteenth century. Also has a growing contemporary collection and a multidisciplinary exhibition programme.

Submission policy A biennial open art exhibition. A small number of solo and group shows each year by artists from Cheshire and North Wales.

Talks/Events/Education A full programme of public events including lectures, gallery tours, and art and craft workshops for children and adults. Some are free.

Harris Museum and Art Gallery

Market Square, Preston
PR1 2PP
T 01772 258248
F 01772 886764
E harris.museum@preston.gov.uk
W www.lancashiretourism.com
A grade I-listed building and an outstanding
example of Greek Revival architecture. Opened in
1893, it houses a major collection of historical and
contemporary painting and sculpture, including
work by L.S. Lowry, Lucian Freud, Stanley Spencer,
Walter Sickert, Jacob Epstein and J.W. Waterhouse.
Decorative art includes ceramics, costume
and glass. Also runs programme of temporary
exhibitions including international contemporary
art, historical art and local history.
Submission policy Opportunities for a small
number of professional artists to exhibit as part of
the stairway exhibitions programme. Contact
Exhibitions Assistant.
Talks/Events/Education Occasional artists' talks
held relating to exhibitions on show. Usually a
nominal charge.

Lady Lever Art Gallery

Port Sunlight Village, Wirral
CH62 5EQ
T 0151 4784136
E ladylever@liverpoolmuseums.org.uk
W www.ladyleverartgallery.org.uk
Home to the extensive personal collection of
William Hesketh Lever, first Lord Leverhulme, an
entrepreneur who made his fortune as founder of
Lever Brothers. Holds a large collection of British
eighteenth- and nineteenth-century art, including
Victorian and Pre-Raphaelite paintings by artists
such as Leighton and Rossetti. Also exhibits a
collection of the 'Sunlight Soap' paintings.
Talks/Events/Education Free talks and tours.

The Lowry

Pier 8, Salford Quays, Salford
M50 3AZ
T 0161 8762020
F 0161 8762021
E info@thelowry.com
W www.thelowry.com
Centred around the L.S. Lowry Collection, with
regularly changing displays encouraging visitors
to take a fresh look at the artist. Other exhibitions
place emphasis on the work of contemporary
artists and photographers, and particularly on the
locality and context of the Lowry. These shows
often complement the Lowry Collection.
Submission policy Welcomes applications but
recommends that artists contact the Exhibition
Programmer before submitting a proposal.

Manchester Art Gallery

Mosley Street, Manchester
M2 3JL
T 0161 2358888
F 0161 2358899
E t.wilcox@manchester.gov.uk
W www.manchestergalleries.org
Houses an extensive art collection with a varied
programme of special exhibitions and events.
Particularly strong collections of nineteenth- and
twentieth-century British paintings in both oil and
watercolour. Featured artists include Henry Moore,
Paul Nash, Ben Nicholson, Francis Bacon, Lucian
Freud and David Hockney. Also important
collections of Impressionist and seventeenth-
century Dutch paintings, and decorative art, craft
and design.

Ruskin Gallery

Ruskin Museum, Coniston
LA21 8DU
T 015394 41164
W www.ruskinmuseum.com
Gallery contains works by John Ruskin, J.M.W.
Turner and W.G. Collingwood.

Saddleworth Museum

High street, Uppermill, Oldham
OL3 6HS
T 01457 874093
E curator@saddleworthmuseum.co.uk
W www.saddleworthmuseum.co.uk
Opened in 1962 and housed in a Victorian Mill.
Exhibitions change every six weeks and showcase
the best local and regional contemporary art.

Salford Museum and Art Gallery

Peel Park, Crescent, Salford
M5 4WU
T 0161 7362649
F 0161 7459490
E salford.museum@salford.gov.uk
W www.salford.gov.uk
Houses an extensive collection of paintings,
pottery and fine art.

Sudley House

Mossley Hill Road, Liverpool
L18 8BX

T 0151 7243245
E sudleyhouse@liverpoolmuseums.org.uk
W www.sudleyhouse.org.uk
Situated in Mossley Hill, the house belonged to
Victorian ship-owner George Holt, whose
extensive art collection is exhibited. Highlights
include works by Landseer, Turner, Millais,
Romney, Reynolds, Gainsborough, Benjamin
Spence and Conrad Dressler. NB The museum is
closed until April 2006 for refurbishment.

Tate Liverpool
Albert Dock, Liverpool
L3 4BB
T 0151 7027400
F 0151 7027401
E liverpoolinfo@tate.org.uk
W www.tate.org.uk/liverpool
Opened in 1988, displaying modern and
contemporary art from 1900 to the present day.
Submission policy Send a covering letter, CV and
visuals to the Exhibitions Department at Tate
Liverpool.
Talks/Events/Education A programme of free
introductory tours, exhibition talks and lectures.
Also special events around exhibitions and
displays.

Tullie House Museum and Art Gallery
Castle Street, Carlisle
CA3 8TP
T 01228 534781 ext. 246
F 01228 810249
E enquiries@tulliehouse.co.uk
W www.tulliehouse.co.uk
Established since 1893, with significant collections
of fine and decorative arts, human history and
natural sciences. Underwent redevelopment
in 1990, which included building the Border
Galleries and a purpose-built art gallery. The
latter hosts a changing programme of primarily
contemporary-art exhibitions of regional, national
and international significance.
Submission policy Artists' proposals should be
submitted in the form of an exhibition outline,
CV(s) and a selection of good-quality images.
Talks/Events/Education Presents a wide range
of events and activities, from free drop-ins to
workshops and illustrated talks.

Turnpike Gallery
Civic Square, Leigh
WN7 1EB
T 01942 404469

F 01942 404447
E turnpikegallery@wlct.org
W www.wlct.org
Built in 1971. The only purpose-built public
gallery in the borough of Wigan. Presents around
six to eight exhibitions per year, including new
commissions, solo, group, community and touring
shows, reflecting contemporary visual arts practice
by artists with a local, regional or national profile.
The gallery has a commitment to developing
learning and outreach opportunities for the local
community.
Submission policy Artists are welcome to submit
exhibition proposals to the gallery at any time, but
only a few of such proposals will make up part of
the programme.
Talks/Events/Education Talks associated with
exhibitions and other educational/training events
for artists are usually free, and arranged on an
occasional basis.

University of Liverpool Art Gallery
3 Abercromby Square, Liverpool
L69 7WY
T 0151 7942348
F 0151 7942343
E artgall@liv.ac.uk
W www.liv.ac.uk/artgall/
Fine and decorative art from the university
collections, displayed in an elegant Georgian
house. Includes works by Turner, Wright of Derby,
Burne-Jones, Augustus John, Epstein, Freud and
Frink.
Submission policy Apply in writing to the Curator.
Talks/Events/Education Talks and events
advertised on website. Free of charge.

Viewpoint Photography Gallery
The Old Fire Station, The Crescent, Salford
M6
T 0161 7371040
Has a programme of regularly changing
photography exhibitions.

Walker Art Gallery
William Brown Street, Liverpool
L3 8EL
T 0151 4784199
E stephen.guy@liverpoolmuseums.org.uk
W www.thewalker.org.uk
Founded in 1877 and popularly regarded as
the National Gallery of the north. Exhibits an
internationally important collection of art from the
fourteenth to the twenty-first centuries. Especially

rich in European Old Masters, Victorian and Pre-Raphaelite pictures and modern British works.
Submission policy Artists are invited to enter the John Moores Exhibition, a painting biennial to be next held between September and December 2006.
Talks/Events/Education Extensive free talks and educational events open to all. Often themed on exhibitions or particular art works.

Whitworth Art Gallery

University of Manchester, Oxford Road, Manchester
M15 6ER
T 0161 2757450
F 0161 2757451
E whitworth@manchester.ac.uk
W www.manchester.ac.uk/whitworth
Founded in 1889, the gallery has been part of the university since 1958. Houses important collections of watercolours, prints, drawings, modern art and sculpture, as well as the largest collections of textiles and wallpapers outside London.
Submission policy Gallery exhibition policy available on website.
Talks/Events/Education Education Department organizes a full programme of activities for formal and informal learning. Special events and talks are available from time to time.

Wordsworth Trust

Dove Cottage, Grasmere
LA22 9SH
T 01539435544
F 01539435748
E enquiries@wordsworth.org.uk
W www.wordsworth.org.uk
Established in 1891 to house a selection of Wordsworth's furniture, memorabilia and working manuscripts. The fine-art collection has been built to reflect the themes of the trust. Includes paintings by John Constable, Joseph Wright of Derby, James Gillray, David Cox, David Wilkie, Sir Joshua Reynolds and an extensive collection of landscape drawings. There is also a small sculpture holding.

Scotland

Aberdeen Art Gallery

Schoolhill, Aberdeen
AB10 1FQ
T 01224 523700
F 01224 632133

E info@aagm.co.uk
W www.aberdeencity.gov.uk
Houses an important fine-art collection with particularly good examples of nineteenth-, twentieth- and twenty-first century works and a diverse applied art collection. Hosts a programme of special exhibitions.
Submission policy Submissions should be sent to Jason Williamson (Exhibitions Officer) at the above address. To discuss proposals prior to submisson, phone 01224 523713.

An Tuireann Arts Centre

Ross Memorial Building, Struan Road, Portree, Isle of Skye
IV51 9EG
T 01478 613306
F 01479 613156
E exhibitions@antuireann.org.uk
W www.antuireann.org.uk
Established since 1989. A public space with two galleries. Exhibitions change every six weeks and the programme covers all disciplines (fine arts, craft, design, architecture and new media), showing artists at various stages of their career.
Submission policy Welcomes applications from all disciplines; supply high-quality images on CD, transparency or photo with CV and statement. No deadline.
Talks/Events/Education TALK ART, an informal discussion around themes of the current exhibitions, is free and held every six weeks.

Burrell Collection

Pollok Country Park, 2060 Pollokshaws Road, Glasgow
G43 1AT
T 0141 2872550
F 0141 2872597
E museums@cls.glasgow.gov.uk
W www.glasgowmuseums.com
Major collections include medieval art, tapestries, alabasters, stained glass, English oak furniture, European paintings by Degas and Cézanne, Islamic art, and modern sculpture by Epstein and Rodin. Also has collection of works from ancient China, Egypt, Greece and Rome.
Talks/Events/Education Ongoing events programme, mostly free.

Centre for Contemporary Arts (CCA)

350 Sauchiehall Street, Glasgow
G2 3JD
T 0141 3524900

F 0141 3323226
E gen@cca-glasgow.com
W www.cca-glasgow.com
Six flexible arts spaces presenting the best in
contemporary visual art, film, music,
performance, etc.
Talks/Events/Education 'CCA:Participate' includes
events for adults and children as well as special
seminars for artists and practitioners, providing a
platform for discussion, learning and sharing
experience of the contemporary arts.

Changing Room
35 The Arcade, King Street, Stirling
FK8 1AX
T 01786 479361
F 01786 479361
E info@changingroom.sol.co.uk
W www.stirling.gov.uk/changingroom
Established in 1997 to support the development
of contemporary visual art in Scotland. Hosts a
year-round programme of exhibitions, events and
projects.
Submission policy Takes exhibition proposals at an
annual deadline. Artists can submit material for
the artist directory at any time.
Talks/Events/Education Regular talks with artists,
ranging from recent graduates to the well-known,
local to international. Holds an annual
professional-development and networking event,
as well as events and classes open to anyone.

City Art Centre (CAC)
2 Market Street, Edinburgh
EH1 1DE
T 0131 5293993
F 0131 5293977
E enquiries@city-art-centre.demon.uk
W www.cac.org.uk
Founded in 1980, the CAC is home to a large
range of Edinburgh's fine-art collections.
Temporary exhibits in the past have ranged from
Star Wars to the Glasgow Boys, the Titanic to Cecil
Beaton.
Submission policy Submissions from artists
welcome.
Talks/Events/Education Occasional events
(prices vary).

Collective Gallery
22–28 Cockburn Street, Edinburgh
EH1 1NY
T 0131 2201260
E mail@collectivegallery.net

W www.collectivegallery.net
Originally established as an artist-run space
in 1984, the Collective has developed into
an independent, publicly funded exhibition,
commissioning and development agency. Aims to
support emergent Scottish contemporary art and
artists within the context of an international
programme. Membership fees: £5 for Scottish-
based artists; £15 for non-Scottish-based artists.
Submission policy Strong committiment to
developing and initiating a wide range of education,
outreach and community-based projects.

Crawford Arts Centre
93 North Street, St Andrews
KY16 9AD
T 01334 474610
F 01334 479880
W www.crawfordarts.free-online.co.uk
Founded in 1977 and run by a charitable
company since 1988. A programme of mostly
contemporary visual art and craft is shown
throughout the year.
Submission policy Professional artists should send
visuals, CV and info. (NB: the centre's structure is
to change from 2006 and will affect programming
in the short term.)
Talks/Events/Education Talks and exhibition tours
held several times per year (mostly free); open to
all. Art classes (e.g. life drawing) held in autumn
and winter (not free).

Dean Gallery
73 Belford Road, Edinburgh
EH4 3DS
T 0131 6246200
F 0131 3432802
E deaninfo@nationalgalleries.org
W www.nationalgalleries.org
An art centre situated in parkland opposite
the Scottish National Gallery of Modern Art.
Opened in 1999, it provides a home for the
Eduardo Paolozzi gift of sculpture and graphic
art, including a reconstruction of Paolozzi's
studio. Also houses the Scottish National
Gallery of Modern Art's renowned Dada
and Surrealist collections, one of the best
collections of Surrealist art in the world.
Contains a library and archive, and a gallery
fitted out as a library for the display of artists'
books. Shows temporary exhibitions on a
regular basis. In the grounds are sculptures by
Bourdelle, Rickey, Hamilton Finlay, Paolozzi
and Turnbull.

Talks/Events/Education Various talks, events and lectures throughout the year. Contact the gallery for further information.

Dick Institute

Dean Castle Country Park, Dean Road, Kilmarnock
KA3 1XB
T 01563 522702
F 01563 573333
W www.east-ayrshire.gov.uk/comser/
arts_museums/joint_di_page.asp
Opened in 1901. Two art galleries and three museum galleries house permanent and temporary displays of fine and contemporary art and craft.

Duff House Country House Gallery

Banff
AB45 3SX
T 01261 818181
F 01261 818900
E duff.house@aberdeenshire.gov.uk
W www.duffhouse.com
Duff House was designed by William Adam and built between 1735 and 1740 for the Earls Fife. It now houses a permanent collection, including furniture, tapestries, and Old Masters by artists such as Sir Henry Raeburn, El Greco and François Boucher. Regular visiting exhibitions are held.

Dundee Contemporary Arts

152 Nethergate, Dundee
DD1 4DY
T 01382 909900
F 01382 909221
E dca@dca.org.uk
W www.dca.org.uk
An internationally renowned centre for the arts, opened in 1999. Houses five floors of cinemas, galleries, artists' facilities, education resources and the University of Dundee Visual Research Centre.

Fruitmarket Gallery

45 Market Street, Edinburgh
EH1 1DF
T 0131 2252383
F 0131 2203130
E info@fruitmarket.co.uk
W www.fruitmarket.co.uk
Established in 1984 as an independent public gallery. Committed to exhibiting contemporary art made by established and emerging international and Scottish artists. Major recent exhibitions include Ellen Gallagher, Fred Tomaselli and Louise Bourgeois in 2004, Hiroshi Sugimoto in 2002 and Shirin Neshat in 2000. Exhibitions emphasize new work as part of a consistent and developing artistic practice, and seek to engage new and existing audiences through an integrated education, interpretation and publishing programme.
Submission policy Submissions made directly to the Gallery Director. The gallery programme is subject to fourteen months' lead time.
Talks/Events/Education Free gallery tours and artist's talk for each exhibition. Workshops for adults, young people and small children for a small fee.

Gallery of Modern Art

Royal Exchange Square, Glasgow
G1 3AH
T 0141 2291996
F 0141 2045316
E museums@cls.glasgow.gov.uk
W www.glasgowmuseums.com
Opened in 1996. Housed in an elegant Neoclassical building in the heart of Glasgow city centre. Refurbished to hold the city's contemporary-art collection, the building is an appealing combination of old and new architecture, incorporating a number of artists' commissions. Displays work by local and international artists as well as addressing contemporary social issues through major biannual projects.
Talks/Events/Education Ongoing events programme, mostly free.

Hunterian Art Gallery

82 Hillhead Street, University of Glasgow,
Glasgow
G12 8QQ
T 0141 3305431
F 0141 3303618
E hunter@museum.gla.ac.uk
W www.hunterian.gla.ac.uk
In 1783 William Hunter bequeathed his substantial and varied collections to the University of Glasgow and the museum was opened to the public in 1807. In 1870 the Hunterian collections were transferred to the university's present site. The art collection is now housed separately. There are five collections: Mackintosh House, Glasgow Boys, Mackintosh Collection, Scottish Colourists and the Whistler Collection.

Inverleith House

The Royal Botanic Garden, Edinburgh
EH3 5LR
T 0131 2482983
F 0131 2482901
E ihouse@rbge.org.uk
W www.rbge.org.uk
Designed by David Henderson in 1774, Inverleith House was the founding home of the Scottish National Gallery of Modern Art (1960–1984). It is now run by the Royal Botanic Garden Edinburgh and presents a programme of temporary exhibitions by established and emerging artists in addition to botanical works from the garden's collection. Recent exhibitions have included Ed Ruscha, Agnes Martin, Franz West, Laura Owens and Richard Wright.
Talks/Events/Education Talks and workshops accompany most exhibitions.

Kelvingrove Art Gallery and Museum

Argyle Street, Glasgow
G3 8AG
W www.glasgowmuseums.com
Reopening in summer 2006, one hundred years after first opening its doors. Large fine- and applied-art collections, including several major European works.
Submission policy All exhibition proposals are considered by an exhibition committee that meets monthly. In the first instance email museums@cls.glasgow.gov.uk.

Kirkcaldy Museum and Art Gallery

War Memorial Gardens, Kirkcaldy
KY1 1YG
T 01592 412860
F 01592 412870
E Kirkcaldy.museum@fife.gov.uk
W www.fifedirect.org.uk/museums
Founded in 1925, housing a collection of fine and decorative arts of local and national importance. Holds an outstanding collection of eighteenth- to twentieth-century Scottish paintings, including large bodies of work by William McTaggart and Scottish Colourist S.J. Peploe. Also has three galleries showing a changing programme of temporary exhibitions.
Submission policy Applications should be in writing to the Exhibitions Officer.
Talks/Events/Education Occasional talks and workshops, advertised in the local press.

The Lighthouse

Scotland's Centre for Architecture, Design and the City, 11 Mitchell Lane, Glasgow
G1 3NU
T 0141 2216362
F 0141 2216395
E enquiries@thelighthouse.co.uk
The building comprises 1,400m² of exhibition space. Annually shows fifteen to twenty exhibitions, many of which are of international stature. Also contains a Charles Rennie Mackintosh interpretation centre and a dedicated education floor, including workshop, computer laboratory, gallery space and an innovative project called the Urban Learning Space.

McLellan Galleries

270 Sauchiehall Street, Glasgow
G2 3EH
T 0141 5654137
F 0141 5654111
E museums@cls.glasgow.gov.uk
W www.glasgowmuseums.com
Built in 1856. The galleries were ravaged by fire in the 1980s, but reopened in 1990 following a £3m restoration, when it was the largest high-quality, air-conditioned, temporary exhibition space outside London.
Talks/Events/Education Ongoing events programme, mostly free.

Mount Stuart

Isle of Bute
PA20 9LR
T 01700 503877
F 01700 505313
E contactus@mountstuart.com
W www.mountstuart.com
Opened to the public in 1995. Aims to promote public interest in contemporary visual arts by bringing exhibitions of an international standard to Bute and Argyll.
Talks/Events/Education The programme for each exhibition includes artists' talks and school and adult workshops. Free of charge.

Museum of Scotland

Chambers Street, Edinburgh
EH1 1JF
T 0131 2474422
F 0131 2204819
E info@nms.ac.uk
W www.nms.ac.uk/scotland

The museum presents the history of Scotland through collections ranging from everyday objects to some of Scotland's most precious treasures.
Talks/Events/Education Regular educational events for families.

National Gallery Of Scotland

The Mound, Edinburgh
EH2 2EL
T 0131 6246200
F 0131 2200917
E nginfo@nationalgalleries.org
W www.nationalgalleries.org
Home to Scotland's greatest collection of European paintings and sculpture from the Renaissance to Post-Impressionism. The collection of watercolours, prints and drawings features some twenty thousand items and is particularly rich in Italian and Netherlandish drawings. Also has a comprehensive collection of Scottish art, representing all the major names including Ramsay, Raeburn, McTaggart and Wilkie. The Playfair Project recently extended and upgraded the gallery's site on the Mound to incorporate the newly refurbished Royal Scottish Academy Building, which hosts a series of exhibitions all year round, and the Weston Link, which is connected by means of a modern underground visitor facility including a state-of-the-art education centre and lecture theatre.
Talks/Events/Education Various talks, events and lectures throughout the year. Contact the gallery for further information.

National War Museum

Edinburgh Castle, Edinburgh
EH1 2NG
T 0131 2474413
F 0131 2253848
E info@nms.ac.uk
W www.nms@ac.uk/war
Collections of paintings, prints, ceramics and glass illustrating everything from world-changing events to the everyday lives of Scottish servicemen.

Peacock Visual Arts

21 Castle Street, off the Castlegate, Aberdeen
AB11 5BQ
T 01224 639539
F 01224 627094
E info@peacockvisualarts.co.uk
W www.peacockvisualarts.co.uk

A contemporary visual arts organization supported by Aberdeen City Council and the Scottish Arts Council. Established in 1974 as a printmaking workshop, the facility has developed into a centre for the promotion of art and visual media.
Submission policy All submissions for projects and proposals welcome. Contact Monika Vykonkal (Assistant Curator) in the first instance at monika@peacockvisualarts.co.uk.
Talks/Events/Education Frequent talks, educational events and courses throughout the year. Admission is free.

The Queen's Gallery, Palace of Holyroodhouse

The Palace of Holyroodhouse, Edinburgh
EH8 8DX
T 0131 5565100
F 020 79309625
E press@royalcollection.org.uk
W www.royal.gov.uk
Opened in 2002 to celebrate the Queen's Golden Jubilee, the gallery hosts a series of changing exhibitions of works of art (predominantly works on paper) from the Royal Collection.
Talks/Events/Education Private evening tours available for pre-booked groups (admission charged).

Royal Museum

Chambers Street, Edinburgh
EH1 1JF
T 0131 2474422
F 0131 2204819
E info@nms.ac.uk
W www.nms.ac.uk/royal
Covers life, the universe and beyond with international collections of decorative arts, science and industry, archeology and the natural world.
Talks/Events/Education Regular educational events for adults and families, plus a series of evening lectures and concerts.

Royal Scottish Academy Building

The Mound, Edinburgh
EH2 2EL
T 0131 6246200
F 0131 6237126
E enquiries@nationalgalleries.org
W www.nationalgalleries.org
Designed by architect William Henry Playfair at the junction of Princes Street and the Mound. Has undergone refurbishment by the National Galleries of Scotland and offers nearly 1,500m² of

international exhibition space, housed in eleven galleries.

Talks/Events/Education A range of free public events is created to appeal to as many people as possible.

Scottish National Gallery of Modern Art

75 Belford Road, Edinburgh
EH4 3DR
T 0131 6246200
F 0131 6237126
E enquiries@nationalgalleries.org
W www.nationalgalleries.org
Opened in 1960, with a small number of twentieth-century works from the National Gallery of Scotland. Now comprises more than five thousand items, ranging from the late nineteenth century to the present and encompassing a wide variety of media, from paintings, bronzes and works on paper, to kinetic sculpture and video installations.
Talks/Events/Education A range of free public events.

Scottish National Portrait Gallery

1 Queen Street, Edinburgh
EH2 1JD
T 0131 6246200
F 0131 5583691
E pginfo@nationalgalleries.org
W www.nationalgalleries.org
Situated in the heart of the New Town on Queen Street. Provides a unique visual history of Scotland, told through portraits of the figures who shaped it. Includes work not only by Scottish artists but by great English, European and American masters such as Van Dyck, Gainsborough, Rodin and Kokoschka. Also displays sculptures, miniatures, coins, medallions, drawings and watercolours. The Scottish National Photography Collection is also based at the gallery.
Talks/Events/Education Various talks, events and lectures held throughout the year.

St Mungo Museum of Religious Life and Art

2 Castle Street, Glasgow
G4 0RH
T 0141 5532557
F 0141 5524744
E museums@cls.glasgow.gov.uk
W www.glasgowmuseums.com
Opened in April 1993. The aim of the museum is to promote understanding and respect between people of different faiths and none. Displays occupy three floors and are divided into four exhibition areas: the Gallery of Religious Art, the Gallery of Religious Life, the Scottish Gallery and a temporary exhibition space.
Submission policy All exhibition proposals are considered by an exhibition committee that meets monthly. In the first instance email museums@cls.glasgow.gov.uk.
Talks/Events/Education Ongoing events programme, mostly free.

Talbot Rice Gallery

University of Edinburgh, Old College, South Bridge, Edinburgh
EH8 9YL
T 0131 6502211
F 0131 6502213
E info.talbotrice@ed.ac.uk
W www.trg.ed.ac.uk
Established in 1975. The public art gallery of the University of Edinburgh. Shows a temporary exhibition programme alongside the university's permanent fine-art collection. Presents up to five major exhibitions per year in the White Gallery, showing a variety of painting, sculpture, drawing and installation. Also runs the Round Room programme in a unique architectural space showing small installations and experimental projects. Admission is free.
Submission policy To be considered for either the White Gallery or Round Room programme, submit an exhibition proposal for the attention of Pat Fisher (Principal Curator). Include a statement outlining the content of the exhibition, visuals (preferably 35mm slides or digital prints), a brief biography and any other information the artist feels is important. The proposal will then be considered at a monthly programming meeting. For gallery plans or further advice, contact the gallery.
Talks/Events/Education Has a broad educational remit, including a programme of regular tours, lectures, seminars and artists' talks accompanying each exhibition (free to the public).

Timespan

Dunrobin Street, Helmsdale, Sutherland
KW8 6JX
T 01431 821327
F 01431 821058
E enquiries@timespan.org.uk
W www.timespan.org.uk

A museum and gallery with changing exhibitions of contemporary art.

Transmission
28 King Street, Glasgow
G1 5QP
T 0141 5524813
F 0141 5521577
E info@transmissiongallery.org
W www.transmissiongallery.org
Set up in 1983 by graduates from Glasgow School of Art who were dissatisfied with the lack of exhibition spaces and opportunities for young artists in Glasgow. Through support from the Scottish Arts Council, they manage and maintain a space in which to exhibit their work and that of local artists and invited artists working nationally and internationally.
Membership policy One year's membership costs £5 for students or the unemployed, and £15 for those with a wage (anyone may invigilate for a day at the gallery in lieu). For legal reasons, members choose either a full or associate membership: full members are required to attend Transmission's annual general meeting; associate members are not required to attend.
Talks/Events/Education Maintains an image bank of slides, which are made available to visiting curators and artists. Members also gain the use of gallery facilities such as fax, photocopier, video equipment and slide projector and receive ten to twelve mailouts per year.

Verdant Works
West Henderson's Wynd, Dundee
DD1 5BT
T 01382 225282
F 01382 221612
E admin@dundeeheritage.co.uk
W www.verdantworks.com
A museum of Dundee's textile industries (primarily focused on jute), opened in 1996 and housed in a nineteenth-century mill building.
Submission policy The Exhibitions Director assesses all potential exhibitions for quality and suitability. Two- and three-dimensional material can be shown. Booked up a year in advance.

South-east

ArtSway
Station Road, Sway
SO41 6BA
T 01590 682260
F 01590 681989
E mail@artsway.org.uk
W www.artsway.org.uk
Establish in 1997 as a lottery project, ArtSway is a contemporary visual arts venue deep in the New Forest. Besides a programme of high-quality contemporary-art exhibitions, the gallery hosts artists-in-residence and offers professional-development and production facilities for artists. Creative opportunities for audiences are also available through a range of workshops, talks and courses. The white cube galleries were designed by architect Tony Fretton.
Submission policy See website for information on residency opportunities and deadlines for the ArtSway open exhibition held annually in December and January.
Talks/Events/Education Offers free gallery talks throughout the year, regular life-drawing sessions and a range of workshops.

Ashmolean Museum
Beaumont Street, Oxford
OX1 2PH
T 01865 278000
F 01865 278018
W www.ashmol.ox.ac.uk
Founded in 1683, the Ashmolean is one of the oldest museums in the world. The collection includes everything from Chinese watercolours to Renaissance drawings and Picasso paintings.
Submission policy For artist submissions please send information to Dr Christopher Brown (Director of the Ashmolean).
Talks/Events/Education Presents study days, lectures and talks. All groups must book. Telephone 01865 278015 for further information.

Aspex Gallery
27 Brougham Road, Southsea, Portsmouth
PO5 4PA
T 023 92812121
F 023 92812121
E info@aspex.org.uk
W www.aspex.org.uk
Exists to provide the people of Portsmouth, the locality and visitors with opportunities to experience some of the most innovative contemporary visual arts locally, nationally, and internationally. The exhibitions policy is to show work of high quality that reveals the full potential of the artist or artists chosen. In the main it has concentrated on younger artists who are in the

possession of a body of work that has not been seen in public (or in the region), and comes up to all the standards set by the artist and gallery. Access Aspex, a small exhibition and project space, focuses on the work of artists based in Portsmouth and the south-east region. This space is suited to small-scale work or that of an experimental nature.

Submission policy Proposals from artists and curators are welcomed. See the background section on the website.

Talks/Events/Education Programme of free gallery talks alongside each exhibition.

Brighton Museum and Art Gallery
Royal Pavilion Gardens, Brighton
BN1 1EE
T 01273 290900
F 01273 292871
E museums@brighton-hove.gov.uk
W www.virtualmuseum.info
Following a £10m redevelopment in 2002, the gallery has become one of the most visited museums in the south-east. Includes nationally important collections of twentieth-century art and design, fashion, paintings, ceramics and world art.

Submission policy Every two years the museum holds the Sussex Open, a selected open-submission exhibition for artists who are living and working in Sussex. Artists can also show work on the café balcony. Contact the Exhibition Manager for further details on 01273 292885.

Talks/Events/Education Special events, talks and courses.

Buckinghamshire Art Gallery
Buckinghamshire County Museum, Church Street, Aylesbury
HP20 2QP
T 01296 331441
F 01296 334884
E museumwebsiteenquiries@buckscc.gov.uk
W www.buckscc.gov.uk/museum/index.stm
Housed in a fifteenth-century building refurbished in 1995, the gallery has a permanent collection. Up to five exhibitions, ranging across a variety of art forms and subjects, are held annually.

Talks/Events/Education Events, activities and gallery talks.

Cass Sculpture Foundation
Sculpture Park, Goodwood, Chichester
PO18 0QP
T 01243 538449
F 01243 531853
E info@sculpture.org.uk
W www.sculpture.org.uk
Focusing on twenty-first century British sculpture, the park consists of twenty-six acres of woodland in an area of outstanding natural beauty, containing over sixty large-scale sculptures by Britain's leading artists. The foundation was established in 1994 as a charity and aims to empower sculptors (both young and established) to take their careers to a new level.

Charleston Farmhouse and Gallery
The Charleston Trust, Firle, Lewes
BN8 6LL
T 01323 811626
F 01323 811628
E info@charleston.org.uk
W www.charleston.org.uk
Founded in 1981 to conserve Charleston Farmhouse, a unique example of the decorative art and bohemian ideals of the Bloomsbury artists Vanessa Bell and Duncan Grant. Open to visitors and stages workshops and events. Two exhibitions spaces, the gallery and the tearoom.

Submission policy The gallery is open to established artists in all media (applications close 30 September for the following season; contact c.baron@charleston.org.uk or s.philp@charleston.org.uk). The tearoom is open to artists and photographers (applications close in December each year; contact c.garner@charleston.org.uk). Free to exhibit. Twenty per cent commission taken.

Talks/Events/Education Welcomes applications by artists to lead workshops for children and young people. Work should use Charleston as the inspiration (contact c.garner@charleston.org.uk). In addition, there is a full annual programme of special events, lectures and creative workshops open to all.

Christ Church Picture Gallery
Christ Church, St Aldates, Oxford
OX1 1DP
T 01865 276172
F 01865 202429
E picturegallery@chch.ox.ac.uk
W www.christ-church.ox.ac.uk
Houses an internationally important collection of Old Master paintings, drawings and prints in a listed modern building. Especially known for its holdings of Italian art, dating from the early Renaissance to the eighteenth century. Among

its highlights are paintings by Filipino Lippi, Veronese, Tintoretto, Annibale Carracci and Salvator Rosa, together with drawings by Leonardo, Michelangelo and Raphael. Also possesses a small number of works by renowned northern European artists, including Van Dyck, Rubens, Frans Hals and Hugo Van der Goes. The gallery holds regular exhibitions of its Old Master drawings and shows by local living artists.

Submission policy Artists should consider what will fit into the gallery and exhibition programme. Send illustrative material, CV and covering letter. No hire charge. Twenty-five per cent commission.

Talks/Events/Education Free guided tours every Thursday at 2.15 p.m. Special talks relating to current exhibitions or the collection held from time to time.

Crafts Study Centre

The Surrey Institute of Art & Design, University College, Falkner Road, Farnham
GU9 7DS
T 01252 891450
F 01252 891451
E craftscentre@surrart.ac.uk
W www.craftscentre.surrart.ac.uk
Founded in 1970. Located at the front of the Farnham campus of the Surrey Institute of Art & Design. A new purpose-built museum and research centre for the major craft collection was opened to the public in 2004, featuring two exhibition galleries and a study room. The permanent collection includes ceramics, textiles, lettering and furniture. The temporary exhibition programme showcases the work of contemporary craft practitioners.

Submission policy Programme is selected up to two years in advance. Proposals from contemporary craft practitioners should be made in writing to the Director.

Talks/Events/Education Held on an occasional basis, with a modest charge.

De La Warr Pavilion

Marina, Bexhill on Sea
TN40 1DP
T 01424 787949
F 01424 787940
E sally.ann.lycett@dlwp.com
W www.dlwp.com
Built in 1935, this grade I-listed Modernist building is a leading centre for contemporary art, architecture and live performance.

Submission policy Contact Celia Davies (Head of Exhibitions) at celia.davies@dlwp.com.

Talks/Events/Education Talks are a major part of the programme.

Ditchling Museum

Church Lane, Ditchling
BN6 8TB
T 01273 844744
E info@ditchling-museum.com
W www.ditchling-museum.com
Home to the artists Eric Gill, Edward Johnston and Frank Brangwyn in the twentieth century. Gill founded the artists' community of St Joseph and St Dominic, which included artists, letterers, weavers and silversmiths. Much of their work and that of other artists drawn to the area is represented in the collection. The museum has a temporary exhibition space and holds three or four exhibitions per year.

Submission policy Open to written submissions only. The museum cannot return images, etc. and will only be able to respond to artists that it feels may be suitable to exhibit.

Talks/Events/Education Talks and events throughout the year.

Eastleigh Museum

25 High Street, Eastleigh
SO50 5LF
T 023 80643026
F 023 80653582
E gill.budden@hants.gov.uk
W www.hants.gov.uk/museum/eastlmus
Holds regularly changing special exhibitions, which include art, crafts, photography, local and natural history. National and regional touring exhibitions shown, as well as the work of local artists, societies and collectors.

Talks/Events/Education Talks accompany some exhibitions. Admission is free.

Foyer Gallery and James Hockey Gallery

The Surrey Institute of Art & Design, University College, Falkner Road, Farnham
GU9 7DS
T 01252 892646 / 892668
F 01252 892667
E galleries@surrart.ac.uk
W www.surrart.ac.uk/galleries
Established in 1998 and 1969 respectively, the Foyer Gallery and James Hockey Gallery are public exhibition spaces showing a wide range of work, including art, craft, design and lens-based media.

They aim to present work of lasting and educational importance. Respect for professional practice remains vital.
Submission policy The exhibitions programme focuses on contemporary work. Application procedures are available from the Galleries Office.
Talks/Events/Education Workshops and public events are associated with most exhibitions and open to an inclusive audience of professionals, amateurs and general visitors.

Gardner Arts Centre

University of Sussex Campus, Falmer, Brighton
BN1 9RA
T 01273 685447
F 01273 678551
E info@gardnerarts.co.uk
W www.gardnerarts.co.uk
Based on the campus of the University of Sussex and housed in an eccentric grade II-listed building designed by Sir Basil Spence, the Gardner Arts Centre was opened in 1969 as the first university campus arts centre. It has a 480-seat purpose-built theatre, a visual-art gallery and studio space, and runs a programme of exhibitions of modern art.
Talks/Events/Education An extensive range of art classes and workshops is offered. To request an education resource guide, contact Gardner Education on 01273 685447 or go to the website.

Guildford House Gallery

155 High Street, Guildford
GU1 3AJ
T 01483 444741
F 01483 444742
E guildfordhouse@guildford.gov.uk
W www.guildfordhouse.co.uk
Home of Guildford Borough's art collection since 1959. Has a varied programme of temporary exhibitions including local groups, touring exhibitions and the borough collection.
Submission policy Artists must be connected to Guildford or Surrey. The waiting list is approximately two years.
Talks/Events/Education A programme of free talks, workshops and tours accompanies the exhibition programme.

Hastings Museum and Art Gallery (HMAG)

Johns Place, Bohemia Road, Hastings
TN34 1ET
T 01424 781155
F 01424 781165
E museum@hastings.gov.uk
W www.hmag.org.uk
Houses historical and cultural displays, a local studies room and an art gallery, with collections of fine and applied art. The gallery focuses on contemporary visual art, with occasional art history exhibitions. There are five exhibitions in each year's programme.
Submission policy Artists should submit exhibition proposals in writing (with illustrations of their work) to the Exhibitions Officer. Submissions for the 2007–8 programme can be made after January 2006.
Talks/Events/Education Workshops and talks are arranged with each exhibition. These are usually free, but on occasion may have a nominal fee.

Hove Museum and Art Gallery

19 New Church Road, Hove
BN3 4AB
T 01273 290200
E museums@brighton-hove.gov.uk
W www.virtualmuseum.info
Houses permanent collections of toys, film, local history, paintings and contemporary craft. Underwent major redevelopment in 2003. Hosts temporary exhibitions of varying forms of art (paintings, photography, craft, etc.).
Submission policy Contact the Exhibitions Office for more details on 01273 292852.
Talks/Events/Education Runs a programme of events, talks and courses.

Jelly Leg'd Chicken

The Town Hall, Blagrave Street, Reading
RG1 1QH
T 0118 9507926
F 0118 9507936
E babes@jelly.org.uk
W www.jelly.org.uk
Opened in Reading Town Hall in 2004 after five years in Reading's Oracle Shopping Centre. Set up in 1993 to exhibit quirky, innovative and enduring art. Has worked across many art forms including drawing, sculpture, mosaic, painting, jewelry, ceramics, textiles, architectural drawing, mixed media, printmaking, masks and digital animation.
Submission policy Artists are welcome to apply by email to curator@jelly.org.uk.
Talks/Events/Education Offers workshops, gallery visits, a database of tutors, training, consultancy and a mentoring scheme. For details contact Morag Scally or Marje Doyle on 0118 9507926, or by email at education@jelly.org.uk.

John Hansard Gallery

University of Southampton, Highfield,
Southampton
SO17 1BJ
T 023 80592158
F 023 80594192
E info@hansardgallery.org.uk
W www.hansardgallery.org.uk
Created in 1980 to promote all aspects of
contemporary visual art. Delivers a programme by
British and international artists.
Submission policy The gallery does not represent
artists. The selection process is made at the
discretion of the Director and Exhibitions Officer.
Talks/Events/Education Presents a wide
programme of talks, symposia and conferences,
tours and workshops. Talks are free and normally
accompany each new show. For symposia and
conferences, a fee is charged.

Manor House Gallery

Chipping Norton
OX7 5LH
T 01608 642620
E luigi@manorhousegallery.co.uk
W www.manorhousegallery.co.uk
Shows oils and watercolours by contemporary
British painters.

Metropole Galleries

The Leas, Folkestone
CT20 2LS
T 01303 244706
F 01303 851353
E info@metropole.org.uk
W www.metropole.org.uk
Founded in 1960. Has hosted a broad range of
exhibitions over the years. Current priorities are
to present contemporary art with meaning and
resonance for the locale and physical space. In
most cases the galleries work with artists to devise
exhibitions. Has a strong education and audience
development programme.
Submission policy Artists should send details
about themselves, their work and what they would
like to produce for the Metropole. Applicants are
advised to visit the gallery in advance as the space
is rather unusual.
Talks/Events/Education Hosts occasional talks,
discussions, etc.

Millais Gallery

Southampton Institute, East Park Terrace,
Southampton
SO14 0YN
T 023 80319916
F 023 80334161
E millais.gallery@solent.ac.uk
W www.millais.solent.ac.uk
A city-centre public art gallery committed to the
exhibition of mainly contemporary visual arts that
address issues of relevance to culturally diverse
communities locally, regionally and nationally.
The programme of exhibitions and events
complements the work of staff and students in
art, design and media.
Submission policy Artists may submit proposals to
the Curator.
Talks/Events/Education Public talks during each
exhibition. All are welcome; admission is free.

Milton Keynes Gallery

900 Midsummer Boulevard, Central Milton
Keynes
MK9 3QA
T 01908 676900
F 01908 558308
E info@mk-g.org
W www.mk-g.org
Opened in 1999 and presents six to eight free
exhibitions of contemporary art per year.

Modern Art Oxford

30 Pembroke Street, Oxford
0X1 1BP
T 01865 722733
F 01865 722573
E kirsty.brackenridge@modernartoxford.org.uk
W www.modernartoxford.org.uk
Founded in 1965, and now one of the UK's
leading centres for modern and contemporary art.
The gallery does not have a permanent collection
but recent exhibitions have included Mike Nelson
and Jannis Kounellis, Yael Bartana, Emily Jacir and
Lee Miller. Also hosts group shows. Admission is
free.
Talks/Events/Education During exhibitions,
gallery runs workshops for families, students,
teachers and schools. Artist talks and free
exhibition tours are open to all. Booking is
essential for workshops, courses and artist talks
and entry is subject to availability. Some events are
subject to ticket prices, for which concessions are
often available.

Open Hand Open Space

571 Oxford Road, Reading
RG30 1HL
T 0118 9597752
E info@ohos.org.uk

W www.ohos.org.uk
Artist-run studios and public gallery, established
over twenty-three years ago by former Reading
University MA students to provide arts and artists'
provisions for the local area (while showing
international shows). Previous members include
Cornelia Parker and Paul Bonaventura.
Submission policy Members' applications should
include a CV and slides. The gallery welcomes
detailed proposals for shows by artists, which are
then presented to a programming committee that
declares whether suitable by group vote.
Talks/Events/Education All events are free. Hosts
numerous artists' talks, seminars and visiting
artists throughout the year, usually corresponding
to the current exhibit.

Pallant House Gallery

9 North Pallant, Chichester
PO20 3QZ
T 01243 774557
F 01243 536038
E info@pallant.org.uk
W www.pallant.org.uk
The gallery of modern art in the south, located in
a Queen Anne townhouse and a contemporary
building holding a major collection of twentieth-
century British art. Extensive exhibition programme
includes international touring exhibitions and print
room shows. The collection includes important
works by, among others, Auerbach, Blake,
Bomberg, Caulfield, Freud, Goldsworthy, Hamilton,
Hodgkin, Langlands and Bell, Moore, Nicholson,
Paolozzi, Piper, Sickert and Sutherland.
Talks/Events/Education Talks and educational
events throughout the year.

Parham House

Parham Park, Storrington, Pulborough
RH20 4HS
T 01903 742021
F 01903 746557
E enquiries@parhaminsussex.co.uk
W www.parhaminsussex.co.uk
Opened to visitors in 1948. An important
collection of paintings by artists such as
Gainsborough, Lely, Barlow, Stubbs, Badmin,
Muncaster, Devis, Castro, Lutterhuys, Peake,
Wootton and Zoffany. Shown in light panelled
rooms of Elizabethan house. Open from Easter to
September on Wednesdays, Thursdays, Sundays
and Bank Holiday Mondays, as well as Tuesdays
and Fridays in August.
Submission policy Does not show any living artists.

Pitt Rivers Museum

South Parks Road, Oxford
OX1 3PP
T 01865 270927
F 01865 270943
E prm@prm.ox.ac.uk
W www.prm.ox.ac.uk
Founded in 1884 when General Pitt Rivers gave
18,000 objects to the university, the museum now
houses over 500,000 objects from around the
world and across time. Collections include textiles
and looms, Benin brasses and ivories, masks,
sculpture, jewelry and ceramics.
Submission policy Welcomes submissions by
1 October each year for its occasional programme
of exhibitions and installations relating to the
collections (and developed in collaboration with
curatorial staff).
Talks/Events/Education A changing programme
of activities and events are listed on the website.

Portsmouth City Museum and Records Office

Museum Road, Portsmouth
PO1 2LJ
T 023 92827261
F 023 92875276
E Christopher.Spendlove@portsmouthcc.gov.uk
W www.portsmouthmuseums.co.uk
The museum's main display is 'The Story of
Portsmouth'. It also features a fine- and decorative-
art gallery (which holds regular temporary
exhibitions) and picture gallery.

Quay Arts

Ser Street, Newport Harbour, Newport
PO30 5BD
T 01983 822490
F 01983 526606
E info@quayarts.org
W www.quayarts.org
Founded in 1979. Has three gallery spaces
showing work by international, national and local
artists. Also has seven artists' studios for hire.
Submission policy Submit images of work to
Jo Johnson (Exhibitions Organizer) at
j.johnson@quayarts.org.
Talks/Events/Education Has a full programme of
talks and courses for artists of all levels. Some are
free. In July and August there is a summer school
for artists.

Robert Phillips Gallery

Riverhouse Barn, Manor Road, Walton-on-Thames
KT11 2HT

T 01932 254198
F 01932 254198
E arts@riverhousebarn.co.uk
W www.riverhousebarn.co.uk
Part of the Riverhouse Community Arts Centre, the gallery has a changing programme of curated shows, touring exhibitions and opportunities for artists and groups to exhibit in a dramatic display space.
Submission policy Occasional open-submission exhibitions and rental opportunities (information given on website).
Talks/Events/Education Regular series of art talks, workshops, courses and children's activity sessions.

Rochester Art Gallery

95 High Street, Rochester
ME1 1LX
T 01634 338319
E arts@medway.gov.uk
Holds regularly changing exhibitions of fine art and photography.

Royal Borough Museum Collection (RBMC)

1st Floor, 24 High Street, Windsor
SL4 1LH
T 01628 796829
F 01628 796121
E museum.collections@rbwm.gov.uk
W www.rbwm.gov.uk/museum
A small local history collection that became a registered museum in 2002. Aims to make the rich history of the borough accessible to residents, visitors and researchers. The collection includes a wide variety of over six thousand objects including textiles, manuscripts, paintings and ephemera.
Submission policy Can only accept proposals from artists with a strong local connection, reflecting the local history or area. Planning two years ahead.
Talks/Events/Education Friends of the RBMC have an annual calendar of talks and visits. Talks cost approximately £2 each.

Russell-Cotes Art Gallery and Museum

East Cliff, Bournemouth
BH1 3AA
T 01202 451858
F 01202 451851
W russelll-cotes@bournemouth.gov.uk
Home to three permanent collections: art, Japan and sculpture.

Sidney Cooper Gallery

St Peter's Street, Canterbury
CT1 2B Q
T 01227 7822797
E al83@canterbury.ac.uk
W www.canterbury.ac.uk
Founded in 2004 by Canterbury Christ Church University College, the gallery shows contemporary work by local, national and international artists. Aims to show the process of making art, supported by lectures and a public programme.
Submission policy Welcomes portfolio-backed submissions from artists in all media. Yearly programme decided by November. Exclusive university use from mid-June to mid-September.
Talks/Events/Education Each exhibition is supported by free lectures, workshops and sometimes concerts.

Southampton City Art Gallery

Civic Centre, Commercial Road, Southampton
SO14 7LP
T 023 80832277
F 023 80832153
E art.gallery@southampton.gov.uk
W www.southampton.gov.uk/leisure/arts/art%2Dgallery
Collection comprises 3,500 works, with the earliest being Allegretto Nuzzi's fourteenth-century altarpiece. Also includes seventeenth-century Dutch landscapes and French Impressionist paintings. The modern-art holdings include works by Sir Stanley Spencer, Philip Wilson Steer, Tony Cragg, Richard Long, Shirazeh Houshiary, Antony Gormley, Michael Craig-Martin and Chris Ofili.
Talks/Events/Education Workshops for children and adults and also gallery talks.

St Barbe Museum and Art Gallery

New Street, Lymington
SO41 9BH
T 01590 676969
F 01590 679997
E office@stbarbe-museum.org.uk
W www.stbarbe-museum.org.uk
Opened in 1999, with art works related to the local area.

Stanley Spencer Gallery

The Kings Hall, High Street, Cookham
SL6 9SJ
T 01628 471885
E info@stanleyspencer.org.uk

W www.cookham.com/about/spencer.htm
Opened in 1962, devoted exclusively to Spencer's
work and life.

Towner Art Gallery

High Street, Old Town, Eastbourne
BN20 8BB
T 01323 417961
F 01323 648182
E townergallery@eastbourne.gov.uk
W www.eastbourne.gov.uk
A local-authority art gallery founded in 1923.
The permanent fine-art collection holds in excess
of four thousand works by artists including Eric
Ravilious, Christopher Wood and Alfred Wallis.
Has a lively temporary (contemporary) exhibitions
programme. Relocating to a new purpose-built
facility in 2006–7.
Submission policy Welcomes exhibition proposals
from living artists, addressed for the attention of
the Curator.
Talks/Events/Education Talks accompany some
temporary exhibitions, changing approximately
every six to eight weeks (some are free). Often held
on Thursday evenings or Saturday afternoons.

Trinity Gallery

Trinity Theatre, Church Road, Tunbridge Wells
TN1 7JP
T 01892 678670
F 01892 678680
E info@trinitytheatre.net
W www.trinitytheatre.net
Founded in 1977, the gallery runs a programme
aimed at showing diverse contemporary art.
Submission policy Contact the gallery for an
application form. Can only accommodate work
that can hang on the wall. Exhibitions are generally
monthly.

Tunbridge Wells Museum and Art Gallery

Civic Centre, Mount Pleasant, Tunbridge Wells
TN1 1JN
T 01892 554171
E museum@tunbridgewells.gov.uk
Has a programme of frequently changing art and
craft exhibitions consisting of the works of artists
and art societies, touring displays from major
British and European museums, and special
exhibitions from the museum's reserve
collections. Regular showings of the Ashton
Bequest of Victorian oil paintings, Pamela
McDowall flower collages, photographs by
Henry Peach Robinson and Thomas Sims,

and paintings by Charles Tattershall Dodd and
members of his family.

University of Brighton Gallery

Grand Parade, Brighton
BN2 0JY
T 01273 643010
F 01273 643038
E g.wilson@brighton.ac.uk
W www.brighton.ac.uk/gallery-theatre/
Housed within the university's Faculty of Arts
and Architecture and curated by the Centre for
Contemporary Visual Arts. Holds between eight
to twelve exhibitions per year, including the
university's own student shows, touring
exhibitions, shows by leading contemporary artists
and installations.
Submission policy Only exhibits contemporary
collections. Proposals are welcomed from
interested artists or groups.
Talks/Events/Education The university has a
number of full- and part-time courses, plus talks
and lectures open to the public.

Waddesdon Manor

Waddesdon, nr Aylesbury
HP18 0JH
T 01296 653211
E vicky.darby@nationaltrust.org.uk
W www.waddesdon.org.uk
Waddesdon Manor was built between 1874 and
1889 by Baron Ferdinand de Rothschild to display
his collection of art treasures and entertain the
fashionable world. Contains textiles and decorative
arts from the eighteenth century, important
examples of English portraiture and several Dutch
Old Masters.
Talks/Events/Education Many public events are
organized each season.

Winchester Gallery

Winchester School of Art, Park Avenue,
Winchester
SO23 8DL
T 01962 852500 / 596900
E sates@soton.ac.uk
Part of the Winchester School of Art. Offers a
programme of contemporary professional visual
arts, crafts and design, mostly through the
Southern Arts Touring Exhibition Service.

Worthing Museum and Art Gallery

Chapel Road, Worthing
BN11 1HP

T 01903 221150
F 01903 236277
E museum@worthing.gov.uk
W www.worthing.gov.uk/Leisure/
MuseumArtGallery
Collections include British works (by artists
including Hitchens, Pissarro and Hunt), European
works (by artists including Roerich, Hobbema and
Wynants) and a piece from the School of Bassano.
Works by local artists are also represented. There is
a small sculpture collection and decorative arts and
textiles. The Studio was opened in the early 1990s
as a temporary exhibition space for the museum's
collections as well as invited artists and groups.

South-west

Arnolfini
16 Narrow Quay, Bristol
BS1 4QA
T 0117 9172300
F 0117 9172303
E info@arnolfini.org.uk
W www.arnolfini.org.uk
Created in 1961. An internationally renowned
contemporary arts centre situated in Bristol's
vibrant harbourside, presenting new, innovative
work in visual arts, performance, dance, film,
literature and music. Closed for a major
refurbishment in autumn 2003 and reopened in
summer 2005 with upgraded and extended
facilities. Open seven days a week, with free
admission to the building, exhibitions and café–bar.
Submission policy For further information,
contact the Exhibitions Department.
Talks/Events/Education Education programme
includes talks, tours, workshops and events.

The Art Gym
Petherton Road, Hengrove, Bristol
BS14 9BU
T 0117 3772800 ext. 268
F 0117 3772807
E rfitzger@hengrove.bristol.sch.uk
W www.theartgym.co.uk
Purpose-built in 2002, a non-commercial gallery
space hosting exhibitions from contemporary
artists working in all media. Ongoing exhibition
programme shows established, international
artists, emerging contemporary artists, and
individual curatorial projects. Based in the
grounds of Hengrove Community Arts College.
Submission policy The gallery accepts proposals
from artists and curators. Contact the Art College

Manager for a submission pack. Artists and
curators are advised to consider the context of
the space when developing a proposal.
Talks/Events/Education Ongoing programme
of educational activities and workshops. For
full details contact the Gallery Manager on
0117 3772800 ext. 268.

Barbara Hepworth Museum and Sculpture Garden
Barnoon Hill, St Ives
TR26 1AD
T 01736 796226
W www.tate.org.uk/stives/hepworth.htm
Run by the Tate since 1980 and now an integral part
of Tate St Ives. Hepworth, who died in 1975, asked
in her will that Trewyn Studios and the adjacent
garden, with a group of her sculptures placed as she
wished, be permanently open to the public.

Bristol's City Museum and Art Gallery
Queens Road, Bristol
BS8 1RL
T 0117 9223571
F 0117 9222047
E general_museum@bristol-city.gov.uk
W www.bristol-city.gov.uk/museums
Includes important collections of Eastern art and
seven galleries of fine and applied art. Has an ever-
changing programme of temporary exhibitions
and a public events programme.

Burton Art Gallery and Museum
Kingsley Road, Bideford
EX39 2QQ
T 01237 471455
F 01237 473813
E burtonartgallery@torridge.gov.uk
W www.burtonartgallery.co.uk
Founded in 1951 with a core collection of English
watercolours and ceramics. Rebuilt in 1993 and
extended to three gallery spaces, a craft gallery
and a local museum. Shows about twenty visiting
exhibitions a year, ranging from national touring
shows to mixed exhibitions and the work of
individual artists.
Submission policy Interested in all kinds of art and
craft, with a leaning towards accessible art.
Talks/Events/Education Hosts artists' talks and
workshops.

Cheltenham Art Gallery and Museum
Clarence Street, Cheltenham
GL50 3JT

T 01242 237431
E ArtGallery@cheltenham.gov.uk
W www.cheltenham.artgallery.museum
Houses a major collection relating to the Arts
and Crafts Movement including furniture and
metalwork made by Cotswold craftsmen, inspired
by William Morris. Additional collections include
rare Chinese and English pottery, four hundred
years of painting by Dutch and British artists,
and the story of Edward Wilson, Cheltenham's
Antarctic explorer. Also discover the history of
Britain's most complete Regency town and
archaeological treasures from the neighbouring
Cotswolds. Special exhibitions are held throughout
the year and the museum also has a shop and café.
Submission policy Artists should write in
with a CV and photos or slides of their work.
Artists should have some connection with
Cheltenham, the Cotswolds or Gloucestershire.
Talks/Events/Education Workshops, talks and
events held at various times throughout the year.

Design Collection Museum

Arts Institute at Bournemouth, Fern Barrow,
Wallisdown, Poole
BH12 5HH
T 01202 533011
F 01202 537729
E designcollection@aib.ac.uk
W www.aib.ac.uk
Founded in 1988. Became a registered museum
in 2001. A study and research resource that
facilitates an understanding and appreciation
of international mass-produced popular design
and culture of the twentieth and twenty-first
centuries. Diverse yet cohesive collections
consists of approximately 7,500 items, which
relate directly to the academic courses and
specialist areas of study offered at the Institute.
Organized into key collection categories that
identify specific object types (e.g. electrical,
product design, fashion, printed ephemera,
plastics, packaging, etc.).
Submission policy The collection comprises
examples of mass-produced twentieth- and
twenty-first-century design only.

Dorset County Museum

High West Street, Dorchester
DT1 1XA
T 01305 262735
F 01305 257180
E dorsetcountymuseum@dor-mus.demon.co.uk
W www.dorsetcountymuseum.org

Founded in 1846. Has a diverse art collection,
including works by Gainsborough, Sir James
Thornhill, Alfred Wallis, Christopher Wood and
several thousand watercolours by Henry Joseph
Moule, a prolific nineteenth-century Dorset
watercolourist. Only a small proportion of the
museum's several thousand engravings, oil
paintings and watercolours are on show. However,
the museum has a policy to show this work as part
of its temporary exhibition programme and it is
possible to make an appointment to see items that
are not on display.
Submission policy All media accepted for the
regular temporary exhibitions programme.
Proposals submitted to a selection committee,
which meets five times a year. Thirty per cent
commission.

Fox Talbot Museum

High Street, Lacock, nr Chippenham
SN15 2LG
T 01249 730459
W www.foxtalbot.museum
Commemorates the life and work of William
Henry Fox Talbot (1800–1877), who in 1835
discovered the negative–positive photographic
process. The museum is located inside a medieval
barn at the entrance to Lacock Abbey, with
the upper gallery hosting two to three annual
exhibitions showing work by contemporary and
nineteenth-century photographers.

Gloucester City Museum and Art Gallery

Brunswick Road, Gloucester
GL1 1HP
T 01452 396131
F 01452 410898
Opened in 1860, with important collection of fine
and applied art.

Holburne Museum of Art

Great Pulteney Street, Bath
BA2 4DB
T 01225 466669
E holburne@bath.ac.uk
W www.bath.ac.uk/Holburne
Located in the former Georgian Sydney Hotel,
displaying the treasures collected by Sir William
Holburne, including English and continental
silver, porcelain, maiolica, glass and Renaissance
bronzes. The picture gallery contains works by
Turner, Guardi, Stubbs and others plus portraits of
Bath society by Gainsborough. There are also
temporary exhibitions.

Kelmscott Manor
Kelmscott, nr Lechlade
GL7 3HJ
T 01367 253348
F 01367 253754
E admin@kelmscottmanor.co.uk
W www.kelmscottmanor.co.uk
The country home of William Morris (poet, craftsman, artist and socialist) from 1871 until his death in 1896. The house contains a collection of the possessions and works of Morris and his associates, including furniture, textiles, ceramics and paintings.

Lighthouse Gallery
Poole's Centre for the Arts, Kingland Road, Poole
BH15 1UG
T 01202 685222
F 01202 670016
E oliviah@lighthousepoole.co.uk
W www.lighthousepoole.co.uk
Reopened in 2002 following major refurbishment. Part of the largest arts centre outside London, and programmes six exhibitions a year of photography, digital art and artists' film and video.
Submission policy Annual open exhibition (details on website) open to residents of the BH postcode area.

Museum of East Asian Art
12 Bennett Street, Bath
BA1 2QL
T 01225 464640
F 01225 461718
E museum@east-asian-art.freeserve.co.uk
Opened in 1993. Home to one of the most important collections of East Asian art outside London.

National Monuments Record Centre
Kemble Drive, Churchward, Swindon
SN2 2GZ
T 01793 414600
W www.english-heritage.org.uk
The centre is home to the archive of England's heritage. Holds a stock of over ten million photographs, drawings and other documents recording the archaeology and architecture of England.

Nature In Art
Wallsworth Hall, Twigworth, Gloucester
GL2 9PA
T 01452 731422
F 01452 730937
E ninart@globlnet.co.uk
W www.nature-in-art.org.uk
The world's first museum dedicated exclusively to art inspired by nature.

New Art Centre Sculpture Park and Gallery
Roche Court, East Winterslow, Salisbury
SP5 1BG
T 01980 862244
F 01980 862447
E nac@globalnet.co.uk
W www.sculpture.uk.com
Founded in 1957, the sculpture park specializes in work from 1950 onwards and is the sole representative of the Estate of Barbara Hepworth (1903–1975). Works closely with the family on a global exhibitions and sales programme and exhibits works by Barbara Hepworth including pieces in polished bronze, marble and wood. Other featured artists include Antony Gormley, Richard Long, Alison Wilding, Richard Deacon and Gavin Turk.

P.J. Crook Foundation
39 Priory Lane, Bishop's Cleeve, Cheltenham
GL52 8JL
T 01242 675963
E museum@pjcrook.com
W www.pjcrook.com/museum.html
Established in 2004 with the aim of opening and maintaining Crook's studios and house as an educational resource and for the benefit of the public. Exhibits significant paintings from throughout Crook's career, as well as works by artists who taught her, are from the region or have relevance to the main collection (particularly women artists and Surrealism, and prints and works on paper).
Submission policy Hopes to curate shows by living artists in future years but is not seeking applications at present.
Talks/Events/Education Due to extensive building works the museum is open by appointment only, but regular talks and tours still take place.

Penlee House Gallery and Museum
Morrab Road, Penzance
TR18 4HE
T 01736 363625
F 01736 361312
E info@penleehouse.org.uk
W www.penleehouse.org.uk

Founded in 1839, Penlee House is the district museum and art gallery for Penzance and Penwith. A programme of changing art exhibitions focuses on the historic art of west Cornwall, often featuring the Newlyn and Lamorna artists' colonies (1880–1940).
Talks/Events/Education Talks, educational events and occasional artists' workshops.

Penwith Galleries and Penwith Society of Arts
Back Road West, St Ives
TR26 1NL
T 01736 795579
Founded in 1949. Aims to encourage practising artists and craftworkers in Cornwall and to promote public interest in the arts. The organization includes public galleries, artists' studios and a bookshop and a print workshop. Holds continuous exhibitions of paintings, ceramics and sculpture.

Plymouth City Museums and Art Gallery
Drake Circus, Plymouth
PL4 8AJ
T 01752 304774
F 01752 304775
E plymouth.museum@plymouth.gov.uk
W www.plymouthmuseum.gov.uk,
www.cottoniancollection.org.uk
The current museum opened in 1910 and houses the designated Cottonian Collection featuring paintings by Plymouth-born Joshua Reynolds. The collection includes maritime pictures, oil paintings, watercolours, prints, drawings and ceramics. Good examples of works from the Newlyn School and by other important local painters. Free, regularly changing exhibitions.
Submission policy Annual exhibitions open to non-members by Plymouth Society of Artists and Plymouth Arts Club. Phone for details.
Talks/Events/Education Free Tuesday-lunchtime talks, regular family and children's activities and other events.

Prema
South Street, Uley, nr Dursley
GL11 5SS
T 01453 860703
E info@prema.demon.co.uk
W www.prema.demon.co.uk
Founded over twenty-five years ago as a small, independent rural arts centre. Has a year-round programme of arts activities (performances, classes, workshops, exhibitions, installations, etc.).

The main exhibition space is multifunctional; a smaller space is available, though less often used. Exhibitions last five to six weeks.
Submission policy First contact by phone or email, then send in a CV and images (as attachments, on CD or as hard copies), and then discuss with the Director.
Talks/Events/Education Regular classes and workshops, all artist-led. Occasionally artists' talks.

ROOM
4 Alfred Place, Redcliffe, Bristol
BS1 6ST
T 0117 9273778
F 0117 9273788
E sandie.macrae@netgates.co.uk
W www.roomartspace.co.uk
Founded in 2003. An artist-led space in a new building made specially for the purpose. Shows have been mainly film, video and photography, with a strong critical and theoretical grounding.
Submission policy Interested in innovative work showing different approaches, with a particular focus on lens-based works including photography, film and video. Also shows performance, and there is potential for installation, taking account of the space, which can be extended into the courtyard.
Talks/Events/Education Hosts artists' talks and single-evening events called 'VIEWINGROOMS', which are about artists' methodologies.

Red House Museum and Art Gallery
Quay Road, Christchurch
BH23 1BU
T 01202 482860
F 01202 481924
W www.hants.gov.uk/museum
Built as a workhouse in 1764, the building now houses several locally relevant collections, including an extensive range of Arts and Crafts pieces. Also hosts temporary exhibitions.

Royal Cornwall Museum
River Street, Truro
TR1 2SJ
T 01872 272205
F 01872 240514
E enquiries@royalcornwallmuseum.org.uk
W www.royalcornwallmuseum.org.uk
Founded in 1818. Owned and managed by the Royal Institution of Cornwall, which was created to provide lectures, facilities for study and a museum.

Offers a varied programme for both children and adults.

Royal West of England Academy (RWA)
Queen's Road, Clifton, Bristol
BS8 1PX
T 0117 9735129
F 0117 9237874
E info@rwa.org.uk
W www.rwa.org.uk
Founded in 1944 as Bristol's first art gallery. Houses five naturally lit galleries. Stages major solo, mixed and open exhibitions all year round, and has a collection of works spanning the nineteenth, twentieth and twenty-first centuries. **Talks/Events/Education** A programme of educational activities accompanies each exhibition. These include lectures, gallery tours, demonstrations and workshops. Charges may apply.

SPACEX
45 Preston Street, Exeter
EX1 1DF
T 01392 431786
F 01392 213786
E mail@spacex.co.uk
W www.spacex.co.uk
Established in 1974 by an Exeter-based artists' cooperative, extending the SPACE philosophy of artist-led studios and exhibition initiatives beyond London. The gallery became publicly funded in the early 1990s and runs a programme of contemporary-art exhibitions, projects and education activities. Focuses on emerging artists and process-based work, including site-specific projects in 'non-art' contexts. **Talks/Events/Education** A regular programme of talks, symposia and workshops, as well as participatory projects out of the gallery. Also weekly after-school and Saturday Art Club activities for children and young people.

St Ives Society of Artists Gallery
Norway Square, St Ives
TR26 2SX
T 01736 795582
E gallery@stisa.co.uk
W www.stivessocietyofartists.com
The society first organized exhibitions of members' work in 1927. The main gallery houses its annual exhibitions of paintings, prints, woodcarvings and sculptures. The Mariners' Gallery is available for hire.

Study Gallery
North Road, Parkstone, Poole
BH14 0LS
T 01202 205200
F 01202 205240
E info@thestudygallery.org
W www.thestudygallery.org
Opened in 2000. Runs feature exhibitions presenting work in different forms on changing themes and of high professional status. Also has a programme of project exhibitions, displaying the results of projects that the gallery initiates or is involved in through partnerships. Home to Bournemouth and Poole College's mid-twentieth-century art collection, including work by Henry Moore, Barbara Hepworth, Ivon Hitchens and Bridget Riley.

Swindon Community Heritage Museum and Art Gallery
Bath Road, Swindon
SN1 4BA
T 01793 466556
W www.steam-museum.org.uk
A museum and art gallery telling the story of local history.

Tate St Ives
Porthmeor Beach, St Ives
TR26 1TG
T 01736 796226
E tatestivesinfo@tate.org.uk
W www.tate.org.uk/stives
Open since 1995. Aims, through its exhibition and education programmes drawing on the Tate's collection, to encourage a greater understanding and enjoyment of modern and contemporary art in the cultural context of St Ives. **Talks/Events/Education** An extensive programme of talks, events and study days (some free and some chargeable).

text + work – The Gallery
Arts Institute at Bournemouth, Wallisdown, Poole
BH12 5HH
T 01202 363351
F 01202 537729
E vmcclean@aib.ac.uk
W www.textandwork.org.uk
'text + work' is the exhibitions programme of the gallery of the Arts Institute, aiming to provide a forum for dialogue between contemporary art and design practice and commentary. As well as gallery events, there are shared and networked exhibitions.

Submission policy Only open on Saturdays in term time. See website for access information.
Talks/Events/Education All exhibitions are supported by a 'text + work' event.

Victoria Art Gallery

Bridge Street, Bath
BA2 4AT
T 01225 477232
F 01225 477231
E victoria_enquiries@bathnes.gov.uk
W www.victoriagal.org.uk
The permanent collection occupies two rooms on the first floor, while the ground floor is given over to two temporary exhibition spaces, which change every two months. Permanent collections range from the fifteenth century to the present day and were formed mainly by gift and bequest since the building first opened in 1900. Highlights include eighteenth-century portraits, views of Bath, Victorian paintings, English Delftware and Staffordshire ceramic dogs. Modern artists include John Nash, Walter Sickert, William Roberts and Kenneth Armitage.

Watershed

1 Canon's Road, Harbourside, Bristol
BS15TX
T 0117 9276444
E info@watershed.co.uk
W www.watershed.co.uk
A media centre for the digital age, with a programme of feature films, video, digital media, courses and events presented in three cinemas, three event suites and online.
Talks/Events/Education Runs an extensive education programme and a programme of digital courses. Other events include talks such as the 'Alternative Series', run by the Centre for Critical Theory at Bristol UWE in conjunction with Watershed.

Wales

Aberystwyth Arts Centre

Penglais Hill, Aberystwyth
SY23 3DE
T 01970 621634
F 01970 622883
E s2s@aber.ac.uk
W www.aber.ac.uk/artscentre
Houses a concert-hall theatre, gallery spaces specializing in large-scale contemporary-art shows and photography exhibitions, studio-theatre workshop spaces, two cafés, a cinema, craft design shop, bookshop and bars. Hosts one of Britain's most important collections of studio ceramics.
Submission policy Apply in writing with visuals to Eve Ropek. Applications are put before a programming committee.
Talks/Events/Education Courses, workshops and talks are held on a weekly basis. Other specialized events covering all art forms are held annually.

Andrew Logan Museum of Sculpture

Berriew, nr Welshpool
SY22 8AH
T 01686 640689
E info@andrewlogan.com
W www.andrewlogan.com
A collection of works by sculptor Andrew Logan.

Bleddfa Centre

Knighton
LD7 1PA
T 01547 550377
F 01547 550370
E enquiries@bleddfacentre.com
W www.bleddfacentre.com/centre.htm
The Old School Gallery hosts exhibitions of paintings, sculpture and crafts, while the Hall Barn hosts meetings, talks and workshops.

Chapter Gallery

Chapter Arts Centre, Market Road, Cardiff
CF5 1QE
T 029 20311055
F 029 20311059
E visual.arts@chapter.org
W www.chapter.org
Established more than thirty years ago, the centre comprises a gallery with two residency studios, a theatre, two cinema screens, a bar–restaurant and fifty additional artists' studios. Operates an international programme of contemporary visual arts activity. This is achieved through commissioning new work, touring exhibitions, developing a programme of international residencies and exhibitions, publishing, and creating forums for critical reflection via commissioned essays and a programme of talks and events. Recent commissions and exhibitions have included Olaf Breuning, Mariele Neudecker, Geraint Evans, Anna Bjerger, James Aldridge, Beagles and Ramsay, Bedwyr Williams, Shizuka Yokomizo, Paul Granjon and Gintaras Makarevicius.
Submission policy Exhibition is generally by invitation only, although the gallery undertakes an

annual residency and solo-exhibition programme
that is advertised internationally and selected by a
panel of invited judges.

Ffotogallery
c/o Chapter, Market Road, Cardiff
CF5 1QE
T 029 20341667
F 029 20341672
E info@ffotogallery.org
W www.ffotogallery.org
The national development agency for photography
in Wales. Initiates exhibitions that explore
mainstream documentary photography as well
as more expansive uses of the medium, which
may involve the use of projection and other
forms of extended and digital media. The gallery's
exhibition programme is run from the grade II-
listed Turner House Gallery in Penarth, a ten-
minute drive from Cardiff. Hosts touring
exhibitions, collaborates with other organizations
and runs education and outreach programmes.
Submission policy All work by artists working with
any form of lens-based art considered.
Talks/Events/Education Runs a regular
programme of gallery talks and an extensive
programme of photography and digital courses
and classes. The talks programme is free.

Glynn Vivian Art Gallery
Alexandra Road, Swansea
SA1 5DZ
T 01792 516900
F 01792 516903
E glynn.vivian.gallery@swansea.gov.uk
W www.swansea.gov.uk
Founded in 1911. An Edwardian gallery offering
a broad range of visual arts from the original
bequest of Richard Glynn Vivian (1835–1910)
to art of the twentieth century. The latter is
well represented with painting and sculpture by
Hepworth, Nicholson and Nash alongside Welsh
artists such as Ceri Richards, Gwen John and
Augustus John. The exhibitions programme in the
modern wing gives a contemporary overview of the
arts in local, national and international contexts.
Submission policy Applications are considered
throughout the year, and should include a CV,
examples of the work (on slides, CD, video, DVD,
etc.), plus publications and support material.
Talks/Events/Education An education service
for schools and a programme of artists' talks and
events, plus lectures organized by Friends of the
gallery.

Howard Gardens Gallery
Cardiff School of Art and Design, UWK Howard
Gardens, Cardiff
CF24 0SP
T 029 20418608
F 029 20416944
E rcox@uwk.ac.uk
Situated at the centre of Cardiff School of Art and
Design, the programme presents a combination of
contemporary fine-art and craft exhibitions from
local, national and international sources. Also
holds annual BA degree and MA postgraduate
exhibitions in the summer and autumn terms.
Submission policy Contemporary visual artists and
craftspeople may apply during the academic year
(September to June) with a CV, ten slides and sae.
Talks/Events/Education Occasional seminars and
conferences associated with specific exhibitions.

National Museum and Gallery, Cardiff
Cathays Park, Cardiff
CF10 3NP
T 029 20397951
E art@nmgw.ac.uk
W www.nmgw.ac.uk/www.php/art/
Collections include the Williams-Wynn Collection,
the De Winton Collection of European porcelain,
the Morton Nance Collection of Welsh ceramics,
the Davies Sisters' Collection, historical paintings,
works on paper and contemporary craft. The
Davies Collection is one of the great British art
collections of the twentieth century and was
donated to the museum in the 1950s. Historical
paintings includes sixteenth-century Welsh
portraits, a collection of miniatures and works
from across Europe.

Oriel Davies Gallery
The Park, Newtown
SY16 2NZ
T 01686 625041
F 01686 623633
E enquiries@orieldavies.org
W www.orieldavies.org
Formerly Oriel 31, Oriel Davies Gallery was started
in Newtown in 1985 as a contemporary-art gallery
in Mid-Wales. Following an extensive three-year
refurbishment beginning in 2002, it now
boasts two new galleries that cater specifically to
displaying temporary exhibitions of modern and
contemporary art.
Submission policy Welcomes applications from
contemporary artists to exhibit, but does not
represent artists.

Talks/Events/Education Runs a wide and varied programme of workshops and events at the gallery alongside the exhibitions programme. Gallery talks are free but some workshops carry a small fee.

Oriel Mostyn Gallery

12 Vaughan Street, Llandudno
LL30 1AB
T 01492 879201
F 01492 878869
E info@mostyn.org
W www.mostyn.org

Founded in 1978 as a gallery for contemporary arts. Shows five or six changing exhibitions of all contemporary art forms per year.

Submission policy The gallery references and curates its own shows and collaborates with other galleries, but submissions from artists are considered. There is an annual open exhibition with a £6,000 prize, where entries are solicited from artists without conditions of age, theme or any other restriction.

Talks/Events/Education Free 'Artists Talking' series, where exhibiting artists discuss their work. Other events are also organized, some of which are free.

Riverfront

Bristol Packet Wharf, Newport
NP20 IHG
T 01633 232039
E riverfront@newport.gov.uk
W www.newport.gov.uk/_dc/
index.cfm?fuseaction=riverfront.homepage

In 1999 Newport received funding for a new arts centre, which includes a small gallery displaying exhibitions of art, design and photography. Rooms are available for hire.

Royal Cambrian Academy of Art

Crown Lane, Conwy
LL32 8AN
T 01492 593413
E rca@rcaconwy.org
W www.rcaconwy.org

Founded in 1881. Home to a significant collection of Welsh art.

School of Art Gallery and Museum

The University of Wales, Aberystwyth, Buarth Mawr, Aberystwyth
SY23 1NG
T 01970 622460
F 01970 622461
E neh@aber.ac.uk
W www.aber.ac.uk/museum

Has changing exhibitions from the permanent collection and touring shows. The collection includes graphic art from fifteenth century to present, art in Wales since 1945, contemporary Welsh and post-war Italian photography, early twentieth-century pioneer and contemporary British studio pottery, eighteenth- and nineteenth-century slipware, Swansea and Nantgarw porcelain, art pottery and Oriental ceramics. Studies of the collection by appointment.

Tabernacle – MOMA Wales

Heol Penrallt, Machynlleth
SY20 8AJ
T 01654 703355
F 01654 702160
W www.momawales.org.uk

MOMA Wales has grown up alongside the Tabernacle, a former Wesleyan chapel, which in 1986 reopened as a centre for the performing arts. It has six exhibition spaces, which house, throughout the year, the Tabernacle Collection and modern Welsh art. Individual artists are spotlighted in temporary exhibitions.

Talks/Events/Education Workshops for adults and children in July. Tabernacle Art Competition in August, with winners chosen by expert judges and the public. Many works in MOMA Wales for sale.

Tenby Museum and Gallery

Castle Hill, Tenby
SA70 7BP
T 01834 842809
E tenbymuseum@hotmail.com
W www.tenbymuseum.free-online.co.uk

The permanent collection includes works by Augustus John, Gwen John, Nina Hamnet, E.J. Head, Julius Caesar Ibbetson, John Piper and David Jones.

Wrexham Arts Centre

Rhosddu Road, Wrexham
LL11 1AU
T 01978 292093
F 01978 292611
E arts.centre@wrexham.gov.uk
W www.wrexham.gov.uk/arts

Established in 1970, the centre is a local-authority-administered venue. Exhibits temporary exhibitions highlighting a variety of contemporary artists and media. Works in collaboration with many partners (including Yale Memorial Gallery) and hosts touring exhibitions.

Submission policy Artists can send in exhibition proposal, including images, CV and vision of proposed exhibition.

Talks/Events/Education An education programme supports every exhibition and can include talks and workshops.

West Midlands

Barber Institute of Fine Arts

University of Birmingham, Edgbaston, Birmingham
B15 2TS
T 0121 4147333
F 0121 4143370
E info@barber.org.uk
W www.barber.org.uk
Comprises works from the thirteenth to the twentieth centuries, with particularly important Old Master and Impressionist collections. The gallery includes work by Baschenis, Bellini, Botticelli, Degas, Delacroix, Gainsborough, Gauguin, Holbein, Ingres, Magritte, Manet, Matisse, Monet, Picasso, Poussin, Rembrandt, Rodin, Rossetti, Rubens, Schiele, Stom, Turner, Van Dyck, van Gogh, Veronese and Whistler.

Birmingham Museum and Art Gallery

Chamberlain Square, Birmingham
B3 3DH
T 0121 3032834 / 3031966
F 0121 3031394
E bmag_enquiries@birmingham.gov.uk
W www.bmag.org.uk/museum_and_art_gallery/
Founded in 1885. The collections cover fine and applied arts, archaeology and ethnography, and local and industrial history. The fine- and applied-art collections include paintings and drawings, British watercolours and arts and crafts. There is an ever-changing programme of temporary exhibitions and the permanent collection includes the Pre-Raphaelites. Major shows are housed in the restored gas hall. Entrance to the museum and art gallery is free.

Compton Verney

Compton Verney, Warwickshire
CV35 9HZ
T 01926 645500
F 01926 645501
E info@comptonverney.org.uk
W www.comptonverney.org.uk

Launched in 2004. Collections include Naples (1600 to 1800), German (1450 to 1650), Chinese bronzes, British portraits, British folk art and the Marx-Lambert Collection of popular art. Also runs a major temporary exhibitions programme.

Talks/Events/Education An extensive events programme accompanies each exhibition. Events are charged for.

Herbert Museum and Art Gallery

Jordan Well, Coventry
CV1 5QP
T 024 76832381
F 024 76832410
E artsandheritage@coventry.gov.uk
W www.coventrymuseum.org.uk
The visual arts collection features mainly British twentieth-century art (particularly of the 1950s and 1960s). Other main areas collected include British watercolours and prints, pre-1900 British paintings, British figure drawings from 1800, images of Lady Godiva, works by local nineteenth-century artist David Gee, Far Eastern ceramics, Western seventeenth-century art, world art, and topographical views of Coventry and Warwickshire.

Hereford Museum and Art Gallery

Broad Street, Hereford
HR4 9AU
T 01432 260692
F 01432 342492
E herefordmuseums@herefordshire.gov.uk
W www.herefordshire.gov.uk (click on Leisure and Museums)
The museum was founded in 1874 and the gallery added as an extension in the 1920s. Houses changing exhibitions of a wide variety of media and styles. Has an extensive collection of fine art, costume and social history, as well as natural history and archaeology.

Submission policy All submissions welcome, but especially interested in applications from artists who have considered accessibility for the visually impaired.

Talks/Events/Education Exhibitions are often accompanied by talks (a small fee is usually charged). Workshops are usually aimed at non-professionals.

Ikon Gallery

1 Oozells Square, Brindleyplace, Birmingham
B1 2HS
T 0121 2480708

F 0121 2480709
E programming@ikon-gallery.co.uk
W www.ikon-gallery.co.uk
Founded about forty years ago and originally a small kiosk in the Bull Ring. It is now housed in the neo-Gothic Oozells Street School. Holds temporary exhibitions in a variety of media and organizes programmes outside the gallery.
Talks/Events/Education A variety of talks, tours, workshops and seminars are held. For education enquiries, email education@ikon-gallery.co.uk. In addition, a limited number of placements are offered to third-year art students; for details contact Andrew Tims at a.tims@ikon-gallery.co.uk or telephone the number above.

Impressions Gallery

29 Castlegate, York
YO1 9RN
T 01904 654724
F 01904 651509
W www.impressions-gallery.com
Opened in 1972. One of the oldest specialist contemporary-photography galleries in Europe. Shows photography and digital art.

Mead Gallery

Warwick Arts Centre, University of Warwick, Coventry
CV4 7AL
T 024 76522589
F 024 76572664
E meadgallery@warwick.ac.uk
W www.warwickartscentre.co.uk
Hosts curated exhibitions of international contemporary art and runs an access programme utilizing expertise within the university. The university art collection was founded in 1966 and includes over eight hundred works of modern and contemporary art on open display across campus, including paintings, prints, sculptures, photographs and ceramics.
Submission policy Welcomes submissions with previous permission from the Senior Curator, although the programme is booked up well in advance.
Talks/Events/Education Open during term time only and holds talks and events relating to each exhibition.

Meadow Gallery

Burford House, Tenbury Wells
WR15 8HQ
T 01584 891659

E info@meadowgallery.co.uk
W www.meadowgallery.co.uk
A three-acre landscaped site adjacent to Burford House. The gallery provides the environmental setting for an annual summer-long exhibition of specially commissioned site-specific sculpture and installations.

New Art Gallery, Walsall

Gallery Square, Walsall
WS2 8LG
T 01922 654400
F 01922 654401
E info@artatwalsall.org.uk
W www.artatwalsall.org.uk
Has collections of European art, including major paintings by Rembrandt, Goya, Constable, Manet, Degas and Freud. The Garman Ryan Collection galleries chart the career of Jacob Epstein. There is also an interactive children's gallery, library and changing exhibitions programme.
Talks/Events/Education Holds events and activities, artists' talks about exhibitions, introductory talks about the Garman Ryan collection and family workshops.

Potteries Museum and Art Gallery

Bethesda Street, City Centre, Stoke-on-Trent
ST1 3DW
T 01782 232323
F 01782 232500
E museums@stoke.gov.uk
W www.stoke.gov.uk/museums
Opened in 1981, the museum houses the world's greatest collection of Staffordshire ceramics, plus displays of art and local history. There is also a lively programme of exhibitions and events, with the emphasis on contemporary art and craft.
Submission policy Shows work by artists either based in the region or with a national or international reputation.
Talks/Events/Education Organizes talks and events for specific exhibitions on a regular basis. There is a charge for each event.

Royal Pump Rooms –
Art Gallery and Museum

The Parade, Leamington Spa
CV32 4AA
T 01926 742700
F 01926 742705
E prooms@warwickdc.gov.uk
W www.royal-pump-rooms.co.uk
The gallery and museum opened at the historic

Royal Pump Rooms in 1999. Facilities include an art gallery, a museum with a historic *hammam* room, a temporary exhibition space, an interactive learning gallery and an education room. The permanent exhibition of art works from the collection changes every eighteen months. A new collection of contemporary works explores links between art and medical science. Shows exhibitions of contemporary art, historical art and social history for an average of six to eight weeks at a time.

Submission policy Exhibition proposals from individuals or groups should be addressed to the Art Gallery Curator at the postal address above.

Talks/Events/Education Details of all events given in the quarterly *What's On* publication.

Rugby Art Gallery and Museum

Little Elborow Street, Rugby
CV21 3BZ
T 01788 533201
F 01788 533204
E rugbyartgalleryandmuseum@rugby.gov.uk
W www.rugbygalleryandmuseum.org.uk
For more than half a century, Rugby has been collecting work by modern artists, including Spencer, Freud, Lowry, Hepworth and Sutherland. In 2000 the collection was moved to a new gallery, giving it a permanent home for the first time.

Shire Hall Gallery

Market Square, Stafford
ST16 2LD
T 01785 278345
E shirehallgallery@staffordshire.gov.uk
Dedicated to promoting the visual arts and crafts across a range of subjects and styles. Comprises seven hundred prints, drawings, watercolours, maps and oil paintings.

Shrewsbury Museum and Art Gallery

Rowley's House, Barker Street, Shrewsbury
SY1 1QH
T 01743 361196
F 01743 358411
E museums@shrewsbury.gov.uk
W www.shrewsburymuseums.com
www.darwincountry.org
Housed in two sixteenth- to seventeenth-century buildings. Includes collections of fine and applied arts. Special exhibitions link heritage and contemporary visual arts, including media arts.
Submission policy Artists may submit information about their work. All such information will be

assessed on a one-off basis, within the overall context of a long-term, pre-planned exhibition programme.
Talks/Events/Education Occasional exhibition-related events, on a one-off basis.

Wolverhampton Art Gallery

Lichfield Street, Wolverhampton
WV1 1DU
T 01902 552055
F 01902 552053
E info@wolverhamptonart.org.uk
W www.scit.wlv.ac.uk/university/sles/gallery/web_page/wag_intro.htm
Built in 1884 and situated in the heart of the town centre. The gallery's collections include contemporary Pop Art, displays of Victorian and Georgian paintings and video and digital media. Work began in January 2005 to build a new extension to house the Pop Art collection and provide a temporary exhibition gallery. The gallery also manages The Makers Dozen Studios, artist studios situated within the art gallery complex, purpose-designed for artists and makers.

Yorkshire and Humberside

Cartwright Hall Art Gallery

Lister Park, Bradford
BD9 4NS
T 01274 431212
F 01274 481045
E cartwright.hall@bradford.gov.uk
W www.city-of-bradford.com/cartwright-hall.html
Built in 1904 in Baroque style as an art gallery. Houses permanent collections of nineteenth- and twentieth-century British art (particularly strong in Victorian art), arts from the Indian subcontinent and contemporary South Asian art. Also shows temporary exhibitions.

Cooper Gallery

Church Street, Barnsley
S70 2AH
T 01226 242905
F 01226 297283
W www.barnsley.gov.uk/tourism/coopergallery/index.asp
Founded in 1912 to house the collection of Samuel Joshua Cooper. The permanent collection holds paintings, watercolours and drawings from the seventeenth to the twentieth centuries. Also hosts

visiting contemporary exhibitions, such as the South Yorkshire Open Art Exhibition.

Dean Clough Galleries
Halifax
HX3 5AX
T 01422 250250
F 01422 255250
E dean.clough.ltd@deanclough.com
W www.deanclough.com
An arts, business and design complex created on the derelict site of what was once the world's largest carpet mill. Eight galleries host a range of exhibitions spanning the arts. The Dean Clough Studios, based in Mill House, the Stable Yard and the Band Room, house twenty-four fine artists, designers and craftworkers working in a variety of media.

Ferens Art Gallery
Queen Victoria Square, Hull
HU1 3RA
T 01482 613902
F 01482 613710
E museums@hullcc.gov.uk
W www.hullcc.gov.uk/museums
Opened in 1927, the gallery combines an internationally renowned permanent collection and a programme of temporary exhibitions. Particular strengths of the collection include European Old Masters (notably Dutch and Flemish), portraiture, marine paintings, and modern and contemporary British art.
Submission policy Welcomes written proposals from artists involved in fine art. For the temporary exhibitions programme include a CV, statement and good-quality visuals.
Talks/Events/Education Frequently holds talks and education events, most of which are free.

Graves Art Gallery
Surrey Street, Sheffield
S1 1XZ
T 0114 2782600
F 0114 2782604
W www.shef.ac.uk/city/artgals/graves.html
Founded in 1934, the gallery covers all periods of British art from the sixteenth century to the present. Other collections include French, Italian, Spanish and Dutch paintings of all major periods, watercolours, drawings and prints, and a collection of decorative art from diverse cultures (including the Grice Collection of Chinese ivories). Also hosts temporary exhibitions.

Harewood House
Harewood, nr Leeds
LS17 9LQ
T 0113 2181010
F 0113 2181002
E info@harewood.org
W www.harewood.org
In addition to displaying the collections of the house, there is a programme of temporary exhibitions of historical and contemporary art.
Talks/Events/Education A programme of lectures, demonstrations and workshops given by experts and artists, which runs all year.

Henry Moore Institute
74 The Headrow, Leeds
LS1 3AH
T 0113 2467467
F 0113 2461481
E info@henry-moore.ac.uk
W www.henry-moore-fdn.co.uk
A centre for the study of sculpture, with exhibition galleries and an active research programme. Originally set up in partnership between the Henry Moore Foundation and Leeds City Council in the city where Moore began his training as a sculptor, it is now concerned with a wide variety of sculpture, both historical and contemporary. The institute, an award-winning, architecturally designed building, opened in 1993, and comprises a suite of galleries on the ground floor, the library and archive on the first floor, and a seminar room in the basement.
Submission policy Welcomes applications for research fellowships from artists and academics. Deadline for applications each year is usually end of first week in January.
Talks/Events/Education Runs a series of complementary Wednesday-evening talks for each of its main exhibitions, as well as seminars and conferences. Events are usually free.

Huddersfield Art Gallery
Princess Alexandra Walk, Huddersfield
HD1 2SU
T 01484 221962
F 01484 221952
E robert.hall@kirklees.gov.uk
W www.kirklees.gov.uk/art
In current building (along with library) since 1945. The collection consists mainly of twentieth-century British art in all media. Exhibitions throughout the year include one-person and group shows, and touring (Arts Council, Crafts Council, etc.).

Current interests particularly in post-war British art, especially sculpture and Constructivism.
Submission policy Written or emailed submissions with slides or CD are accepted. Unlikely to exhibit without local or regional link.
Talks/Events/Education Events held. Contact the Education and Outreach Officer.

Hull Maritime Museum

Queen Victoria Square, Hull
HU1 3DX
T 01482 613902
F 01482 613710
E Arthur.Credland@hullcc.gov.uk
W www.hullcc.gov.uk/museums
Maritime collections go back to 1822. Includes marine paintings (chiefly by local artists), decorative arts of the sea and an outstanding collection of scrimshaw work (carved whale bone and ivory). Recent exhibitions have shown the work of David Bell and Colin Verity.
Submission policy Interested in work incorporating maritime themes, decorative art with sea connections, or marine painting in the traditional sense.

Leeds City Art Gallery

The Headrow, Leeds
LS1 3AA
W www.leeds.gov.uk/artgallery/
Emphasis is on significant and interesting new developments in contemporary art and exhibitions that explore the history of nineteenth- and twentieth-century art. Works on paper include pieces by Turner, Rembrandt, Cotman, Cozens, Girtin, Derain, Sisley, Rose Garrard and Atkinson Grimshaw. Recent contemporary-art acquisitions include works by Bill Woodrow, Paula Rego, Mark Wallinger, Stephen Willats, Alison Wilding and Bridget Riley. With support from the Henry Moore Foundation, the modern sculpture collection is second only to that of the Tate.
Submission policy The exhibitions programme is put together twelve to eighteen months in advance, and larger-scale exhibitions at least two years in advance. Welcomes applications from artists. Send a proposal outlining the exhibition, supporting visual material (preferably transparencies or slides; five or six and not more than fifteen), which will be returned, a CV and an outline of what makes the proposal distinctive and how it might be of interest to the gallery's audiences. Send to Nigel Walsh (Exhibitions Curator).

Leeds Metropolitan University Gallery and Studio Theatre

Civic Quarter, Leeds
LS1 3HE
T 0113 2833140
E gallerytheatre@leedsmet.ac.uk
W www.lmu.ac.uk/arts/
Founded in 1990. Six exhibitions held each year, including shows based on artists' proposals, initiated projects and occasional hired-in exhibitions.
Submission policy Submissions should contain good-quality visuals in a format that best represents the work (e.g. slides, video, DVD, CD; digital images should be PC-compatible). Also include a statement about the content of the work, a CV and supporting website links. Do not send full proposals by email. Proposals will be considered by the curator in consultation with education and technical staff at fixed points in the year (mid-November, mid-March and mid-June).

Mercer Art Gallery

Swan Road, Harrogate
HG1 2SA
T 01423 556188
F 01423 556130
E museums@harrogate.gov.uk
W www.harrogate.gov.uk/museums
Harrogate's fine-art collection began in the 1880s and the first gallery opened in the 1930s. Opened on current site in 1991. Home to two thousand works of art, mainly from the nineteenth and twentieth centuries.
Submission policy Artists wishing to exhibit should contact the Curator of Art on the above number.
Talks/Events/Education Runs a regular programme of talks and workshops. Costs vary from free to a few pounds for talks, and from £10 for workshops.

Millennium Galleries

Arundel Gate, Sheffield
S1 2PP
T 0114 2782600
W www.sheffieldgalleries.org.uk/coresite/html/millennium.asp
Displays visual arts, craft and design. Incorporates a special exhibition gallery, a craft and design gallery, a metalwork gallery and the Ruskin Gallery, containing a collection compiled by John Ruskin over many years.
Talks/Events/Education The learning centre organizes talks, events and practical workshops.

National Museum of Photography,
Film and Television
Pictureville, Bradford
BD1 1NQ
T 0870 7010200
F 01274 723155
E talk.nmpft@nmsi.ac.uk
W www.nmpft.org.uk
Founded in 1983, with collections covering the past, present and future of the three media. Includes the Royal Photographic Society Collection, the National Collection, the Daily Herald Archive and the National Cinematography Collection.
Submission policy All three of the museum's subject media, taking account of new technologies (such as digital imaging), are covered. The submission of exhibition proposals is encouraged. New work is regularly commissioned. For more details, telephone 01274 203325.
Talks/Events/Education The frequency of events changes depending on subject matter and time of year. Some are subject to charges.

Newby Hall and Gardens
Ripon
HG4 5AE
T 01423 322583
F 01423 824452
W www.newbyhall.co.uk
Highlights include the Gobelins Tapestry Room, a gallery of classical statuary and a contemporary sculpture garden.

North Light Gallery
Armitage Bridge, Huddersfield
HD4 7NR
T 01484 340003
F 01484 340001
W www.northlightgallery.org.uk
Opened in 2000 to show contemporary British art. A charity, the gallery was created out of a nineteenth-century wool textile mill and is available to hire by artists or groups of artists or other museums. Houses a collection of Yorkshire artists in 15,000 sq. ft of airy industrial space.
Submission policy To show, the artist must finance the costs of transport, catalogue, insurance, invitation cards and printing.
Talks/Events/Education Artists must be prepared to give one talk as part of exhibition.

S10 Gallery
Ashgate House, Ashgate Road, Sheffield
S10 3BZ

T 0114 2678883
F 0114 2678894
E s10gallery@aol.com
W www.s10gallery.com
Holds monthly exhibitions covering a cross-section of the arts. Run by the charity For A Better Life with Epilepsy (FABLE).

Salts Mill
Shipley, Saltaire
BD18 3LB
T 01274 531185
F 01274 531184
E post@saltsmill.demon.co.uk
W www.saltsmill.org.uk
Includes an extensive collection of works by David Hockney.

Scarborough Art Gallery
The Crescent, Scarborough
YO11 2PW
T 01723 374753
W www.scarboroughmuseums.org.uk/art_gallery.html
Includes works by Grimshaw, H.B. Carter, Frank Mason, Ernest Dade, Lord Leighton, Ivan Hitchens, Matthew Smith, E. Bawden and Eric Rivilious. Also runs a temporary exhibition programme featuring contemporary work by professional artists.

Site Gallery
1 Brown Street, Sheffield
S1 2BS
T 0114 2812077
F 0114 2812078
E info@sitegallery.org
W www.sitegallery.org
Founded as Untitled Gallery in 1978 by a group of photographers who set up a darkroom and gallery in a small shop. Site Gallery launched in 1995, giving a new direction to the gallery's programming of exhibitions and events by incorporating the new and experimental, digital and multimedia alongside traditional forms of image production. Also runs commissioning and residency programme.
Talks/Events/Education Education and training activities and open-access production facilities.

Wakefield Art Gallery
Wentworth Terrace, Wakefield
WF1 3QW
T 01924 305901

F 01924 305770
E museumsandarts@wakefield.gov.uk
W www.wakefield.gov.uk
Houses a distinguished collection of modern
British art, including internationally significant
works by locally born sculptors Barbara Hepworth
and Henry Moore. The Gott Collection contains
over a thousand works on paper relating to the
topography and architecture of Yorkshire from the
1700s. Also has notable Edwardian and Victorian
paintings, British portraiture and seventeenth-
century Italian and northern European paintings
and drawings. The decorative-art collection
contains a range of eighteenth-century British and
European wares and a small collection of studio
pottery from 1950 to the present.
Submission policy Exhibition proposals accepted
from regional and national artists. Art and design
relevant to the region or permanent collection
particularly welcome.
Talks/Events/Education Events and activities for
children and adults.

West Yorkshire Print Workshop
75a Huddersfield Road, Mirfield
WF14 8AT
T 01924 497646
F 01924 497646
E print.workshop@btconnect.com
W westyorkshireprintworkshop.co.uk
Founded in 1981, showing all areas of print
including photography and etching. Workshop
facilities available for members. Artists' studios
and courses offered.
Submission policy All areas of print considered.

York City Art Gallery
Exhibition Square, York
YO1 7EW
T 01904 687687
E art.gallery@ymt.org.uk
W www.york.art.museum
Founded in 1879 and houses notable collections of
continental Old Masters from the fourteenth to the
eighteenth centuries, British paintings from the
seventeenth to the twentieth centuries, and
twentieth-century studio ceramics. The galleries
were rehung in 2005 in thematic displays.

Yorkshire Sculpture Park
West Bretton, Wakefield
WF4 4LG
T 01924 832515
F 01924 832600
E info@ysp.co.uk
W www.ysp.co.uk
Founded in 1977, an outdoor centre for modern
sculpture. The five hundred acres of historical
gardens and parkland were designed in the
eighteenth and nineteenth centuries. Outdoor
sculpture includes work by Barbara Hepworth,
Anthony Caro, Antony Gormley, Elisabeth Frink
and Sol LeWitt as well as one of the world's largest
open-air displays of bronzes by Henry Moore.
Indoor galleries also show a variety of temporary
exhibitions and projects by international artists.
Talks/Events/Education Educational events are
held throughout the year and include workshops,
sculpture courses, lectures, talks and tours.

03

The Internet

'The big fat pipe dream': The challenges of the Internet as a site for artistic creativity

Nick Crowe

Once upon a time there was a story about a big fat pipe – one that, if you possessed it, would make all your dreams come true. Within the small community of artists that make art for, and on, the Internet, there was a firmly held belief that 'net art' would really take off after the introduction of broadband. Now that the roads have been dug up and the cables relaid, it is clear that superior connectivity has not greatly altered the output or position of Internet-based practice.

It is worth considering why this is the case, why the big fat pipe has not fundamentally altered the fact that digital art still occupies a minor role within the contemporary visual arts. Certainly it is now usual for artists, critics, curators, journals and galleries to have broadband access. However, it is in the interface between the Internet and the gallery that work remains to be done, and this relationship will ultimately determine how net art develops within the UK over the next few years.

Plugging in

The challenge that Internet art presents to the rest of the culture is not one of technology or connectivity – these are problems for which there are simple cash solutions. The expansive timeframes and accretive structures of the Internet defy simple snapshot comprehension and are often difficult to grasp for those museums or galleries used to programming and working with traditional artistic media. Fortunately, Internet art can take place on any home computer and be viewed around the clock, regardless of when galleries are open or shut, but this same quality becomes a problem when considering what to present within the 'serious' acreage of the white-walled exhibition space. Put bluntly, the problem with Internet art is that is doesn't fit.

Consider the model of video art. There was no reason why video art should not have developed along the Blockbuster video rental model, or the CD market model. The technology was very suited to reproduction and home-distribution – as is the Internet.

But it was the video projector and the presentation of videos in galleries that started to make sense of video as an art form for the curators, the museums and, it would seem, the wider public. In a sense, it was the video projector rather than the video camera that enabled video art to occupy a central position within visual culture – a victory of presentational form over creative technology. Is that a depressing observation? It depends on your view of the commodification and collectability of art. Undoubtedly the fact that net art is widely available and freely distributed for domestic consumption has protected it from commodification and continues to limit the scope for its cultural reification.

Not for sale

For many digital artists, this disjuncture between technology-based art and the space of the gallery is precisely what attracts them to working in networked spaces. The Internet is free of that most pernicious influence – the need to render ideas as commodities – and acts as an unmediated site of correspondence between the artist and the viewer. This is a partial and idealized view, but as a narrative of production it continues to exert a considerable influence on the choices artists make when they engage in digital practice. There is also a persuasive argument in favour of this narrative in which net art – perpetually estranged from institutional patronage – finds its natural home in the hinterland of the suburban bedroom, fulfilling J.G. Ballard's observation that 'the periphery is where the future reveals itself.'

In the real world

It should not go unnoted, however, that digital art has its own, highly developed institutional forms: exhibition spaces such as ZKM in

Germany (www.zkm.de), V2 in Rotterdam (www.v2.nl) or Deluxe in London (www.deluxe-arts.org.uk), specialist publications including *MUTE* and *Leonardo*, websites such as Nettime (www.nettime.org) or Rhizome (www.rhizome.org), as well as international festivals such as ISEA (www.isea-web.org), Transmediale (www.transmediale.de) and Ars Electronica (www.aec.at). It even has its own nobility – both artistic and curatorial – that dominates the field in terms of reputation and general visibility.

While many within the digital art world still feel themselves to be excluded from the traditional art world as typified by the gallery–dealer–collector matrix, the more interesting developments that have occurred in the past few years have come from artists who seem to reject the dichotomy that the art world versus digital world model implies. Artists such as John Thomson and Alison Craighead (www.thomson-craighead.net) in the UK or Cory Archangel in the USA have managed to cross over to the mainstream to a certain extent, and it seems likely that others will follow suit.

Furthermore, as the Internet and other communication technologies have become more integral to the everyday experience of non-specialist users, the opportunities for artists to move beyond the ghetto structures of digital art, however reassuring and supportive these may have been in the early years of the form, becomes almost a cultural obligation. It is surely no accident that some of the most exciting digital work around today integrates aspects of Internet technology with performance, satellite communications, video or audio or with a physical presence in one or more real spaces. Jen Southern's experimentation with Global Positioning System and light aircraft or the urban game works of Blast Theory (www.blasttheory.co.uk) present themselves as examples of this expanded field of digital practice.

Politics and power

One cannot close this brief overview of net practice without considering the political framework within which it occurs. The early years of net art were characterized by its socially progressive, even utopian, politics. Now digital art has adopted a harder and more embattled stance, primarily in response to the violation – at national, European and global levels – of the idea that the Internet should be a free space of expression and articulation. In the USA, recent arrests of art activists working with technology, and the use of unspecified legal powers against independent news feeds under the auspices of the ongoing war on terrorism, have shifted and to a certain extent revitalized the focus of net art as an innately political activity. Remember, we're not talking about the Great Firewall of China here. These are the actions of European and American police forces, and it will be interesting to see how these developments impact on digital practice.

Initiatives such as Creative Commons (creativecommons.org), an organization dedicated to protecting copyright control for digital artists and musicians, provide some glimmer of hope that other models of digital-art practice may emerge in the cultural mainstream. The sheer political muscle of the media conglomerate, armed with copyright lawyers and lobbyists, leaves one in little doubt that artists will have to be bold and someone will have to be prepared to challenge these laws through the courts if the corporate takeover of digital culture is to be anything other than complete.

Nick Crowe is an artist based in Manchester. He has exhibited widely in the UK and abroad, and is currently a research fellow in the Faculty of Art and Design at Manchester Metropolitan University. His digital projects can be viewed and downloaded at www.nickcrowe.net.

Internet resources

24 Hour Museum
E info@www.24hourmuseum.org.uk
W www.24hourmuseum.org.uk
The UK's national virtual museum, offering
content including daily arts and museum news,
exhibition reviews and in-depth online trails.
Promotes publicly funded UK museums, galleries
and heritage attractions and seeks to develop
new audiences for UK culture. Venue and listings
information is driven by a searchable database of
over three thousand museum, gallery and heritage
sites.
Submission policy Welcomes press releases from
not-for-profit galleries and museums.

a-n The Artists Information Company
E info@a-n.co.uk
W www.a-n.co.uk
UK representative body for professional artists
and publishers of *a-n Magazine*. Subscriber access
to online resources on making a living, profile
and promotion, time and space, professional
practice and professional-development toolkits.
Weekly updated UK and international opportunities,
international contacts, artists' networks, and
professional-development organizations.

absolutearts.com and World Wide Arts Resources Corp.
E help@absolutearts.com
W www.absolutearts.com, www.wwar.com
Contact Janet Thomas
Since 1995, the largest arts site on the Internet.
In 1999, wwar.com expanded to include
absolutearts.com, which began as a daily arts
news outlet and has adapted to include a
comprehensive contemporary art online
portfolio programme.
Submission policy For absolutearts.com online
arts news, submissions must be complete press
releases, written in English and received two weeks
before the exhibition opening. A website must be
associated with the venue, project, exhibition or
artists.

ADAM
E adam@adam.ac.uk
W www.adam.ac.uk
The Art, Design, Architecture & Media (ADAM)
Information Gateway is being developed to help
find quality-assured information on the Internet in
the areas of fine art, design, architecture, applied

arts, media, theory, museum studies and
conservation, and professional practice.

AHDS Visual Arts
E info@visualarts.ahds.ac.uk
W vads.ahds.ac.uk
Based at the Surrey Institute of Art & Design,
University College. Aims to support research,
learning and teaching by providing visual arts
digital resources through robust systems for
Internet access and long-term preservation.

APD
E apd@a-n.co.uk
W www.apd-network.info
The Artists' Professional Development (APD)
network, initiated by a-n in 2001, is a UK-wide
intelligence and exchange forum for organizations
that are proactively developing information,
advice, training and professional-development
services for visual and applied artists.

Art & Architecture Thesaurus Online
E AAT@getty.edu
W www.getty.edu/research/conducting_research/
vocabularies/aat
A structured vocabulary of 133,000 terms,
descriptions, bibliographic citations and other
information relating to fine art, architecture,
decorative arts, archival materials and material
culture.

Art Guide
E info@artguide.org
W www.artguide.org
Founded in the late 1990s. A free online database
of museums and galleries across the UK and
Ireland. Visitors can search the site by artist and by
special interest. Also a comprehensive, up-to-date
exhibitions guide.

Art in Context
W www.artincontext.org
Established in 1995, offering free public access to
information added by curators, dealers, artists,
writers and others from around the world.

Art in the City
E admin@artinthecity.co.uk
W www.artinthecity.co.uk
Contact Sylvia Swiffin
Enables artists to promote themselves and their
work by offering sixteen picture spaces, gallery
function, biography and artist's photo. Automated

system for changing pictures, details and prices. Commission only on sales via the site using credit cards.

Submission policy Artists complete Internet application and submit work. Small annual charge on acceptance.

Art Industri

W www.artindustri.com

Promotes the work of students, amateur and professional artists, and art galleries via a network of sites offering promotional tools, reference information and resource services to the art community.

Art Movements

W www.artmovements.co.uk

A concise reference guide to the major art movements and periods.

Art on the Net

E webmasters@art.net

W www.art.net

An international collective of artists sharing their works on the Internet. Currently represents over one hundred artists.

art-online – The Fine Art Directory

W www.art-online.com

Contains links to editor-reviewed websites organized into the subject categories of art history, the art market, art venues, artists, education, employment, events, galleries, governments, legal, museums, professionals, resources, rewards and shopping.

artquest

E stephen@artquest.org.uk

W www.artquest.org.uk

Contact Stephen Beddoe (Programme Manager)

Provides advice, information and support to visual artists living in London.

Art Search UK

W www.artsearchuk.org

A free, independent search engine that indexes webpages relevant to contemporary art from mainly (but not exclusively) UK-based sites.

artart.co.uk

E curator@artart.co.uk

W www.artart.co.uk

Contact Lawrie Simonson

Founded in 2000, offering a platform to

professional artists to exhibit and offer for sale works of art. Has a varied stable of professional artists and welcomes recent arts graduates onto the site. Tends to show predominantly modern painting and sculpture but also a good selection of other specialized media including ceramics and photography.

Submission policy Requires eight to twelve images/jpegs of good quality, CV and statement.

artcourses.co.uk

E thah@artcourses.co.uk

W www.artcourses.co.uk

Contact Jonathan Wickens

An online directory of art classes, craft workshops, painting holidays, etc. Europe-wide coverage of all media and all levels. Course providers with or without their own website can apply for an entry via the website. Offers a starter webpage service for artists without websites.

Artcyclopedia

E jmalyon@artcyclopedia.com

W www.artcyclopedia.com

Aims to be 'the definitive guide to museum-quality fine art on the Internet'.

artdaily.com

E ignacio@artdaily.com

W www.artdaily.com

Contact Ignacio Villarreal (Editor and Publisher)

Founded in 1996. The 'first art newspaper on the net'.

artefact

W www.artefact.co.uk

Online editions of *Galleries* and *The Collector* magazines, with searchable databases.

Artifact

E artifact@mmu.ac.uk

W www.artifact.ac.uk

Contact Jayne Everard

A free, searchable guide to the best of the web for the arts and creative industries' teaching, learning and research community. Part of the Resource Discovery Network (RDN), aimed at Internet users in UK further and higher education but freely available to all.

the-artists.org

W www.the-artists.org

A database of biographical information on leading twentieth-century and contemporary visual artists.

Artlex Art Dictionary
W www.artlex.com
Offers over 3,500 definitions of terms relevant to art and visual culture. Includes images, pronunciation notes, quotations and cross-references.

artnet
E jlaplaca@artnet.com
W www.artnet.com
A site for buying, selling and researching fine art online. Serves dealers and buyers alike by providing a survey of the market and its pricing trends. A price database represents auction results from over five hundred international auction houses since 1985, covering more than 2.6 million art works by over 180,000 artists.

artrat
E enquiries@artrat.co.uk
W www.artrat.co.uk
Contact Thomas Fazzini
Founded in 2003. A platform for new and established artists to exhibit and sell their work. Free to exhibit. Commission applies if sold through the site. Also features regularly updated interviews with cutting-edge artists, musicians and actors as well as current views and reviews.

artroof.com
E info@artroof.com
W www.artroof.com
Helps artists to establish an online art gallery in a few minutes.

Arts Connect
E richard@metier.org.uk
W www.arts-connect.net
A web-based search engine for the arts, searching thousands of database items across specialized arts websites to find information about arts and artists that may not be found by more general web searches.

Arts Hub
E info@artshub.co.uk
W www.artshub.co.uk
A resource for UK arts workers, containing news and information on jobs and events.

Arts Journal
E mclennan@artsjournal.com
W www.artsjournal.com
A weekday digest of some of the best arts and cultural journalism in the English-speaking world. Combs more than two hundred English-language newspapers, magazines and publications every day.

ArtsCurator Ltd
E info@artsCurator.co.uk
W www.artscurator.co.uk
Contact Simon Clark
Formed in 2004 to provide a fully supported service for artists who wish to promote their work via the Internet. Each artist gets their own content-managed website, which takes no technical expertise to update. Subscription to the service is £25 per month.

Artshole.co.uk
E tony@artshole.co.uk
W www.artshole.co.uk
Founded in 2002, providing professional, emerging and student artists with a free platform to showcase and sell their art work. Currently shows over two thousand artists. Free listings section and many online links and resourses.

artsNETWORKS
E artsNETWORKS@thinkeq.org.uk
W www.artsnetworks.net
An online directory of creative, cultural and media support organizations.

ArtSouthEast
E editor@artsoutheast.co.uk
W www.artsoutheast.co.uk
An online gateway to arts events and information in the south-east of England.

Artupdate.com
E info@artupdate.com
W www.artupdate.com
A contemporary art information service publishing in print and online for a worldwide audience.

Asian Arts Access
E kalwant.ajimal@which.net
W www.asianartsaccess.org
The website for Asian Arts Access, an arts development agency, research and development organization and production house.

axis
E info@axisweb.org
W www.axisartists.org.uk

An online guide to practising artists in the UK. For each artist there is detailed information, examples of art works, projects and links to further information.

Backspace

E info@backspace.org
W www.bak.spc.org
An 'open environment for exploration and expression on the Internet and the focal point for related events, audio, visual and otherwise, with particular bias toward the diverse talents of its subscribers'.

britart.com

W www.britart.com
An online forum for buying and selling UK art works.

British Arts

E arts@britishservices.co.uk
W www.britisharts.co.uk
Contact Annabel (Customer Services Manager)
Founded in 1999. An online artists' and patrons' information resource. Free for any artist, relevant individual or company to list their website and services.
Submission policy All artists from amateur to professional included free of charge. Suppliers, jobs, competitions and companies selling art-related services are also included for free.

Counter–

E info@countereditions.com
W www.countereditions.com
A website of prints and multiples by contemporary artists.

Creative Futures

E hday@surrart.ac.uk
W www.creativefutures.cadise.ac.uk
Contact Helen Day (Project Administrator)
A specialist careers resource for creative and performing arts, design and communications students to connect with arts and creative industry employers.

CreativePeople

E info@creativepeople.org.uk
W www.creativepeople.org.uk
Contact Barbara Brunsdon
An online UK network of organizations, individually supplying training and professional-development information, advice and guidance services to current and aspiring arts and crafts practitioners. Details of and links to the partners are provided on the site. The member organizations affiliate themselves to regional, art form or special-interest partnerships. Creative People was launched as a pilot in 2001 with the support of the Arts Council England. The network is a virtual organization and it is intended that it will extend in stages.

culturebase.net

E info@culturebase.net.
W www.culturebase.net
An online information source on contemporary international artists from all fields.

Cybersalon

E lewis@cybersalon.org
W www.cybersalon.org
Contact Lewis Sykes
Aims to be a forum for debate and discussion on digital-media issues, a showcase for new work and a meeting place for people to exchange ideas and make new contacts.

digital art source

E contact@digitalartsource.com
W www.digitalartsource.com
An online resource for digital art and culture information.

The Digital Artist

E carol@thedigitalartist.com
W www.thedigitalartist.com
Contact Carol Pentleton
An exhibition site for artists, designers and artisans. Free exhibits include name, contact information, biography, artist's statement, webpage link and one image. Exhibitors are from around the world, from students to established professionals. Offers free monthly newsletters and e-books, classifieds, forums and articles.
Submission policy Artists, designers and artisans in all media welcome.

Digital Arts Network (DAN)

E bruno@digitalartsnetwork.org
W www.digitalartsnetwork.org
Contact Bruno Martelli (DAN Coordinator)
A network of people working at the intersection of art and technology in the east of England. Online resources include a searchable database of members, electronic news

services, peer-to-peer communication and live networking events.

Digital Consciousness
W www.digitalconsciousness.com
A public database of contemporary art, with art and biographies of emerging and established artists exhibited through galleries and artists' pages.

electronic flux corporation (e-flux)
W www.e-flux.com
A New York-based information bureau dedicated to worldwide distribution of intelligence via the Internet for contemporary visual arts institutions.

eyestorm
E emma.poole@eyestorm.com
W www.eyestorm.com
Contact Angie Davey
Founded in 1999. An online company offering exclusive signed limited-edition prints by many leading contemporary artists, including Damien Hirst, Jeff Koons, Peter Blake and Helmut Newton.

Fine Artz Virtual Gallery
E enquiries@fineartz.com
W www.fineartz.com
A virtual art gallery displaying work from new and emerging fine artists from the UK and beyond.

Fotonet
E office@fotonet.org.uk
W www.fotonet.org.uk
Contact Susie Medley (Director)
A website showing curated online exhibitions and a source of information for photographers. Run by Fotonet (founded in 1999), a photography development organization based at the Winchester Gallery, Winchester School of Art.

Foundation for Art and Creative Technology (FACT)
E info@fact.co.uk
W www.fact.co.uk
The website of one of the UK's leading organizations for the development, support and exhibition of film, video, and new and emerging media.

Furtherfield
E info@furtherfield.org
W www.furtherfield.org
Contact Marc Garrett

Creates 'imaginative strategies that actively communicate ideas and issues in a range of digital and terrestrial media contexts'. Features works online and organizes global, contributory projects on the Internet, the streets and at public venues simultaneously.

The Gallery Channel
E support@thegallerychannel.com
W www.thegallerychannel.com
A searchable database of galleries, venues, artists and exhibitions.

Global Art Jobs
E info@globalartsjobs.com
W www.globalartjobs.com
A website with details of international visual arts vacancies.

Hidden Art
E info@mazorcaprojects.co.uk
W www.hiddenart.com
A forum for design talent based in the wider east London area and beyond.

irational
E irational@irational.org
W www.irational.org
An 'international system for deploying "irational" information, services and products for the displaced and roaming'. Supports independent artists and organizations creating work that pushes the boundaries between the corporate realms of business, art and engineering.

Londonart.co.uk
E info@londonart.co.uk
W www.londonart.co.uk
Contact Paul Wynter
Set up in 1997 to provide artists with an opportunity to show their work online, and buyers with a wide choice of original contemporary art. The site now offers fifteen thousand works for sale from over nine hundred artists, with prices ranging from £50 to over £40,000. There are five painting categories (figurative, landscape, abstract, still life and drawing) and four other categories (digital, sculpture, photography and other).
Submission policy Welcomes applications from visual artists making original contemporary art. All applications will be carefully considered.

MadforArts
W www.madforarts.org
A web and television project that aims to
encourage people with mental health issues to talk
about public art that inspires them.

metamute
E mute@metamute.com
W www.metamute.com
A web platform for debates on culture, politics and
globalization.

Mini Gallery
E enquiries@minigallery.co.uk
W www.minigallery.co.uk
Contact Hazel Semple & Chris Storey
Established in 2002. A website that showcases art
by self-representing British artists. Each member
artist is set up with a mini-website, including
online gallery space to display and sell art
commission-free, and is provided with all the
tools necessary to manage their online profile.
Membership subscriptions are available from £25.
Also offered is a wide range of art-related content
and a forum-based online community of practising
artists.
Submission policy There is an online application
form only. Refer to the website for a step-by-step
guide.

National Disability Arts Forum (NDAF)
E silvie@ndaf.org
W www.ndaf.org
Contact Silvie Fisch
NDAF's ArtsAccessUK is an online database of
disabled access provided by art venues throughout
the UK. Also displays the work of disabled artists
on its website.

nettime
W www.nettime.org
A mailing list and 'an effort to formulate an
international, networked discourse that neither
promotes a dominant euphoria (to sell products)
nor continues the cynical pessimism, spread by
journalists and intellectuals in the "old" media
who generalize about "new" media with no clear
understanding of their communication aspects'.

New Exhibitions of Contemporary Art
E listings@newexhibitions.com
W www.newexhibitions.com
Founded in 1978. A bimonthly, free-of-charge
contemporary art listings service.

Own Art
W www.artscouncil.org.uk/ownart
An online guide to Arts Council England's
interest-free loan scheme for purchasing art.

Paintings and Prints 2 – Artists of the World
W www.paintingsandprints2.com
Contact John and Susan Wood
Founded in 1999. An artists' directory including
paintings and prints by various amateur and semi-
professional artists.

Rhizome.org
E webmaster@rhizome.org
W www.rhizome.org
A non-profit organization founded in 1996 to
provide an online platform for the global new-
media art community.

scotlandart.com
E enquiries@scotlandart.com
W www.scotlandart.com
The largest original art website in Scotland.

stot
E stot@stot.org
W www.stot.org
Contact Jonathan Rust
A not-for-profit contemporary art platform
that, in addition to producing artist projects,
facilitates a comprehensive online resource
of thousands of links to international galleries,
festivals, fairs, biennials, publications and
residencies. Also includes an extensive section
devoted to new media, and user forums providing
an outlet for news and opportunities in related
arts.

theSeer.info
E culturalservices@brent.gov.uk
W www.theSeer.info
Contact Abi Palmer
An arts directory and information website
piloted by the London Borough of Brent and
Royal Borough of Kensington and Chelsea in
partnership with Arts Council England in
London. The longer-term aspiration for the
site is to be a free resource for all thirty-three
of London's boroughs.
Submission policy Registrants living and/or
working in participating London boroughs can
register their presence on the website and find
advice, information and opportunities free of
charge.

Trans Artists
E info@transartists.nl
W www.transartists.nl
Offers independent information to artists, artist-run initiatives and cultural institutions about cultural exchanges, residency programmes and work opportunities in the Netherlands and abroad.

UK Sponsorship Database
E info@uksponsorship.com
W www.uksponsorship.com
Founded in 2000. Offers those seeking sponsorship a means of displaying their sponsorship offering and requirements to sponsors via a categorized, online database. A range of formats and prices for listings is available.

Universes in Universe – Worlds of Art
E info@universes-in-universe.de
W www.universes-in-universe.de
A non-commercial online information system focusing on the visual arts of Africa, Latin America and Asia within the context of international art processes.

Visual Collections
E carto@luna-img.com
W www.davidrumsey.com/collections
A searchable archive of over 300,000 images of fine art works, photographs, maps and other items from thirty-five major international museum, academic and private collections. Administered by Cartography Associates.

04
Suppliers and services

Construct your ambition: Making grand ideas become realities

Mike Smith

The range of materials, techniques and services available to artists is becoming more astonishing every day. As you might expect, any choice of materials derives naturally from the sorts of references and influences required of the work. For example, you may want the traditional associations of bronze-casting and marble sculpture, the highly finished industrial aesthetic, or even something in between made from plaster or wood. The crucial factor in these artistic choices is to know what you want and why you want it, in which case many of your problems will solve themselves.

An artist needs to be interested in the process of making their own work, but if they do not have access to the facilities, space or skills to make the work they have envisioned, there are others who can help. Art fabricators such as myself can work with artists in lots of different ways – we can advise or consult on a project, aid the design of an object, make a part of something or make the whole work from start to finish, including transportation and installation.

I started out as a studio assistant while at Camberwell College in the 1980s, working for painters such as Ian McKeever and Christopher Le Brun, stretching, preparing and priming canvases. It is vital to learn these skills because even if you get to a position where you can employ someone else to help out, then at least you can explain whether you like the painting surface to be loose or as tight as a drum.

My knowledge grew as I began to experiment in different materials such as wax, steel and formica, while assisting the sculptor Edward Allington as well as hanging shows and making pieces of furniture for galleries in my spare time and at weekends.

As soon as I finished college in 1989, I set up as a business and went into production full-time. Eventually in 1994 I stopped my own art practice because the prospect of making work with others was more exciting and offered more possibilities. Initially I worked with a relatively small number of artists and galleries. It was during this period that I constructed a number of works for Damien Hirst's first major London show, 'Internal Affairs', at the Institute of Contemporary Arts in 1991, developing a method of manufacturing his trademark vitrines of glass and steel. More recently the studio produced a large-scale, site-specific house by Michael Landy called *Semi-Detached* for Tate Britain in 2004 that weighed around thirteen tonnes and consisted of ten truckloads of panels and components, which was later demolished.

Although you can get emotionally attached to a work of art, what I really enjoy is the collaboration, the whole discursive process of bringing something new into the world; from the initial exchange of information via conversations and sketches through to the finished three-dimensional object. Of course, the big projects are more risky, challenging and ultimately more rewarding, but even if you are not working on a grand scale, there are some points to bear in mind before attempting to realize your project.

Sourcing materials

The Internet has made it much easier to find materials, specialist equipment or companies that can supply and cut material to order. Advances in technology have produced the means to create very particular objects. One particular technique is known as rapid prototyping; this involves constructing a computer model that is then rendered in plastic by a machine, so avoiding the costs and trouble of making a mould and then casting a maquette, although it also has limitations because of the cost and the size of objects that can be produced.

A problem you may face is finding companies that are sympathetic and prepared to engage in what you are doing. They needn't know the philosophical reasoning behind your work, but the more artists have thought about their work and developed the structure of a piece themselves, the better informed an engineering firm or a cabinetmaker will be in achieving the desired specification. Once you have invested a little time and effort into research and development (especially in the details of a project), try to go with an open mind – avoid being too vague or getting overly defensive – as this will allow the technical or material dialogue with a third party to be far more productive.

Fabrication

There has been a steady demise in artists' ability to handle materials, partly because there are so many health and safety conditions at colleges that students can no longer use machinery anymore owing to the institution's fear of being sued. Much of a work's fabrication – whether it is in plastic or resin, made from copper, stainless steel, brass or aluminium, painted, carved, handmade or machined – is down to your curiosity about how things are made and how you can manipulate a material to suit your aims and ideas.

A lot of people think that if they can imagine a work of art, then it can be made, but often the creation of an object is subject to all sorts of negotiation and compromise. Again, if you know what you want and have a sense of why you want it to look a certain way, then your aesthetic concerns are more likely to prevail.

Budget

There are many things to bear in mind when drawing up an initial budget for a work of art, including its making, delivering, installing and the all-important VAT. Artists often waive the idea that they are actually going to make any money from it themselves, but you should nonetheless value your own time – especially if you are not yet making a living from your art – and only consider doing something for an insignificant financial return if it is potentially an investment in your future. Depending on where you are in your career and your position in the art market, there is no reason to invest everything you have in making one piece. Someone once asked me to make a two-metre-deep water tank for a performance that had to be big enough for someone to swim in but also had to be built in a tiny venue in half a day. Apart from the fact that it would have buckled the hollow gallery floor, the £2,500 budget would only have bought a few square metres of glass. So, make sure that absolutely everything is accounted for in your budgets, and factor in all logistics such as manoeuvrability, specialist equipment, planning permission, and health and safety requirements.

Planning and safety

Many artists involved in commissioned, semi-permanent or public art for the first time make assumptions about what they can do in a public space, without proper regard for the complicated issues of planning permission or health and safety. Much of it is common sense – knowing that if you mix bleach and chlorine you get a deadly gas, for instance – so always read the labels and take your work seriously.

If you are not well prepared on these topics, you can waste a lot of time putting forward a proposal that will fall foul of the rules and regulations in the final reckoning. We have had a lot of experience with these issues and found ways to circumvent or incorporate them without prohibitive compromise. Before we went to install Rachel Whiteread's *Monument* on the empty plinth in Trafalgar Square, we discovered that it was not possible to drive vehicles onto the square and we were not permitted to drill holes in the plinth. Not only did we have to get the eleven-tonne resin piece there by closing major roads and avoiding low bridges, but we then had to crane it into position between two and five o'clock in the morning, when the centre of London was full of drunks, and figure out a way to secure it that wasn't mechanical or architecturally invasive.

Crating and conservation

Although custom-made crates may seem excessive and expensive, they can protect and greatly prolong the life of a sculpture or installation, or even keep a painting clean almost indefinitely. There is always a chance that a work might get damaged because you cannot be there every time it is handled or moved, but if it is in a box it will hopefully arrive at its destination in one piece. If your work is in multiple parts already, then these should definitely be crated and kept together.

Conservation and cost are intrinsically linked, so if an art work is not worth a huge amount of money then people will not be up in arms about conserving it. However, all artists, whatever their age or status, should think in the long term. We manufacture a variety of painting supports including aluminium panels for artists such as Gary Hume, Jason Martin and Ian Davenport. Apart from its rigidity, the aluminium substrate is profoundly stable; museum conservators know that if you put household paint on aluminium it will last a long time, but if you apply it to canvas it will rot and fall off, even if the surface is properly primed. Also, it is wise to keep some sort of record of a work's manufacture. Take note of what colours, materials and adhesives you used, and hold on to early sketches, computer drawings and invoices, in case something needs to be repaired, restored or even refabricated.

Mike Smith provides technical and intellectual engineering solutions for artists and has been designing and fabricating works of art for many prominent British artists for over fifteen years (www.mikesmithstudio.com).

Art materials retailers

East Anglia

The Art Shop
Buckenham House, 81 High Street, Southwold
IP18 6DS
T 01502 725390
E thewoodhouse@supanet.com
Contact Mrs Wood
A retail art and craft materials supplier since 1993, serving professionals and amateurs.

Berkhamsted Arts & Crafts
29–31 Lower Kings Road, Berkhamsted
HP4 2AB
T 01442 866632
E info@art4crafts.co.uk
W www.art4crafts.co.uk
Contact Paula Gibbs
Established in 1972, stocking an extensive range of art and craft materials. Small classes held on site.

Boons
48 The Howard Centre, Howardsgate, Welwyn Garden City
AL8 6HA
T 01707 325875
F 01707 325875
E sales@tuppers.co.uk
Contact Sandy Weller or Muriel Montgomery
A long-established retailer of art, craft and graphic materials. Bespoke picture-framing service. Limited-edition prints and framed art in gallery.

David Potter Ltd
The Old Forge, Rockland St Mary, Norwich
NR14 7AH
T 01508 538570
F 01508 538636
E info@davidpotter.co.uk
W www.davidpotter.co.uk
A manufacturer of a range of high-quality artists' easels, studio furniture and accessories.

Heffers Art & Graphics
15–21 King Street, Cambridge
CB1 1LH
T 01223 568495
F 01223 568411
E michelet@heffers.co.uk
Suppliers of art materials to Cambridge artists and students for the past thirty years. Orders by post, email, telephone and fax welcome.

Hertfordshire Graphics Ltd
6 St Andrew Street, Hertford
SG14 1JE
T 01992 503636
F 01992 503244
E sales@hertfordshiregraphics.co.uk
W www.hertfordshiregraphics.co.uk
Contact Rod Lewis
Founded in 1983, originally supplying solely to Hertfordshire graphic designers but now including an art shop and gallery. A sponsor of many local art events.

Hobbycraft – The Arts & Crafts Superstore
Westgate Park, Fodderwick, Basildon
SS14 1WP
T 0126 82240100
W www.hobbycraft.co.uk
Suppliers of arts and crafts materials with branches nationwide.

Hussey and Greades Ltd
94 Hutton Road, Shenfield
CM15 8ND
T 01277 226262
F 01277 261289
E shen@husseyandgreades.co.uk
W www.husseyandgreades.co.uk
Contact Dan Culliton
Founded in 1955. Suppliers of art materials from leading manufacturers.
Branches 52 Moulsham Street, Chelmsford
CM2 0JA T 01245 268601.

Jarrold's
1 London Street, Norwich
NR2 1JF
T 01603 660661
F 01603 611295
E info@jarroldthestore.co.uk
W www.jarroldthestore.co.uk
Contact Patrick Clarke (Art and Craft Head Buyer)
Founded in 1823. Respected retailer of leading-brand art and craft materials.

KRC Brushes
110 Tolmers Road, Cuffley
EN6 4JR
T 01707 888091
E krcbrushes@hotmail.com
W www.krcbrushes.co.uk
Contact Karen Rice
Established in 2004. Suppliers of discount, quality artists' brushes to artists and students.

Laurence Mathews Art & Craft Store
1 Queens Road, Southend-on-Sea
SS1 1LT
T 01702 435196
F 01702 435377
E laurence.mathews@madasafish.com
An art and graphics materials supplier in business since 1948. Also offers a bespoke picture-framing service.

Tim's Art Supplies
85 Tilehouse Street, Hitchin
SG5 2DY
T 01462 455376
F 01462 421898
E info@timsartsupplies.co.uk
W www.timsartsupplies.co.uk
Contact Tim Farr
Founded in 1976, specializing in fine art, craft, graphic and office supplies, and offering a picture-framing service. Holds regular classes covering a range of subjects, for both adults and children. Mail order available via the website.

Tina's
38 The Causeway, Burwell, Cambridge
CB5 0DU
T 01638 742785

Tindalls the Stationers Ltd
50–52 High Street, Newmarket
CB8 8LE
T 01638 668855
F 01638 663633
E sales@tindalls.co.uk
W www.tindalls.co.uk
Contact Jamie Gaskin
Branches 8 Bridge Street, St Ives
PE27 5EG **T** 01480 493765 **F** 01480 493766;
4 Market Place, Ely CB7 4NP **T** 01353 669498
F 01353 669382.

Windsor Gallery
167 London Road South, Lowestoft
NR33 0BL
T 01502 512278
E products@windsorgallery.fsnet.co.uk
W www.windsorgallery.fsnet.co.uk
Contact Ray Glanfield
Established in 1981. Stocks art and craft materials from a wide range of manufacturers. Also offers a bespoke framing service.

Wrights
15–16 Stanley Road, Great Yarmouth
NR30 1QJ
T 01493 844618
E wrights.norfolk@btopenworld.com
W www.wrightsofnorfolk.co.uk
A family business, started in 1957. Stocks a comprehensive range of all artist materials. Offers a full framing service, from supplying mouldings to framing finished articles.

East Midlands

Art & Craft Centre
86–88 Chilwell Road, Beeston, Nottingham
NG9 1ES
T 0115 9223743

Art Essentials
26 Main Street, Kimberley, Nottingham
NG16 2LL
T 0115 9385551

The Art Shop
45a High Street, Oakham, Rutland
LE15 6AJ
T 01572 723943
F 01572 770068
E hopsdavis@aol.com
W www.artshop.co.uk
Contact Christine Davis
Founded in 1985. An independent retailer specializing in art and craft materials. Knowledgeable staff always available to give directions. Mail order and student discounts offered.

The Artist's Shop
185 Mansfield Road, Nottingham
NG1 3FS
T 0115 9474421

Boston Artstore
13a Pen Street, Boston
PE21 0BE
T 01205 353349
F 01205 353349
Contact Stephen Eede
Founded in 1985, providing a comprehensive range of art supplies for amateur and professional artists. Also offers classes for all ages in most media and can put on one-person or group exhibitions in gallery space.

Colemans of Stamford

39 High Street, Stamford
P69 2BE
T 01780 480635
F 01780 766424
E Stamford@colemangroup.co.uk
W www.colemans-online.co.uk
Contact Joan Dale
Established in 1969, stocking a wide range of
materials and now operating twelve branches
across Northants, Cambridgeshire, Bedfordshire
and Herefordshire.

Dominoes of Leicester Ltd

66 High Street, Leicester
LE1 5YP
T 0116 2533363
F 0116 2628066
E ann.land@dominoestoys.co.uk
W www.dominoestoys.co.uk
Contact Tony Wilmot or Darroll Cramp
A large, independent retailer of arts and crafts, toys
and models. Two artists staff the art room.

Gadsby's

22 Market Place, Leicester
LE1 5GH
T 0116 2517792
F 0116 2517792
E info@gadsbys.co.uk
W www.gadsbys.co.uk, www.artshopper.co.uk
An art materials retailer.
Branches 260 High Street, Lincoln LN2 1LH
T 01522 527485; 7 Braunstone Gate, Leicester
LE3 5LH **T** 0116 2550558; 347 High Street, Lincoln
LN5 7DQ **T** 01522 527487; 9 Bradford Street,
Walsall WS1 1PB **T** 01922 623104; 33 New
Briggate, Leeds LS3 8JD **T** 0113 2455326;
15 Darlington Street, Wolverhampton WV1 4HW
T 01902 424029; Beatties (in store), 16–28
Corporation Street, Birmingham B2 4RR
T 0121 6444000.

Hills of Newark Ltd

34–38 Barnbygate, Newark
NG24 1PZ
T 01636 702240
F 01636 612627
E sales@hillsofnewark.co.uk
W www.hillsofnewark.co.uk
Contact Nick Hill
Established in 1977. A family-run artists' materials
shop with picture-framing service on the premises.

J. Ruddock Ltd

287 High Street, Lincoln
LN2 1AW
T 01522 528285
F 01522 532162
E shop@ruddocksoflincoln.co.uk
W www.ruddocksoflincoln.co.uk
Contact Milana Bontoft (Manageress) or
Henry Ruddock (MD)
Has supplied art materials from this shop for
over a hundred years and runs courses in its own
studios, including watercolour and life drawing.
Price range £25 per day for main studios (e.g. for
teaching or workshops).

John E. Wright

Blueprint House, 115 Huntingdon Street,
Nottingham
NG1 3NF
T 0870 2408136

Shawe's the Art Shop

68–70 Mansfield Road, Nottingham
NG1 3GY
T 0115 9418646

London

A.S. Handover Ltd

Unit 8, Leeds Place, Tollington Park, London
N4 3RF
T 020 72729624
F 020 72638670
E m_venus@handover.co.uk
W www.handover.co.uk
Contact Michael Venus
Founded in 1949, manufacturing artists' brushes
in London. Will make small orders to customers'
specifications. Also supplies tools, paints and
sundries for artists and craftsmen.

A.P. Fitzpatrick

142 Cambridge Heath Road, Bethnal Green,
London
E1 5QJ
T 020 77900884
A leading stockist of artists' pigments.

The Art Shop

117c High Street, Wanstead, London
E11 2RL
T 020 89890154
F 020 85188110

Contact Dill

Established in 1955 to serve local artists with all products needed. Runs a service whereby specialist materials can be ordered on a weekly basis. Also sells craft materials for adults and children.

Atlantis Art

7–9 Plumber's Row, London
E1 1EQ
T 020 73778855
F 020 73778850
W www.atlantisart.co.uk
One of London's leading suppliers of arts and crafts materials. Mail order available.

Bird & Davis Ltd – The Artist's Manufactory

45 Holmes Road, Kentish Town
NW5 3AN
T 020 74853797
F 020 72840509
E birdltd@aol.com
W www.birdanddavis.co.uk
Contact Rob or Johnny
Established in 1928. One of the UK's leading stretcher-frame manufacturers, specializing in made-to-measure stretchers. Can provide bespoke canvases to any size and has extensive stock of fine-artist materials.
Branches The Royal Academy, Students Schools Entrance, nr Burlington Arcade, Piccadilly W1 (open during term time, from 10 a.m. to 12 p.m.).

Booer & Sons Ltd

216–218 Eltham High Street, Eltham, London
SE9 1BA
T 020 88502503
F 020 88506323
Contact Brenda Jackson
Established for nearly ninety years. Stocks artists' materials and has a large commercial stationery department.

Canonbury Arts

266 Upper Street, Islington, London
N1 2UQ
T 020 72264652
F 020 77041781
E sc@canonburyarts.co.uk
W www.canonburyarts.co.uk
Contact Shaun, Lucy or Emelie
Established in 1949. A specialist art and sculpting materials supplier, moulder and caster. Also offers a picture-framing service.

Cass Art

13 Charing Cross Road, London
WC2H OEP
T 020 79309940
E info@cassart.co.uk
W www.cassart.co.uk
Stocks a wide range of materials for the artist, including brushes, canvases, paints, pastels, portfolios, easels, drawing pads and books.
Branches Three central London stores on Charing Cross Road, Kensington High Street and Berwick Street.

Chromacolour International

Unit 5 Pilton Estate, Pitlake, Croydon
CR0 3RA
T 020 86881991
F 020 86881441
E sales@chromacolour.co.uk
W www.chromacolour.co.uk
Contact Miss Joanne Hogan
Established over twenty-five years ago as animation suppliers, and still a market-leader in this field. Manufactures and supplies unique artist colours in eighty tones, which can be used as watercolour, acrylic, gouache, ink, wash or as an impasto, all from the same tube or pot. Also offers a full range of artist products including brushes, artists' paper and canvases.

Colart Fine Art & Graphics Ltd

Whitefriars Avenue, Harrow
HA3 5RH
T 020 84243339
F 020 84243328
E n.montgomery@colart.co.uk
W www.windsornewton.com
Contact Neil Montgomery
Among the world's largest suppliers and manufacturers of fine-art materials. Main brands include Windsor & Newton, Liquitex and Conte A Paris. Also distributes Artcare, Copic Canson and Slater Harrison in the UK.

L. Cornelissen & Son

105 Great Russell Street, London
WC1B 3RY
T 020 76361045
F 020 76363655
E info@cornelissen.com
W www.cornelissen.com
Established in 1855. Suppliers of materials and equipment for painting, drawing, gilding and printmaking. Bespoke canvas-stretching service.

Fast and efficient worldwide mail-order service. Two minutes' walk from the British Museum.

Cowling & Wilcox Ltd

26–28 Broadwick Street, London
W1V 1FG
T 020 77349557
F 020 74344513
E art@cowlingandwilcox.com
W www.cowlingandwilcox.com
Stocks a wide selection of portfolios, carrying cases and presentation books. Also fine-art, craft and graphic materials. Mail-order service offered.

D & J Simons & Sons Ltd and SimonArt

SimonArt House, 122–150 Hackney Road, London
E2 7QS
T 020 77393744
F 020 77394452
E dsimons@djsimons.co.uk
W www.djsimons.co.uk
Contact Sales
Company founded in 1900. Major stockists of Ferrario paints from Italy. Wide range of paints, artist's brushes, canvas products, pallets, painting mediums and accessories. Catalogue available on request.

Daler-Rowney Percy Street

12 Percy Street, London
W1T 1DW
T 020 76368241
F 020 75807534
E dr@artmat.co.uk
W www.dalerrowney.co.uk
Situated on the site of the original 1952 George Rowney 'showroom', this is still the only shop to stock the entire range of Daler-Rowney art materials. Also offers a complete framing service including gilded and hand-finished frames and twenty-four-hour mount-cutting.

Falkiner Fine Papers

76 Southampton Row, London
WC1B 4AR
T 020 78311151
F 020 74301248
E falkiner@ic24.net
Contact Nicolaas Aukes
Founded in 1973, specializing in selling a large range of papers for all art, craft and conservation purposes. Artists are able to experiment with unusual papers and can buy in volumes as low as

a single sheet. Experienced staff are happy to guide the novice through the finer points of paper.

Fielders

54 Wimbledon Hill Road, London
SW19 7PA
T 020 89465044
F 020 89441320
E shop@fielders.co.uk
W www.fielders.co.uk
Founded in 1928, specializing in art and craft materials, framing, copying/design services and art-related books.
Branches 8 High Street, Kinston-upon-Thames
KT1 1EY **T** 020 85471304 **F** 020 85472066.

Gallery Gifts Ltd

157–159 High Street, Sutton, Surrey
SM1 1JH
T 020 86432945
F 020 86420990
E gallerygifts@hotmail.com
Contact Judith Palmer
Trading in art materials since 2001 and stocking major brands.

Green and Stone of Chelsea

259 Kings Road, London
SW3 5EL
T 020 73520837
F 020 73511098
E sales@greenandstone.com
W www.greenandstone.com
Established in 1927. One of the most highly respected artists' material shops in Europe. Stock includes painting and display easels in oak, beech and mahogany, oil paints by leading manufacturers, linen and cotton canvas, balanced palettes, handmade and antique papers, and handmade picture frames designed and made to order. Mail-order service offered.

Harris Fine Art Ltd

710–712 High Road, North Finchley, London
N12 9QD
T 020 84452804
E sales@harrisfineart.co.uk
W www.harrisfineart.co.uk
Contact Mr C. Harris
Established in 1971, stocking a wide range of art and craft materials from leading manufacturers. Also offers a picture-framing service and a large modern gallery space. Website gives secure online ordering and guaranteed delivery.

Holloway Art & Stationers
222 Holloway Road, Islington, London
N7 8DA
T 020 76074738
F 020 77004943
E hollowayartandstationers@ouvip.com
A family business since 1874, stocking leading
brands of art, graphic and drafting materials
including airbrushes and compressors.
Branches Perrys, 777 Fulham Road SW6 5HA
T 020 77367225 **F** 020 77366893. Perrys,
109 East Street, Southampton SO14 3HD
T 023 80339444 **F** 023 80231644.

Jackson's Art Supplies
1 Farleigh Place, Farleigh Road, London
N16 7SX
T 0870 2411849
F 0870 7700360
E sales@jacksonsart.com
W www.jacksonart.com
A mail-order supplier of quality art materials,
catering especially for the professional artist.
Products available by phone, fax, post or via secure
online ordering system.

John Jones Framing and Art Shop
4 Morris Place, Stroud Green Road, London
N4 3JG
T 020 72815439
F 020 72815956
E info@johnjones.co.uk
W www.johnjones.co.uk
A family business offering bespoke picture-
framing and artist materials. The shop is based in
a large industrial warehouse and stocks a wide
range of products for professional and student
artists, plus a mail-order service on a national
basis. Specializes in artists' surfaces; bespoke
stretchers can be ordered to any format and size
and are produced in wood or aluminium. Also
produces panel surfaces in aluminium or paper.
Extensive contemporary framing service.

John Purcell Paper
15 Rumsey Road, London
SW9 0TR
T 020 77375199
F 020 77376765
E jpp@johnpurcell.net
W www.johnpurcell.net
A wholesale paper merchant based in south
London, supplying an extensive range of
papers and boards from stock suitable for many

applications including printmaking, drawing and
watercolour, inkjet printing, picture-framing,
bookbinding and commercial printing.
Comprehensive price list available on request.

London Art Ltd
132 Finchley Road, London
NW3 5HS
T 020 74331571/ 74356830
F 020 74331747
E email@londonart-shop.co.uk
W www.londonart-shop.co.uk
Specialists in art and craft materials with over
fifteen years of experience. Runs an online shop.

London Graphic Centre
16–18 Shelton Street, Covent Garden, London
WC2H 9JL
T 020 77594500
F 020 77594585
E info@londongraphics.co.uk
W www.londongraphics.co.uk
Contact Andrew Parsonage
Established for over thirty years. One of Europe's
largest independent dealers in art and graphic
supplies. Over twenty thousand products available
to order over the phone or by visiting flagship retail
store in Covent Garden. As well as traditional
artists' materials, also offers wide range of
specialist papers and portfolios.

Lyndons Art & Graphics
197 Portobello Road, London
W11 2ED
T 020 77274357
F 020 77929429
Contact Peter Kalyan
Established in 1904. Supplies art and graphics
materials.
Branches 164 Portobello Road, London W11 2EB.

Michael Harding's Artists Oil Colours
88 Mile End Road, Whitechapel, London
E1 4UN
T 020 77028338
F 020 77910060
E oilpaint@michaelharding.freeserve.co.uk
W www.michaelharding.co.uk
Contact Michael Harding
Wholesale only (not open to the public). Founded
in 1980, manufacturing the finest-quality oil paint
available using recipes that date prior to the
Industrial Revolution. Involved in restoration
for, among others, the National Trust, English

Heritage and the Tate. Seventy-four colours available, soon extending to over one hundred. Available throughout the UK and through some major suppliers worldwide.

Owen Clark & Co. Ltd
129–133 Cranbrook Road, Ilford
IG1 4QB
T 020 84788478
F 020 84783983
E sales@owen-clark.fsnet.co.uk
W www.owenclark.com
Contact Tony Clark
A retail art and stationery store established in 1928. Specializes in educational supplies, serving hundreds of local secondary schools and colleges with art materials, technical drawing equipment and educational stationery. Also caters for needs of amateur and professional artists and offers a mail-order service with generous discounts.

Paintworks Ltd
99–101 Kingsland Road, London
E2 8AG
T 020 77297451
F 020 77390439
E shop@paintworks.biz
W www.paintworks.biz
Contact Dorothy Wood
An artist-run shop and mail-order service founded in 1985. A major national stockist of fine-art paints, canvas and papers, supplying the education sector. Offers a product and technical information resource and a conservation-framing service for contemporary art works in all media. Specialist advice available.

Paperchase Products Ltd
213–215 Tottenham Court Road, London
W1T 7PS
T 020 74676200
E write@paperchase.co.uk
W www.paperchase.co.uk
A flagship store for innovative papers and stationery for over thirty years. Specializes in imported and effect papers, with a full selection of media and artists' requisites.

Perrys Art & Office
777 Fulham Road, Fulham, London
SW6 5HA
T 020 77367225
F 020 77366893
E info@perrysartoffice.com

Contact Nish Chande
Established in 1986. Stockists of a comprehensive range of art and craft materials including all leading brands.
Branches 222 Holloway Road, London N7 8DA
T 020 76074738.

R.K. Burt & Co. Ltd
57 Union Street, London
SE1 1SG
T 020 74076474
F 020 74033672
E sales@rkburt.co.uk
W www.rkburt.co.uk
Established in 1892. One of the largest wholesale paper merchants in the UK, specializing in high-quality paper for every type of artist use. The first wholesale distributor in the UK for many leading mills, with a reputation for commissioning paper produced to its own specifications as required.

Rembrandt Art & Crafts
P.O. Box 252, Twickenham
TW1 1XU
T 020 88980973
W www.craftwithus@aol.com
Contact Russell
Offers a bespoke canvas-making service. Stretching and framing services also available.

Russell & Chapple
68 Drury Lane, London
WC2B 5SP
T 020 78367521
F 020 74970554
E info@randc.net
W www.randc.net
Contact Andrew Milne
Founded in 1770. One of the UK's leading specialist suppliers of artists' canvas, selling a wide range of cottons, linens and canvases, both primed and unprimed. Products include canvases for digital printing, artists' stretcher bars and professional-quality artists' paints. Also offers a bespoke stretching service and can restretch original art work and inkjet prints to order.

Selwyn-Smith Studio
148 High Street, Teddington
TW11 8HZ
T 020 89730771
F 020 89730772
Contact Jo Selwyn-Smith
Founded in 2001. A traditional supplier of art

materials specializing in the provision of drawing and painting equipment. The shop is always well stocked with both student- and artist-quality paint, a selection of stretched canvases, watercolour papers, easels and brushes.

Unik Art & Craft
4 Astoria Parade, Streatham High Road, London
SW16 1PR
T 020 87690422
F 020 86773737
E nwacke@btinternet.com
Founded in 2000, specializing in the supply of professional-artist materials and a wide range of craft materials.

Vandy's Art and Graphic Centre
621 Forest Road, Walthamstow, London
E17 4NE
T 020 85273492
Contact Zahir Mawani (Proprietor)
Stockists of fine-art and graphic materials. All major brands stocked.

Wheatsheaf Art Shop
56 Baker Street, London
W1U 7BU
T 020 79355510
F 020 79353794
E sales@wheatsheaf-art.co.uk
Contact Tony Berrington
Founded in 1946. Stockists of art materials from leading manufacturers. Mail-order service available and experienced team on hand to answer questions.

North-east

The Art Shop
11–12 Bondgate,
Darlington
DL3 7JE
T 01325 465484

The Art Shop
15 Station Road, Whitley Bay
NE26 2QY
T 0191 2511726

The Art Shop and Kemble Gallery
62 Saddler Street,
Durham
DH1 3NU
T 0191 3864034

City Art
76 North Road, Durham
DH1 4SQ
T 0191 3831919

City Art Store
23 Vine Place, Sunderland
SR1 3NA
T 0191 5659254

Details
67 Westgate Road, Newcastle-upon-Tyne
NE1 1SG
T 0191 2615999

Jarred's Arts & Craft
59 Borough Road, Middlesbrough
TS1 3AA
T 01642 222531

R.R. Bailey
12 Grange Road, Newcastle-upon-Tyne
NE4 9LD
T 0191 2746126

Stratford & York Ltd
Whickham Industrial Estate, Swalwell,
Newcastle-upon-Tyne
NE16 3BY
T 0191 4960111
F 0191 4960211
E andrew.eccles@delbanco.com
Contact Andrew Eccles (Sales Manager)
Manufacturers of fine-art brushes in the UK since 1939. Seeks to serve both professional artists and accomplished amateurs. Each brush is made by hand.

Superstamp
Station Road, Moorside, Backworth,
Newcastle-upon-Tyne
NE27 0RU
T 0191 2687309

Team Valley Brush Co.
Whickham Industrial Estate, Swalwell,
Newcastle-upon-Tyne
NE16 3BY
T 0191 4960111

Ward's Arts & Crafts
Halifax Road, Dunston Industrial Estate,
Gateshead
NE11 9HW
T 0191 4605915

F 0191 4608540
E info@doart.co.uk
W www.doart.co.uk
Established for over 150 years. One of the north's leading retailers of arts and crafts supplies and materials. Also offers a professional photographic and repro lab providing high quality giclée printing to artists.

Northern Ireland

Artquip
31a Upper Dunmurry Lane, Dunmurry, Belfast
BT17 0AA
T 028 90605552

Bradbury Graphics
3 Lyndon Court, Queen Street, Belfast
BT1 6BT
T 028 90233535
F 028 90572065
E art@bradbury-graphics.co.uk
W www.bradburygraphics.co.uk
Contact Richard or Una
A city-centre store stocking a wide range of branded art materials, stationery items and presentation goods. Caters for all, from children to established career artists and those associated with creative industries such as technical drawing, design and communication.

EDCO
47–49 Queen Street, Belfast
BT1 6HP
T 028 90324687

G.E. Kee
17 Bridge Street, Coleraine
BT52 1DR
T 028 70343525
E shop@kee-arts.demon.co.uk
W www.kee-arts.demon.co.uk
Opened in 1948. An arts and crafts retailer, gallery and framing service.

Proctor & Co. Ltd
201–213 Castlereagh Road, Belfast
BT5 5FH
T 028 90456582
F 028 90732500
E proctors@btclick.com
W www.proctors.uk.com

Contact Carol McNaughton
Established for forty years, offering an extensive range of art, craft and stationery supplies. Printing service also available.

Scarva Pottery Supplies
Unit 20, Scarva Road Industrial Estate, Scarva Road, Banbridge
BT32 3QD
T 028 40669699
F 028 40669700
E david@scarvapottery.com
W www.scarvapottery.com
Contact David Maybin
In business for over twenty years. Stocks quality products for the professional potter, from raw materials to tools and equipment. Competitive pricing structure and delivery charges.

Vision Applied Arts & Crafts
42 Waring Street, Belfast
BT1 2ED
T 028 90246665

North-west

The Art House
The Triangle, Hanging Ditch, Manchester
M4 3TR
T 0161 8345545

Artcoe Ltd
Unit C5, Wardley Point, Fallons Road, Wardley Industrial Estate, Manchester
M28 2NY
T 0161 7278388

Artisan
115 Penny Lane, Allerton, Liverpool
L18 1DF
T 0151 7350707

Artstat
P.O. Box 4, 621 Liverpool Road, Irlam, Manchester
M44 5BB
T 0161 7779543
Contact Patrick Swindell
Established in 1978. Wholesale distributors of artists' materials, craft and stationery products. Over eleven thousand items held in stock at the Manchester warehouse and showroom. Cash-and-carry facility or delivery by carrier.

Blots Pen & Ink Supplies

14 Lyndhurst Avenue, Prestwich, Manchester
M25 0GF
T 0161 7206916
F 0161 7206916
E sales@blotspens.co.uk
W www.blotspens.co.uk
Contact John Winstanley
Trading since 1993, specializing in the mail
order of calligraphy pens, inks and sundries.
Manufacturers of Iron Gall Ink, a medieval ink
suitable for fine sketching and line and wash.
Orders accepted online or via a paper catalogue.

Bluecoat Books & Art Ltd

Gostins Building, 32 Hanover Street, Liverpool
L1 4LN
T 0151 7095449

Blyth's Artshop Ltd

Amazon House, 3 Brazil Street, Manchester
M1 3PJ
T 0161 2361302

Bottomleys Ltd

The Wheatsheaf Centre, Yorkshire Street,
Rochdale
OL16 1JZ
T 01706 653211
F 01706 653229
E janice@bottomleys.com
W www.bottomleys.com
Contact Janice Bottomley
An art and craft retailer situated in the centre of
Rochdale, stocking all manner of artists' supplies.
Operates a mail-order service and an online shop.
Does not charge for delivery within UK. Regularly
holds product demonstrations in the shop.

Chapter 1

35 Derby Street, Leek
ST13 6HU
T 01538 399885
F 01538 399885
E chapter.1@btconnect.com
Contact Ann Vaughan
Founded in 1990. A retailer of art materials,
stationery and books.

Colours and Crafts

61 London Road, Alderley Edge
SK9 7DY
T 01625 586100
F 01625 586100

E seahorse6259@aol.com
Contact Stella Batchelor
Founded in 2003. An art and craft retail outlet on
two sites (Alderley Edge and Victoria Mill, Foundry
Bank, Congleton, Cheshire). Workshops in all art
and craft media available, lasting from half an hour
to a full day.

Creative Shop Ltd

79 Strand Street, Douglas, Isle of Man
IM1 2EN
T 01624 628618
Founded in 1991, stocking artists' materials and
craft supplies. Also sells fine-art prints and offers a
framing service.

Daisy Designs (Crafts) Ltd

Hutpine House, 21 Sandown Lane, Liverpool
L15 8HY
T 0151 7341385

Edwin Allen Arts & Crafts

14–16 Buttermarket Street, Warrington
WA1 2LR
T 01925 630264
F 01925 444620
E mike@edwinallen.co.uk
W www.edwinallen.co.uk
Contact Michael Allen
Founded in 1894 and still a family-run business.
Specializes in the supply of fine-art materials, craft
products, picture-framing and mount-cutting
services.

Fred Aldous Ltd

37 Lever Street, Manchester
M1 1LW
T 0870 7517302

Galleria Fine Arts

6 Green Street, Sanbach
CW11 1GX
T 01270 753233
F 01270 753233
Contact Peter Brown
Established in 1995, supplying a full range of
artists' materials. Bespoke framing a speciality.

Granthams Art Discount

Graphics House, Charnley Road, Blackpool
FY1 4PE
T 01253 624402
F 01253 295743
E info@artdiscount.co.uk

W www.artdiscount.co.uk
Contact John Thompson
Founded in 1890, originally as a signwriting business. Moved into art materials supplies in the late 1960s and today operates out of two major sites. Orders can be made via website.

Grin

Afflecks Palace, Church Street, Manchester
M4 1PW
T 0161 8396392

Heaton Cooper Studio Ltd

Grasmere, Ambleside
LA22 9SX
T 015394 35280
F 015394 35797
E info@heatoncooper.co.uk
W www.heatoncooper.co.uk
Contact John Heaton Cooper
Suppliers of high-quality art materials with worldwide mailing service available online or by phone. Stocks artists' accessories of all kinds, including a large range of brand-name and handmade papers. The retail shop is attached to the Heaton Cooper studio, selling originals and prints of works by the Heaton Cooper family.

Icthus Arts & Graphics

Graphic House, 106–110 School Lane, Didsbury, Manchester
M20 6HR
T 0161 4342560

Ken Bromley Art Supplies

Curzon House, Curzon Road, Bolton
BL1 4RW
T 0845 3303234
F 01204 381123
E sales@artsupplies.co.uk
W www.artsupplies.co.uk
Contact Laureen Bromley
Suppliers of art materials at discount prices. The company originated from the success of the Ken Bromley Perfect Paper Stretcher (invented during World War II). Since 1994, the shop has increased its stock of paints, paper, brushes and accessories.

The Potters' Barn

Roughwood Lane, Hassall Green, Sandbach
CW11 4XX
T 01270 884080
E info@thepottersbarn.co.uk
W www.thepottersbarn.co.uk

Contact Andrew Pollard, Steve Marr
Founded in 1979. Suppliers of discus potter's wheels. Producers of handthrown reduction-fired stoneware, raku and pit-fired ware. Regular classes for adults and children in pottery. Courses in other crafts run throughout the year. Group visits, parties, corporate events/team days and personal tuition also available.

Printing House

102 Main Street, Cockermouth
CA13 GLX
T 01900 824984
F 01900 823124
E info@printinghouse.co.uk
Contact Jenny Holliday
Founded in 1968, supplying materials for artists (ordering service available) and secondhand books. Occasional artists' workshops and advice on printing given. Working museum of printing.

R. Jackson & Sons

20 Slater Street, Liverpool
L1 4BS
T 0151 7092647

Rennies Arts & Crafts Ltd

61–63 Bold Street, Liverpool
L1 4EZ
T 0151 7080599
F 0151 7072362
Contact Duncan Rennie
Founded in 1975, offering a wide range of art and craft materials. Also specializes in limited-edition prints and a complete framing service.
Branches 34 Bridge Street, St Helens WA10 1NW; 3 Hill Street, Southport PR9 0PE; 30 Burscough Street, Ormskirk L39 2ES.

Shinglers

Compston Road, Ambleside
LA22 9DR
T 015394 33433
F 015394 34634
Contact Paul Shingler
Suppliers of a broad range of art materials.

Studio Arts – Dodgson Fine Arts Ltd

50 North Road, Lancaster
LA1 1LT
T 01524 271810
F 01524 68013
E tonyd@studioarts.co.uk
W www.studioarts.co.uk

Contact Graeme Atkinson
Founded in 1972. Sells arts, crafts and graphics materials from major suppliers, and houses a gallery featuring a wide selection of self-published limited-edition prints and originals. Mail-order and trade enquiries welcome.

Turners Graphic Art & Drawing Office Supplies
91 Wellington Road South, Stockport
SK1 3SL
T 0161 4804713
F 0161 4764744
E jill@turnersart.co.uk
W www.turnersart.co.uk
Contact Jill Limmack
Founded over one hundred years ago and counts famous artists past and present among its customers. Specializes in all art materials for beginners to the experienced artist, students to drawing offices.

Ziggy Art Ltd
40 Dover Road, Birkdale, Southport
PR8 4TD
T 01704 551322
F 01704 565155
E sales@ziggyart.co.uk
W www.ziggyart.co.uk
Specializes in the online supply of all art and graphic materials, operating a next-day delivery service from a large stockholding.

Scotland

Alexander's Art Shop
58 South Clerk Street, Edinburgh
EH8 9PS
T 0131 6675257

Art Mediums Ltd
Block E, Unit 7 Glenwood Business Park,
50 Glenwood Place, Glasgow
G45 9UH
T 0141 6309339

Artopia Ltd
37 High Street, Johnstone
PA5 8AJ
T 01505 321133
F 01505 321133
E info@artopia.uk.com
W www.artopia.uk.com
Contact Drew Stuart

Opened in 2004, retailing artists' materials from major manufacturers. Internet commerce also available.

Artstore Ltd
94 Queen Street, Glasgow
G1 3AQ
T 0141 2211101

Artwrap Ltd
4–5 West Park Place, Edinburgh
EH11 2DP
T 0131 3467878

Broadford Books and Gallery
Broadford, Isle of Skye
IV49 9AB
T 01471 822748
E broadfordbooks@lineone.net
W www.broadfordbooks.co.uk
Contact Ian and Rosemary Chard
In business since 1987, supplying a wide range of artists' materials and books. Also has a picture gallery and offers a full framing service using conservation-quality materials.

Burns & Harris (Retail) Ltd
97–99 Commercial Street, Dundee
DD1 2AF
T 01382 322591
F 01382 226979
E shop@burns-harris.co.uk
W www.burns-harris.co.uk
Contact Pauline Barker
Established in 1886, stocking art and craft supplies from leading manufacturers. Staff are happy to offer advice to beginners.
Branches 11 The Postings, Kirkcaldy KY1 1HN
T 01592 644004 **F** 01592 644004.

Get Creative
1 Portobello High Street, Edinburgh
EH15 1DW
T 0131 6695214

Greyfriars Art Shop
20 Dundas Street, Edinburgh
EH3 6HZ
T 0131 5566565

Healthcraft
12 Commercial Road, Lerwick, Shetland
ZE1 0LX
T 01595 692924

W mysite.freeserve.com/healthcraft
Contact Lena Miller
Founded in 1990, selling a wide range of artists'
materials. Has a small gallery selling original
paintings by local artists, as well as prints.

Henderson Art Shop
28a Raeburn Place, Edinburgh
EH4 1HN
T 0131 3327800

InkSpot
Castle Street, Hamilton
ML3 6BU
T 01698 286401
F 01698 201300
E shop@inkspot.uk.com
W www.inkspot.uk.com
Contact Craig Moore
Specializes in art materials, stocking a full range of
watercolours, oils, acrylics, gouache, pastels, etc.
for the artist and hobbyist alike. Also provides
classes, workshops and demonstrations for the
not-so-experienced.

Just-Art
81 Morningside Road, Edinburgh
EH10 4AY
T 0131 4471671
E enquiries@just-art-online.co.uk
W www.just-art-online.co.uk
Contact Ritchie Collins
Founded in 1988 by Justine Marjoribanks,
a working artist. Stock a wide range of artists'
materials and also has a gallery. Specializes
in providing advice from professional artists.

Kirkintilloch Fine Arts
110 Townhead, Kirkintilloch, Glasgow
G66 1NZ
T 0141 7750822

Lemon Tree
15, Howard Court, Nerston Industrial Estate, East
Kilbride, Glasgow
G74 4QZ
T 01355 570577

Millers City Art Shop
28 Stockwell Street, Glasgow
G1 4RT
T 0141 5531660

Moray Office Supplies
Edgar Road, Elgin
IV30 6YQ
T 01343 549869
F 01343 549300
E sales@moray-office.co.uk
W www.morayoffice.co.uk
Contact Aileen Neil

Mulberry Bush
77 Morningside Road, Edinburgh
EH10 4AY
T 0131 4475145

Penny's the Art Shop
91 High Street, Selkirk
TD7 4BZ
T 01750 720521
Founded in 1999 to supply artists' materials for
the many border artists and visitors. Selection of
large canvases.

South-east

Alec Tiranti Ltd
70 High Street, Theale, Reading
RG7 5AR
T 01189 302775
F 01189 323487
E enquiries@tiranti.co.uk
W www.tiranti.co.uk
Founded in 1895 by Giovanni Tiranti, a respected
woodcarver from Italy. A manufacturer and
supplier of tools, materials and studio equipment
for carving, modelling, mouldmaking, casting
and restoration. A supplier to sculptors, studios,
film studios, museums, education authorities,
restoration companies, universities, craft
companies and amateur artists.
Branches 27 Warren Street, London W1T 5NB.

Annetts (Horsham) Ltd
7B The Carfax, Horsham
RH12 1DW
T 01403 265878
F 01403 265878
Founded in 1964. An independent family-run art
store retailing artists' and craft supplies from most
major stockists.

Art Centre and Gallery
7 Howard Street, Bedford
MK40 3HS

T 01234 344784
F 01234 360237
E info@artcentre.biz
Founded in 1923. A large store specializing in art and craft materials and offering a complete picture-framing service from own stocks. The gallery holds regular exhibitions displaying works by established artists. Gallery available for private exhibitions. Phone for more information.

Art for All
230 High Street, Bromley
BR1 1PQ
T 020 83139368
Founded in 1990. Supplies a range of art materials to suit all levels in all media. Also runs art classes and courses. Other services include framing.

Art-Write (Hythe) Ltd
90a High Street, Hythe
CT21 5AJ
T 01303 261925
F 01303 237933
E artwritehythe@hotmail.com
W www.artwritehythe.co.uk
Contact Clive Brown, Helen Brown or Louise Moore
A recently established family-run art supplier. Stocks a comprehensive ranges of artists' materials and textbooks. A diary detailing daily classes, courses and demonstrations in the attached studio is available on request.

Artworker
Unit 1–3, 1–6 Grand Parade, Brighton
BN2 9QB
T 01273 689822

Bovilles Art Shop
59 Woodside Road, Amersham
HP6 6AA
T 01494 725144
F 01494 433601
E sales@bovilles.co.uk
W www.bovilles.co.uk
Founded in 1904 as a picture framer and artists' colourman. Agents for all the well-known makes.
Branches 16–18 Station Road, Gerrards Cross
SL9 8EL **T** 01753 884966 **F** 01753 890602.

Brackendale Arts
1 Sparvell Way, Camberley
GU15 3SF
T 01276 681344

F 01276 681344
W www.brackendalearts.co.uk
A family-owned company established for over twenty years. Keeps a well-stocked and comprehensive range of art and craft supplies.

Broad Canvas
20 Broad Street, Oxford
OX1 3AS
T 01865 244025

Chromos (Tunbridge Wells) Ltd
58 High Street, Tunbridge Wells
TN1 1XF
T 01892 518854
F 01892 528967
Contact Suna Lambert
Established in 1996, stocking a comprehensive range of fine art and craft materials from many leading manufacturers. Also offers a canvas-stretching service (all sizes).

Creative Crafts
11 The Square, Winchester
SO23 9ES
T 01962 856266
E sales@creativecrafts.co.uk
W www.creativecrafts.co.uk
Contact Anthony Wilson
A retailer of fine-art supplies, founded in 1972. Also stocks a large range of craft materials.

Creative World
The Bishop Centre, Bath Road, Maidenhead
SL6 0NX
T 01628 665422
F 01628 665424
E create@creativeworld.co.uk
W www.creativeworld.co.uk
Contact Sue Gowers
An art, craft and gift superstore founded in 1996. Aims to provide a comprehensive, carefully selected range and stocks over seventeen thousand products.

Daler-Rowney Ltd
P.O. Box 10, Bracknell
RG12 8ST
T 01344 461000
F 01344 486511
E customer.service@daler-rowney.com
W www.daler-rowney.com
Founded over two hundred years ago. Manufactures and distributes fine-art materials in

more than 150 countries worldwide. A range of quality art materials encompasses more than 7,500 products.

Economy of Brighton
82 St Georges Road, Kemptown, Brighton
BN2 1EF
T 01273 682831

EKA Services Ltd
11–12 Hampton Court Parade, East Molesey
KT8 9HB
T 020 89793466
F 020 89414332
E ekaservices@btclick.com
W www.ekaservices.co.uk
Contact Anup Patel
Established for over fifty years, stocking all major manufacturers of art and graphic materials.

Expressions
49 Kings Road, St Leonards-on-Sea
TN37 6DY
T 01424 437136
F 01424 442652
Contact Mr or Mrs King
Retails wide range of art and craft supplies and canvases.

Forget Me Not
69–70 St James Street, Newport (Isle of Wight)
PO30 1LQ
T 01983 522291
F 01983 522291
Contact Anne Toogood
Founded in 1984, supplying artists' materials, stationery, etc.

Godalming Art Shop
45 Bridge Street, Godalming
GU7 1HL
T 01483 423432
F 01483 423432
Contact Charlotte Albrecht or Alan Watson
Stocks a wide range of artists' materials from leading manufacturers, technical equipment and ancillary and craft materials.

Hearn & Scott
10 Bridge Street, Andover
SP10 1BH
T 01264 400200
F 01264 400205
E sales@hearnscott.co.uk

Contact Maureen Mallett
Established in 1973. A stationer, printer, digital copy shop and art shop. Also has a gallery where local artists exhibit their work.

Hockles
166 Kennington Road, Kennington, Oxford
OX1 5PG
T 01865 736611

Lunns of Ringwood
13 Christchurch Road, Ringwood
BH24 1DG
T 01425 480347
F 01425 480347
E lunnsofringwood@btconnect.com
Contact Heidi Killen
A family-run business for nearly forty years. Stocks leading brands of art materials. Discounts on bulk orders and mail order available.

Oxford Craft Studio
443 Banbury Road, Oxford
OX2 8ED
T 01865 513909

Paint Pots
39 Trafalgar Street, Brighton
BN1 4ED
T 01273 696682

Pure South
6 Meeting House Lane, Brighton
BN1 1HB
T 01273 321718

Rural Art Company
Milton Ernest Garden Centre, Radwell Road,
Milton Ernest
MK44 1SH
T 01234 823592
F 01234 823562
Contact Pauline Hurst
An art materials shop and on-site framer. Also sells original paintings and prints, displayed on walls and in the garden-centre coffee shop. No charge for display but thirty per cent commission plus VAT taken on anything sold.

Sevenoaks Art Shop
45 London Road, Sevenoaks
TN13 1AR
T 01732 452551
E sevenoaksartshop@hotmail.com

Established in 1927, supplying fine-art materials and offering a picture-framing service.

Smitcraft
Unit 1, Eastern Road, Aldershot
GU12 4TE
T 01252 342626
F 01252 311700
E info@smitcraft.com
W www.smitcraft.com
Founded in 1938, a mail-order supplier predominantly serving the institutional market e.g. hospitals, prisons, schools. Supplies over fifteen thousand art and craft items.

T.S. Two
41 Queensway, Bletchley, Milton Keynes
MK2 2DR
T 01908 646521
F 01908 646526
E sales@tuppers.co.uk
Contact Olga Prentice of Jeff Wyatt
Retails art, craft and graphic materials and offers a bespoke framing service.

T.N. Lawrence & Son Ltd
208 Portland Road, Hove
BN3 5QT
T 01273 260260
F 01273 260270
E artbox@lawrence.co.uk
W www.lawrence.co.uk
Established in 1859, specializing in printmaking and painting supplies. Operates worldwide mail-order and online purchasing systems.
Branches 38 Barncoose Industrial Estate, Pool, Redruth, Cornwall TR15 3RQ **T** 01209 313181.

Terry Harrison
28 Cove Road, Farnborough
GU14 0EN
T 01252 545012
F 01252 545012
E harrisonarts@aol.com
W www.terryharrison.com
Contact Terry Harrison or Derek Whitcher
Books, videos, DVDs, brushes and art materials are available via website. Terry Harrison himself is available to give demonstrations to art societies and other groups and holds workshops all over the UK.

ToolPost
35 Brunstock Beck, Didcot
OX11 7YG
T 01235 810658
F 01235 810905
E peter@toolpost.co.uk
W www.toolpost.co.uk
Contact Peter Hemsley
An online vendor of tools and materials, specializing in quality tools for woodturning, woodcarving and handcrafted woodworking. Other materials available include timber (hardwoods), finishes, adhesives, polishing systems, lathes and copy-carving machines. Delivers worldwide.

Tuppers
696 North Row, Lloyds Court, Central Milton Keynes
MK9 3AP
T 01908 678033
F 01908 663695
E sales@tuppers.co.uk
W www.tuppers.co.uk
Contact Nick Lambert
Retails art and graphic materials and provides bespoke framing service.

South-west

Alms House
20 Silver Street, Trowbridge
BA14 8AE
T 01225 776329
F 01225 774740
E mjcreek@almshouse.net
W www.almshouse.net
Contact Jim Creek
Founded in 1987, stocking a wide range of materials and offering art classes. Mail order available via website. Studio space occasionally available; rates on application.

Art at Bristol
44 Gloucester Road, Bishopston, Bristol
BS7 8AR
T 0117 9232259

Art Centre and Tamar Valley Gallery
Block A, Florence Road Business Park, Kelly Bray
PL17 8EX
T 01579 383523
F 01579 384043
E aafc@fsmail.net
Contact Darren Gardiner
Discount art and craft materials retailer. Also offers commercial framing service, art and craft

classes and workshops, and an art gallery. Studios, classrooms and gallery space for hire.
Price range £10–£50 per week.

Art Centre
135 High Street, nr Playhouse Theatre,
Weston-super-Mare
BS23 1HN
T 01934 644102
E mikekbeaumont@aol.com
W www.artysus.co.uk
Contact Mike Beaumont
Established since 1992, with a large range of artists' materials including grounds, easels, brushes, paints and mounting boards. A comprehensive range of acrylics and pastels are held in stock. Silk, glass painting and other specialist materials are also available.

The Art Shop
54 Castle Street, Trowbridge
BA14 8AU
T 01225 765139

Artboxdirect
23–25 The Pollet, St Peter Port, Guernsey
GY2 4GB
T 01481 701351
F 01481 710383
E info@artboxdirect.co.uk
W www.artboxdirect.co.uk
Contact Julie Queripel
A [remier art store for over twenty-five years. The Internet selling arm of the Lexicon, with sales primarily to the UK and Europe. Four thousand products online from major manufacturers.

Artrageous
21 Sevier Street, Bristol
BS2 9LB
T 0117 9143025

Arts & Interiors Ltd
48 Princes Street, Yeovil
BA20 1EQ
T 01935 477790
F 01935 434183
E brenda.phil@ramlands.freeserve.co.uk
Contact Brenda Drayton

Axworthys' Group
4 Palace Avenue, Paignton
TQ3 3HA
T 01803 663320

F 01803 558869
E steveperry@axworthys.co.uk
W www.axworthys.co.uk
Contact Maureen Turpin
Established in 1868, stocking a full range of products to suit the beginner up to the expert.

Blue Gallery
16 Joy Street, Barnstaple
EX31 1BS
T 01271 343536
F 01271 321896
E sales@bluegallery.co.uk
W www.bluegallery.co.uk
Contact Roy Smith
Specialist retailers of art and craft materials for over forty years. Most leading suppliers stocked. Online shopping.

Bristol Fine Art
72–74 Park Row, Bristol
BS1 5LE
T 0117 9260344

Ceres Crafts Ltd
Lansdown Road, Bude
EX23 8BH
T 01288 354070
Contact Mr T. A. Miell
Established in 1981, selling a complete range of artist materials and a comprehensive range of craft materials and kits.

Cherry Art Centre
18–20 Ellacombe Road, Longwell Green, Bristol
BS30 9BA
T 0117 9048287
E mail@cherryartcentre.com
Contact Lynne & Martyn Holehouse
Artists' materials retailer and picture framer. Tuition also offered, with demonstrations to clubs, societies, businesses, etc.

Compleat Artist
102 Crane Street, Salisbury
SP1 2QD
T 01722 335928
E martyn.kennard@tesco.net
W www.artmail.co.uk
Contact Martyn Kennard
Founded in 1952 by Edna Trott and now owned by Martyn Kennard. Caters for the student, intermediate and professional artist. Situated on the River Avon.

Creativity
7–9 Worrall Road, Bristol
BS8 2UF
T 0117 9731710

F.J. Harris & Son
13 Green Street, Bath
BA1 2JZ
T 01225 462116
F 01225 338442
Contact Jackie Gluschke or Luke Elston
Founded in 1821. A retail outlet for all art materials
for artists and students. A wide range of stretched
canvases.

Finelife
Foxcombe, Exford, Minehead
TA24 7NY
T 01643 831336
W www.artnetdirectory.co.uk/artistsmaterials/
pochade
Contact Peter Waymouth
Pochade (French for 'sketch') oil painter's field box
reintroduced in 2004. Takes three wet canvas
boards (8" × 6" or 10" × 8"), in-built palette, space
for tubes, brushes, etc.

Fred Keetch Gallery
46 The Strand, Exmouth
EX8 1AL
T 01395 227226
An art materials stockist, framer and gallery,
exhibiting local artists' work.

Harberton Art Workshop
27 High Street, Totnes
TQ9 5NP
T 01803 862390
F 01803 867881
Founded in 1970, selling a comprehensive range
of artists' materials from all the main suppliers.

Hardings
59–61 High Street, Shaftesbury
SP7 8JE
T 01747 852156
F 01747 851587
E hardshaf@freenetname.co.uk
Contact Tracey
Retail shop founded in the late nineteenth century.

Inside Art
18 Colliers Walk, Nailsea, Bristol
BS48 1RG
T 01275 859990

Jim's Mail Order
56 Fore Street, Redruth
TR15 2AQ
T 01209 211903
F 01209 313994
E enquiries@jims.org.uk
W www.jims-mail-order.co.uk
Founded in 1984, supplying a range of art and craft
materials.

Lexicon
23–25 The Pollet, St Peter Port, Guernsey
GY2 4GB
T 01481 721120
F 01481 710383
E sales@thelexicon.co.uk
W www.thelexicon.co.uk
Contact Julie Queripel
Operating as an art materials retailer for over
twenty-five years.

Minerva Graphics
12a Trim Street, Bath
BA1 1HB
T 01225 464054

Riverbank Centre
1a Pool Road, Kingswood, Bristol
BS15 1XL
T 0117 9674804
E riverbank.centre@tiscali.co.uk
Contact Gill Punter
Started in 2001. Sells art materials. Has teaching
studio for up to fourteen people (covering range of
media and age groups). Holds stock of original
works. One exhibition per year (for charity).

Sanders
22 Grants Walk, St Austell
PL25 5AA
T 01726 73814
F 01726 69044
E enquiries@sandersartsupplies.co.uk
W www.sandersartsupplies.co.uk
Contact Ellie Atkinson
Started in 2001, stocking supplies from major
manufacturers to suit all, from the beginner to the
accomplished artist. Upstairs gallery to open
imminently.

Stationery/Art Ltd
104–105 High Street, Tewkesbury
GL20 5JZ
T 01684 273100

F 01684 273300
Contact Gordon Bird or Rikki Meads
Established on current site for over twenty years, carrying a wide range of artists' materials and craft and hobby materials.

Thornbury Arts
3a High Street, Thornbury, Bristol
BS35 2AE
T 01454 413722

Wales

Artbox
7 De La Beche Street, Swansea
SA1 3EZ
T 01792 455433
F 01792 455433
E brian.harris@artbox-swansea.com
W www.artbox-swansea.com
Contact Brian Harris
Founded in 1997 and run by a qualified artist with over twenty years' experience of art materials and techniques. Complete picture-framing service also available, along with colour-copying, laminating service and comb-binding.

B Creative
1 Temperance Lane, Ystradgynlais, Swansea
SA9 1JP
T 01639 845091

Blades the Art Works
2 Cornwall Place, Mumbles, Swansea
SA3 4DP
T 01792 366673

Browsers Bookshop
73 High Street, Porthmadog
LL49 9EU
T 01766 512066
F 01766 512066
Contact Dave Cowper, Sharon Grifith, Helen Moran, Ben Cowper, Shaun Cowper or Sara Cowper
Founded in 1976. A retailer of artist and craft materials. For unusual and not-stocked items, a regular ordering service exists. A daily search-and-order service operates for all books.

Crafty Bits
2 Pen-y-Lan Road, Cardiff
CF24 3PF
T 029 20499229

Major Brushes Ltd
Units C2 and C3, Capital Point, Capital Business Park, Parkway, Cardiff
CF3 2PY
T 029 20770835

Makit
21 Rectory Road, Cardiff
CF5 1QL
T 029 20343609

Mumbles Art & Craft Centre
Treasure, 29–31 Newton Road, Mumbles, Swansea
SA3 4AS
T 01792 410717

Pen and Paper Stationery Co.
13–17 Royal Arcade, Cardiff
CF10 1AE
T 029 20373738
F 029 20373038
E sales@penandpaper.co.uk
W www.penandpaper.co.uk
Contact Wendy
Stationery and art-materials store selling quality pens and materials for the general artist. Also holds a wide-ranging stock of papers for art and craft.

Pots of Fun
Unit 2, Danescourt Shopping Precinct, Danescourt Way, Cardiff
CF5 2QF
T 029 20565600

West Midlands

Cromartie Hobbycraft Ltd
Park Hall Road, Longton, Stoke-on-Trent
ST3 5AY
T 01782 313947
F 01782 599723
E enquiries@cromartie.co.uk
W www.cromartie.co.uk
Over fifty years' experience of making kilns in Britain and one of the UK's leading distributors of colours and glazes.

Everyman
10 Calthorpe Road, Edgbaston
B15 1QT
T 0121 4550099
F 0121 4565983
E everymans@tiscali.co.uk

Contact David Argall
Founded in 1910, offering a full range of supplies for professional and amateur artists, including canvases on the roll. Mail-order service.

Fearnside's Art Ltd
34 Belle Vue Terrace, Malvern
WR14 4PZ
T 01684 573221
E fearnsides_arts@tiscali.co.uk
Contact John Edwards
A long-established business selling a wide range of art materials from all major suppliers. Signed prints also available and art tutoring classes held.

Fly Art & Crafts Company
Unit E5, The Pallasades, Birmingham
B2 4XA
T 0121 6436388

Harris-Moore Canvases Ltd
Unit 108 Jubilee Trades Centre, 130 Pershore Street, Birmingham
B5 6ND
T 0121 2480030
E sales@stretchershop.co.uk
W www.stretchershop.co.uk
Contact Louise Moore
A maker of bespoke artists' stretched canvases and linens. Specializes in deep-sided and gallery-wrapped canvases with a wide choice of fabrics and finishes. Any size made to order. National delivery from £6. Online shop on website.

Oasis Art & Graphics
68 East Meadway, Birmingham
B33 0AP
T 0121 7862988

Paper House
19a Greengate Street, Stafford
ST16 2HS
T 01785 212953
F 01785 606611
Contact Martin Dalgarno
Founded in 1984. A retailer of fine-art materials operating from a large store in the centre of Stafford.

Spectrum Fine Art & Graphic Materials
5 Fletchers Walk, Paradise Place, Birmingham
B3 3HJ
T 0121 2331780

Tales Press
7 Dam Street, Lichfield
WS13 6AE
T 01543 256777
Contact Peter Mott
Established in 1970, selling artists' materials and needlework.

Vesey Arts & Crafts
48–50 Chester Road, New Oscott, Sutton Coldfield
B73 5DA
T 0121 3558747
Contact Jackie
Started in 1972 and moved to larger premises in 1987. Specializes in selling artist and craft supplies, stocking all main manufacturers. Also offers a bespoke picture-framing service with workshop on site.

Yorkshire and Humberside

Art Centre
6 Albion Street, Halifax
HX1 1DU
T 01422 366936
Stocks a wide range of materials for arts and crafts from leading manufacturers.
Branches 47 Cleveland Street, Doncaster, DN1 3DS
T 01302 761245.

Art Express
Design House, Sizers Court, Yeadon, Leeds
LS19 7DP
T 0113 2500077

The Art Shop
27 Shambles, York
YO1 7LX
T 01904 623898
Contact Mr or Mrs Fletcher
Situated in York's famous medieval street, stocking a comprehensive range of art, craft and graphics materials.

Artcraft
Stephen H. Smith's Garden & Leisure, Pool Road, Otley
LS21 1DY
T 01943 462195
F 01943 850074
E wharfe@artcraft.co.uk
W www.artcraft.co.uk
Established in 1966, stocking thousands of artists' and craft materials items.

Branches Doncaster Road, Scunthorpe, North Lincolnshire; Wilsden Road, Harden, nr Bingley, West Yorkshire; Radcliffe Moor Road, Bradley Fold, Bolton, Lancashire.

Bar Street Arts Ltd
14 Bar Street, Scarborough
YO11 2HT
T 01723 507622
F 01723 507622
Contact Dave Colley
Founded in 1996. A specialist supplier of fine-art materials and papers, stocking many of the leading brands.

Biskit Tin
6 Regent Buildings, York Road, York
YO26 4LT
T 01904 787799

Calder Graphics
5 Byram Arcade, Westgate, Huddersfield
HD1 1ND
T 01484 422991
F 01484 421191
E calderg@brighousecomputers.co.uk
Founded in 1979, retailing a wide range of fine-art and craft products from most of the major manufacturers.

Centagraph
18 Station Parade, Harrogate
HG1 1UE
T 01423 566327
F 01423 505386
E info@centagraph.co.uk
W www.centagraph.co.uk
Large retail art and craft shop, offering a full range of fine-art materials from all the leading manufacturers.

Discount Art
18 Wood Street, Wakefield
WF1 2ED
T 01924 201772
F 01924 369171
E info@discountart.co.uk
W www.discountart.co.uk
Contact Robert Burgess
Offers a large selection of art materials at discounted prices. A total studio service in art supplies with bulk prices on canvas and colour.

Drawing Group Ltd
3–9 West Street, Hull
HU1 3UR
T 01482 324263
F 01482 325176
E christine@drawgroup.co.uk
W www.drawgroup.co.uk
Contact Trevor Dixon
A family business established in 1950, specializing in art and craft materials. Special orders and mail orders taken.

Mulberry Bush
Barkers Tower, Lendal Bridge, York
YO1 7DP
T 01904 642032

Rainbow Arts & Crafts Of Easingworld
Chapel Street, Easingwold, York
YO61 3AE
T 01347 823962

S & A Frames and Art Centre
The Old Post Office, Yarra Road, Cleethorpes
DN35 8LS
T 01472 697772
E saframes@aol.com
W www.artmaterial.co.uk
Contact Rolf Sperr
A large arts and crafts materials centre with regular art classes for adults and children.

Samuel Taylors
10 Central Road, Leeds
LS1 6DE
T 0113 2459737

York Art & Framing
7 Castlegate, York
YO1 9RN
T 01904 637619

Art photography suppliers, developers and printers

artistsprinting
Southgate Studios, 2–4 Southgate Road, London
N1 3JJ
T 01608 641070
F 08700 549825
E mail@artistsprinting.com
W www.artistsprinting.co.uk

Contact Stephan
Offers large-format digital printing and unique installation and mounting techniques (specializing in one-off billboard format digital photography). Hosts workshops for artists in, among other subjects, file-processing for digital printing and mounting and display applications for digital prints. Collaborates with individual artists and groups working on digital printing or web-based projects.

Calumet Photographic UK
Promandis House, Bradbourne Drive, Tilbrook, Milton Keynes
MK7 8AJ
T 01908 366344
F 01908 366322
E website@calumetphoto.co.uk
W www.calumetphoto.co.uk
A leading supplier of high-quality imaging products since 1939.

Camden Camera Centre
28 Parkway, Camden Town, London
NW1 7AH
T 020 74857247
F 020 79160841
W www.camdencameracentre.co.uk
A photographic retailer established in 1989.

Direct Lighting
North London Freight Depot, York Way, London
N1 0UZ
T 07000 272727
F 07000 262626
E mail@directlighting.co.uk
W www.directlighting.co.uk
One of London's leading rental suppliers of camera and lighting equipment.

Films Ltd
1–5 Poland Street, London
W1F 8QB
T 020 7494 4508
Stock includes film, paper, boards, and processing and contact sheets.

Flash Centre
54 Brunswick Centre, London
WC1N 1AE
T 020 78376163
Stocks cameras and films, and distributes flash equipment to photographic studios.
Branches 2nd Floor, Mill 1, Mabgate Mills,

Mabgate, Leeds LS9 7DZ **T** 0113 2470937;
2 Mount Street Business Centre, Mount Street, Birmingham B7 5RD **T** 0121 3279220.

Fuji Photo Film (UK) Ltd
125 Finchley Road, London
NW3 6HY
T 020 75865900
F 020 77224259
W www.fujifilm.co.uk

Genie Imaging
Unit D4, Jaggard Way, Wandsworth, London
SW12 8SG
T 020 87721700
F 020 87721710
E info@genieimaging.co.uk
Established in 1987. A London-based photographic and digital-imaging laboratory.

Ilford Imaging UK Ltd
Town Lane, Mobberley, Knutsford
WA16 7JL
W www.ilford.com
T 01565 684000

Jessops
Jessop House, Scudamore Road, Leicester
LE3 1TZ
T 0116 2326000
W www.jessops.com
Founded in 1935. A photographic retailer with over two hundred and seventy stores nationwide.

John Jones
4 Morris Place, Stroud Green Road, London
N4 3JG
T 020 72815439
E photo@johnjones.co.uk
W www.johnjones.co.uk
Provides a range of photographic services for artists, photographers, collectors and businesses.

Kentmere Photographic Ltd
Staveley, Kendal
LA8 9PB
T 01539 821365
F 01539 821399
E sales@kentmere.co.uk
W www.kentmere.co.uk
Specialists in photographic paper, especially black and white.

Kodak UK Ltd
P.O. Box 66, Station Road, Hemel Hempstead
HP1 1JU
T 01442 845945
F 01442 844458
W www.kodak.com

London Camera Exchange Group
98 Strand, London
WC2R 0EW
T 020 73790200
E strand@lcegroup.co.uk
W www.lcegroup.co.uk
Offers new, used and digital cameras and
parts. Runs a mail-order service. Branches
nationwide.

Metro Imaging Ltd
76 Clerkenwell Road, London
EC1M 5TN
T 020 78650000
F 020 78650001
W www.metroimaging.co.uk
Specialists in photographic and digital services.

Outback Printworks
Unit 27, Cremer Business Centre, Cremer Street,
London
E2 8HD
T 020 77291144
F 020 77296555
W www.outbackprintworks.com
Photographic printworks.

PhotoArtistry Ltd
Unit 5, 2 Pennard Close, Brackmills Industrial
Estate, Northampton
NN4 7BE
T 01604 700608
F 01604 763834
E info@photoartistry.co.uk
W www.photoartistry.co.uk
Offers bespoke large-format digital printing
service.

Potosi Ltd
Unit 23, Cremer Business Centre, 37 Cremer
Street, London
E2 8HD
T 020 77295353
A photographic printworks, specializing in black
and white.

Process Supplies (London) Ltd
13–25 Mount Pleasant, London
WC1X OAR
T 020 78372179
F 020 78378551
E sales@process-supplies.co.uk
W www.process-supplies.co.uk
Contact Neil Willes, Paul Willes
Established in 1928. Offers a specialist supply
service for all conventional and digital
photographic materials, including archival storage
and presentation, inkjet papers and inks, CD- and
DVD-Rs and -RWs.

Professional Film Co. Ltd
65 Great Portland Street, London
W1W 7LW
T 020 75800700
F 020 75800701
Stocks films and photographic accessories. Also
offers processing and printing services.

SamedaySnaps – Mitcham Arts
256 London Road, Mitcham
CR4 3HD
T 020 86850010
F 020 86408666
E samedaysnaps@mitchamarts.fsnet.co.uk
Contact Vijay
Specializes in digital imaging, printing on a variety
of media, from photographic paper to canvas, from
miniature to poster size. In-house picture-framing
and stretching of canvas provided.

Sky Photographic Services Ltd
Ramillies Street, London
W1F 7AZ
T 020 74342266
Photo processing and printing chain.
Branches 64a Cannon Street, London EC4N
T 020 72361019; 17–23 Southampton Row,
London WC1B **T** 020 72422504; 16 Andrews
Road, London E8 **T** 020 72544313.

Tapestry.MM Ltd
51–52 Frith Street, London
W1D 4SH
T 020 78963100
F 020 78963109
E info@tapestrymm.com
W www.tapestrymm.com
Established in 1972. An independent creative
services company with wide experience of
photographic services.

Tetenal Ltd
Tetenal House, Centurion Way, Meridian Business
Park, Leicester
LE3 2WH
T 0116 2630306
A photographic materials manufacturer.

Art book publishers

A&C Black Publishing
37 Soho Square, London
W1D 3QZ
T 020 77580200
W www.acblack.com
Founded in 1807. Subject areas include visual arts,
glass, ceramics and printmaking.

Antique Collectors' Club
Sandy Lane, Old Martlesham, Woodbridge
IP12 4SD
T 01394 389950
F 01394 389999
E sales@antique-acc.com
W www.antiquecc.com
Publishes specialist books on antiques, the
decorative arts and architecture.

Art Data
12 Bell Industrial Estate, 50 Cunnington Street,
London
W4 5HB
T 020 87471061
F 020 87422319
E orders@artdata.co.uk
W www.artdata.co.uk
Contact Tim Borton
Established in 1978, primarily to distribute books
and catalogues of contemporary visual arts (fine
art, sculpture, architecture, photography, design,
illustration and fashion). Handles over five
thousand titles and sells throughout the world.
Also produces about six titles of its own a year.

Art Sales Index Ltd
194 Thorpe Lea Road, Egham
TW20 8HA
T 01784 451145
F 01784 451144
E info@art-sales-index.com
W www.art-sales-index.com
Founded in 1968 to record the price and details of
works of fine art sold at auction to help collectors

and dealers to value art. The database has over
2.8 million entries and is available in book form,
on CD-ROM and on the web.

Ashgate Publishing Ltd
Gower House, Croft Road, Aldershot
GU11 3HR
T 01252 331551
F 01252 344405
W www.ashgate.com
List ranges from scholarly research
monographs and specialist *catalogues raisonnés*
to illustrated artist monographs and exhibition
catalogues.

Ashmolean Museum Publications
Ashmolean Museum, Beaumont Street, Oxford
OX1 2PH
T 01865 278010
F 01865 278018
W www.ashmol.ox.ac.uk/ash/publications
Publishes widely on fine and applied arts.

Bardon Enterprises
6 Winter Road, Southsea
PO4 9BT
T 07752 873831
F 023 92874900
Specializes in books about art and music.

Black Dog Publishing
Unit 4.4 Tea Building, Shoreditch High Street,
London
E1 6JJ
T 020 76131922
F 020 76131944
E info@bdp.demon.co.uk
W www.bdpworld.com
Specializes in books on contemporary art,
architecture, design and photography.

Blackwell Publishing
9600 Garsington Road, Oxford
OX4 2DQ
T 01865 778315
F 01865 471775
E customerservices@oxon.blackwellpublishing.
com
W www.blackwellpublishing.com
A humanities and social sciences publisher
with an art and theory list. Longstanding
relationships with the journals *Art History* and
The Art Book.

Book Works Publishing
19 Holywell Row, London
EC2A 4JB
T 020 72472203
F 020 72472540
E mail@bookworks.org.uk
W www.bookworks.org.uk
A publicly funded contemporary visual arts
publisher, dedicated to distributing significant and
cutting-edge work to a wide audience.

Brepols Publishers
1 Jane Street, Saltaire, Shipley
BD18 3HA
The UK office of a Belgian academic publisher
of monographs and collections across the
humanities. Its imprint, Harvey Miller Publishers,
specializes in academic studies of medieval and
Renaissance art history.

British Museum Press
38 Russell Square, London
WC1B 3QQ
T 020 76371292
F 020 74367315
Founded in 1973. Publishes around sixty books
each year.

BT Batsford
The Chrysalis Building, Bramley Road, London
W10 6SP
T 020 7314 1400
F 020 7314 1594
E saul.rice@chrysalisbooks.co.uk
W www.chrysalisbooks.co.uk
Contact Saul Rice
A Chrysalis Books Group imprint. Produces a
range of practical books for artists.

Cambridge University Press
The Edinburgh Building, Shaftesbury Road,
Cambridge
CB2 2RU
T 01223 312393
F 01223 315052
W www.cambridge.org/uk
The oldest printing and publishing house in the
world, with an extensive art and architecture
backlist.

Collins and Brown
The Chrysalis Building, Bramley Road, London
W10 6SP
T 020 73141400

F 020 73141594
E sales@chrysalisbooks.co.uk
W www.chrysalisbooks.co.uk
Contact Laura Brudenell
A Chrysalis Books Group imprint. Publishes high-
quality practical art books for those keen to
improve their techniques or broaden their
specialities. Authors include John Raynes and
Albany Wiseman.

Constable & Robinson Ltd
3 The Lanchesters, 162 Fulham Palace Road,
London
W6 9ER
T 020 87413663
F 020 87487562
E enquiries@constablerobinson.com
W www.constablerobinson.com
A general publisher with several landscape
photography titles.

David & Charles
Brunel House, Forde Close, Newton Abbot
TQ12 4PU
T 01626 323200
F 01626 323319
E postmaster@davidandcharles.co.uk
W www.davidandcharles.co.uk
An international publisher of illustrated non-
fiction books.

Dorling Kindersley Ltd
The Penguin Group (UK), 80 Strand, London
WC2R 0RL
T 020 70103000
F 020 70106060
W www.dk.com
An international publisher of highly illustrated
books, with a specialist arts and culture list.

Enitharmon Editions Ltd
26b Caversham Road, London
NW5 2DU
T 020 74825967
F 020 72841787
E books@enitharmon.co.uk
W www.enitharmon.co.uk
Contact Stephen Stuart-Smith
Established in 2001 as an associated company of
Enitharmon Press (founded in 1967). Specialist
publisher of artists' books, commissioning
collaborations between artists and writers, which
take the form of deluxe books incorporating
original art works.

Frances Lincoln Ltd
4 Torriano Mews, Torriano Avenue, London
NW5 2RZ
T 020 72844009
F 020 72675249
W www.franceslincoln.com
Publishes highly illustrated non-fiction, including
art and design.

Garnet Publishing
8 Southern Court, South Street, Reading
RG1 4QS
T 0118 9597847
F 0118 9597356
E info@garnetpublishing.co.uk
W www.garnetpublishing.co.uk
Independent publishers, producing some art
and architecture titles.

Giles de la Mare Publishers Ltd
P.O. Box 25351, London
NW5 1ZT
T 020 74852533
F 020 74852534
E gilesdelamare@dial.pipex.com
Publishes mainly non-fiction, especially art and
architecture.

Golden Cockerel Press Ltd
16 Barter Street, London
WC1A 2AH
T 020 74057979
F 020 74043598
E aup.uk@btinternet.com
An academic publisher with list of art titles.

Halsgrove Publishing
Halsgrove House, Lower Moor Way, Tiverton
TQ13 9UY
T 01884 243242
F 01884 243325
E sales@halsgrove.com
W www.halsgrove.com
Contact Simon Butler
A publisher of books about art and artists,
specializing in illustrated studies of individual
artists and on books with a regional content. Often
works with galleries and their artists to create
publications to coincide with exhibitions.

Harvard University Press
Fitzroy House, 11 Chenies Street, London
WC1E 7EY
T 020 73060603
F 020 73060604
E info@HUP-MITpress.co.uk
W www.hup.harvard.edu
Produces scholarly books and serious works of
general interest.

Hilmarton Manor Press
(Who's Who in Art), Hilmarton Manor, Calne
SN11 8SB
T 01249 760208
F 01249 760379
E whoswhoinart@tiscali.co.uk
W www.hilmartonpress.co.uk
Contact Charles Baile de Laperriere
The first edition of *Who's Who in Art* was published
in 1927 and every two years thereafter. Hilmarton
Manor Press, founded in 1969, specializes in the
publishing and distribution of fine art and art
reference books.

I.B. Tauris & Co. Ltd
6 Salem Road, London
W2 4BU
T 020 72431225
F 020 72431226
W www.ibtauris.com
An independent publishing house, producing both
general and academic titles. Operates strong lists
in art, architecture and visual culture.

Koenig Books London
The Serpentine Gallery, Kensington Gardens,
London
W2 3XA
T 020 77064907
F 020 77064911
E info@koenigbooks.co.uk
W www.koenigbooks.co.uk
The UK art-book imprint of Buchhandlung
Walther Koenig in Cologne.

Laurence King Publishing Ltd
71 Great Russell Street, London
WC1B 3BP
T 020 74308850
F 020 74308880
E enquiries@laurenceking.co.uk
W www.laurenceking.co.uk
Founded in 1991. Publishes books on art history,
architecture, interior design, graphic design, film,
fashion, photography, the decorative arts and craft.
Books cater for students of art or design and
professional architects or designers, as well as
interested general readers.

Liverpool University Press
4 Cambridge Street, Liverpool
L69 7ZU
T 0151 7942233
F 0151 7942235
E J.M.Smith@liv.ac.uk
W www.liverpool-unipress.co.uk
Publishes academic books and journals on a range
of subjects including art and architecture.

Lund Humphries
Mecklenburgh House, 11 Mecklenburgh Square,
London
WC1N 2AE
T 020 78419800
F 020 78376322
E info@lundhumphries.com
W www.lundhumphries.com
Contact Lucy Clark (Commissioning Editor) or
lclark@lundhumphries.com
Publishers of illustrated art books for specialists
and academics. In over fifty years of fine-art
publishing, the imprint has built up a strong
reputation in the areas of contemporary artists'
monographs, twentieth-century British art,
museum-related publications, and typography
and graphic design.

Mainstream Publishing
7 Albany Street, Edinburgh
EH1 3UG
T 0131 5572959
F 0131 5568720
E enquiries@mainstreampublishing.com
W www.mainstreampublishing.com
Contact Bill Campbell
Founded in 1978. A publisher of a wide-ranging
general list including art, photography and popular
culture.

Manchester University Press
Oxford Road, Manchester
M13 9NR
T 0161 2752310
F 0161 2743346
E mup@manchester.ac.uk
W www.manchesteruniversitypress.co.uk
Includes a programme of paperbacks in art history
and design.

Marston House
Marston Magna, Yeovil
BA22 8DH
T 01935 851331

F 01935 851372
Publishes on fine art, architecture and ceramics.

Merrell Publishers
42 Southwark Street, London
SE1 1UN
T 020 74032047
F 020 74071333
E mail@merrellpublishers.com
W www.merrellpublishers.com
Publishers of books on all aspects of visual culture,
from key titles on major artists to surveys of
international architecture and explorations of
cutting-edge developments in world design.

National Portrait Gallery Publications
National Portrait Gallery, St Martin's Place, London
WC2H 0HE
T 020 73060055
F 020 73060092
E sellis@npg.org.uk
W www.npg.org.uk/live/pubs.asp
Aims to support the work of the gallery and to
increase visitors' knowledge and enjoyment of its
collections.

NMS Publishing Ltd
Royal Museum, Chambers Street, Edinburgh
EH1 1JF
T 0131 2474026
F 0131 2474012
E ltaylor@nms.ac.uk
W www.nms.ac.uk
Publishes non-fiction related to the National
Museums of Scotland collections.

Octopus Publishing Group
2–4 Heron Quays, London
E14 4JP
T 020 75318400
F 020 75318650
E firstnamelastname@octopus-publishing.co.uk
W www.octopus-publishing.co.uk
Contact Derek Freeman or Henri Masonlel
Imprints include Cassell Illustrated (illustrated
books for the international market) and Conran
Octopus (quality illustrated books).

Oxford University Press
Great Clarendon Street, Oxford
OX2 6DP
T 01865 556767
F 01865 556646
E WebEnquiry.UK@oup.com

W www.oup.com
Founded in the sixteenth century, producing
scholarly and reference works.

Pavilion
The Chrysalis Building, Bramley Road, London
W10 6SP
T 020 73141400
F 020 73141594
E sales@chrysalisbooks.co.uk
W www.chrysalisbooks.co.uk
Contact Laura Brudenell
A Chrysalis Books Group imprint. Publishes quality
art books. Published artists include Jack Vettriano.

Phaidon Press Ltd
Regent's Wharf, All Saints Street, London
N1 9PA
T 020 78431234
F 020 78431111
W www.phaidon.com
A publisher on the visual arts since 1923. Offices
in New York, London, Paris and Berlin.

Philip Wilson Publishers Ltd
109 Drysdale Street, The Timber Yard, London
N1 6ND
T 020 70339900
F 020 70339922
E pwilson@philip-wilson.co.uk
W www.philip-wilson.co.uk
Contact Philip Wilson
Publishers of art books, museum and exhibition
catalogues, monographs of contemporary artists
and complete catalogues of twentieth-century
artists.

Prestel Publishing Ltd
4 Bloomsbury Place, London
WC1A 2QA
T 020 73235004
F 020 76368004
E sales@prestel-uk.co.uk
W www.prestel.com
Contact Andrew Hansen
Established in Germany in 1923. A leading
publisher of high-quality, illustrated books on art,
architecture, design and photography. The London
office opened in 1997 and has its own publishing
programme.

Primrose Hill Press Ltd
Stratton Audley Park, nr Bicester
OX27 9AB

T 01869 278000
F 01869 277820
E info@primrosehillpress.co.uk
W www.primrosehillpress.co.uk
Specializes in the art of wood-engraving.

Reaktion Books Ltd
79 Farringdon Road, London
EC1M 3JU
T 020 74049930
F 020 74049931
E info@reaktionbooks.co.uk
W www.reaktionbooks.co.uk
Founded in 1985. Publishing programme includes
titles on art history, architecture and design.

Routledge Publishers
2 Park Square, Milton Park, Abingdon
OX14 4RN
T 020 70176000
F 020 70176708
E tom.church@tandf.co.uk
W www.routledge.com
Publishers in the fields of art, art history, design,
visual culture and aesthetics.

Royal Jelly Factory
11 Kemp House, 103 Berwick Street, London
W1F 0QT
T 020 77346032
F 0870 0549832
E info@royaljellyfactory.com
W www.royaljellyfactory.com
Publishers of New Art Up-Close, a series of pocket-
sized books on living artists.

Sangam Books Ltd
57 London Fruit Exchange, Brushfield Street,
London
E1 6EP
T 020 73776399
F 020 73751230
Traditionally a publisher of textbooks but with
some art titles.

Search Press Ltd
Wellwood, North Farm Road, Tunbridge Wells
TN4 8UT
T 01892 510850
F 01892 515903
E searchpress@searchpress.com
W www.searchpress.com
A specialist art and craft publisher for thirty-five
years. Series include Leisure Arts, Watercolour

Tips & Techniques, Design Source Books and Handmade Greetings Cards.

Seren Books

1st and 2nd Floors, 38–40 Nolton Street, Bridgend
CF31 3BN
T 01656 663018
F 01656 649226
E general@seren-books.com
W www.seren-books.com
An independent literary publisher, specializing in English-language writing from Wales. Publishes on Welsh art.

Taschen UK Ltd

13 Old Burlington Street, London
W1S 3AJ
T 020 74374350
F 020 74374360
E contact-uk@taschen.com
W www.taschen.com
Founded in 1980 by Benedict Taschen in Cologne, Germany. All editorial submissions are handled by the German office.

Tate Publishing Ltd

Millbank, London
SW1P 4RG
T 020 78878869
F 020 78878878
E tp.enquiries@tate.org.uk
W www.tate.org.uk/publishing
Publishing since 1932, including scholarly works, series and exhibition catalogues.

Textile & Art Publications

12 Queen Street, Mayfair, London
W1J 5PG
T 020 74997979
F 020 74092596
E post@textile-art.com
W www.textile-art.com
Publishes a limited number of titles each year, covering a variety of subjects from Oriental and Islamic art to Pre-Columbian and medieval art.

Thames & Hudson

181A High Holborn, London
WC1V 7QX
T 020 78455000
F 020 78455050
E editorial@thameshudson.co.uk
W www.thamesandhudson.com

Founded in 1949. An international publisher of books on visual culture throughout the world, from prehistory to the twenty-first century. Art titles include the World of Art series, monographs, artists' books (collaborations with David Hockney, Lucian Freud and many others), art theory, practical instruction and art history (all periods). Target audiences include students, professionals and the general public.

V&A Publications

160 Brompton Road, London
SW3 1HW
T 020 79422966
F 020 79422977
E vapubs.info@vam.ac.uk
W www.vandashop.co.uk
Publishers of popular and scholarly illustrated books on fashion and interior design, fine and decorative arts, architecture and photography.

Worple Press

P.O. Box 328, Tonbridge
TN9 1WR
T 01732 368958
E theworpleco@aol.com
Contact Amanda Knight or Peter Carpenter
Founded in 1997, specializing in poetry and alternative arts titles. Three to four titles per year.

Yale University Press

47 Bedford Square, London
WC1B 3DP
T 020 70794000
F 020 70794901
E sales@yaleup.co.uk
W www.yalebooks.co.uk
The London headquarters were established in 1967. Publishes scholarly books in the humanities, with a particular emphasis on art history.

Art bookshops

Antique Collectors' Club Ltd

Sandy Lane, Old Martlesham, Woodbridge
IP12 4SD
E sales@antique-acc.com
W www.antiquecc.com

Arnolfini Bookshop

16 Narrow Quay, Bristol
BS1 4QA

T 0117 9172304
E bookshop@arnolfini.org.uk
W www.arnolfini.org.uk

Art Books Etc
81 Westwater Way, Didcot
OX11 7TY
T 01235 812834
F 01235 813535
E sales@artbooksetc.co.uk
W www.artbooksetc.co.uk

Art Books International
Unit 14 Groves Business Centre, Shipton Road,
Milton-under-Wychwood, Chipping Norton
OX7 6JP
T 01993 830000
F 01993 830007
E sales@art-bks.com
W www.art-bks.com

The Art Bookshop
3 Quality Square, Ludlow
SY8 1AR
T 01584 872758

Art Data
12 Bell Industrial Estate, 50 Cunington Street,
London
W4 5HB
T 020 87471061
F 020 87422319
E orders@artdata.co.uk
W www.artdata.co.uk

Arts Bibliographic
37 Cumberland Business Park, Cumberland
Avenue, London
NW10 7SL
T 020 89614277
F 020 89618246
E sales@artsbib.com
W www.artsbib.com

Artwords at the Whitechapel
Whitechapel Art Gallery, 80 Whitechapel High
Street, London
E1 7QX
T 020 72476924
F 020 77294400
E shop@artwords.co.uk
W www.artwords.co.uk

Artwords Bookshop
65A Rivington Street, London
EC2A 3QQ
T 020 77292000
F 020 77294400
E shop@artwords.co.uk
W www.artwords.co.uk

Ashmolean Museum Shop
Beaumont Street, Oxford
OX1 2PH
T 01865 288070
E dec.mccarthy@ashmus.ox.ac.uk
W www.ashmol.ox.ac.uk/ash/shop

Baltic Shop
South Shore Road, Gateshead
NE8 3BA
T 0191 4404947
E shop@balticmill.com
W www.balticmill.com/html/conboo.html

Bircham Contemporary Arts
14 Market Place, Holt
NR25 6BW
T 01263 713312
E Birchamgal@aol.com
W www.birchamgallery.co.uk

Blackwell's Art & Poster Shop
27 Broad Street, Oxford
OX1 3BS
T 01865 333642
F 01865 794143
E art@blackwell.co.uk
W www.blackwell.co.uk
Contact Alan Pointer
A specialist art bookshop including sections
on fashion, design, fine art, architecture, art
techniques and decorative arts. Part of the
Blackwell's chain, originally founded in
Oxford in 1879.

British Bookshops and Sussex Stationers
Unit 6, Crowhurst Road, Hollingbury Industrial
Estate, Brighton
BN1 8AF
T 01273 507999
F 01273 502630
E tclark@britishbookshops.co.uk
A bookseller and retailer of artists' materials. Fifty
stores throughout south-east England.

CCA Shop
350 Sauchiehall Street, Glasgow
G2 3SD
T 0141 3324133
E gen@cca-glasgow.com
W www.cca-glasgow.com/shop

Cornerhouse Shop
70 Oxford Road, Manchester
M1 5NH
T 0161 2287621
E info@cornerhouse.org

Dundee Contemporary Arts Shop
152 Nethergate, Dundee
DD1 4DY
T 01382 909900
F 01382 909221
E mail@dca.org.uk
W www.dca.org.uk

Falmouth Art Books
8 Webber Street, Falmouth
TR11 3AU
T 01326 316918
E info@falmouthartsbooks.co.uk
W www.falmouthartsbooks.co.uk
Contact Francis Platt
Opened in September 2004. Stocks books on art, photography, architecture, design, graphic design, illustration and other related subjects.

Fitzwilliam Museum Enterprises
Fitzwilliam Museum, Trumpington Street, Cambridge
CB2 1RB
T 01223 470474
F 01223 744788
E sales@fitzwilliammuseum.org
W www.fitzwilliammuseum.org

Foyles Bookshop
113–119 Charing Cross Road, London
WC2H 0EB
T 020 74375660
E gallery@foyles.co.uk
W www.foyles.co.uk/
Founded in 1903 and situated at the heart of Soho, Foyles is among the world's most famous bookshops. The shop is divided into fifty-six specialist subject areas over five floors and has its own gallery space on the second floor.

Fruitmarket Gallery Shop
45 Market Street, Edinburgh
EH1 1DF
T 0131 2252383
F 0131 2203130
E info@fruitmarket.co.uk
W www.fruitmarket.co.uk/bookshop.html

Grenville Books – The Book People Ltd
Bryn Derwen, Parc Menai, Bangor
LL57 4FB

Hayward Gallery Shop
Belvedere Road, London
SE1 8XZ
T 020 79605226
E hginfo@hayward.org.uk

Heffers Academic & General Books
20 Trinity Street, Cambridge
CB2 1TY
T 01223 568568
F 01223 568591
E heffers@heffers.co.uk
W www.heffers.co.uk

Ian Shipley Books Ltd
70 Charing Cross Road, London
WC2H 0BQ
T 020 78364872
F 020 73794358
E enquiries@shipley.co.uk
W www.artbook.co.uk

ICA Bookshop
The Mall, London
SW1Y 5AH
T 020 77661452
F 020 78730015
E bookshop@ica.org.uk
W www.ica.org.uk/bookshop
Contact Russell Herron (Manager)
Stockists of books on cultural theory, philosophy, art, art theory and new media. Also has a range of hard-to-find magazines.

John Sandoe (Books) Ltd
10 Blacklands Terrace, London
SW3 2SR
T 020 75899473
F 020 75812084
E sales@johnsandoe.com
W www.johnsandoe.com

An independent bookshop in Chelsea, founded in 1957. Stocks a wide range of art titles covering individual artists, the decorative arts and architecture.

Koenig Books Ltd
The Serpentine Gallery, Kensington Gardens, London
W2 3XA
T 020 77064907
F 020 77064911
E info@koenigbooks.co.uk
W www.koenigbooks.co.uk
Contact Franz Koenig (Bookshop Manager and Company Director)
An independent bookshop in the Serpentine Gallery with a wide range of stock on modern and contemporary art, photography, architecture and art theory. Specializes in artists' books, monographs and catalogues. Has full access to the stock and services of Buchhandlung Walther Koenig in Cologne.

Leeds City Art Gallery Shop
Headrow, Leeds
LS1 3AA
E info@bridgeman.co.uk

Magma Design Ltd
117–119 Clerkenwell Road, London
EC1R 5BY
T 020 72429503
F 020 72429504
W www.magmabooks.com ·

Manchester City Gallery Shop
Mosley Street, Manchester
M2 3JL
T 0161 2358888
F 0161 2358899

Marcus Campbell Art Books
43 Holland Street, Bankside, London
SE1 9JR
T 020 72610111
F 020 72610129
E info@marcuscampbell.co.uk
W www.marcuscampbell.co.uk

Modern Art Oxford Shop
30 Pembroke Street, Oxford
OX1 1BP
T 01865 722733
F 01865 722573

W www.modernartoxford.org.uk/Visit/shopandcafe.php

National Gallery of Scotland Shop
The Mound, Edinburgh
EH2 2EL
T 0131 6246200
F 0131 2200917
E shops@nationalgalleries.org

National Gallery Shop
National Gallery, Sainsbury Wing, Whitcomb Street, London
WC2
T 020 77472870
E help@nationalgallery.co.uk

National Portrait Gallery Shop
2 St Martin's Place, London
WC2H 0HE
T 020 73122463
F 020 73060056

Oriel Mostyn Art Gallery Shop
12 Vaughan Street, Llandudno
LL30 1AB
T 01492 879201
F 01492 878869
E post@mostyn.org
W www.mostyn.org

Photographer's Gallery Shop
8 Great Newport Street, London
WC2H 7HY
T 020 78311772 ext. 227
F 020 72400591
E bookshop@photonet.org.uk
W www.photonet.org.uk

Royal Academy of Arts
Unit C Elm Village, 114 Camley Street, London
NW1 0PS
T 0800 6346341
E mailorder@royalacademy.org.uk

Tate Britain Shop
Millbank, London
SW1P 4RG
T 020 78878000
E info@tate.org.uk

Tate Modern Shop
Bankside, London
SE1 9TGT

T 020 74015167
E info@tate.org.uk

Thomas Heneage Art Books
42 Duke Street, St James's, London
SW1Y 6DJ
T 020 79309223
F 020 78399223
E artbooks@heneage.com
W www.heneage.com
Founded in 1977 and among the UK's largest art bookshops, selling art reference books, *catalogues raisonnés*, monographs and exhibition catalogues worldwide. Shop policy is to stock the most authoritative book on any subject and in any language, irrespective of it being new or secondhand.

Three Counties Bookshop
6 High Street, Ledbury
HR8 1DS
T 01531 635699
E threecountiesbookshop@supanet.com
Contact Alan Cowan
Stockists of artists' materials by leading manufacturers as well as books.

V&A Shop
Victoria & Albert Museum, Cromwell Road, London
SW7 2RL
T 020 79422696
W www.vandashop.co.uk

Walker Art Gallery Shop
William Brown Street, Liverpool
L3 8EL
T 0151 478 4199
E thewalker@liverpoolmuseums.org.uk

Whitworth Gallery Shop
The University of Manchester, Oxford Road, Manchester
M15 6ER
T 0161 2757450
F 0161 2757451
E Whitworth@man.ac.uk

Conservators

C.S. Wellby
The Malt House, 4 Church End, Haddenham, Aylesbury
HP17 8AH

T 01844 290036
E candm@wellby.plus.com
Contact Christopher Wellby
Practising since 1973. Specializes in the conservation and restoration of oil paintings on canvas and panel. Also provides reports and surveys of collections. Fellow of the British Association of Paintings Conservator Restorers.

Christine Bullick
5 Belford Terrace, Edinburgh
EH4 3DQ
T 0131 3326948
F 0131 3326948
E mail@bullickconservation.com
W www.bullickconservation.com
Contact Christine Bullick, painting conservator
An accredited painting conservator with thirty years' experience in the conservation of paintings on panel, canvas and metal supports. Works for public collections and private clients.

Clare Finn & Co. Ltd
38 Cornwall Gardens, London
SW7 4AA
T 020 79371895
F 020 79374198
E FinnClare@aol.com
Contact Clare Finn
Founded in 1983, offering a full range of conservation services for paintings, including consolidation, tear repair, cleaning, lining, filling, retouching and varnishing. Clare Finn herself has wide-ranging specialist knowledge of different periods and styles from Old Masters through to contemporary painting techniques. Additional services offered include scientific examination of paintings, mounting, framing, and treatment of existing frames. Advice to purchasers and research projects are undertaken.

Conservation Studio
59 Peverells Wood Avenue, Chandler's Ford
SO53 2FX
T 023 80268167
F 023 80268267
E winstudio@aol.com
W www.conservationstudio.org
Contact Paul Congdon-Clelford
A specialist studio workshop that provides a full and complete restoration and conservation service. Specializes in oils and works of art on paper. Provides home and business consultations and offers collection and delivery nationwide. Clients

include museums, institutions, dealers and private individuals.

Consultant Conservators of Fine Art
North Staffordshire
ST10 3BT
T 01538 702928 / 07974 791627
E huonweaver@aol.com
Contact Marilyn Jackson-Mooney or Ian Mooney
Founded in 1974, providing conservation and restoration of paintings, prints and watercolours by qualified conservation graduates of Gateshead Conservation College. Undertakes work for museums, church dioceses and private clients. Relining, wood panel and miniatures repairs, and large paintings are specialities.
Price range Subject to an hourly rate or quote.

Eddie Sinclair
10 Park Street, Crediton
EX17 3EQ
T 01363 775552
E eddie@sinclair-polychromy.co.uk
Operating since 1979, conserving and researching medieval materials and techniques in historic buildings such as Exeter and Salisbury Cathedrals. Has published and lectured widely on aspects of historical painting techniques and has acted as a consultant to the BBC.

Egan, Matthews & Rose
12 Douglas Court, West Henderson's Wynd, Dundee
DD1 5BY
T 01382 229772
F 01382 229772
E eganmatthewsrose@uk2.net
Carries out all aspects of structural work, cleaning and restoration of easel paintings, including works on fabric, wood and metal supports. Experienced in working on site, on collections and on outsized paintings. Also undertakes collection surveys and loan reports. Welcomes enquiries seeking advice on any aspect of the care of easel paintings.

Ellen L. Breheny
10 Glenisla Gardens, Edinburgh
EH9 2HR
T 0131 6672620
E ellen@breheny.com
Contact Ellen L Breheny
Founded in 1988 for the conservation and restoration of ceramics, vessel glass and related

materials, e.g. enamels, jade, plastics and non-architectural plaster.

Fitzgerald Conservation
The Rise, Sevenoaks
TN13
T 01732 460096
F 01732 460096
E julie.fitzgerald1@virgin.net
Specializes in the conservation of works of art on paper, including prints and drawings, watercolours, photographs, parchment, pith and wallpapers. Conservation assessments and treatments carried out. Consultations, surveys, preservation programs and environmental advice and disaster advice given. Also offers training seminars and workshops.

Graham Bignell Paper Conservation
Standpoint Studios, 45 Coronet Street, London
N1 6HD
T 020 77293161
F 020 77293161
E graham.bignell@talk21.com
Contact Graham Bignell
Founded in 1980, the studio specializes in the conservation of art on paper, prints and drawing, maps, posters and archives. Experts in flood damage and framing.

Halahan Associates
38 Kitson Road, London
SE5 7LF
T 020 77030806
F 020 77030806
E halahan@dircon.co.uk
Contact Frances Halahan
Offers pragmatic advice on collection care issues. Specializes in exhibition work, condition surveys, audits of collections, advising on storage solutions and environmental regulation and pest control for museums and galleries. Also undertakes remedial conservation work for museums and galleries and private collections. Over fifteen years of experience in the museum sector.

Hamish Dewar Ltd
14 Mason's Yard, Duke Street, St James's, London
SW1Y 6BU
T 020 79304004
F 020 79304100
E hamish@hamishdewar.co.uk
Contact Hamish Dewar

Established in 1980, specializing in the conservation and restoration of paintings.

Ines Santy Paintings Conservation and Restoration
15 Leopold Place, Edinburgh
EH7 5LB
T 0131 5565002
F 0131 5565002
E santy.restorer@virgin.net
Started in 1998, specializing in conservation and restoration of oil paintings on canvas and panel. Undertakes interventive treatment (e.g. surface cleaning, varnish removal, retouching) and structural work (consolidation of paint or ground layers, strip-lining, lining, replacement of stretchers, conservation framing). Small repairs may be undertaken to accompanying frames.

International Fine Art Conservation Studios Ltd
43–45 Park Street, Bristol
BS1 5NL
T 0117 9293480 / 020 85491671
F 0117 9225511
E enquiries@ifacs.co.uk
W www.ifacs.co.uk
Contact Richard Pelter ACR FBAPCR
Established in 1969 and has been involved in conservation projects throughout the UK and overseas. A fully qualified team can accommodate paintings of any size. Other services include technical research and paint analysis schemes.

Jane McAusland Ltd
Flat 3, 41 Lexington Street, Soho, London
W1F 9AJ
T 020 74371070
F 01449 770689
E janemca@globalnet.co.uk
Contact Jane McAusland
A large, well-equipped studio founded in 1970. Conserves fine art on paper from any period including pastels and Oriental works. Also offers advice on general conservation of paper supported art through storage and display.
Price range From £100

Judith Gowland
Leases Barn, Braiseworth, Eye
IP23 7DS
T 01379 871556 / 07714 895916
E paperdoc@madasafish.com

Established in 1992, specializing in conservation of works of art on paper.

Judith Wetherall (trading as J.B. Symes)
28 Silverlea Gardens, Horley, Surrey
RH6 9BB
T 01293 775024
F 01293 775024
E judith@thewetheralls.org.uk
Contact Judith Wetherall
A studio set up in 1977. Conservation, restoration and new work undertaken. Expert knowledge of gilding and paint history and techniques.

Julian Spencer-Smith
The Studio, 30a College Road, Woking
GU22 8BU
T 01483 726070
F 01483 726070
E jupastudio@btconnect.com
W www.picturerestorer.com
Contact Julian Spencer-Smith
Founded in 1982. Restorers and conservators of oil paintings. Cleaning and restoration work uses minimal intervention and follows ethical restoration standards in reversibility. Does all lining and structural work in-house.

Julie Crick Art Conservation
The Conservation Studio, Anstey Hall,
Maris Lane, Trumpington, Cambridge
CB2 2LG
T 01223 410586
E julie@crickcollins.com
Contact Julie Crick (Dip. Con.)
Founded in 1984. Undertakes the conservation and care of easel paintings on canvas or wood for museums, churches and collections large and small. Also offers advice on packing and transportation of paintings, on the best methods of protecting works of art and on repairing paintings if they become damaged. Will work on extremely large paintings down to very small ones.

Lesley Bower Paper Conservation
34 Park House Gardens, Twickenham
TW1 2DE
T 020 88929391
E bower@blueyonder.co.uk
W www.westlondonartists.co.uk
Provides surveys for small museums and undertakes preventive conservation including environmental control. Offers advice on storage and display and provides staff training.

Life – A New Life for Old Documents
87 St Georges Road, Great Yarmouth
NR30 2JR
T 01493 854395
E lorraine.pinch@paperconservation.fsnet.co.uk
W www.paperconservation.fsnet.co.uk
Has over a decade of experience in providing
conservation and preservation services to
institutions and individuals. All aspects of archives
and art on paper conservation and preservation are
undertaken, from large-scale projects to single
items, as well as photographic conservation.

Lucia Scalisi
13 Burnsall Street, London
SW3 3SR
T 020 73511532
E luciascalisi@ukonline.co.uk
Conservation of easel paintings. Formerly Senior
Conservator of Paintings at the Victoria & Albert
Museum.

Rachel Howells
61 Geraints Way, Cowbridge
CF71 7AY
T 01446 773038
F 01446 773038
E Rachel@RachelHowells.co.uk
W www.RachelHowells.co.uk
Working on a freelance basis since 1990. Main
activities include conservation and restoration,
including structural work, tear repair, linings,
and also surface treatments, cleaning and
consolidation. Work with artists in the past
has included giving advice on materials and
techniques, treating accidental damages, treating
mould growth, improving structural conditions
of canvases and accessory supports, and offering
advice on framing.

Ronald Moore Fine Art Conservation
Upper Sydcombe, Dorstone, Hay-on-Wye
HR3 6BA
T 01497 831566
E moorerestoration@aol.com
Thirty years' experience, with particular expertise
in fire, water, bomb and structural damage to
oil paintings and works on paper. Also offers
consultation and valuation services.

Rupert Harris Conservation
Studio 5c, Block A, No 1 Fawe Street, London
E14 6PD
T 020 75152020
F 020 79877994
E enquiries@rupertharris.com
W www.rupertharris.com
Contact Rupert Harris
Established in 1982 and appointed metalwork
conservation adviser to the National Trust in the
same year. Work covers bronze, lead, zinc and
electrotype sculpture, modern and contemporary
art, historical lighting, casting and replication,
gilding, consultancy and maintenance. Can advise
artists on the use of materials and paint finishes,
security fixings and maintenance of public
sculpture.

Simon Gillespie Studio
16 Albemarle Street, London
W1S 4HW
T 020 74930988
F 020 74930955
E info@simongillespie.com
W www.simongillespie.com
Founded in 1982, specializing in restoring
paintings. Advice on techniques and conservation
given.

Sophia Fairclough Ltd
34 Wellington Park, Clifton, Bristol
BS8 2UW
T 0117 3179615
E sophia@sophiafairclough.co.uk
Established a studio in 1980. Specializes in the
conservation of works of art on paper, particularly
twentieth-century and contemporary work. Also
gives advice and consultation on materials for
contemporary artists.
Price range Varies according to the nature of the
work. Estimates are always given before starting
work.

Taylor Pearce Ltd
Fishers Court, Besson Street, London
SE14 5AF
T 020 72529800
F 020 72778169
E admin@taylorpearce.co.uk
Founded in 1986. Sculpture conservators by
appointment to the Queen. Lists all major public
galleries and collections on client list. Carries out
restoration and conservation to sculpture, ranging
from classical to medieval to contemporary. Also
makes and installs (mainly stone) sculpture for
prominent contemporary artists and acts as
consultant exhibitions conservators to institutions
such as the Royal Academy and National Gallery.

Textile Conservancy Company Ltd
3A Pickhill Business Centre, Smallhythe Road, Tenterden
TN30 7LZ
T 01580 761600
F 01580 761600
E alex@textile-conservation.co.uk
W www.textile-conservation.co.uk
Contact Alexandra Seth-Smith
Founded in 1998, providing the cleaning and repair of historical textiles, rugs and tapestries. Clients include English Heritage, and National Maritime Museum, the Wellcome Trust Library and a variety of private collectors.

Valentine Walsh
3 Whitehorse Mews, London
SE1 7QD
T 020 72611691
F 020 74019049
E valentine@valentinewalsh.co.uk
W www.valentinewalsh.co.uk
Contact Valentine Walsh
Over twenty years' experience of conservation of easel paintings and polychrome sculpture and works for West End dealers and national museums on pieces from all art periods. Works to museum standards and advises on transport, insurance, care and maintenance and preventive conservation. Services include disaster response, collection surveys, condition reporting and scientific analysis. All work is fully documented.

Consultants

Artquest
University of the Arts London, 65 Davies Street, London
W1K 5DA
T 020 75146493
F 020 75146211
E info@artquest.org.uk
W www.artquest.org.uk
Contact Stephen Beddoe (Programme Manager)
Provides advice and information to London's visual arts sector. The programme responds to the professional needs of artists in the region throughout their careers by providing a website, telephone and email helpline, advisory sessions, and training and seminars. Support covers areas such as presenting and selling work, research and development of new work practices and techniques, financial advice and ongoing professional-development and training opportunities. Also provides a comprehensive legal advice archive and advice service for visual artists. The programme is funded by Arts Council England and University of the Arts London.

Bridgeman Art Library
17–19 Garway Road, London
W2 4PH
T 020 77274065
F 020 77928509
E celia.cokesteel@bridgeman.co.uk
W www.bridgemanart.co.uk
Contact Celia Coke-Steel
A commercial picture library established in 1972 by Harriet Bridgeman and specializing in images of art, history and culture. The archive holds approximately one million images from collections around the world, covering every aspect of art and including works by over five hundred artists in copyright. Operates a no-fee service for contemporary artists to administer their copyright and to sell reproduction licences in their work. Accepts 5 × 4 colour transparencies or digital files of 50-megabyte RGB tiffs.

Business Art Galleries
Curwen & New Academy Gallery, 34 Windmill Street, London
W1T 2JR
T 020 73234700
F 020 74363059
E gallery@curwengallery.com
W www.curwengallery.com
Among Britain's most established art consultancies, having been set up in 1978 as part of the Royal Academy to provide art to businesses. In 1988 the company moved premises and set up the New Academy Gallery in Fitzrovia. In the following years the company purchased the Curwen Gallery at 4 Windmill Street, originally set up in the area by the famous Curwen Studio in 1958. At the start of 2005, the galleries combined in one space at 34 Windmill Street.

Central House
Unit 12.1, 29 Fashion Street, London
E1 6PX
T 07973 439026
E elle@thecentralhouse.com
W www.thecentralhouse.com
Contact Elyse Eales

Founded in 2002, representing young contemporary British artists. Acts as consultants for developers, interior designers and corporate clients.

Contemporary Art Holdings
The Old Chapel, 14 London Road, Cirencester
GL7 1AE
T 01285 644990
F 01285 644992
E cah@contemporary-art-holdings.co.uk
W www.contemporary-art-holdings.co.uk
Contact Celia Wickham
A corporate art consultancy established in 1990. Specializes in providing art work for offices and commercial environments such as conference centres, hotels and exhibition spaces. Pieces range from original prints and paintings to fabric wall hangings, tapestries, contemporary glass and site specific sculpture. The consultancy also operates an art rental scheme. Artists wishing to submit their work for consideration should send images on disk together with an sae for returns.

Dickson Russell Art Management
23 St Peter's Square, London
W6 9NW
T 020 87419577 / 77337137
F 020 85639249
E dickson.russell@ntlworld.com
W www.dicksonrussell.co.uk
Contact Emma Russell or Rachel Dickson
Established in 1992 to offer comprehensive art-management services to public, corporate and private clients. Deals with acquisition, exhibition curation, commissioning and management of existing collections. Contemporary and period work sourced according to client requirements. Additional services offered include shipping, art handling, framing, restoration and valuation.

east73rd
19 Tintern Close, London
SW15 2HF
T 020 82465821
F 020 82465821
E info@east73rd.com
W www.east73rd.com
Contact Nicki Makris
A gallery established in 2000. Recently started concentrating solely on consultancy work, offering corporate and private clients a cross-section of contemporary art, ranging from highly representational to completely abstract. Artists supported are up-and-coming painters, photographers and sculptors with work at affordable prices.

HS Projects
51 Balcombe Street, London
NW1 6HD
T 020 72842614
E info@hsprojects.com
W www.hsprojects.com
Over ten years' experience working with artists and businessmen. Work undertaken includes exhibitions, commissions, project management, contracts, workshops and advice. Does not represent artists except on a project basis when retained by the artist. Arrange appointment to visit office.

Impact Art
The Lodge, Warren Cottage, Station Road, North Chailey
BN8 4HQ
T 01444 473878
E art@impactart.co.uk
W www.impactart.co.uk
Contact Belinda Holden
An independent art consultancy that delivers professionally managed programmes of site-specific art and environmental works involving artists from a broad spectrum of disciplines. Projects range from large-scale public commissioning programmes to commercial headquarters and smaller-scale projects sourcing art works. Notice of open-competition projects are through the national art press. However, as commissioners they will view new work for consideration. Initial contact via email.

International Intelligence on Culture
4 Baden Place, Crosby Row, London
SE1 1YW
T 020 74037001
F 020 74032009
E enquiry@intelculture.org
W www.intelculture.org
An international cultural consultancy, operating a free enquiry service on behalf of Arts Council England, providing information for UK-based arts practitioners and organizations seeking to work internationally. This includes international contacts, opportunities and sign posting to funding.

Mac Medicine Ltd
90 Elmore Street, London
N1 3AL
T 07968 271048
E help@macmedicine.net
W www.macmedicine.net
Offers web design advice to artists.

nobleART
63 Stanley Road, Cambridge
CB5 8LF
T 01223 306298
E nobleart@nobleart.plus.com
W www.noble-art.co.uk
Contact Guy Noble
Founded in 2000. An art consultancy for homes
and businesses offering contemporary art at
affordable prices.

plan art consultants
63 Squirries Street, Bethnal Green, London
E2 6AJ
T 020 77393007
F 020 77393189
E art@plan-art.co.uk
W www.plan-art.co.uk
Contact Ivan Tennant
Founded in 1997. Includes a multidisciplinary
team of consultants who advise on all aspects of
the development and implementation of public,
corporate and hotel art strategies.

Royal Jelly Factory
11 Kemp House, 103 Berwick Street, London
W1F 0QT
T 020 77346032
F 0870 0549832
E info@royaljellyfactory.com
W www.royaljellyfactory.com
Web-design and coding services aimed primarily at
those involved in the arts, particularly individual
artists and small-scale organizations.

Sheeran Lock Ltd
The Mansion House, Church Lane, Market Hill,
Framlingham
IP13 9EQ
T 01728 621126
E imogenlock@sheeranlock.com
W www.sheeranlock.com
Contact Imogen Lock
Founded in 1990 by John Sheeran, an art curator,
and Imogen Lock, a specialist in communications.
Creates art exhibitions, competitions, events and

education programmes, and is best known for the
ways it cross-fertilizes art, education and business.
Helps artists maximize their potential and
develop their careers through its artist consultancy
service, as well as by organizing retrospective and
thematic exhibitions, publishing catalogues and
monographs, and creating websites for artists.
Also generates cultural projects commissioned
and sponsored by the corporate sector.

Snowgoose
12 Chaytor Terrace South, Craghead
DH9 6AZ
T 01207 290639
F 01207 299791
E info@snowgoose.co.uk
W www.snowgoose.co.uk
Designs and builds websites for artists and
designers.

Southern Arts Touring Exhibition Service
Winchester School of Art, Park Avenue,
Winchester
SO23 8DL
T 01962 852500
E sates@soton.ac.uk
W www.soton.ac.uk/~sates/
Contact Kate Maple (Exhibitions Coordinator)
An exhibition service operated by the Winchester
Gallery at Winchester School of Art, University of
Southampton, and supported by Southern Arts. Its
role is to provide exhibitions of contemporary
visual art, including craft, for venues of all kinds,
and to manage related visual projects.

Thomas Corman Arts
24 Daleham Gardens, London
NW3 5DA
T 020 74331339
F 020 74331339
E tca@btinternet.com
W www.thomascormanarts.com
Contact Ruth Corman
Specializes in consultancy for both corporate and
private clients. Clients can choose from over three
hundred artists and makers producing paintings,
prints, photography, textile art, wall hangings,
contemporary ceramics, metalwork and sculpture.

Workplace Art Consultancy
Studio G1, Tea Building, 56 Shoreditch High
Street, London
E1 6JJ
T 020 77397500

F 020 77298170
E enquiries@wacart.com
W www.wacart.com
Contact Kelvin Graham
A corporate, residential, healthcare and digital-art consultancy established in 1990. Also has a 3,000 sq. ft gallery in Shoreditch, which holds regular exhibitions. Clients include the Bank of England, the Ministry of Defence, the Bank of New York, Reuters and the Institute of Directors. Also works extensively with architects and designers both in the UK and abroad. Current interest is the application of digital art for the built environment.

Founders and art manufacturers

AB Fine Art Foundry Ltd
1 Fawe Street, London
E14 6PD
T 020 75158052
F 020 79877339
E enquiries@abfineart.com
W www.abfineart.com
Contact Henry or Jerry

Art Bronze Foundry (London) Ltd
1–3 Michael Road, Kings Road, London
SW6 2ER
T 020 77367292
F 020 77315460
E service@artbronze.co.uk
W www.artbronze.co.uk
Contact Philip Freiensener

Art Cast
36 Southwell Road, London
E5
T 020 77338424

Art Founders Ltd
9 Swinborne Drive, Springwood Industrial Estate, Braintree
CM7 2YP
T 01376 343222
F 01376 341793
E info@artfounders.co.uk
W www.artfounders.co.uk

Bronze Age Sculpture Casting Foundry Ltd and Limehouse Gallery
272 Island Row, Basin Approach, Limehouse, London
E14 7HY

T 020 75381388
F 020 75389723
E info@bronzeage.co.uk
W www.bronzeage.co.uk
Contact Susan Rolfe (Production and General Manager)
Established for over fifteen years, offering a full service to artists looking to cast their sculpture into bronze. Service includes scaling up and on-site moulding.

Cast Iron Co. Ltd
8 Old Lodge Place, Twickenham
TW1 1RQ
T 020 87449992
F 020 87441121
E info@castiron.co.uk
W www.castiron.co.uk
Contact Gary Young
Founded in 1987, specializing in casting in iron, bronze, etc. and in fabrication. Specialists in architectural metalwork and restoration. Able to work with sculptor to produce patterns, moulds and castings in any metal type.

Castle Fine Art Foundry
N6b Inchbrook Trading Estate, Bath Road, Woodchester, Stroud
GL5 5EY
T 01453 836123

Lakeland Mouldings
Soulby, Pooley Bridge, Penrith
CA11 0JF
T 017684 86989
F 017684 86989
E anne@lakelandmouldings.co.uk
W www.lakelandmouldings.co.uk
Contact Anne Woods
A freelance mouldmaking and resin casting company with over fifteen years' experience. Offers a professional service to individual sculptors, businesses, galleries and giftware manufacturers. Able to produce silicone moulds and resin casts from original pieces of work.

Livingstone Art Founders
Maidstone Road, Matfield, Tonbridge
TN12 7LQ
T 01892 722474

LS Sculpture Casting
367 Westcott Venture Park, Westcott, Aylesbury
HP18 0XB

T 01296 658884
F 01296 658882

Lunts Castings Ltd
Unit 7, Hawthorns Industrial Estate, Middlemore Road, Birmingham
B21 0BJ
T 0121 5514301
F 0121 5237954
W www.luntscastings.co.uk

MFH Art Foundry
Unit 1, Product Work Shop, Lains Farm, Quarley, Andover
SP11 8PX
T 01264 889898

Mike Smith Studio
Unit 4, 709 Old Kent Road, London
SE15 1JZ
T 020 72775377
F 020 72775420
E mail@mikesmithstudio.com
W www.mikesmithstudio.com
The studio was started in 1989 by Michael Smith. Works with all materials and processes appropriate to realizing a project, with the exception of metal casting. Studio occupies 10,000 sq. ft and is fully equipped to handle projects of any scale. Works with artists, architects, designers and other clients in a variety of ways, including fabricaton, consultancy, design development, production, installation and project management. Has a worldwide client base.

Milwyn Casting
Old Brook Farm, Murthering Lane, Navestock, nr Romford
RM4 1HL
T 01277 373779
E mwcast@artistsfolio.com
Contact Alex Davies
A fine-art foundry offering bronze-casting, steel fabrication and a silicon mouldmaking service.

Morris Singer Ltd
Highfield Site, Church Lane, Lasham
GU34 5SQ
T 01256 381033
F 01256 381565
E info@morrissinger.co.uk
W www.morrissinger.co.uk
Contact Chris Boverhoff

A sculpture-casting foundry, founded in 1848. Services include art-work enlarging, lost wax and sand casting, installation and restoration.

Pangolin Editions
Unit 9, Chalford Industrial Estate, Chalford
GL6 8NT
T 01453 886527
F 01453 731499
E sales@pangolin-editions.com
W www.pangolin-editions.com

Powderhall Bronze
29–30 Stewartfield, Edinburgh
EH6 5RQ
T 0131 5553013
F 0131 5553013
E briancaster@caster.worldonline.co.uk
W www.powderhallbronze.co.uk

Framers

A. Bliss
5 Bakers Yard, Bakers Row, London
EC1R 3HF
T 020 78374959
F 020 78378244
E edward@abliss.co.uk
W www.abliss.co.uk
Contact Edward Mawby
Specialist fine-art dry-mounters of photographs and digital prints onto many surfaces, including aluminium and glass.

Acacia Works
20 Gayal Croft, Shenley Brook End, Milton Keynes
MK5 7HX
T 01908 501268
E trudy@acaciaworks.co.uk
W www.acaciaworks.co.uk
Contact Trudy Phillips
Offers picture-framing and mount-cutting up to museum standard. Art commissions also undertaken and full consultancy service available. Original art and prints available.

Alec Drew Picture Frames Ltd
7 Cale Street, Chelsea Green, London
SW3 3QT
T 020 73528716
F 020 73528716
E framing@alec-drew.demon.co.uk

W www.alec-drew.co.uk
Founded in 1977. A bespoke framer, mainly catering to the local area. Offers a full framing service from simple certificates to Gesso and gilded frames via perspex or hand-laid veneer. Can also recommend restorers or picture-hangers.

Art & Frame
35 South Parade, Yate Shopping Centre, Yate
BS37 4BB
T 01454 327010
E info@artandframe.co.uk
W www.artandframe.co.uk
Contact John Evans
Offers a full range of framing services, with a wide selection of frames to choose from in both traditional and contemporary styles. Mounts are only cut from conservation- and museum-quality boards, with a choice of many colours and textures. Also stocks a large range of artist materials, readymade frames and mounts.

Art and Soul
G14 Belgravia Workshops, 157 Marlborough Road, London
N19 4NF
T 020 72630421
E becxb@hotmail.com
W www.artandsoulframes.com
Contact Rebecca Bramwell
A framing service with a wide range of mouldings, box-frames, acid-free mounts, etc. Established in 1989 by St Martin's graduate Rebecca Bramwell. Happy to offer advice to artists.

Artisan for Unusual Things
80 London Road, Teynham
ME9 9QH
T 01795 522121
F 01795 520744
Contact Melanie Clews
Established in 1985. A retail shop and workshops specializing in design-led miscellanea for contemporary and classic interiors. Offers bespoke on-site framing for two- and three-dimensional items, whenever possible utilizing recycled materials.

Attic Picture Framing Supplies
11 Boulton Industrial Centre, Hockley, Birmingham
B18 5AU
T 0121 5515454
F 0121 2135072

E frame.tec@virgin.net
Contact Peter Frith
Supplies framing materials to the trade and public. A large range of mouldings in stock and a full range of mounting boards, along with all the sundries required for framing. Can either frame art work from start to finish or supply kits that include frame rims, pre-cut mounts, glass and backing. Will send samples of frames on request.

Barbers
18 Chertsey Road, Woking
GU21 5AB
T 01483 769926
Contact Stuart Herring
Under present management since 1985. Offers a full bespoke and contract picture-framing service. Stocks a wide range of artist materials and houses a modern gallery providing exhibition possibilities.

Bourlet Fine Art Frame Makers
32 Connaught Street, London
W2 2AF
F 020 77244837
E gabrielle@bourlet.co.uk
W www.bourlet.co.uk
Contact Gabrielle Rendell
Founded in 1838. Gilders, carvers and restorers specializing in making fine-art frames for period and contemporary art. Clients include museums in the UK and overseas, interior designers, West End galleries, artists and private collectors.
Price range From £150

Campbell's of London
1–5 Exhibition Road, London
SW7 2HE
T 020 75849268
F 020 75813499
E wendel.clement@campbellsoflondon.co.uk
W www.campbellsoflondon.co.uk
Contact W. Clement
Founded in 1966, stocking one of the largest collections of handmade frames in the UK. Campbell's gallery (£1,000 to £3,000 per week) also carries a range of original paintings and signed limited-edition prints. Consultancy service available.

Darbyshire Frame Makers
90 Leather Lane, London
EC1N 7TT
T 020 78310028
F 020 78311128

E enquiries@darbyshire.uk.com
W www.darbyshire.uk.com
Contact Sharon Simons, Dan Edwards or
Laura Beveridge
Founded in 1992. A leading framer and art
fabricator to the contemporary art world. Aims
to provide the right creative solution through a
process of collaborative consultation.

Frame Tec
8 Greenfield Road, Harborne, Birmingham
B170EE
T 0121 4281038
E frame.tec@virgin.net
Contact Peter Frith
Founded in 1988, a picture-framer and art gallery
specializing in original art exhibited on a sale-or-
return basis. Although art work is vetted, it is
not necessary that it is framed as the gallery can
undertake this and add the cost onto the selling
price. Charges a commission on sales of thirty-
three per cent plus VAT, but does not charge for
hanging space.

Framework Picture Framing
5–9 Creekside, Deptford, London
SE8 4SA
T 020 86915140
F 020 86922266
E enquiries@frameworkgallery.co.uk
W www.frameworkgallery.co.uk
Contact Adrian Morris-Thomas
Founded in 1988. A specialist bespoke picture-
framer with a large range of mouldings. All
materials used are of conservation quality.
Acrylic frames and dry-mounting available.
A large workshop and experienced team of framers
can accommodate most framing requirements.
Free consultation. Also available are exhibition-
standard readymade frames. Premises include
the Framework Gallery, showing contemporary
fine art.

Framing Fantastic
149 Sevenmile Straight, Muckamore, Antrim
BT41 4QT
T 028 94432009
F 028 94439287
E info@framingfantastic.co.uk
W www.framingfantastic.co.uk
Contact Shane Noble
A bespoke picture-framing and computerized
mount-cutting service. Online ordering of
standard core mounts available.

Framing Workshop
80 Walcot Street, Bath
BA1 5BD
T 01225 482748
F 01225 422910
E framing@theframingworkshop.com
W www.theframingworkshop.com
Offers a comprehensive framing service.
Expertise in hand-finishing skills including
gilding, painting, liming and staving. Stocks
over 120 plain wood and five hundred finished
mouldings including swept, oral and circular
frames. Also home to art work by established local
artists including Peter Brown and Nick Cudworth.

Frandsen Fine Art Framers Ltd
7 Lillie Yard, Fulham, London
SW6 1UB
T 020 73859930
F 020 76101404
E frandsenframes@msn.com
Contact Derek Tanous
A family business for nearly one hundred years.
Specializes in handmade frames and the
restoration of frames, colouring and guilding.

Frank B. Scragg & Co.
68 Vittoria Street, Birmingham
B1 3PB
T 0121 2367219
F 0121 2363633
E sales@frankscragg.co.uk
W www.frankscragg.co.uk
Contact John Lewis
A long-established company distributing a wide
range of items for framing and hanging pictures,
including the Gallery Hanging System of rods and
sliding hooks. Free catalogue on request.

Fringe Arts Picture Framers
'Great Down', Hog's Back, Seale, Farnham
GU10 1HD
T 01483 810555
F 0870 7482254
E lyn@fringearts.co.uk
W www.fringearts.co.uk
Contact Lyn Hall
Run by Lyn Hall, with over twenty-one years
of bespoke framing experience. Offers a wide
range of specialisms, including handling textiles
(modern and traditional), conservation framing,
specialist mount-cutting skills, and canvas-
stretching. Currently working for a large number
of well-known and amateur artists.

Gallery 2000
11–13 Windle Court, Clayhill Park, Neston
CH64 3UH
T 0151 3531522
F 0151 3531300
E art@gallery2000.co.uk
W www.gallery2000.co.uk
Contact Jenny Holland
A family business founded in 1986 by resident
artist Jenny Holland. Prints and originals,
watercolours and oils. Local scenes, Lake District,
North Wales and Anglesey, Isle of Man, Ireland,
Wirral, Liverpool and Chester. Specialist framer of
pictures and all memorabilia. Readymade frames
and decorative mounts, 'while-you-wait' service.
Comprehensive stock of artists' materials. In-
house, scanning and wide-format giclée printing.
Illustrated website with international shopping
basket for UK local scenes, dispatched worldwide.

Goslings
50 Station Road, Sudbury
CO10 2SP
T 01787 371932
Contact Miss W. Allen
In business for over twenty-five years, offering
a full picture-framing service and stocking art
materials. Accompanying gallery holds exhibitions
throughout the year.

Ian Dixon GCF Bespoke Framers
White Timbers, Forest Road, East Horsley
KT24 5ER
T 01483 282059
F 01483 282059
E dixonframes@btinternet.com
Contact Ian Dixon GCF
All types of framing undertaken including
originals, photographs, prints, needlework,
medals, memorabilia and sports equipment.
Conservation framing and repairs. Computerized
mount-cutting service (single or multi-aperture).
Corporate work welcomed.

J&M Framework
5 Station Parade, Woodthorpe Road, Ashford
TW15 2RX
T 01784 258800
F 01784 250503
E info@jandmframework.com
W www.jandmframework.com
Contact Jim Cowell
Established for twenty years, specializing in
readymade picture frames and mounts. Can also
make frames to size from an extensive range of
mouldings.

J.A. & G.J. Cowell (trading as Thomas Ellis)
7 Beaumont Street, Hexham
NE46 3LZ
T 01434 602050
Established 1829. Picture-framing (tapestries,
needleworks, etc.). Artists' supplies by Daler-
Rowney. Picture sales, including local artists.

Largs Hardware Services & Gallery Eight
3–11 Stanlane Place, Largs
KA30 8DA
T 01475 672634
F 01475 672634
Founded in 1888, offering a picture-framing
service in an on-site workshop. Also houses a
gallery and sells artists' materials.

Leighswood Art and Publishing
Unit 10, Lion Industrial Park, Northgate Way,
Aldridge nr Walsall
WS9 8AY
T 01922 458424
E duncan@leighswoodart.com
W www.leighswoodart.com
Founded in 1996 as a picture-framing business
alongside selling local artists' works. Specializes in
all aspects of framing and also produces giclée
prints. Recently started publishing fine-art prints
and marketing them to galleries throughout the
UK. Currently represents seven artists, covering all
styles and subjects. New artists and all quality
submissions will be considered.

Litchfield Artists' Centre
6 Southampton Road, Lymington
SO41 9GG
T 01590 672503
E artistsmaterials@yahoo.co.uk
W www.litchfieldartistscentre.co.uk
Contact P.D. Merrick
Founded in 1974 and still owned and run by the
same husband-and-wife team, offering a complete
framing service, undertaken by the proprietors in
own workshop. Also sells artists' materials,
stocking many major brands. Postal service
available.

Michael Hackman
Kite Hill Studios, Kite Hill, Selborne, Alton
GU34 3LA
T 01420 511524

F 01420 511491
E m.hackman@btclick.com
Contact Michael Hackman
Has been producing frames for clients including designers, hotels, artists and retail stores for the past fifteen years. Specializes in hand-finished frames using gesso, oil and water gilding, and a variety of paint finishes to client's specification. Works in solid woods, producing frame widths of up to 180mm in one section.

Millennium Fine Art & Framing Ltd

43 Drury Lane, Solihull
B91 3BP
T 0121 7053323
E solihull@millenniumfineart.co.uk
W www.millenniumfineart.co.uk

Newcastle Arts Centre

67 Westgate Road, Newcastle-upon-Tyne
NE1 1SG
T 0191 2615618
F 0191 2330525
E venue@newcastle-arts-centre.co.uk
W www.newcastlearts.co.uk
Contact Mike Tilley
Founded in 1981, the centre includes Frameshop for framing, a recently upgraded art gallery and an arts materials store online at www.details.co.uk.

Old Church Galleries

98 Fulham Road, Chelsea, London
SW3 6HS
T 020 75918790
F 020 75918791
E sales@oldchurchgalleries.com
W www.oldchurchgalleries.com
A bespoke picture-framing and mounting service, from conservation to museum standards. Offers a large choice of handmade and manufactured frames and decorative mounts, as well as stretching and oil and paper restoration services.

Paul Mitchell Ltd

17 Avery Row, Brook Street, London
W1K 4BF
T 020 74938732
F 020 74097136
E admin@paulmitchell.co.uk
W www.paulmitchell.co.uk
Contact Paul Mitchell or Mary Ross-Trevor
Provides a comprehensive framing and conservation service. From an extensive inventory of antique European frames, the company is able to supply dealers, auctioneers, museums and private collectors worldwide with expertly researched framing proposals.

Paul Treadaway

Field Cottage, North Road, Widmer End
HP15 6ND
T 01494 713918
F 01494 713918
E paul@fineartframes.co.uk
W www.fineartframes.co.uk,
www.verre-eglomise.com
Founded in 1970. A maker and gilder of replica antique frames for drawings, watercolours and prints. Also offers restoration and gilding of antique picture frames. A maker of *verre-eglomise* glass mounts for antique and contemporary art work.

Pendragon Frames

1–3 Yorkton Street, London
E2 8NH
T 020 77290608
F 020 77297711
E sales@pendragonframes.com
W www.pendragonframes.com
Dedicated to producing fine handmade frames using conservation techniques. Has undertaken much work in the museums and galleries sector. Portfolio of clients also includes photographers, artists, private collectors, consultants and companies.

pictureframes.co.uk

Unit 22d, Wincombe Business Park, Shaftesbury
SP7 9QJ
T 0845 2267249
E mail@pictureframes.co.uk
W www.pictureframes.co.uk
Contact Hope Elletson
A professional framer since 1989, offering full bespoke framing up to museum standard including gilding, etc. Website offers custom-made picture frames direct to the door. Experienced in large-scale projects including installation and offers training in hand-finishing and gilding.

Railings Gallery

5 New Cavendish Street, London
W1G 8UT
T 020 79351114
F 020 74869250
E artists@railings-gallery.com
W www.railings-gallery.com

Contact Geihle Sander
Founded in 1980. An in-house framing workshop offering artists and photographers advice and competitive prices for framing for exhibitions and one-off bespoke frames, using conservation materials. Also stocks contemporary limited-edition original prints and paintings with a figurative or abstract feel.

Renaissance 2
36 Town End, Golcar, Huddersfield
HD7 4NL
T 01484 659596
E info@renaissance2.co.uk
W www.renaissance2.co.uk
Contact Diane Myzak
Offers bespoke and small-run picture-framing services to artists and photographers with an emphasis on innovative design. Also produces and sells limited-edition giclée prints.

Riccardo Giaccherini Ltd
39 Newman Street, London
W1T 1QB
T 020 75801783
F 020 76375221
E louise.liddell@riccardogiaccherini.co.uk
Contact Louise Liddell (Proprietor)
A traditional Florentine-style workshop, specializing in handmaking, joining, carving and gilding mirror and picture frames. Old Master and contemporary works framed by international staff.

Simon Beaugié Picture Frames Ltd
Manor Farm Workshops, Ashford
TN26 1NL
T 01233 733353
F 01233 732354
E framing@simonbeaugie.com
Established for over ten years, offering a comprehensive conservation picture-framing service. Also provides gilding and photography services. Free collection and delivery service in Central London.

Wallace Brown Studio
10 Duke Street, Bedford
MK40 3HR
T 01234 360237
F 012234 360237
Contact Wally Greenaway
Founded in 1960. A framer offering a complete bespoke and readymade contract service to the trade, industry and professionals alike. The

modern studio incorporates up-to-date equipment together with an experienced workforce.

Art insurance

Aon Artscope
8 Devonshire Square, Cutlers Gardens, London
EC2M 4PL
T 020 78820470
F 020 78820383
E artscope@aon.co.uk

AXA Art Insurance Ltd
106 Fenchurch Street, London
EC3M 5JE
T 020 72654600
F 020 77020016
E info@axa-art.co.uk
W www.axa-art.co.uk
Contact Helen George
Provides specialist cover to private and corporate collectors, museums, galleries, exhibitions and dealers worldwide.

Carroll & Partners
2 White Lion Court, Cornhill, London
EC3V 3NP
T 020 76232228

Crowley Colosso
Friary Court, Crutched Friars, London
EC3N 2NP
T 020 75603104
F 020 75603655

Gwennap Stevenson Brown Ltd
1 Tomlins Corner, Queen Street, Gillingham
SP8 4DJ
T 01747 821188
F 01747 821177

Hallett Independent
1 Wellington Place, Captains Row, Lymington
S041 9RS
T 01590 672888
F 01590 673222
E info@hallettindependent.com

Heath Lambert Group
Friary Court, Crutched Friars, London
EC3N 2NP
T 020 72344227

F 020 72344267
E rnorthcott@heathlambert.com
W www.heathlambert.com
Contact Richard Northcott
One of the largest brokers in the London market for fine art, collectibles and private jewelry. Caters for clients ranging from galleries and museums to individual private collectors, corporate collectors, art and antique dealers and shippers. Acts for many major museums and galleries in the UK and Europe as well as arranging exhibitions worldwide.

Hiscox PLC
1 Great St Helen's, London
EC3A 6HX
T 020 74486000
F 020 74486797
E enquiry@hiscox.co.uk
W www.hiscox.com

HSBC Insurance Brokers Ltd
Jewelry and Fine Arts Division, Bishops Court, 27–33 Artillery Lane, London
E1 7LP
T 020 72475433
F 020 73772139
W www.insurancebrokers.hsbc.com/hsbc/jewellery
Contact Bruno LeRoy

Insurancenow Services Ltd
1st Floor, 413a Chingford Road, Walthamstow, London
E17 5AF
T 020 85315336
F 020 85274527
E paul@insurancenow.co.uk
W www.insurancenow.co.uk
Contact Paul
Established in 1999, incorporating an insurance directory website that provides links to specialist fine-art insurers.

Masterpiece
Chubb Insurance Company of Europe S.A., 106 Fenchurch Street, London
EC3M 5NB
T 0800 111511
W www.chubb.com/international/uk/personal/jewellery.html

Phillippa Levy & Associates
19 Louisa Street, London
E1 4NF

T 020 77901963
F 020 77904100
E leavypitt@aol.com
Contact Phillippa Levy
Established in 1981, offering insurance to artists and craftspeople (public/employers' liability, exhibitions, studio contents). All policies are tailormade to individual needs. Exhibitions covered worldwide, including transit to and from venue. Personal accident cover also available.

Society for All Artists (SAA)
P.O. Box 50, Newark
NG23 5GY
T 01949 844050
F 01949 844051
E info@saa.co.uk
W www.saa.co.uk

T.H. March & Co. Ltd
Hare Park House, Yelverton Business Park, Yelverton
PL20 7LS
T 01822 855555
F 01822 855566
E insurance@thmarch.co.uk
W www.thmarch.co.uk

Willis
Fine Art, Jewelry and Specie Division, 10 Trinity Square, London
EC3P 3AX
T 020 74888111
E molloyl@willis.com

Windsor Insurance Brokers Ltd
Fine Art and Antiquities Division, Lyon House, 160–166 Borough High Street, London
SE1 1JR
T 020 74077144

Packers and shippers

01 Art Services Ltd
Unit 2, Towcester Road, London
E3 3ND
T 020 75157510
F 020 75382479
E info@01artservices.co.uk
W www.01artservices.co.uk
Contact Liz Cooper
Founded in 1992, specializing in the transportation, installation and storage of fine art

within the UK. Can cater for all types of project, from the carriage or hanging of a single art work to the management and coordination of whole exhibitions and collections. Client base includes leading artists, galleries, museums, consultants, fine framers, designers, and corporate and private collectors.

3 Lanes Transport Ltd
5 Albany Terrace, St Ives
TR26 2BS
T 07970 948324
F 01736 798400
E info@3lanes.com
W www.3lanes.com

Anglo Pacific
Units 1 & 2 Bush Industrial Estate, Standard Road, North Acton, London
NW10 6DF
T 020 89651234
F 020 89654954
E info@anglopacific.co.uk
W www.anglopacific.co.uk

Art Move Ltd
Unit 3, The Arches, Grant Road, London
SW11 2NU
T 020 75851801
F 020 72230241
E mail@artmove.co.uk
W www.artmove.co.uk
Contact Alistair Adie
Founded in 1983. Transports, stores and installs art works, from single pieces to whole shows. Also provides an export packing service and ships worldwide. Has regular (weekly) run between London and Scotland at part-load prices from £70 plus AT (also the minimum charge for work around London).

C'Art
Unit 7, Brunel Court, Enterprise Drive, Four Ashes, Wolverhampton
WV10 7DF
T 01902 791797
F 01902 790687
E info@cart.uk.com
W www.cart.uk.com

Cadogan Tate Fine Art Logistics
6–12 Ponton Road, London
SW8 5BA
T 020 78196611
F 020 78196601
E c.evans@cadogantate.com
W www.cadogantate.com
Contact Chris Evans
Professional packers and shippers of art. Offices in London, New York and Paris. Weekly shuttle service to Paris, Geneva and Zurich. London warehouse is bonded allowing art to be stored in bond VAT unpaid. Private temperature-controlled vaults also available.

Constantine Ltd
Constantine House, 134 Queen's Road, London
SE15 2HR
T 020 77328124
F 020 77322631
E reception@const.co.uk
W www.constantinemoving.com

Damon Bramley
Box Cottage, Viney Woodside, Lydney
GL15 4LX
T 01599 510365
F 01599 510365
E damon@boxcottage.plus.com
Contact Damon Bramley
A sculpture transport and installation company, trading for seven years. All aspects of transport and installation undertaken. Exhibitions moved. Insurance cover to £75,000.

Davies Turner Worldwide Movers
49 Wates Way, Mitcham
CR4 4HR
T 020 76224393
F 020 77203897
E T.Hutchison@daviesturner.co.uk
W www.daviesturner.com

Hedley's Humpers
3 St Leonard's Road, North Acton, London
NW10 6SX
T 020 89658733
F 020 89650249
E london@hedleyshumpers.com
W www.hedleyshumpers.com

HMC Logistics Ltd
Unit 21, Newington Industrial Estate, Crampton Street, London
SE17 3AZ
T 020 77031666
F 020 77036999
E info@hmclogistics.com

W www.hmclogistics.com
Contact Andy Keir

Kent Services Ltd

Unit 3 Phase 2, Grace Road, Sheerness
ME12 1DB
T 01795 660812
F 01795 669906
E ksl@kent-services.com
W www.kent-services.com
Contact Sheila Amey (Director)
Provides economical and ready access to a large
quantity of high-standard containers for safe and
secure transportation of art objects. Containers
also for sale. Small-quantity materials service.
Transportation and storage of cases for temporary
exhibitions.

Lockson UK

Unit 1, Heath Park Industrial Estate, Freshwater
Road, Chadwell Heath
RM8 1RX
T 020 85972889
F 020 85975265
E shipping@lockson.co.uk
W www.lockson.co.uk

M+G Transport & Technical Services

18 Maple Crescent, Rishton, Blackburn
BB1 4RJ
T 01254 884244
F 01254 884244
E enquiries@museumtransport.co.uk
W www.museumtransport.co.uk
Contact Karen Yates
Founded in 1997, providing transport and
technical services to museums, galleries, artists,
collectors, etc. Also offers picture-hanging,
exhibition installation, mounting and framing
services.

Momart Ltd

199–205 Richmond Road, London
E8 3NJ
T 020 89863624
F 020 85330122
E enquiries@momart.co.uk
W www.momart.co.uk
An acknowledged authority on the handling
of fine arts and antiquities. Services offered
include project management, transportation,
shipping, installation, case making, collection
management, bonded storage and airport
services.

Moving Experience

19A Alexandra Road, St John's Wood, London
NW8 0DP
T 020 74832501
F 020 74834088
E roberto@movexp.co.uk
W www.movexp.com
In business since 1997, offering picture-hanging
and art-installation services. Clients include
private individuals, artists, galleries, museums
and commercial companies. Charges are per art
installer and are for half a day (up to four hours) or
a full day (four to eight hours). Only installs and
hangs pictures; does not supply hanging systems.

MTec Freight Group

Unit 10, Gentlemans Field, Westmill Road, Ware
SG12 0EF
T 01920 461800
F 01920 466606
E info@mtechfreightgroup.com
W www.arttransport.com

Oxford Exhibition Services Ltd

Station Road, Uffington, Faringdon
SN7 7QD
T 01367 820713
F 01367 820504
E enquiries@oxex.co.uk
W www.oxex.co.uk
Contact Michael Festenstein (Managing Director)
Provides safe packing, secure domestic and
international shipping, storage and installation
of museum objects and works of art to the highest
standards of conservation and security.

Seabourne Mailpack Worldwide

13 Saxon Way, Moor Lane, Harmondsworth
UB7 0LW
T 020 83221700
F 020 83221701
E info@seabourne-mailpack.com
W www.seabourne-mailpack.com
Founded in 1962, offering a specialist collection,
packing and delivery service worldwide. In
conjunction with parent company Seabourne
Express Courier Ltd, any transit time can be
catered for. Services are often tailormade.

Sovereign International Freight Ltd

Sovereign House, 8–10 St Dunstans Road,
Feltham
TW13 4JU
T 020 87513131

F 020 87514517
E info@sovereignlondon.co.uk
W www.sovereignlondon.co.uk

T. Rogers & Co. Ltd
P.O. Box 8, 1a Broughton Street, London
SW8 3QL
T 020 76229151
F 020 76273318

Team Relocations
Drury Way, London
NW10 0JN
T 020 87840100
F 020 84510061
W www.teamrelocations.com

Printers, print publishers and printmakers

107 Workshop
The Courtyard, Bath Road, Shaw, Melksham
SN12 8EF
T 01225 791800
F 01225 790948
E 107w@shirrett.demon.co.uk
Established in 1976, with 7,000 sq. ft of fully
equipped studio space designed to enable artists
to create an environment suitable to their own
individual specifications. Processes available
include multiplate-printing using copper,
carborundum, liftground, aquatint, handpainting,
relief woodcut and mono-printing. Artists include
Ayers, Hodgkin, Hughes, Aitcheson, Heindorf and
Ackroyd. *Livres d'artiste* by Howard Hodgkin,
Kidner and Hayter.
Price range £800–£15,000

Abacus (Colour Printers) Ltd
Lowick House, Lowick, nr Ulverston
LA12 8DX
T 01229 885361
F 01229 885348
E sales@abacusprinters.co.uk
W www.abacusprinters.co.uk
The company has been established in Cumbria for
over eighteen years. Specializes in turning artists'
images into print. Offers high-quality 'waterless'
offset printing of postcards, greetings cards,
folders, posters, catalogues, calendars, limited-
edition prints and giclée prints. Potential

customers should contact Abacus for a free sample
pack.

Art Marketing Ltd
Unit 3, Redbourn Industrial Park, High Street,
Redbourn, nr St Albans
AL3 7LG
T 01582 794541
F 01582 792664
E sales@artmarketing.co.uk
W www.artmarketing.co.uk
Contact The Design Manager
A family company formed in 1980, developing
trading relationships with major high-street
retailers as well as 1,500 independent galleries
and lifestyle and home-interior stores. Employs
and publishes artists working on open edition,
original or limited-edition bases and supplies
products in many formats. Aims to develop and
encourage artists to identify popular furnishing
colour trends and themes to maximize their
success.

ArtChroma
P.O. Box 627, Portsmouth
PO6 2WZ
T 023 92387831
E info@artchroma.com
W www.artchroma.co.uk
Contact Roland Clarke
A UK giclée printer providing services for artists,
photographers, galleries and fine-art publishers.
Specializes in giclée printing onto fine-art paper or
canvas, and large-format poster printing.

Artline Media
Gloucester Place, Briston, Melton Constable
NR24 2LD
T 01263 860103
F 01263 860138
E phillip@artlinemedia.co.uk
W www.artlinemedia.co.uk
Contact Phillip Round
A division of a company established for thirty
years. Original roots were in the photographic
industry before moving over completely to digital
technology. For many years it has been supplying
high-quality prints, up to A3-size and, with a
recent investment in new equipment, it has
expanded range to include greetings cards and
up to A1-size giclée prints. Also in the process
of setting up an online art gallery where
customers can sell cards, prints and original
art work.

Beaver Lodge Prints Ltd

Units 25–26 Broomhills Industrial Estate, Braintree
CM7 2RW
T 01376 552558
F 01376 553881
E sales@beaverlodgeprints.co.uk
W www.beaverlodgeprints.co.uk
Contact James Arnold
A print-distribution company for over twelve years,
sourcing artists of modern and contemporary
art work to be published. Works on behalf of
publishers in Germany, Italy and the USA.

Broad Oak Colour Ltd

Units A&B 254 Broad Oak Road, Canterbury
CT2 7QH
T 01227 767856
F 01227 762593
E enquiries@broadoakltd.co.uk
W www.broadoakltd.co.uk
Contact Simon Young or Terry Tilbury
Colour printers for twenty-two years, producing
limited-edition prints on Bockingford paper, etc.

Dayfold Solvit

27 Black Moor Road, Ebblake Industrial Estate,
Verwood
BH31 6BE
T 01202 827141
F 01202 825841
E mark@dayfold.com
W www.dayfold.com
Contact Mark Smith
Founded in 1979. A fine-art lithographic printer
specializing in the production of high-quality
limited-edition prints and promotional material,
including show catalogues and leaflets.

DesignerPrint

8 Stafford Road, Southampton
SO15 5EA
T 023 80333564
F 023 80333564
E info@designerprint.co.uk
W www.designerprint.co.uk
Contact Peter Horner
A newly established Southampton-based company
specializing in printing images onto canvas, block-
mounting and poster-printing.

Digital Fine Art & Print

47 Great Western Studios, Paddington (New) Yard,
Great Western Road, London
W9 3NY
T 07754 702090
E info@dfap.co.uk
W www.dfap.co.uk
Contact Mat Sant
Established in 2003, producing large-format
digital giclée prints on artists' papers and canvas.
Specializes in printing limited editions for artists
and designers.

Dolphin Fine Art Printers

37 Nuffield Road, Nuffield Estate, Poole
BH17 0RA
T 01202 673048
F 01202 661500
E info@dolphin-printers.co.uk
W www.dolphin-printers.co.uk
Founded in 1970, producing open- and limited-
edition prints and giclée. Specializes in offering
guidance for those starting out.

East London Printmakers

Printmaking Studio, SPACE Studios,
The Triangle, 129 Mare Street, Hackney
E8 3RH
T 020 85254344 (SPACE Studios)
E info@eastlondonprintmakers.co.uk
W www.eastlondonprintmakers.co.uk
Contact Nick Morley (Studio Manager) or Anna
Alcock (Chairperson)
A group of contemporary artist–printmakers,
formed in 1998, running a spacious, modern
and newly equipped printmaking studio with
open access. Has equipment for water-based
screenprinting, copper-etching/intaglio, relief-
printing and fabric-printing. The studio is used
by rent-paying members, who have twenty-four-
hour access, and by open-access users who pay
per session.

Eyes Wide Digital Ltd

The Old Coach House, Unit 1, Charman Road,
Redhill
RH1 6AH
T 01737 780789
F 01737 780987
E info@eyeswidedigital.com
W www.eyeswidedigital.com
Contact Ian Ingle
Specializes in bespoke canvas printing.
Reproduces fine art onto canvas or art paper for
artists and galleries throughout Europe. Images
can be supplied in print format, as negatives or
transparencies, or as a digital file through email
or on CD.

Gemini Digital Colour Ltd
North Road, Bridgend Industrial Estate, Bridgend
CF31 3TP
T 01656 652447
F 01656 661266
E info@geminidigitalcolour.co.uk
W www.geminidigitalcolour.co.uk
Contact Craig Whitney
Fine-art printers, specializing in print-on-demand, giclée and short-run printing from postcards to limited-edition canvases and prints. Offers personal advice and assistance to the amateur and professional artist alike.

Graal Press
Eskhill Cottage, Roslin, Midlothian
EH25 9QW
T 0131 4402589
E graal@ednet.co.uk
Contact Robert Adam or Carol Robertson
A fine-art print studio, founded in 1998 in a rural location thirty minutes from Edinburgh city centre. Specializes in collaborative projects and innovative approaches to printmaking using media such as artist's water-based paints for screenprinting, recently developed tusches for light-sensitive processes, and acrylic-resist etching. Courses are available in progressive and safer printmaking methods as well as in personal and artistic development.

The Hermit Press
P.O. Box 3863, Stratford-upon-Avon
CV37 6TZ
T 01789 415676
E info@thehermitpress.com
W www.thehermitpress.com
Contact Webmaster
Produces prints from artists' original work, with no restriction on the size of order. Uses digital technology coupled with lightfast pigment inks and natural, acid-free papers or canvas for long-lasting, high-quality prints.

imagiclée
48 Wynford Terrace, Leeds
LS16 6HY
T 0113 2744954
F 0113 2948769
E printit@imagiclee.com
W www.imagiclee.com
Contact Peter Learoyd
Produces fine-art prints from art work, scans, photographs and digital files. Prints with light-fast pigmented inks on to a wide range of materials. Also helps customers sell prints by providing space in online gallery at www.shopforprints.com which allows worldwide customers to buy images on different materials at a variety of sizes.
Price range From less than £2 per print.

J. Thomson Colour Printers Ltd
14 Carnoustie Place, Glasgow
G5 8PB
T 0141 4291094
F 0141 4295638
E production@jtcp.co.uk
W www.jtcp.co.uk
Specialists in lithographic fine-art reproduction and high-quality scanning from transparencies. Over fifty years' experience in the production of fine-art prints, catalogues, brochures, fine-art books and fine-art cards.

Kustom
76 Clerkenwell Road, London
EC1M 5TN
T 020 78650000
F 020 78650001
E comments@metroimaging.co.uk
W www.metroimaging.co.uk
Contact Michael Mardon
Whether from file or digital files, Kustom works collaboratively with clients to create conventional prints, digital Lambdas or giclée prints. Able to call upon the resources of parent company Metro Imaging, one of London's leading specialists in photographic and digital services.

London Print Studio
425 Harrow Road, London
W10 4RE
T 020 89693247
F 020 89640008
E info@londonprintstudio.org.uk
W www.londonprintstudio.org.uk
An independent, not-for-profit arts organization providing low-cost training and access to artists' print and graphic arts facilities. The studio has a printmaking studio with facilities for screenprinting, etching, blockprinting and lithography, a computer facility with computers, scanners and printers, and a large-format digital printing service. Also incorporates gallery with a changing programme of exhibitions and events. Services offered include an MA in Printmaking & Professional Practice, various education and training programmes, and editioning. Use of

facilities open to artists, community organizations, members of the general public and anyone interested in art.

Price range Studio hire from £1.56 per hour.

Loudmouth Postcard Printing

23 Hall Road, Sheffield
S13 9AG
T 0845 2309805
F 0114 2880044
E info@loudworld.co.uk
W www.loudworld.co.uk
Contact Paul Jenkinson
Design-led printers to the arts, media and crafts industries for over twenty years. Specializes in producing thick colour postcards, business cards, product cards, greetings cards etc. No minimum quantity. Turnaround from four days. Free sample pack available.

Mark Harwood Photography

12 The Waterside, 44–48 Wharf Road, London
N1 7SF
T 020 74908787
F 020 74901009
E mail@markharwood.plus.com
W www.markharwoodstudio.co.uk
Contact Mark Harwood
A practising photographer offering in-house scanning and fine-art printing to very large sizes.

New North Press

Standpoint Studios, 45 Coronet Street, London
N1 6HD
T 020 77293161
F 020 77293161
E graham.bignell@talk21.com
Contact Graham Bignell
Founded in 1985, specializing in the editioning of linocuts, woodcuts and wood engravings and editions of letter press artist's books. The studio has a broad range of types available for small editions.

Newnum Art

29 Oxford Road, Worthing
BN11 1UT
T 01903 821191
F 01903 820507
E enquiries@newnumart.co.uk
W www.newnumart.co.uk
Contact Mandy Newnum
Founded in 2001 as an offshoot of a litho and digital-printing company and consequently has considerable print expertise. Specializes in giclée printing as well as conventional litho and waterless litho using a Heidelberg DI press.

Price range Studio of 600 sq. ft available for hire from £75.

Oberon Art Ltd

Chess Castle, 112 Latimer Road, Chesham
HP5 1QQ
T 01494 774004
E sales@oberonart.co.uk
W www.oberonart.co.uk
Contact Susie Lipman
Founded in 2002. An artist-run fine-art publishing company. Supplies limited-edition prints by seventeen selected artists. Also offers a bespoke framing service.

Paulsharma.com

91 Blackheath Park, London
SE3 0EU
E enquires@paulsharma.com
W www.paulsharma.com
Contact Paul Sharma
Founded in 2002. Offers high-quality limited-edition prints for the home or office.

Pratt Contemporary Art and Pratt Editions

The Gallery, Ightham, Sevenoaks
TN15 9HH
T 01732 882326
F 01732 885502
E pca@prattcontemporaryart.co.uk
W www.prattcontemporaryart.co.uk
Contact Bernard Pratt
Printers, publishers and dealers, founded in 1977. Alongside a regular publishing programme, the studios also provide an editioning service to artists and galleries. Working in close collaboration with a master printer, artists are given time to fully explore and experiment with the various processes available, including screenprinting, intaglio, relief and large-format digital printing. Gallery open by appointment.

Printmaker Studio

Manton, Bath Road, Padworth, Reading
RG7 5HR
T 0118 9712896
E enquiries@printmaker.co.uk
W www.printmaker.co.uk
Contact Chris Mercier
A silkscreen and giclée editioning studio founded in 1990. Specializes in screenprinting projects and

editioning for artists and printmakers. Also offers a large-format digital giclée printing service for digital art work and reproductions.

Prism
Unit 28 School Close, Chandlers Ford, Eastleigh
SO53 4RA
T 023 80266256
F 023 80266256
E stewart.goldsmith@ntlworld.com
Contact Ian Goldsmith
A lithographic reprographics and printing company founded in 1991. Reproduces originals from A5 cards up to large B1 posters. Sample pack available and advice given.

Reprotech Studios Ltd
22 Trinity Lane, Micklegate, York
YO1 6EL
T 01904 644006
F 01904 611264
E repstudios@aol.com
Contact John Hall
Founded in 1986, specializing in digital printing and fine-art reproduction. Produces limited-edition giclée prints onto watercolour, paper and canvas.

shopforprints.com
48 Wynford Terrace, Leeds
LS16 6HY
T 0113 2744954
F 0113 2948769
E shopforprints@shopforprints.com
W www.shopforprints.com
Contact Peter Learoyd
An online shop for art prints, photographic prints and posters. Helps artist, cartographer and photographer customers sell fine-art giclée reproduction prints of their work by providing space in the online gallery. This gives worldwide customers twenty-four-hour access to buy prints online at a variety of sizes and on a range of different materials. Pays fifty per cent of the selling price to the artist every month.

St Ives Printing & Publishing Co.
High Street, St Ives
TR26 1RS
T 01736 795813
F 01736 795813
E toni@stivesnews.co.uk
W www.stivesnews.co.uk
Contact Mr Toni Carver (Proprietor)
A printer and publisher of a local newspaper and

books, founded in 1951. Offers a range of services for artists, including fine-art lithographic prints and photo-litho reproductions, private-view invitations, greeting cards, catalogues and fine-art photographs.

Terracotta Press Ltd
273 Abbeydale Road, Wembley
HA0 1QE
T 020 89974655
F 020 89987842
E print@terracotta-press.co.uk
W www.terracotta-press.co.uk
Contact Karen Low
Established in 1995. A commercial printer of brochures, postcards, posters, fine-art prints, etc. Has undertaken work for some of the biggest galleries and studios in London.

Think Ink Ltd
11–13 Philip Road, Ipswich
IP2 8BH
T 01473 400162
F 01473 400163
E charles@think-ink.co.uk
W www.think-ink.co.uk
Specializes in the production of printing for artists, e.g. greeting cards, postcards, private view cards, giclée prints.

Wall Candi Ltd
High Street, Lane End, High Wycombe
HP14 3JG
T 01494 883250
F 01494 883250
E info@wallcandi.com
W www.wallcandi.com
Contact Jonathan Burns
Specializes in giclée digital fine-art reproduction. Uses state-of-the-art giclée and colour management technology and prints onto a variety of media, producing archival quality prints. Other services include a professional in-house photographic studio for capturing original art work digitally or onto traditional transparency film.

Studio space

36 Lime Street Ltd
36 Lime Street, Ouseburn Valley, Newcastle-upon-Tyne
NE1 2PQ

E limest36@yahoo.co.uk
W www.36limestreet.co.uk
Founded in 1984, a tenants' cooperative and the
largest artists' studio group in the north-east,
representing an eclectic mix of artists, designers,
makers, performers and musicians in the region.
Price range Low-cost studio space. Purchase of a
lease for each studio is required.

Acme Studios

44 Copperfield Road, Bow, London
E3 4RR
T 020 89816811
F 020 89830567
E mail@acme.org.uk
W www.acme.org.uk
A charity formed in 1972 to provide artists with
low-cost studio and living space. Provides 380
studios (over 170,000 sq. ft) throughout east
and south-east London, as well as twenty-five
accommodation units. Active in other residency
and studio and accommodation programmes. Also
offers free advice on property issues to artists.
Price range £6.50–£8 per sq. ft per year,
inclusive.

Amberney Studio

32A Goldney Road, Maida Vale, London
W91 JR
T 020 72891122
F 0871 2426134
E amberneystudio@tiscali.co.uk
W www.amberneystudios.co.uk
Contact Kathy Roche
Light day studio (60ft × 20ft × 25ft) available for
hire, complete with equipment, catering and other
services.
Price range £200 per day.

Art Space Portsmouth Ltd

27 Brougham Road, Portsmouth
PO5 4PA
T 02392 874523
E marcia@artspace.co.uk
W www.artspace.co.uk
Contact Marcia Allen (Studio Manager)
Formed in 1980, providing affordable studio space
for artists working in a wide range of art forms
and media. Runs an education programme from
its Omega Centre site and offers a sponsored
studio at its Mile End site. Aims to encourage
the widest audience for the visual arts through
workshops, residencies, open studios and
exhibitions.

Price range £38.56–£106 per month, inclusive of
heating, lighting, etc.

Artists and Restorers (A&R) Studios

7 Farm Mews, Farm Road, Hove
BN3 1GH
T 01273 207470
F 01273 207470
E artistandrestorer@fastmail.com.uk
Contact Caroline
Founded in 1996, with the aim of giving artists
and craftspeople an affordable place to practice
their craft in an art environment. Members include
artists, jewelers, textile makers and designers, and
picture-restorers.
Price range £100–£130 per month.

artists @ redlees

Redlees Studios, Redlees Park, Worton Road,
Isleworth
TW7 6DW
E artists@redlees.org
W www.redlees.org
Contact John Carbery
A diverse group of artists formed to organize and
promote the collective and individual work of the
residents of Redlees Studios. Members' work
includes jewelry, glass, ceramics, painting,
sculpture and mixed media. Works closely with the
Community Initiative Partnership, who maintain
the buildings, to organize shows of members'
creations.
Price range £100–£200 per month.

ASC

3rd Floor, 246 Stockwell Road, Brixton
SW9 9SP
T 020 72747474
F 020 72741744
E info@ascstudios.co.uk
W www.ascstudios.co.uk
Contact Lisa Wilson
A London-based registered charity that provides
studio and exhibition space to visual artists and
not-for-profit arts organizations. Currently
manages 350 artists' studios across six buildings.
Registration is free and there is a waiting list for
most studios. There is studio space available in
Bethnal Green, E2, Newcross, SW14, Brixton,
SW9, and Camberwell, SE5. Exhibition space is
offered free of charge to visual artists and not-for-
profit arts organizations. Selection is through a
committee of ASC artists. The organization also
provides free advice on all matters relating to

studio development and can help with property negotiation.

Price range Rents are inclusive of building insurance, service charges, heating and electric and are based on £9.50–£12 per sq. ft per year.

Ashley Studios

19 Staithe Street, Wells-next-the-Sea
NR23 1AG
T 01328 710923
F 01328 710923
Contact Hazel Ashley
Founded in 1979. A small studio with a comprehensive range of artists materials. Contacts with local artists and Wells's thriving art group. Open all year round.

Association for Cultural Advancement through Visual Art (ACAVA)

54 Blechynden Street, London
W10 6RJ
T 020 89605015
F 020 89609269
Provides three hundred studios for artists and arts organizations throughout north, west and south-west London. Associate members are placed on a waiting list.

Bedford Hill Gallery and Workshops, Chelsea Bridge Studios

1 The Field, 103 Prince of Wales Drive, London
SW11 3UN
T 020 74988730
F 020 74988730
E chelseabridge.studios@btinternet.com
Contact Roy Woods
Managing and letting artist studios since 1979, the Bedford Hill Gallery currently manages twelve exclusive artist studios in a Victorian mansion house, which stands in its own grounds near Chelsea Bridge. All studios have high ceilings, and come equipped with 'natural daylight' secondary lighting.
Price range Around £130 per week for 200 sq. ft studios.

Bow Arts Trust and Nunnery Gallery

183 Bow Road, London
E3 2SJ
T 020 89807774
F 020 89807770
E info@bowarts.com
W www.bowarts.com

Contact Jeremy Clarke
Founded in 1995. Designed to provide long-term affordable workspace for artists and to operate as an arts conduit for local communities, and national and international audiences. Offers space for approximately one hundred artists, open studios, employment and training. Nunnery Gallery is a contemporary project space for national and international shows. Education at Bowarts runs an outreach programme with local schools.
Price range £170 for 300 sq. ft (including insurance, education levy) or £248 for 450 sq. ft (open-studio costs, etc).

Can Studios

4th Floor, Oldknows Factory, St Anns Hill Road, Nottingham
NG3 4GP
T 0115 9588601
W www.nottinghamstudios.org.uk/can
Contact Stephen Butler
Founded in 1988 and situated on the top floor of an old textile factory. Has eleven studio spaces offering only minimal facilities. Artists in the group participate in the annual open-studio event.
Price range £44 per month, all-inclusive.

cell project space

4–8 Arcola Street, London
E8 2DJ
T 020 72413600
E info@cell.org.uk
W www.cell.org.uk
Studio space for over one hundred visual artists in four buildings in east London.

Chocolate Factory

Haringey Arts Council, Unit 104, Building B, Clarendon Road, London
N22 6XJ
T 020 83657500
F 020 83658686
W www.chocolatefactory.org.uk
Seventy-five studios in north London for artists and designers in the areas os sculpture, film, crafts, fashion and photography.

Clevedon Craft Centre

Moor Lane, Clevedon
BS21 6TD
T 01275 872149
Contact Mr D.A. Stear or Mr J.J. Bright

Established in 1971, the ten craft design studios and artspace workshops are housed in the outbuildings of a seventeenth-century Somerset 'long farm', which was once part of the Clevedon Court Estate.
Price range £20–£75 per week, exclusive of rates, etc.

Coin Street Community Builders

Oxo Tower Wharf, Barge House Street, London
SE1 9PH
T 020 74013610
F 020 79280111
E info@coin-street.org
W www.oxotower.co.uk
A social enterprise and development trust responsible for thirteen acres on the South Bank of London. Includes design studios, shops and galleries for hire to designers and artists at Oxo Tower Wharf and Gabriel's Wharf.
Price range From £400 per month.

Creekside Artists' Studios

Units A110, A112 and A114 Faircharm Trading Estate, Creekside, Deptford, London
SE8 3DX
E info@creeksideartists.co.uk
W www.creeksideartists.co.uk
Contact Mauricio Vincenzi (Chairman)
Not-for-profit artist-led studios founded in 2000. There are 12 sq. ft × 250 sq. ft units in an open-plan setting, with skylights throughout. The membership of twenty-four artists includes photographers, painters, printmakers, filmmakers, sculptors, and textile and installation artists. The studios have a communal 'chillout' area, as well as a workbench supplied with basic tools for communal use. Twenty-four-hour access. Two open studios a year, as well as exhibitions in London and abroad.

Cuckoo Farm Studios

Boxted Road, Colchester
CO4 5HH
T 01206 843530
E info@cuckoofarmstudios.org.uk
W www.cuckoofarmstudios.org.uk
An artist-run studio group consisting of over thirty studios for artists and craftspeople. Set in a rural location, two miles from Colchester train station. Includes gallery, print workshop and outside space.
Price range £50–£90 per month, inclusive of all bills.

Dalston Underground Studios

The Basement, 28 Shacklewell Lane, Dalston, London
E8 2EZ
T 07941 715888
E info@dalstonunderground.org.uk
W www.dalstonunderground.org.uk
Contact Calum F. Kerr
Established in October 2000 by graduates of the MA Fine Art course at Central St Martins. Provides workspace for contemporary fine artists and supports individuals pursuing their work by offering long-term studio space. Currently has space for ten to twelve artists. Practice is varied and includes painting, film and performance. Examples of work can be viewed through website. Provides a space from which artists can develop projects and exhibit widely in a national and international context. Also organizes critiques, exhibitions and talks involving participating artists at the studios and in other locations.
Price range £80–£160 per month.

Diesel House Studios

Kew Bridge Steam Museum, Green Dragon Lane, Brentford
TW8 0EN
T 020 85698780
F 020 85698781
E thedieselhouse@aol.com
W www.dieselhousestudios.com
Contact Elizabeth Rollins-Scott
Founded in 2001. Specializes in studio rental and consultancy for private and local government arts projects. Currently manages thirty studios in Chiswick, Richmond and Brentford in west London (expected to rise to fifty). All artists are provided with a free website, marketing support, art library and access to digital media as well as advice on commercial career development. Two major exhibitions each year (summer and Christmas), with up to fifty artists and over five hundred works on show.
Price range £100–£525 per calendar month, including all bills.

Flameworks Creative Arts Facility

7 Richmond Walk, Devonport, Plymouth
PL1 4LL
T 01752 559326
E flameworks@tiscali.co.uk
W www.flameworks.co.uk
Contact Katie Lake
Founded in 1999, providing artists' workspaces

and specialist equipment and services. Group activities include exhibitions, commissions, public-art schemes, newsletter production, marketing and schools residencies. Artist workshops and taster sessions available in metalwork, jewelry, ceramics, mosaic, painting, stone- and wood-carving, printmaking and sculpture.
Price range £75–£150 per month.

Flax Art Studios
44–46 Corporation Street, Belfast
BT1 3DE
An artist-run organization founded in 1989 by a group of Belfast-based artists who were looking for space to make large sculptural and installation works. Runs an artist-in-residence programme for four international artists each year and also a graduating student residency. Has initiated a community outreach project in partnership with five community groups.

Gasworks
155 Vauxhall, London
SE11 5RH
T 020 75875202
F 020 75820159
E alessio@gasworks.org.uk
W www.gasworks.org.uk
Contact Alessio Antoniolli
Founded in 1994. A studio and gallery complex with ten studios rented to London-based artists and three reserved for an international residency programme for non-UK-based artists.
Price range Studio spaces rarely available. Enquiries to Alessio Antoniolli.

Great Western Studios
Great Western Road, London
W9 3NY
T 020 72210100
F 020 72210200
E office@greatwesternstudios.com
W www.greatwesternstudios.com
Founded in 1994, providing workspace for over 140 artists and craftspeople. Each space has good natural light, interesting views and high ceilings. Communal facilities include a café, project spaces and general business services.
Price range £7.50–£10 per sq. ft per year.

Green Door Studios
112 Highgate, Kendal
LA9 4HE

T 01539 721147
E artists@greendoorkendal.fsnet.co.uk
W www.greendoorstudios.co.uk
Contact The Administrator
Formed in 1995 and currently has thirteen artists in eleven studio spaces and seventy-eight associate members who join in exhibitions, open studios, professional-development workshops and social events.
Price range Eleven studio spaces ranging in price from £119–£385 per quarter or £476–£1540 per year.

Herford Road Studios
12–14 Herford Road, London
N1
T 020 72410651
Twenty studio spaces available. Artists should send slides of their work, a CV and an sae.

JAM Studios
Lews Castle Grounds, Stornoway
HS2 0XR
T 01851 643261
E info@jam-studios.org
W www.jam-studios.org
Contact Emma Drye
Independent artists' studios running courses including a portfolio course, short courses, evening classes and residential courses on the Isle of Lewis in the Outer Hebrides. Hosts exhibitions and events throughout the year and is interested in exhibiting work of recent graduates.

Kingsgate Workshops Trust and Gallery
110–116 Kingsgate Road, London
NW6 2JG
T 020 73287878
E mail@kingsgateworkshops.org.uk
Around fifty arts and crafts studios available. Email for advice on availability.

Maryland Studios
2nd Floor, 80 Wallis Road, Hackney Wick, London
E9 5LW
T 020 89862555
Contact Joanna Georgiades or Sally Moore
Established in 1995 to provide a secure, affordable and professional environment for the production of art. Architect-designed studios give good light, access and maximum space. Studio members are expected to participate in annual open studios and contribute to educational workshops.
Price range £150–£300 (£6.75 per square foot).

Mivart Street Studios

Epstein Building, Bristol
BS5 6JF
T 0117 3305209
E barbaraorme@hotmail.com
Contact Barbara Orme
Has accommodated artists for over fifteen years,
and now hosts over fifty artists.
Price range £13–£30 per week.

Mother Studios

9 Queens Yard, White Post Lane, Hackney Wick,
London
E9 5EN
T 07968 760550
E info@motherstudios.co.uk
W motherstudios.co.uk
Contact Joanna Hughes
A non-profit-making studio founded in 2001 by
artist Joanna Hughes for fine artists, designers and
makers. There are thirty-four studios with twenty-
four-hour access and parking. On-site 2,000 sq. ft of
exhibition space is available free to all Mother artists.
Price range Space available for hire. Rates
determined on an individual basis, from £80 per
calendar month, inclusive of electricity.

No 19 Cataibh, Dornoch Studio

19 Achavandra Muir, Dornoch
IV25 3JB
T 01862 811099
E sue@cataibh.fsnet.co.uk
Contact Sue Jane Taylor or Ian Westacott
An open-access etching studio located in the north-
east Highlands, four miles from the coastal town
of Dornoch. The studio has two presses, one
800mm wide and one 400mm wide, and uses
non-toxic methods. Artists who have no experience
of the etching process are welcome and offered
technical assistance. Accommodation available for
one to two people (own transport required).
Price range Studio rent per day (plus sundries)
£20; accommodation £15 per person; technical
assistance £20. Rates vary according to season and
availability.

Nottingham Artists' Group

32–36 Carrington Street, Nottingham
NG1 7FG
T 0115 9581450
Contact Geoffrey Grant
Artists' studios founded in 1982 for personal and
professional practice. At present has nine members.
Price range £60–£80

Oldknows Studio Group

3rd Floor, Old Knows Factory Building, St Anns
Hill Road, Nottingham
NG3 4GP
T 0115 9413160
E denisecweston@hotmail.com
W www.oldknows.co.uk
Contact Denise Weston or Simon Withers
Founded in 1987, aiming to provide inexpensive
and spacious studios for artists. Studio group
produces contemporary visual art, from the
traditional through to the avant-garde.
Price range £54 per month.

Open Hand Open Space

571 Oxford Road, Reading
RG30 1HL
T 0118 9597752
E info@ohos.org.uk
W www.ohos.org.uk
Contact Emily Smeaton (Administrator)
Founded in 1980. An artist-led organization
providing affordable artists' studios and facilities
for the production of contemporary visual art. Also
runs an exhibitions and education programme to
promote public access to contemporary visual art
and artists.
Price range £40–£100 per month, inclusive.

Opus Studios

Unit B3, The Oldknows Factory, St Ann's Hill
Road, Nottingham
NG3 4GP
E charlottesmith24@hotmail.com
W www.nottinghamstudios.org.uk/opus
Contact Charlotte Smith
Founded in 1999. A group of ten artists displaying
varied creative practices including painting,
installation, sculpture, photography and
community arts projects. Has exhibited locally,
nationally and internationally.
Price range £35–£70

Pavilion Studios

Market Drive, Chiswick
W4 2RX
T 020 87422225
E info@fodm.org.uk
W www.fodm.org.uk
Contact Kathleen Healy
Founded in 2002, offering private lockable spaces
to ten artists in a converted farm building on the
edge of a park. Twenty-four-hour access, free
parking, central heating and use of a shared

kitchen. Spaces vary in size, but most are around 100 sq. ft.

Price range £150–£260 per month, including all bills and rates.

Phoenix Arts Association

10–14 Waterloo Place, Brighton
BN2 9NB
T 01273 603700
E info@phoenixarts.org
W www.phoenixarts.org
Contact Belinda Greenhalgh (Office Manager)
Established in 1992, providing over one hundred high-quality studios for individual artists as well as larger workspaces for short-term projects. Also a gallery presenting exhibitions of contemporary visual art in all media with an integrated education programme.

Rogue Artists' Studios

2nd Floor, Crusader Works, 66–72 Chapeltown Street, Manchester
M1 2WH
T 0161 2737492
W www.rogueartistsstudios.org.uk
Contact Martin Nash
Founded in 1995. Active in painting, textiles, construction, graphics, photography, performance, video, installation and furniture. Offers an annual platform for artists to exhibit their work to the public. Weekly life-drawing class for studio members and general public. Equipped workshop area and computer suite available.
Price range £33–£86 per calendar month, all-inclusive.

Southgate Studios

2–4 Southgate Road, London
N1 3JJ
T 020 72546485
E adrian@adrianhemming.com
W www.adrianhemming.com
Contact Adam Gray or Adrian Hemming
Founded in 1990, providing approximately ten studio spaces (average size 400 sq. ft).
Price range On application. Two months' deposit required.

SPACE

129–131 Mare Street, London
E8 3RH
T 020 85254330
F 020 85254342
E mail@spacestudios.org.uk
W www.spacestudios.org.uk
Founded in 1968, Studio Provision Artistic Cultural Educational (SPACE) is a charitable organization providing affordable studios across London, with seventeen sites currently serving over five hundred artists. Has a history of commissioning public and community arts. Hosts and collaborates with a wide range of visual arts and performing groups, locally and nationally. Builds audiences through ongoing projects and annual events including the Bow Festival and the Winter Fate.
Price range £70–£600 per month.

SPACE Place

Fish Island, 43–45 Dace Road, London
E3 2NG
T 020 89865998
F 020 89866887
E spaceplace@spacestudios.org.uk
W www.spacestudios.org.uk
Contact Virginia Simpson
A media arts resource centre in Hackney Wick. Offers access to digital-art and video-editing facilities, project space and exhibition space. Also runs a wide variety of courses utilizing two fully equipped editing suites.
Price range £30 per day for Moving Image Suite; £20 per day for Digital Art Suite. £20–£30 for one-day courses.

Studio Voltaire

1A Nelsons Row, Clapham, London
SW4 7JR
T 020 76221294
F 020 76278008
E info@studiovoltaire.org
W www.studiovoltaire.org
Contact Joe Scotland
Founded in 1994. The first and only artist-run gallery and studio complex in south-west London, offering a service for local residents, schools and community groups. Actively promotes access to and participation in contemporary-art practice with its exhibition, education and studio programmes.
Price range £60–£250 per calendar month.

Viking Studios and Bede Gallery

4 Viking Precinct, Jarrow
NE32 3LQ
T 0191 4200560
Contact Vince Rea
Founded in 1996, providing ten artists' studios. Small window space on ground floor used to display work, situated in Jarrow Shopping Centre.

Wakefield Artsmill

Rutland Mills, Kirkgate Bridge, Wakefield
WF1 5JR
T 01924 215873
E w-artsmill@pop3.poptel.org.uk
Contact Ian Smith
Incorporated as a company limited by guarantee in 1997. Provides low-cost studio accommodation, an exhibition space and production facilities for up to forty artists at all stages of their careers.
Price range Spaces are charged at £3.50 per sq. ft per year (£24–£114 per month).

Wasps Artists' Studios

77 Hanson Street, Dennistoun, Glasgow
G31 2HF
T 0141 5548299
F 0141 5547330
E info@waspsstudios.org.uk
W www.waspsstudios.org.uk
Contact Helen Moore (Administration Assistant)
Over the last twenty-five years, Wasps has grown to become the largest visual arts organization in Scotland, providing low-cost studio space to over 650 artists each year at sixteen locations throughout Scotland. Aims to sustain and develop Scotland's visual artist community, provide a network of working spaces and other low-cost services to artists and arts organizations.
Price range Current rental rates are between £3.35 and £5.85 per sq. ft per year, fully inclusive. This translates to between £55 to £100 per month, with £75 being the average rental for a 200 sq. ft studio.

Waygood Gallery and Studios

548–560 Shields Road, Byker, Newcastle-upon-Tyne
NE6 2UT
T 0191 2656857
F 0191 2244187
E art@waygood.org
W www.waygood.org
Contact Alex Evans
Founded in 1995 with the aims of providing a place of practice for artists and engaging audiences with contemporary art. Its site on High Bridge is currently being redeveloped into new, state-of-the-art accommodation and will include a gallery with an international programme of contemporary visual art and live art, fully accessible studios, a visual arts learning centre, workshop facilities and an international residency programme. Until completion in late 2006,

Waygood will be based at Harkers Building in Byker, Newcastle.
Price range £30–£150 per month for studio rent, depending on size of space.

West Walls Studios

53 West Walls, Carlisle
CA3 8UH
T 01228 515127
E west.walls@virgin.net
W www.westwallsstudios.com
Contact Paul Taylor
Established in 1993, an artists' cooperative working collaboratively and individually on projects, community activities and exhibitions. twelve artists' spaces and small gallery/project space are available to hire, subject to application. Studios open to public by appointment and on annual open weekend.
Price range £60–£150 per month for studios; £150 per month for gallery/project space.

Westbourne Studios

242 Acklam Road, London
W10 5JJ
T 020 75753000
F 020 75753001
E lettings@westbournestudios.com
W www.westbournestudios.com
Contact Natalie Clarke
Situated underneath the Westway, ninety-two studios are available to hire as well as a space for gallery exhibitions, a screening room and a project space.
Price range From £700

Widcombe Studios Ltd

The Old Malthouse, Comfortable Place, Upper Bristol Road, Bath
BA1 3AJ
T 01225 482480
E admin@widcombestudios.co.uk
W www.widcombestudios.co.uk
Contact Anny Colgan (Studios Administrator)
Founded in 1996, comprising forty-five studios. Also runs courses and has a gallery space available for hire.
Price range £10.50 per square metre per calendar month. Average studio is 10m², but in reality are all different sizes.

Wimbledon Art Studios

Riverside Yard, Riverside Road, London
SW17 0BA

T 020 89471183
F 020 89445162
E wimbledonartstudios@yahoo.co.uk
W www.WimbledonArtStudios.co.uk
Contact Jane Cavanagh (Art Studio Coordinator)
Established ten years ago and now one of
the largest art studios in Europe, with over
one hundred artists, sculptors, ceramacists,
photographers, jewelers and costume designers
under one roof. There are two open-studio shows
each year. Twenty-four-hour access, seven days a
week, and a good community atmosphere.
Price range From £2 for rental space.

Wollaton Street Studios

179 Wollaton Street, Nottingham
NG1 5GE
E bobrobinsonrig@hotmail.com
W www.nottinghamstudios.org/wollaton
Contact Bob Robinson or Rob Hart
Formed in 1985 and located close to the city centre.

Six separate studios arranged around a central
stairwell, with two studios to each floor.
Completely artist-run and predominantly
encouraging the activity of painting.
Price range £65–£100 per month, inclusive.

Yorkshire Artspace Society

Persistence Works, 21 Brown Street, Sheffield
S1 2BS
T 0114 2761769
F 0114 2761769
E info@artspace.org.uk
W www.artspace.org.uk
Contact Viv Mager
Established in Sheffield in 1977. Based in a
purpose-built studio complex for artists and
craftspeople (seventy spaces). Offers business
support and training to visual artists and a wide-
ranging community outreach programme to
schools, community groups and the public.
Price range £88–£240 per month, all-inclusive.

O5

Art education

Why art school? Options and approaches for training as an artist

Janet Hand and Gerard Hemsworth

You may want to be an artist and are therefore seriously considering how to turn wanting into doing, and doing into an abiding practice; in this case you may well be asking what art school can offer you. You might already have an involvement in the arts and are at a time in your career when you are considering further study, or you may want to shift the emphasis of your practice. In any case, your first questions will be 'Where do I start?', 'Whom do I approach?' and 'Do I have what it takes?'

Like any practice, art requires commitment and hard work. If you are just starting out, you will need to consider your education and the specific approach to art or design that suits you; this is the first difficult choice on your career path.

Solid foundation

The conventional starting point is a foundation course, which will introduce you to a variety of media and career options, from product design to fashion, textiles and fine art. The availability of courses varies from one institution to another: Byam Shaw School of Art, for example, only offers a foundation in fine art; Central St Martins, on the other hand, has a vast foundation programme with a range of choices across art and design.

This kind of study lasts for a year and aids in choosing the degree that suits your interests and abilities best. Foundation courses are by nature 'diagnostic', so you need not be too concerned that you have not yet come to a decision about which area of art you might wish to pursue eventually. They are geared towards entry into art-school degree courses and will nurture your strengths while guiding you in basic technical requirements. The teaching staff will advise you on which BA programme they think will be most appropriate for the development of your work. Since portfolios need to be ready by Easter, you may consider taking a year out to develop work rather than accepting a place at a college that is not your first choice.

First degree inspection

At BA level, there are numerous art schools vying for your attention through their prospectuses, websites, admissions tutors and admissions offices – all potential first points of contact with colleges on your shortlist. Remember, art schools need your potential as much as you need their expertise, so you will have to identify preferred institutions on your shortlist and visit them on organized open days. Talk to the students who are currently studying there to get a flavour of what is going on, so that you can make an informed choice about which is the right place for you. On college open days you can ask all the questions you need in order to make an appropriate application. A phone call to the admissions office will tell you when and how often these occur.

It is not necessary to have done a foundation course when applying for a degree, although it does give applicants a distinct advantage; some colleges will not interview a student who has not. When making a decision about which BAs to apply for, you should consider the nature of the overall programme in relation to your own aspirations within art practice. Not all applicants to art degrees aspire to be practising artists and many courses offer transferable skills that can be applied in a broader context of art culture.

Consider, also, the ethos of the art school. These generally fall into two categories: the first is interdisciplinary and enables you to move from one medium to another; the second is media-led and will have, for example, a painting department or a stand-alone photography course. Colleges that are media-led may advertise to applicants that you can still make video work within, say, the sculpture department, but make sure this will not be a problem by asking current students.

When you initially visit colleges you are thinking of applying to, you will get a general feel of this ethos. You will also see the size of studio spaces, discover the technical facilities and hear how current students describe the quality of the teaching and learning environment. Students will often volunteer other practical information about their experiences that will help you make a decision. They may tell you how often they get tutorials and from whom. If there are regular visiting tutors to the college, it is worth asking about their involvement in the arts. Are they artists, writers, curators, educationalists?

Students will also give an account of their contextual studies and how these help develop their art practice. Find out if there are separate or integrated history of art or critical studies courses. The way programmes are organized and the courses they offer are not necessarily better or worse from college to college, but they are different. Your understanding of the differences and their appropriateness to you is the basis of making a good choice.

Furthering your education

Some BA graduates acquire professional success as practising artists within months of completion. At Goldsmiths, for example, Damien Hirst, Sarah Lucas, Gary Hume and others had no need for postgraduate studies, but they are the exception and not the rule. In most cases, students who are committed to becoming full-time artists start thinking of applying for postgraduate study after completing their BA.

Postgraduate study is usually when art students begin to consider their practice alongside contemporary artists working in the field. This doesn't mean you have to get to postgraduate level to become a professional artist, but most BA graduates will tell you that the discipline of their profession and their sense of maintaining a serious practice only begins after graduation, and that it is a hard apprenticeship to build a portfolio of interest by working on your own. If you

want or need to continue your study at postgraduate level, you can expect exacting criticism as well as a level of support that artists rarely get otherwise. Remember that your colleagues and fellow students are not only your closest allies but also an embryonic professional network, so it is important that you choose a place to study where you can share ideas and expectations, and most importantly begin to put them into practice through exhibition.

When applying for a postgraduate degree, consider whether or not it is the right time in the development of your career to take full advantage of further study. In the majority of cases, it is worth taking some time between BA and MA in order to develop your concerns and a 'professional practice'.

Generally, you will be asking similar questions of postgraduate programmes as applicants ask of BA programmes. You may also want to know if the MA has an international profile and whether applicants apply from around the world. Again, students are the best people to let applicants know how the college works day to day.

One thing current students may not be able to ascertain is the standard of their programme in comparison to other postgraduate courses. A way to assess the teaching and learning environment of a college is to ask about recent alumni. Is the programme enabling graduates to have careers as practising artists? Is it offering a platform for them to operate? Does it have a network of alumni that can be of help and support?

Recent alumni from the Fine Art MA at Goldsmiths, for example, include many who have gained international recognition, along with many who have been shortlisted for and won the Turner Prize. These include Mark Wallinger, who also represented Great Britain at the Venice Biennale, Yinka Shonibare, who was shortlisted for the 2004 Turner Prize, and Glenn Brown, who had a solo exhibition at the Serpentine in London in 2004. Other major luminaries include Jane and Louise Wilson,

Bob and Roberta Smith, Thomas Demand, David Thorpe, Gillian Wearing, Michael Raedecker and many more.

These days, you can go on to PhD study in art practice – the highest degree of attainment in academic terms, although many colleges also offer fellowships for professional artists and academics. Artists who study towards a PhD often have a commitment to teaching alongside their professional practice, or wish to vitalize their work in a sustained way through research. PhD study is designed for artists and curators who also wish to write a research project proposed and developed by them in support of their practice. Artists pursuing this level of research are most often already exhibiting, curating or working within the profession and continue to do so throughout their course of study. Research students at Goldsmiths, past and present, are working nationally and internationally and have exhibited in venues such as the Whitechapel and Tate galleries.

Status report

Some art schools have independent college status and others operate within a university setting, as is the case with the Department of Visual Arts at Goldsmiths. Goldsmiths is part of the University of London and so has access to the activities, open lectures, libraries and other facilities of the college and university more widely. Independent art schools will organize lectures and talks geared to their student cohort, often in conjunction with galleries.

The learning and teaching environment at any reputable college is as important as its alumni network, with one feeding into the other at all levels. Staff who have contributed significantly in building and maintaining Goldsmiths' reputation have included Professor Nick de Ville, who currently directs our research programme, and Professor Victor Burgin, the current Millard Professor of Fine Art; Peter Creswell, John Thompson and Michael Craig-Martin have also made noteworthy contributions along the way. The department offers programmes in fine art, textiles and curating, as well as a joint BA in art and art history in collaboration with the Department of Visual Culture.

Whatever level of study you wish to pursue, it is always worth asking yourself what kind of support and facilities you will need in the continuation and development of your work. It is then a question of best matching your potential and demonstrable abilities with the most appropriate environment and expertise.

Janet Hand and Gerard Hemsworth are Assistant Director of Research and Director of Postgraduate Studies in Fine Art, respectively, of the Visual Arts Department at Goldsmiths College.

Further, higher and adult education

East Anglia

Anglia Polytechnic University
Bishop Hall Lane, Chelmsford
CM1 1SQ
T 0845 2713333
E answers@apu.ac.uk
W www.apu.ac.uk
In 1858 John Ruskin opened a school of art in
Cambridge, and in 1992 the Privy Council
awarded it university status, thus forming Anglia
Polytechnic University. It has over 28,000
students, studying on two main campuses
in Chelmsford and Cambridge, or at one of
several colleges forming the Regional University
Partnership.
Degrees offered BA (Hons): Fine Art, Fine Art
Printmaking, Illustration, Graphic Design,
Photographic and Digital Media, Modern Visual
Culture (Combined Hons) and Typography
(Combined Hons). MA and PgDip: Book Arts,
Children's Book Illustration; Printmaking;
Typographic Design. Negotiated postgraduate
awards.
Admissions policy Applicants for practice-based
single honours degrees will normally have taken
an art and design foundation, BTEC ND, level 3
GNVQ or AVCE. While academic qualifications
are taken into consideration, admission is based
primarily upon the portfolio of work presented at
interview. Applications from mature students and
those offering other qualifications and/or relevant
professional experience are welcomed and will be
considered on an individual basis.

Colchester Institute
Sheepen Road, Colchester
C03 3LL
T 01206 518000
E info@colchester.ac.uk
W www.colchester.ac.uk
Over ten thousand students at two main
campuses: Sheepen Road in Colchester and
Church Road in Clacton.
Degrees offered BA (Hons): Art and Design.
Other fine-art courses BTEC FD: Art and Design.
Dip. in Foundation Studies: Art and Design (full-
and part-time). HND: Art and Design (full- and
part-time). ND: Graphic Design; Digital Media.
Admissions policy For BA (Hons) Art and Design:
appropriate ND, Dip. in Foundation Studies or
Advanced GNVQ in Art and Design. Mature

students do not need formal qualifications but are
considered on merit. Entry requirements vary
depending on degree.

College of West Anglia
King's Lynn Centre, Tennyson Avenue,
King's Lynn
PE30 2QW
T 01553 761144
F 01553 815555
E enquiries@col-westanglia.ac.uk
W www.col-westanglia.ac.uk
Contact Mike Williams
Founded in 1893.
Degrees offered BA: Fine Art.
Other fine-art courses HND: Fine Art. ND: Fine
Art. Access to Art foundation diploma: Art and
Design.
Admissions policy Entry requirements: a
substantial portfolio; four GCEs A to C for ND;
four GCEs A to C plus at least one A-level for
foundation; no formal qualifications for Access
diploma; four GCSEs A to C, at least one A-level
and foundation diploma or equivalent for BA.

Dunstable College
Kingsway, Dunstable
LU5 4HG
T 01582 477776
F 01582 478801
E enquiries@dunstable.ac.uk
W www.dustable.ac.uk
Other fine-art courses BTEC Dip. in Foundation
Studies: Art and Design. BTEC HND: Graphic
Design. BTEC ND: Fine Art; Three-Dimensional
Art; Graphic Design; Photography. BTEC GNVQ
Foundation: Art and Design. BTEC GNVQ
Intermediate: Art and Design.
Admissions policy Applicants need an aptitude
and enthusiasm for art and design, and to
present a portfolio at an informal interview.

Norwich School of Art & Design
Francis House, 3–7 Redwell Street, Norwich
NR2 4SN
T 01603 610561
F 01603 615728
E info@nsad.ac.uk
W www.nsad.ac.uk
The only specialist art and design institution
in the east of England. Provision ranges from
foundation degree to PhD level.
Degrees offered BA (Hons): Fine Art;
Contemporary Textile Practices; Visual Studies.

MA: Design and Education; Digital Practices; Fine Art; Textile Culture; Photographic Studies. FdA: Arts and the Community.

South East Essex College
Luker Road, Southend-on-Sea
SS1 1ND
T 01702 220400
F 01702 432320
E learning@southend.ac.uk
W www.southend.ac.uk
Contact Admissions Department
Degrees offered BA (Hons): Fine Art. Other HE courses: Digital Animation; Ceramics; Three-Dimensional Product Design; Fashion; Graphic Design; Interior Design; Photography.
Other fine-art courses A wide range of arts courses at FE level, and adult courses in the daytime, evenings and weekends, including oil painting, screenprinting and watercolour classes.
Admissions policy For degrees: 160 UCAS points or mature-entry portfolio. Refer to HE prospectus for full details (phone to request copy).

Suffolk College
Rope Walk, Ipswich
IP4 1LT
T 01473 255885
F 01473 296352
E info@suffolk.ac.uk
W www.suffolk.ac.uk
Contact Sheila Thomas
Has run art and design courses for over one hundred years.
Degrees offered BA (Hons): Fine Art (full- and part-time); Fine Art combined with other subjects such as Psychology, Media Studies, and Early Childhood Studies.
Admissions policy Normal entry requirements: two A-level passes or equivalent; foundation or ND in related subject. All applicants normally interviewed with their portfolios.

University of Hertfordshire
Faculty for the Creative and Cultural Industries, College Lane, Hatfield
AL10 9AB
T 01707 285300
F 01707 285312
E c.mcintyre@herts.ac.uk
W www.herts.ac.uk/artdes
Contact David McGravie
The faculty was originally St Albans School of Art, founded in around 1880. Students have access to

staff who are practising artists, purpose-built studios and workshops, two professional galleries and modern learning-resource centres.
Degrees offered BA (Hons): Fine Art; Fine Art with Marketing (subject to validation); Applied Art; Applied Art with Marketing (subject to validation); Digital and Lens Media; Digital and Lens Media with Marketing (subject to validation). MA: Fine and Applied Arts Practice.
Other fine-art courses All degrees are offered on a part-time basis. Autumn-, spring- and summer-term courses: Drawing and Painting; Photography; Printmaking; Sculpture; Digital Photography; Glass; various design subjects. Sixth-form class: Life Drawing.
Admissions policy Normally foundation diploma, Access certificate, VCE Double Award or BTEC ND/NC in Art and Design, plus GCSE English at grade C or above.

University of Luton
Park Square, Luton
LU1 3JU
T 01582 734111
F 01582 743400
E enquiries@luton.ac.uk
W www.luton.ac.uk
Degrees offered BA (Hons): Art and Design; Digital Photography and Video Art; Fashion Design (top-up); Fine Art. MA: Art and Design.
Other fine-art courses A range of practical courses and workshops such as Painting, Drawing, Graphic Design, Web Design, Printmaking and Illustration.

East Midlands

Bishop Grosseteste College
Newport, Lincoln
LN1 3DY
T 01522 527347
F 01522 530243
E info@bgc.ac.uk
W www.bgc.ac.uk
A church college within the Anglican tradition, founded in 1862. Welcomes students and staff of all faiths and none. Trains schoolteachers. Subjects within the art curriculum are painting, drawing, printmaking, textiles, ceramics, sculpture, glass and computer-manipulated imagery.
Degrees offered BA (Hons): specialist subject and Education Studies (three years) plus PGCE (one year); Primary Education and QTS (three years) with specialization in Art.
Admissions policy An art-and-design-related

A-level (A2) normally at grade C (80 points); another A-level (A2) at grade C (80 points) or two AS levels (A1), each at grade C (40 points); an art portfolio. Alternative qualifications accepted for entry with an art portfolio include: BTEC ND in Art and Design; GNVQ (Advanced/twelve-unit) in Art and Design; art foundation course; an Access course with relevant subject content.

Chesterfield College
Infirmary Road, Chesterfield
S41 7NG
T 01246 500562 / 500563
E advice@chesterfield.ac.uk
W www.chesterfield.ac.uk
Contact Education Helpline on 01246 500562 or Training Helpline on 01246 500553 for short courses, Saturday college and summer college. Started life in 1841 as the Chesterfield and Brampton Mechanics' Institute, and went through various incarnations, including a merger in 1984 of Chesterfield Art College and Chesterfield College of Technology, before becoming Chesterfield College. Over 21,000 students (around 3,600 full-time).
Degrees offered The programmes of the Department of Art and Design centre around dedicated studios and workshops. Courses include: Fine Art; Photography; Ceramics and Silversmithing; Three-Dimensional Design; Fashion and Textiles; Illustration and Graphics.
Other fine-art courses Introductory and Intermediate Access to HE: Art and Design. HNC/HND: Fine Art (Book Arts). BTEC level 1 Introductory Dip.: Art, Design and Media. BTEC FD: Art and Design. BTEC ND: Art and Design. Dip. in Foundation Studies: Art and Design. OCN Photography levels 1 and 2. Drawing for Beginners.
Admissions policy Requirements vary. See website.

De Montfort University
The Gateway, Leicester
LE1 9BH
T 0116 2577570
F 0116 2506281
E artanddesign@dmu.ac.uk
W www.dmu.ac.uk/artanddesign
School of Fine Art established in 1897. The course is studio-based and students can specialize in one discipline, or opt for a broad-based pattern of study across the range of disciplines.
Degrees offered BA (Hons): Fine Art; Design; Crafts.

Other fine-art courses Fashion; Contour Design; Textile Design; Architecture; Graphic Design; Multimedia Design; Interior Design; Photography and Video; Footwear Design; Product, Furniture and Industrial Design.
Admissions policy All offers dependent on interview with portfolio. For further information contact Student Recruitment on 0116 2577555.

Grimsby Institute of Further and Higher Education
Nuns Corner, Grimsby
DN34 5BQ
T 01472 311222
E headmissions@grimsby.ac.uk
W www.grimsby.ac.uk
Contact Helen Geer
Offers an interdisciplinary, contemporary approach. Close links are established between theory and practice. Students benefit from designated studio spaces and a range of appropriate facilities and workshops. First-year students work across painting, printmaking, sculpture, ceramics, art metalwork and textiles, visual language and critical studies. Contemporary practice is introduced through workshops in film, sound, performance and light. Second- and third-year students confirm choice of discipline culminating in the final degree show.
Degrees offered BA Hons: Fine and Applied Arts (three years full-time; six years part-time).
Admissions policy Foundation or AVCE Art and Design required. Exceptions may be made for mature applicants. UCAS route B.

Loughborough University
School of Art & Design, Loughborough
LE11 3TU
T 01509 263171
E R.Turner@lboro.ac.uk
W www.lboro.ac.uk
Contact Rebecca Turner
Has twelve thousand students and a 410-acre campus. In 1966, the college obtained a Royal Charter to become the first university of technology in the country.
Degrees offered BA (Hons): Fine Art (Painting, Printmaking, Sculpture); Visual Communication (Graphic Communication, Illustration); Three-Dimensional Design (Ceramics, Furniture Design, Silversmithing and Jewelry); Textile Design (Printed Textiles, Multi-Media Textiles, Woven Textiles); History of Art and Design.

MA: Art and Design (Studio Practice).
Admissions policy For BA: through UCAS.
For MA: candidates are normally expected to have obtained a good honours bachelor degree or equivalent in an art and design discipline or a closely related subject. A lower-level qualification with appropriate professional or industrial experience may also be considered.

New College Nottingham
P.O. Box 6598, Nottingham
NG1 1NS
T 0115 9 100100
E headmissions@ncn.ac.uk
W www.ncn.ac.uk
Contact Central Admissions
One of the largest colleges of FE in the UK, with a wide range of full- and part-time study programmes.
Degrees offered FdA: Digital Arts.
Other fine-art courses BTEC FD: Art and Design. BTEC ND: Fine Art. Dip. in Foundation Studies: Art and Design.

Nottingham Trent University
Burton Street, Nottingham
NG1 4BU
T 0115 9418418
E reg.web@ntu.ac.uk
W www.ntu.ac.uk
Total student population of around 26,000.
Degrees offered BA (Hons): Decorative Arts; Fine Art; Graphic Design; Photography/Photography in Europe; Textile Design. MA: Art and Design, Language and Culture Bridging Programme; Decorative Arts; Fine Art; Graphic Design; Textile Design and Innovation. MPhil/PhD studies and an art and design international Access programme also offered.
Admissions policy For undergraduate: through UCAS, plus other requirements.

South Nottingham College
West Bridgford Centre, Greythorn Drive, Nottingham
NG2 7GA
T 0115 9146400
F 0115 9146444
E enquiries@south-nottingham.ac.uk
W www.south-nottingham.ac.uk
Other fine-art courses BTEC FD: Design.
BTEC ND: Art and Design; Three-Dimensional Design; Textile Design. Foundation diploma: Art and Design (post-A-level). HND: Design; Three-

Dimensional Design; Graphic Design; Fine Art.
Admissions policy For HND: through UCAS.

Stamford College
Drift Road, Stamford
PE9 1XA
T 01780 484300
F 01780 484301
E enquiries@stamford.ac.uk
W www.stamford.ac.uk
Contact Jayne Olney
The Visual Arts Centre has a specifically equipped life-drawing room, photographic studio, three-dimensional workshops and Apple Macintosh suites. Degrees are validated by Anglia Poytechnic University.
Degrees offered BA (Hons): Fine Art; Graphic Design.
Other fine-art courses Foundation diploma: Art and Design.
Admissions policy All applicants are interviewed. Mature students are encouraged to apply and are considered on a portfolio of work.

University College Northampton
St George's Avenue, Northampton
NN2 6JD
T 01604 735500 / 893210
F 01604 717813
E christine.midgley@northampton.ac.uk
W www.northampton.ac.uk
Contact Judy Jordan
Degrees offered BA (Hons): Fine Art; Fine Art, Painting and Drawing; Photographic Practice.
MA: Fine Art.
Admissions policy Via UCAS routes A and B.
Normally foundation or equivalent. Applicants interviewed. Non-standard applications welcome.

University of Derby
School of Arts, Design and Technology, Britannia Mill Campus, Mackworth Road, Derby
DE22 3BL
T 01332 594008
F 01332 597760
E adtenquiry@derby.ac.uk
W vertigo.derby.ac.uk
Contact Jas Dhillon on 01442 594058.
Courses in fine art date back to the beginning of the nineteenth century. Recent alumni include Nisha Dougal (*Artists' Newsletter*) and Sarah Key (studying for PhD in painting at Loughborough).
Degrees offered BA (Hons): Fine Art; Photography; Film and Video; Illustration.

MA: Advanced Art and Design Theory and Practice (ADAPT).

Other fine-art courses PgCert: Arts Practice.

Admissions policy Applications are invited from students who are studying art and design subjects at A2 level. Application can be through UCAS routes A or B. There will be a portfolio interview for each applicant.

University of Lincoln

Brayford Pool, Lincoln
LN6 7TS
T 01522 882000
E enquiries@lincoln.ac.uk
W www.lincoln.ac.uk

The Art, Architecture and Design Faculty's three schools provide undergraduate, taught postgraduate and postgraduate research programmes. The Hull and Lincoln Schools of Art and Design were both founded in the 1860s while the School of Architecture was established in the 1930s.

Degrees offered BA (Hons): Fine Art; Animation; Conservation and Restoration; Contemporary Decorative Crafts; Contemporary Lens Media; Fashion Studies; Furniture Design and Practice; Graphic Design; Heritage Investigation; Illustration; Museum and Exhibition Design. MA: Fine Art; Design; Art, Architecture and Design. Fine-art research opportunities (MRes/MPhil/ PhD) also offered.

London

Art Academy

201 Union Street, London
SE1 0LN
T 020 74016539
F 020 74016541
E info@artacademy.org.uk
W www.artacademy.org.uk

Incorporates the Sculpture Academy and the Painting Academy. Offers training in fine art, commissioning and using art to stimulate and motivate people. Twelve resident artists teach courses in exchange for studio space.

Other fine-art courses Full- and part-time, evening and weekend courses in painting and sculpture.

Camberwell College of Arts

Peckham Road, London
SE5 8UF
T 020 75146302
F 020 75146310
E enquiries@camberwell.arts.ac.uk
W www.camberwell.arts.ac.uk

Over one hundred years old. Alumni include Howard Hodgkin, Maggi Hambling, Tom Phillips, Gillian Ayres, Richard Long and Cathy de Monchaux.

Degrees offered BA (Hons): Drawing; Painting; Sculpture; Ceramics. MA: Printmaking; Book Arts; Drawing; Digital Arts; Digital Arts (online).

Other fine-art courses An extensive programme of short courses, tailormade courses and summer schools offered in conjunction with Chelsea College of Art and Design. For further details contact Short Course Unit on 020 7514 6311 or email shortcourses@camberwell.arts.ac.uk.

Admissions policy For undergraduate: through UCAS and completion of a foundation year or related qualifications and/or experience (particularly for mature students). For postgraduate: Direct to the college, accompanied by a project proposal. Deadline for AHRB funding: mid-February.

Central St Martins College of Art & Design

Southampton Row, London
WC1B 4AP
T 020 75147000
F 020 75147024
E info@csm.arts.ac.uk
W www.csm.arts.ac.uk

Founded in 1989 by the merger of Central School of Art and Crafts (1869) and St Martin's School of Art (1854). St Martin's was particularly well known for fashion and fine art and the Central School for a wide range of design and art, including theatre design, industrial design and graphic design. In 2003 the Byam Shaw School of Art joined Central St Martins. Alumni include Lucian Freud and Frank Auerbach.

Degrees offered BA (Hons): Fine Art; Art, Design and Environment; Criticism, Communication and Curation: Arts and Design; Ceramic Design. FdA: Fine Art Skills and Practice. PgCert: Drawing; Glass; Printmaking; Photography; Fine Arts. MA: Fine Art. PhD programmes.

Other fine-art courses Fine-art foundation and Foundation Studies in Art and Design. Short courses (summer school, Christmas school, Easter school and evening and weekend courses) and study-abroad courses.

Admissions policy For BA (Hons) undergraduate degree courses: through UCAS. For a place on Foundation Studies, a postgraduate MA course or as a research student, apply direct to Central St Martins on the relevant form, which can be downloaded from website. For details see www.csm.arts.ac.uk/textsite/faq_app.asp.

Chelsea College of Art & Design

John Islip Street, London
SW1
T 020 75147751
F 020 75147778
E enquiries@chelsea.arts.ac.uk
W www.chelsea.arts.ac.uk
Degrees offered BA (Hons): Fine Art; Textile Design; Interior and Spatial Design; Graphic Design Communication. MA: Fine Art; Textile Design; Interior and Spatial Design. PgDip: Fine Art. Foundation Studies: Art and Design.
Other fine-art courses Art foundation: Interior Design. Graduate Dip.: Interior Design (subject to validation). Short course programme, including evening, Saturday and summer schools.
Admissions policy UCAS route B. Portfolio. Two GCE A-levels and three GCSEs (grade C or above). IELTS 6.5. Although most applicants to BA courses have completed foundation studies, Chelsea welcomes applications from a wide range of people with differing qualifications.

Croydon College

College Road, Croydon
CR9 1DX
T 020 87605914
E info@croydon.ac.uk
W www.croydon.ac.uk
Established for over one hundred years. Strong African, Caribbean and Asian influences and links with many other ethnic communities. Two main sites, Fairfield and the adjacent dedicated Higher Education Centre.
Degrees offered BA (Hons): Fine Art (Combined Media) (also Dip./Cert. of HE); Fine Art (Combined Media with Digital Art) (also Dip. of HE); Fine Art (Combined Media with Print and Book) (also Dip. of HE); Photomedia (also Dip./Cert. of HE).
Other fine-art courses BTEC Dip. in Foundation Studies: Art and Design. BTEC FD: Art and Design. All courses offered part-time.
Admissions policy Dependent upon portfolio work and UCAS points.

Goldsmiths College

New Cross, London
SE14 6NW
T 020 79197171
E admissions@gold.ac.uk
W www.goldsmiths.ac.uk
Founded in 1891 and part of the University of London since 1904. Almost 5,400 undergraduates and 3,000 postgraduates. Alumni in art and design include Lucian Freud, Antony Gormley, Damien Hirst, Margaret Howell, Gary Hume, Steve McQueen, Mary Quant, Bridget Riley, Sam Taylor-Wood, Gillian Wearing, Jane and Louise Wilson.
Degrees offered BA (Hons): Fine Art (Studio Practice and Contemporary Critical Studies); Fine Art (extension degree); Fine Art and History of Art; Fine Art and History of Art (extension degree); Design. MA: Design (Critical Theory and Practice); Fine Art. PgDip: Fine Art.
Admissions policy Admission is based on the UCAS system for undergraduates. Postgraduate admission is normally by interview and portfolio inspection. Entrance requirements are normally a first degree of at least second-class standard in Fine Art or the equivalent; or Goldsmiths' PgDip in Fine Art; or a proven record of experience as a practising artist.

Kingston University

River House, 53–57 High Street, Kingston-upon-Thames
KT1 1LQ
T 020 85472000
E admissions-info@kingston.ac.uk
W www.kingston.ac.uk
17,500 students over four campuses.
Degrees offered BA (Hons): Fine Art; Graphic Design; Photography with Graphic Design. MA: Communication Design.
Other fine-art courses Edexcel Dip. in Foundation Studies: Art and Design.
Admissions policy For undergraduate: through UCAS. Requirements vary depending on degree.

London College of Communication

Elephant and Castle, London
SE1 6SB
T 020 75146853
F 020 75146848
E media@lcc.arts.ac.uk
W www.lcc.arts.ac.uk
Founded in 1883 as St Bride Foundation and the North-western Polytechnic. Formerly known as the London College of Printing. Granted university status in 2003. Around nine thousand students.
Degrees offered Digital Media; Film and Video; Photography; Surface Design.

Other fine-art courses FE, Young at Art and professional training courses.

London Metropolitan University

31 Jewry Street, London
EC3N 2EY
T 020 74230000
E admissions@londonmet.ac.uk
W www.londonmet.ac.uk
Can trace its roots back to 1848 with the establishment of the Metropolitan evening classes for young men. Ranks as London's largest unitary university with over 35,000 students.
Degrees offered BA (Hons): Design; Design (Graphics); Fine Art; Fine Art (specialist route); Fine Art Contemporary Theory and Practice. MA by project: Applied Art; Art, Design and Visual Culture; Design; Drawing; Fine Art; Visual Culture.
Other fine-art courses Dip. in Foundation Studies: Art and Design.
Admissions policy See the university's standard entry requirements (for both postgraduate and undergraduate). In addition, students should have undertaken an art foundation course. Students are selected by portfolio inspection and interview.

London South Bank University

103 Borough Road, London
SE1 0AA
T 020 79288989
E enquiry@lsbu.ac.uk
W www.lsbu.ac.uk
Founded in 1892 as the Borough Polytechnic and amalgamated with four other colleges in 1970 to become South Bank Polytechnic. Granted university status in 1992. Nearly eighteen thousand students.
Degrees offered BA (Hons): Digital Media Arts; Digital Photography.
Admissions policy See website.

Middlesex University

North London Business Park, Oakleigh Road South, London
N11 1QS
T 020 84115000
E admissions@mdx.ac.uk
W www.mdx.ac.uk
Degrees offered BA (Hons): Fine Art; Applied Arts; Design; Graphic Design; Illustration; Photography. MA: Fine Art Practice and Theory. MFA: Graphic Design.
Other fine-art courses FdA: Graphic Design;

Fine Art Practice and Theory. Edexcel Dip. in Foundation Studies: Art and Design. Dip. of HE: Three-Dimensional Design; Visual Communication Design (Graphic Design). HND/HNC: Fine Art; Graphic Design; Public Art.
Admissions policy For undergraduate: UCAS (requirements depend on degree). For full- and part-time postgraduate programmes, normally apply direct to the university. See website.

Prince's Drawing School

19–22 Charlotte Road, London
EC2A 3SG
T 020 76138527
F 020 76138599
E enquiry@princesdrawingschool.org.uk
W www.princesdrawingschool.org.uk
An independent educational organization that enables artists to broaden and extend their drawing practice. Founded by the Prince of Wales in 2000. Initially a part of the Prince's Foundation, the Drawing School became a charity in its own right in 2004. Over four hundred students attend classes run by the school each term.
Other fine-art courses Runs twenty-six courses over each ten-week term, during the daytime from Monday to Saturday and most evenings. Geared mainly for students with some experience of drawing, enrolment is open and students don't need to submit a portfolio.

Richmond, The American International University in London

Richmond Hill Campus, Queen's Road,
Richmond-upon-Thames
TW10 6JP
T 020 83329000
F 020 83321596
E enroll@richmond.ac.uk
W www.richmond.ac.uk
Attended by students from over one hundred countries. Degrees recognized in the UK and USA.
Degrees offered BA: Art, Design and Media. Offers a range of contemporary, cross-disciplinary, multimedia core courses dealing with concepts in art, design and media, and the interfaces between them. Students also schooled in professional skills and techniques and appropriate theory.
Admissions policy See website.

Roehampton University

School of Arts, Erasmus House, Roehampton Lane, London
SW15 5PU

T 020 83923000
W www.roehampton.ac.uk
Degrees offered Undergraduate courses: Art Practice and Critical Skills; Childhood and the Arts; Painting and Printmaking. Postgraduate courses: Art Studies.

Royal College of Art
Kensington Gore, London
SW7 2EU
T 020 75904444
F 020 75904500
E admissions@rca.ac.uk
W www.rca.ac.uk
Contact Assistant Registrar
The world's only wholly postgraduate university of art and design, specializing in teaching and research. Alumni include James Dyson, Ridley Scott, Robin Day, Zandra Rhodes, Philip Treacy, Tracey Emin, David Hockney and Henry Moore.
Degrees offered MA, MPhil and PhD degrees. School of Fine Art: Painting; Printmaking; Photography; Sculpture. School of Applied Arts: Ceramics and Glass; Goldsmithing; Silversmithing; Metalwork; Jewelry. School of Communications: Animation; Communication; Art and Design. School of Humanities: Conservation. Curating. Contemporary Art. History of Design. School of Fashion and Textiles: Fashion Menswear; Fashion Womenswear; Constructed Textiles; Printed Textiles. School of Architecture and Design: Architecture and Interiors Design; Products; Industrial Design; Engineering; Interaction Design; Vehicle Design.
Admissions policy Entry requirements and application deadlines all listed on website.

Slade School of Fine Art (UCL)
Gower Street, London
WC1E 6BT
T 020 76792313
F 020 76797801
E slade.enquiries@ucl.ac.uk
W www.ucl.ac.uk/slade
Contact Caroline Nicholas
Concerned with contemporary art and the practice, history and theories that inform it. Provides for the education of professional artists by professional artists and scholars of the history and theory of art. Founded in 1871 as a department of UCL. Located in the centre of London close to many important galleries, museums and theatres.

Degrees offered BA: Fine Art. MA: Fine Art. MFA: Fine Art. Graduate Dip.: Fine Art. MPhil/PhD: Fine Art.
Other fine-art courses Summer, Easter and Saturday classes. Continuing education opportunities including a specialist research development programme.
Admissions policy For BA: UCAS route A. For graduate taught programmes: direct application. Email for further details.

Thames Valley University
Ealing Campus, St Mary's Road, Ealing, London
W5 5RF
T 020 85795000
W www.tvu.ac.uk
Campuses in Ealing, Slough and Reading.
Degrees offered BAs and MAs in digital arts and photography.

University of East London
Longbridge Road, Dagenham
RM17 6UG
T 020 82233333
F 020 82232900
E admiss@uel.ac.uk
W www.uel.ac.uk
Degrees offered BA (Hons): Fine Art (three years full-time; five years part-time); Fine Art with foundation year (four years full-time). MA/PgDip: Fine Art (MA: one year full-time or two years part-time; PgDip: one year part-time with the option of a second year to complete the MA). Professional Doctorate: Fine Art (three years full-time or four to five years part-time).
Admissions policy Contact Beryl Watson on 020 82233400 for details on admission to all fine-art programmes.

University of the Arts London
See entries under: Camberwell College of Arts; Central St Martins College of Art and Design; Chelsea College of Art and Design; London College of Communication.

University of Westminster
309 Regent Street, London
W1B 2UW
T 020 79115000
E cav-admissions@wmin.ac.uk
W www.wmin.ac.uk
Founded in 1838 as Britain's first polytechnic.
Degrees offered BA (Hons): Animation; Mixed

Media Fine Art (full- and part-time); Ceramics; Photographic Arts; Photography (part-time); Digital and Photographic Imaging.
Admissions policy Online for part-time and postgraduate courses. For BA (Hons): through UCAS.

West Thames College
London Road, Isleworth
TW7 4HS
T 020 83262000
E info@west-thames.ac.uk
W www.west-thames.ac.uk
Contact Siobhan Fitzgerald
HND programmes have been running at West Thames since 1985.
Other fine-art courses HND: Graphics and Advertising; Fine Art; Fashion. Foundation diploma: Art and Design. ND: Art and Design. Various part-time classes
Admissions policy ND, AVCE, foundation or A-levels. Mature students with relevant experience welcomed. Portfolio required at interview. Applications accepted from January to September. Enrolment from late August.

Wimbledon School of Art
Merton Hall Road, Wimbledon, London
SW19 3QA
T 020 84085000
F 020 84085050
E info@wimbledon.ac.uk
W www.wimbledon.ac.uk
Contact Linda Tinsley, Admissions Officer
Founded in 1890, a specialist art and design school. Staff are all practising artists, designers and scholars within their specialist fields. Current students show work in exhibitions, performances and costume parades at key venues in London. Alumni include Anthony Cragg, Kenny Ho, Raymond Briggs and Jeff Beck.
Degrees offered BA (Hons): Fine Art (Painting); Fine Art (Sculpture); Fine Art (Graphic Media); Theatre (Costume Design); Theatre (Costume Interpretation); Theatre (Set Design for Stage and Screen); Theatre (Design for Performance); Theatre (Technical Arts and Special Effects). MA: Fine Art (Painting); Fine Art (Drawing); Fine Art (Sculpture); Fine Art (Graphic Media); Theatre (Visual Language of Performance). MPhil and PhD programmes of research.
Other fine-art courses Edexcel BTEC Dip. in Foundation Studies. Full- and part-time orientation course: Art and Design. Pre-

foundation perceptual and analytical drawing programme. Summer short courses.

Working Men's College
44 Crowndale Road, London
NW1 1TR
T 020 72554700 / 0800 3581854 (freephone)
F 020 73835561
E info@wmcollege.ac.uk
W www.wmcollege.ac.uk
Founded in 1854 to provide a liberal arts education for the Victorian skilled artisan class and was associated with the Cooperative Movement. Among the first adult education institutes in the country. Caters for both women and men.
Other fine-art courses Foundation course: Art and Design.
Admissions policy By completion of enrolment form. Concessionary fees for some students.

North-east

City of Sunderland College
Bede Centre, Durham Road, Sunderland
SR3 4AH
T 0191 5116260 / 5116060
W www.citysun.ac.uk
Approximately 24,000 students at five main college centres. Courses also offered by distance learning and at community centres.
Other fine-art courses Art and Design Cert. in Advanced Studies: Calligraphy; Digital Imaging and Photography. FdA: Applied Art; Life Drawing; Oil Painting; Painting and Drawing; Photography; Printed Textiles; Silk Painting; Stained Glass; Watercolours.
Admissions policy Entry requirements vary depending upon the course and level of study. Contact the college for individual fact sheets.

Cleveland College of Art & Design
Green Lane, Linthorpe, Middlesbrough
TS5 7RJ
T 01642 288888
F 01642 288828
E studentrecruitment@ccad.ac.uk
W www.ccad.ac.uk
A specialist art and design college; one of four nationally, offering further, higher and continuing education courses in the creative professions. Has roots that go back to 1880, and was formed by the merger of Teesside and Hartlepool Colleges of Art.
Degrees offered BA (Hons): Fine Art.

Other fine-art courses BTEC Dip.: Fine Art.
Admissions policy Full-time applications through UCAS routes A and B. Part-time direct to college.

Newcastle College
Rye Hill Campus, Scotswood Road, Newcastle-upon-Tyne
NE4 5BR
T 0191 2004000
F 0191 2004517
E enquiries@ncl-coll.ac.uk
W www.newcastlecollege.co.uk
Four hundred staff and thirty thousand students.
Degrees offered BA (Hons): Fine Art. FdA: Contemporary Ceramic Practice; Fine Art Practice; Photographic Practice; Textile Design and Practice.
Other fine-art courses HNC: Photography.

Northumbria University
Arts and Social Sciences, Room 125, Lipman Building, Newcastle-upon-Tyne
NE1 8ST
T 0191 2273280
F 0191 2273696
E liz.candlish@unn.ac.uk
W www.northumbria.ac.uk
Contact Liz Candlish
A visiting programme of artists offer talks on their work. Galleries such as the BALTIC Centre for Contemporary Art and Waygood Gallery collaborate with the university to offer educational opportunities.
Degrees offered BA (Hons): Fine Art. MA: Art Practices (Fine Art); Art Practices (Media); Fine Art and Education; Fine Art (part-time).
Other fine-art courses Foundation certificate: Fine Art (part-time). Foundation diploma: Art and Design (overseas).
Admissions policy By submission of portfolio of recent work and interview. Relevant foundation or degree course required. Each application assessed on individual merit.

University of Newcastle-upon-Tyne
10 Kensington Terrace, Newcastle-upon-Tyne
NE1 7RU
T 0191 2225594
F 0191 2228685
E enquiries@ncl.ac.uk
W www.ncl.ac.uk
Contact Kath Hind
Started life in 1834 as a medical school and gained its own charter in 1963.
Degrees offered BA (Hons): Fine Art (UCAS

codes: W150 route A; E100 route B). MFA: Fine Art (two years full-time).
Other fine-art courses Research areas in fine art.
Admissions policy See website.

University of Sunderland
Edinburgh Building, City Campus, Chester Road, Sunderland
SR1 3SD
T 0191 5153154
W www.welcome.sunderland.ac.uk
Degrees offered BA (Hons): Art and Design; Fine Art; Glass, Architectural Glass and Ceramics; Photography, Video and Digital Imaging.
Admissions policy For degree, foundation degrees and HND programmes applicants need to be at least 18 years of age on 31 December in the proposed year of entry.

University of Teeside
Middlesbrough
TS1 3BA
T 01642 218121
F 01642 342067
E registry@tees.ac.uk
W www.tees.ac.uk
Originally founded as Constantine College, the institution was officially opened in 1930. Has twenty thousand students.
Degrees offered BA (Hons): Fine Art; Contemporary Three-Dimensional Design; Design; Graphic Design. MA: Design. Art foundation: Design for Exhibition and Display; Graphic Design.

Northern Ireland

Ulster University
Belfast Campus, York Street, Belfast
BT15 1ED
T 0870 0400700
E online@ulster.ac.uk
W www.ulst.ac.uk
School of Art and Design located at both York Street campus in Belfast city centre and at the Foyle Arts Centre at the Magee campus. The largest art and design education centre on the island of Ireland. INTERFACE is a new research centre based in the School of Art and Design, part of a multi-million-pound redevelopment of the Belfast campus.
Degrees offered BA (Hons): Art and Design; Fine and Applied Arts; Textiles and Fashion Design.

PGDip/MA: Applied Arts. PgDip/MFA: Fine Art.
Other fine-art courses Foundation Studies: Art and
Design.

North-west

Blackpool and the Fylde College
School of Art and Design, Palatine Road, Blackpool
FY1 4DW
T 01253 352352
E mp@blackpool.ac.uk
W www.art-design.ac.uk
Contact Malcolm Pearson
Offers recently created fine-art course, covering the
specialist disciplines of drawing, painting,
printmaking and digital imaging. Has evolved
from the grade-1 foundation course.
Degrees offered BA (Hons): Fine Art: Professional
Practice (subject to validation by Lancaster
University). MA: Visual Design as Creative Practice.
Admissions policy Fine art applications through
UCAS for BA and direct to the institution for MA.

City College Manchester
Abraham Moss Campus, Crescent Road,
Crumpsall, Manchester
M8 5UF
T 0161 6148000 / 0800 0130123 (freephone)
E admissions@ccm.ac.uk
W www.ccm.ac.uk
Over 29,000 students and 1,200 staff.
Other fine-art courses NVQ level 3, Foundation
and Intermediate: Photography; Black and White
Photography Introduction; Digital Photography
Introduction. NCFE levels 1 and 2: Ceramics
Introduction; Life Drawing.

Cumbria Institute of the Arts
Brampton Road, Carlisle
CA3 9AY
T 01228 400300
F 01228 514491
E info@cumbria.ac.uk
W www.cumbria.ac.uk
Contact Admissions Officer
Around 1,200 full-time students. Founded in the
1820s. Delivers a variety of courses at FE and HE
levels in the visual, performing and media arts,
crafts, design and cultural heritage.
Degrees offered BA (Hons): Fine Art;
Contemporary Applied Arts; Graphic Design;
Multimedia Design and Digital Animation. MA:
Contemporary Fine Art; Contemporary Applied

Arts. Research degrees up to PhD level.
Other fine-art courses Some evening classes.
Phone for part-time brochure.
Admissions policy Entry to undergraduate
programmes through UCAS routes A and B.
Most applicants will have completed a BTEC ND,
Dip. in Foundation Studies, Access to HE course,
Advanced GNVQ or equivalent course, and have
two grade C passes at A2 or, for Scottish students,
three Highers at grades BBC. Applicants for
MAs will normally have a first degree at 2:1
or above. However, applicants with equivalent
professional experience are invited to contact the
institute.

East Lancashire Institute of Higher Education
Blackburn College, Feilden Street, Blackburn
BB2 1LH
T 01254 292594
W www.elihe.ac.uk
Contact Carla Patchett
Offers a range of art and design provision through
full- and part-time study routes.
Degrees offered BA (Hons): Fine Art (Integrated
Media). FdA: Multimedia.
Other fine-art courses HND: Photography; Textile
Design.
Admissions policy All candidates applying to the
school are interviewed for places. For details of
admission requirements see website.

Frink School of Figurative Sculpture
Cross St Mill, Leek
ST13 6BL
T 01538 399210
E info@frinkschool.org
W www.frinkschool.org
Set up to preserve and continue the teaching of
figurative sculpture. Established in 1996 and
named after the sculptor Elisabeth Frink (1933–93).
Operates from the Moorland Arts Centre in Leek on
the edge of the Peak District.
Other fine-art courses Offers a mix of part-time
weekday, weekend and one-week courses, covering
aspects of sculpture and also drawing and
painting, including: Life and Portrait Modelling;
Life Drawing and Painting; Wood Carving; Stone
Carving; Related Modelling and Casting Processes;
Welding; Terracotta Firing.

Lancaster University
Bailrigg, Lancaster
LA1 4YW
T 01524 65201

E ugadmissions@lancaster.ac.uk
W www.lancaster.ac.uk
Degrees offered BA (Hons): Fine Art; Art and Art
History. MA: Art (Studio Practice). MPhil/PhD:
Fine Art.

Liverpool Community College

Bankfield Road, Liverpool
L13 0BQ
T 01512 523214
E enquiry@liv-coll.ac.uk
W www.liv-coll.ac.uk
Other fine-art courses AVCE: Art and Design. BTEC
FD: Design. BTEC GNVQ Intermediate: Art and
Design. BTEC HNC/HND: Fine Arts. BTEC ND:
Foundation Art and Design. BTEC ND: Graphic
Design. BTEC ND: Three-Dimensional Design.
GNVQ Foundation: Art and Design.

Liverpool Hope University College

Hope Park, Liverpool
L16 9JD
T 0151 2913000
F 0151 2913444
E admission@hope.ac.uk
W www.hope.ac.uk
Tradition stretching back over 150 years, when the
Church of England Diocese of Chester and the
Roman Catholic Sisters of Notre Dame established
separate teacher education colleges for women. An
ecumenical Christian foundation.
Degrees offered BA (Hons): Design. BA
(Combined Hons): Fine Art and Design (with
another subject of your choice). BA, QTS: Fine Art
and Design with Teacher Training.
Other fine-art courses Cert. of HE (Combined
Hons): Fine Art and Design (with another subject).
Admissions policy Applications should be made
through UCAS.

Liverpool John Moores University

Rodney House, 70 Mount Pleasant, Liverpool
L3 5UX
T 0151 2312121
E artadmissions@livjm.ac.uk
W www.livjm.ac.uk
Contact Karen Davis
University took its name from Sir John Moores,
the founder of the Littlewoods empire. Originally a
small mechanics institution (Liverpool Mechanics'
School of Arts). Now has over 24,000 students
studying over two hundred courses at
undergraduate and postgraduate level.
Degrees offered BA (Hons): Fine Art; Graphic

Arts; Fashion and Textile Design. PGCE: Art and
Design.
Admissions policy Looks for evidence of creative
ability and motivation regardless of entry route.
Applications through UCAS system and portfolio
interview.

Manchester Metropolitan University

Faculty of Art and Design, Ormond Building,
Lower Ormond Street, Manchester
M15 6BY
T 0161 2471705
F 0161 2476393
E artdes.fac@mmu.ac.uk
W www.mmu.ac.uk
Contact Faculty Office
The faculty has a distinguished history dating back
over 150 years. The painter Adolphe Valette, a
contemporary of L.S. Lowry, was both a student
and a teacher at the faculty.
Degrees offered BA (Hons): Fine Art; Interactive
Arts. MA: Fine Art.
Admissions policy For BA: 160 tariff points plus
foundation course. For MA: good undergraduate
fine-art degree.

Mid-Cheshire College

Hartford Campus, Chester Road, Northwich
CW8 1LJ
T 01606 74444
E info@midchesh.ac.uk
W www.midchesh.ac.uk
Around ten thousand students.
Other fine-art courses BTEC FD: Art and Design.
BTEC Introductory Dip.: Art and Design. BTEC
ND: Graphic Design. BTEC ND: Photography.
Edexcel Dip. in Foundation Studies: Art and
Design. HND: Photography. HND: Graphic
Design. Various part-time courses.
Admissions policy In general, a number of GCSEs
at a certain grade or above, portfolio and interview.

Oldham College

Rochdale Road, Oldham
OL9 6AA
T 0161 6245214
F 0161 7854234
E info@oldham.ac.uk
W www.oldham.ac.uk
Contact Patricia Walkenden
Other fine-art courses HND: Fine Art (two years);
Multimedia (two years). ND: Art and Design
(one year). Adult Access to Art and Design
(two years).

Admissions policy All students receive a one-to-one interview for advice and guidance with an experienced member of teaching staff. Students can apply at any time of year.

Runshaw College

Euxton Lane, Chorley
PR7 6AD
T 01772 642040
E justask@runshaw.ac.uk
W www.runshaw.ac.uk
Established as a sixth-form college in 1974
Other fine-art courses Foundation Studies: Art and Design. HND: Graphic Design; Fine Art.
Admissions policy Apply through UCAS.

Southport College

Mornington Road, Southport
PR9 0TT
T 01704 500606
F 01704 392794
E guidance@southport-college.ac.uk
W www.southport-college.ac.uk
All foundation-degree programmes are offered in conjunction with either the University of Central Lancashire in Preston or Liverpool John Moores University. Around twelve thousand students (two thousand studying on full-time or modular courses).
Other fine-art courses Dip. in Foundation Studies: Art and Design. ND: General Design and Art.
Admissions policy Entry requirements for ND in General Design and Art: four GCSE passes at grade C or above (three if the portfolio presented at interview is exceptionally good). A good standard of Intermediate GNVQ in Art and Design is also acceptable. For Dip. in Foundation Studies (Art and Design), candidates are expected to: possess at least two AS levels supported by a minimum of three GCSEs grades A to C, or equivalent; exhibit a portfolio that shows a satisfactory standard of work, particularly in the area of objective drawing; project a high level of commitment and enthusiasm. If an applicant's work exhibits exceptional ability, the need for minimum number of formal academic qualifications may be waived. Mature students with a good portfolio may be accepted without academic qualifications.

St Helens College

Brook Street, St Helens
WA10 1PZ
T 01744 733766
F 01744 623400

E enquire@sthelens.ac.uk
W www.sthelens.ac.uk
Founded as the Gamble Institute in 1896.
Degrees offered FdA: Photography and Digital Imaging; Multimedia Arts and Animation.
Other fine-art courses Access, BTEC, HND and foundation courses in a wide range of subjects including calligraphy, ceramics, digital video production, painting and drawing, photography, textiles, visual studies, oil and watercolours.
Admissions policy For all HND and degree programmes: through UCAS. For all FE programmes (including part-time HNC): apply directly to the college's admissions unit.

St Martin's College

Bowerham Road, Lancaster
LA1 3JD
T 01524 384384
E admissions@ucsm.ac.uk
W www.ucsm.ac.uk
Founded in 1963 by the Church of England as a College of Education to train teachers. Over ten thousand students (twenty-eight per cent being mature students).
Degrees offered BA (Hons)/Dip. of HE: Fine Art (part-time studies available).
Admissions policy See website.

Stockport College of Further and Higher Education

Wellington Road South, Stockport
SK1 3UQ
T 0845 2303107
F 0161 9583452
E enquiries@stockport.ac.uk
W www.stockport.ac.uk
Founded in 1887. Has fifteen thousand students enrolled within twelve vocational areas offering qualifications from GCSE to degrees validated by local universities.
Degrees offered BA (Hons): Documentary and Fine Art Photography.
Admissions policy Five GCSE passes and two A-levels or satisfactory completion of art and design foundation, Access course, BTEC ND or Advanced GNVQ.

University College Chester

Parkgate Road, Chester
CH1 4BJ
T 01244 375444

E enquiries@chester.ac.uk
W www.chester.ac.uk
Contact For undergraduate admissions,
email enquiries@chester.ac.uk or telephone
01244 375444 / 392780. For postgraduate
admissions, email postgrad@chester.ac.uk or
telephone 01244 392780. For enquiries about
course content, contact Pete Turnbull, Head
of Fine Art, Department of Fine Art, email
fineart@chester.ac.uk or telephone 01244 375444
ext. 3029.

Housed in a modern, custom-built facility, part of
the main campus. Aims of the programme are to
develop practical skills and creative potential
relevant to fine-art practice, and to provide a
theoretical framework that allows students to
engage in informed discourse and constructive
self-evaluation of work.

Degrees offered BA (Single and Combined Hons):
Fine Art; New Media. PgDip/MA: Fine Art.
Admissions policy See website.

University of Bolton

Deane Road, Bolton
BL3 5AB
T 01204 900600
E enquiries@bolton.ac.uk
W www.bolton.ac.uk
Contact Art and Design Admissions, phone
01204 903367.
Formerly known as Bolton Institute. Became the
north-west's newest university in 2005. Of eight
thousand students, approximately seventy-two
per cent are from the north-west.
Degrees offered BA (Hons): Art and Design;
Textile/Surface Design.
Other fine-art courses Art and design foundation.
Admissions policy For BA Art and Design:
art foundation course; or four GCSE passes
and two A-levels including Art; or Intermediate
or Advanced GNVQ in Art and Design or related
subjects; or BTEC ND in Art and Design subjects;
or Access to HE Programme in Art and Design
subjects. For two-year foundation: four GCSEs
at grade C or above. For one-year foundation:
five GCSEs at grade C or above and one A-level,
preferably in Art. Special consideration
given to candidates over 21 without these
qualifications.

University of Central Lancashire

Department of Art and Fashion, Victoria Building,
Room VB338, Preston
PR1 2HE

T 01772 893182
F 01772 892921
E omwells@uclan.ac.uk
W www.uclan.ac.uk/facs/destech/artfash/
index.htm
Contact admissions@uclan.ac.uk
Degrees offered BA (Hons): Fine Art; Photography;
Art and Design. MA: Fine Art: Archive
Interventions; Fine Art: Curatorial Initiatives; Fine
Art: Painting and Printmaking; Fine Art: Site and
Place; Fine Art: Time-Based Media and
Photography.

University of Salford

School of Art and Design, Irwell Valley Campus,
Blandford Road, Salford
M6 6BD
T 0161 2952604
F 0161 2952605
E j.howarth@salford.ac.uk
W www.artdes.salford.ac.uk
Contact Julie Howarth
The BA (Hons) in Visual Arts offers a broad-based
fine-art course, which encourages self-directed
study in the studio across any chosen media.
The students' individual personal development
and study is supported by relevant theory, studio
tutorials and peer learning events. There is an
emphasis on contextualization and a high degree
of freedom in the studio.
Degrees offered BA (Hons): Visual Arts. PgDip:
Contemporary Fine Art. MA: Contemporary
Fine Art.
Other fine-art courses A range of continuing
professional-development courses for
postgraduates or mid-career practitioners.
Admissions policy Normal entry requirements:
foundation diploma in art and design or 160 tariff
points. All applicants are interviewed. Mature
students welcomed.

Wirral Metropolitan College

Conway Park Campus, Europa Boulevard, Conway
Park, Birkenhead
CH41 4NT
T 0151 5517777
F 0151 5517001
W www.wmc.ac.uk
Degrees offered BA (Hons): Fine Art (full- or
part-time).
Other fine-art courses Foundation diploma: Art
and Design. BTEC FD: Art and Design. BTEC:
Introduction to Art, Design and Media. BTEC ND:
Art and Design.

Scotland

Duncan of Jordanstone College of Art and Design

School of Fine Art, University of Dundee, Perth Road, Dundee
DD1 4HT
T 01382 345306
F 01382 200983
E j.a.ritchie@dundee.ac.uk
W www.dundee.ac.uk/fineart/
Contact Jacqueline Ritchie
College founded in 1892 and merged with the university in 1994. Fine Art is one of four schools in the faculty (the others being Architecture, Design and Television and Imaging). Fine Art students work across the full range of contemporary media, including painting, sculpture, printmaking, photography, video and digital, performance, installation and artists' publication. Staff are all practising artists working at national and international levels.
Degrees offered BA (Hons): Fine Art; Art, Philosophy; Contemporary Practices. MA/MLitt: Art and Aesthetics.
Admissions policy See website for details of level 1 (general course) and level 2 entry requirements and dates of application.

Edinburgh College of Art

74 Lauriston Place, Edinburgh
EH3 9DF
T 0131 2216000
F 0131 2216000
E m.wood@eca.ac.uk
W www.eca.ac.uk
Contact Cameron Murdoch (c.murdoch@eca.ac.uk)
Traces its routes back to 1760. The oldest established drawing academy in Britain. Founded on its present site in 1907 in a *beaux-arts* building, which includes a sculpture court built on Palladian principles and has a complete case (made *in situ*) of the Parthenon frieze. Alumni include Dame Elizabeth Blackadder, Sir Eduardo Paolozzi, Alan Davie, John Bellany, Sir Basil Spence, John Arden, Sir Nicholas Grimshaw and Barbara Rae.
Degrees offered BA (Hons): Painting; Design and Applied Arts; Visual Communication; Sculpture.
Other fine-art courses BA: Combined Studies (part-time). ECA Summer School Centre of Continuing Studies offers part-time courses.
Admissions policy Entry through UCAS for all full-time undergraduate courses. Interview and portfolio information is specific to different courses.

Glasgow School of Art

167 Renfrew Street, Glasgow
G3 6RQ
T 0141 3534500
W www.gsa.ac.uk
Founded in 1845 as one of the first government schools of design. International community of over 1,600 (primarily undergraduate) students studying in ten specialist fine art or design departments, or within the Mackintosh School of Architecture. Graduates include the new Glasgow Boys and Girls of the 1980s: Peter Howison, Ken Currie, Steven Campbell, Adrian Wiszniewski, Alison Watt, Christine Borland, Jenny Saville, Douglas Gordon, Roderick Buchanan, Toby Paterson and Rosalind Nashashibi.
Degrees offered BA (Hons): Fine Art; Fine Art Photography. MA: Fine Art; Design Practice. PhD: Art, Design and Architecture Education.

Heriot-Watt University

Edinburgh
EH14 4AS
T 0131 4495111
E edu.liaison@hw.ac.uk
W www.hw.ac.uk
More than 6,300 students on campus in Scotland plus over 9,500 on external programmes in 140 countries worldwide. The eighth oldest HE institution in the UK. Established by Royal Charter in 1966, its origins date back to 1821 through the School of Arts of Edinburgh.
Degrees offered BA (Hons): Design for Textiles. Taught courses at postgraduate level are either MA, PgDip or PCert courses.
Other fine-art courses Part-time study is available.
Admissions policy For undergraduate: through UCAS. For PgDip: applicants need a first degree.

Robert Gordon University

Gray's School of Art, Garthdee Road, Aberdeen
AB10 7QD
T 01224 263600
F 01224 263636
E a.young@rgu.ac.uk
W www2.rgu.ac.uk
Gray's School of Science and Art was founded in 1885. It later merged with Robert Gordon's Technical College and became the Robert Gordon University in 1992.
Degrees offered BA (Hons): Design and Craft; Fine Art; Design for Digital Media. MA: Fine Art.
Admissions policy For admission requirements for specific courses see website.

Studio Art School
St Leonard's House, Lasswade Road, Loanhead
EH20 9SD
T 0131 4402754
E info@studioartschool.co.uk
W www.studioartschool.co.uk
Contact Arlene Stewart
Offers a range of practical, online courses,
designed for those wanting to develop their skills
and knowledge in art and design. Founded in 2004,
the school offers complete flexiblity, enabling
students to work anywhere and at their own pace.
Other fine-art courses Introductory: How to Draw;
How to Paint; Introduction to Mixed Media;
Introduction to Fashion Design; Introduction to
Sketchbooks. Intermediate: Creative Drawing;
Creative Painting; Working with Pastels; Working
with Mixed Media; Designing for Fashion.
Preparation for HE: Portfolio Surgery; Developing
Sketchbooks; foundation course.
Admissions policy There are no specific entry
requirements and students can start at any time.

UHI Millennium Institute
Executive Office, Ness Walk, Inverness
IV3 1JZ
T 01463 279000
F 01463 279001
E EO@uhi.ac.uk
W www.uhi.ac.uk
Granted status of HE Institute in 2001, providing
university level courses throughout the Highlands
and Islands of Scotland. Partnership of fourteen
colleges and research institutions in the region,
coordinated by UHI executive office based in
Inverness.
Degrees offered BA: Creative Media; Fine Art.
Other fine-art courses HND: Art and Design.
HNC: Fine Art.

University of Edinburgh
History of Art, 20 Chambers Street, Edinburgh
EH1 1JZ
T 0131 6504124
F 0131 6508019
E histart@ed.ac.uk
W www.arts.ed.ac.uk/fineart
Contact Lisa Kendall (Arts Admissions)
Founded in 1880, History of Art at the University
of Edinburgh has the oldest chair of Art History in
Britain. A leading centre for the discipline, in a city
with world-class art collections.
Degrees offered MA: Fine Art (five years), jointly
run with Edinburgh College of Art.

Admissions policy UCAS: minimum BBB at A-
level. Portfolio to be submitted to Edinburgh
College of Art in January.

University of Paisley
Ayr Campus, Beechgrove, Ayr
KA8 0SR
T 01292 886388
F 01292 886387
E william.strachan@paisley.ac.uk
Contact William Strachan
Degrees offered BA (Hons): Digital Art. Aims to
unite 'traditional' art skills to skills in digital
technologies. The routes to specialism are digital
media, creative video and filmmaking, and
animation. Some academic study as well as work
in art and digital contexts.
Admissions policy Entry requirements involve
three parts: (1) three SQA Highers (BBC) (or
equivalents), including English; (2) an art and
design portfolio; (3) a brief interview based on (2).

South-east

Bedford College
Cauldwell Street, Bedford
MK42 9AH
T 01234 291000
F 01234 342674
E info@bedford.ac.uk.
W www.bedford.ac.uk
Contact Enquiries and Admissions at Bedford
College, FREEPOST BF 356, Bedford MK42 9BR,
or phone 0800 0740234.
Courses for all levels of ability, both in art and
design and in the more specialist disciplines of
fine art, graphic design, multimedia, three-
dimensional design and textiles. Provide practical
sessions and projects to help develop artistic
skills, and academic study into the social, cultural
and historical development of chosen media.
Other fine-art courses GNVQ levels 1 and 2: Art
and Design. BTEC Dip. in Foundation Studies,
BTEC ND: Fine Art. BTEC ND: Photography.
BTEC ND: Textiles; BTEC HNC/HND: Fine Art.
BTEC HNC/HND: Textiles.
Admissions policy For requirements see website.
Students with no previous qualifications can take
an Access to Art and Design course.

Brighton University
68 Grand Parade, Brighton
BN2 2JY

T 01273 600900
E postmaster@brighton.ac.uk
W www.brighton.ac.uk
Contact Admissions Officer, School of Arts and Communication.
Brighton School of Art opened in the Royal Pavilion Kitchens in 1859. It merged with Brighton Technical College in 1970 to form Brighton Polytechnic. The Polytechnic became Brighton University in 1992. The School of Arts and Communication encompasses painting, sculpture, printmaking, critical fine-art practice, dance, music and theatre with visual practice, graphic design, illustration and editorial photography. With thirty staff and 400 students; the school has an international profile and student exchanges links are established with art schools in Bordeaux, Limoges, Chicago, Kansas, New York and Warsaw. Located at Grand Parade.
Degrees offered BA (Hons): Art and Design; Illustration; Painting; Printmaking; Sculpture. MA/PgDip: Fine Art Printmaking; Printmaking and Professional Practice; Fine Art; Photography. New route PhD: Art and Design.
Other fine-art courses HNC and HND: Fine Art. For part-time evening and Saturday classes contact arthouse@brighton.ac.uk or 01273 643015.
Admissions policy UCAS routes A or B. Candidates are interviewed and should bring a portfolio of work. For MA courses apply by 1 July.

Buckinghamshire Chilterns University College

Faculty of Design, Queen Alexandra Road, High Wycombe
HP11 2JZ
T 01494 603054
F 01494 461196
E desenq@bcuc.ac.uk
W www.bcuc.ac.uk
There has been a School of Art and Design in High Wycombe for over one hundred years. Over 1,300 students studying at all levels from foundation to PhD.
Degrees offered BA (Hons): Fine Art (full- and part-time); Textiles and Surface Design. MA: Art and Design: Illustration; Ceramics with Glass; Printmaking.
Other fine-art courses Edexcel Dip. in Foundation Studies: Art and Design. Part-time drawing course.

Canterbury Christchurch University College

Department of Media and Art, North Holmes Road, Canterbury
CT1 1QU

T 01227 767700
F 01227 782888 / 470442
E M.S.Holt@cant.ac.uk
W www.cant.ac.uk
Contact Department of Admissions,
E admissions@cant.ac.uk.
Founded by the Church of England in 1962, built on what was the old orchard ground of St Augustine's Abbey. Welcomes students from all faiths and none. The Department of Media and Art is located on the Canterbury campus.
Degrees offered BA: Digital Culture, Arts and Media; Ceramics; Fine Art; Painting; Sculpture. Also teacher training with art and design. MA: Ceramics; Fine Art.
Admissions policy All college students must be at least 17 years of age by 1 October in the year of admission and fulfil the minimum entry requirements. Offers will be made in terms of grades rather than points. Candidates who have not had the opportunity to take a recognized qualification in key skills will not be disadvantaged in terms of their application. See website.

Kent Institute of Art and Design

Maidstone Campus, Oakwood Park, Maidstone
ME16 8AG
T 01622 757286
F 01622 621100
E info@kiad.ac.uk
W www.kiad.ac.uk
Campuses Canterbury campus: New Dover Road, Canterbury CT1 3AN **T** 01227 769371. Rochester campus: Rochester ME1 1DZ **T** 01634 830022.
Degrees offered BA (Hons): Applied and Decorative Arts; Contemporary Arts; Fine Art; Illustration; Multimedia; Photography; Video and Photography. MA: Artist's Film, Video and Photography; Fine Art; Fine Art: International Practice; Photography.
Other fine-art courses A wide range of foundation, Access and part-time courses (including evening, and summer school courses) are available.

Northbrook College Sussex

Littlehampton Road, Goring-by-Sea, Worthing
BN12 6NU
T 01903 606060
F 01903 606073
E enquiries@nbcol.ac.uk
W www.northbrook.ac.uk
Formed in 1987 when three local colleges merged, including the West Sussex College of Design.
Degrees offered BA (Hons): Fine Art (Painting);

Fine Art (Sculpture); Fine Art (Printmaking). All courses run full- and part-time.
Other fine-art courses Cert./Dip. of HE: Fine Art.
Admissions policy Applicants should have two A-levels/BTEC ND/GNVQ. All applicants will be interviewed with a portfolio that should include drawing and demonstrate creative, technical, written and visual abilities.

Oxford and Cherwell College
Oxpens Road, Oxford
OX1 1SA
T 01865 550550
F 01865 248871
E enquiries@oxford.occ.ac.uk
W www.occ.ac.uk
Degrees offered BA (Hons): Graphic Design and Illustration; Fine Art.
Other fine-art courses Foundation Studies: Art and Design. HND: Graphic Design; Illustration; Advertising and Multimedia.
Admissions policy See website.

Oxford Brookes University
School of Arts and Humanities, Richard Hamilton Building, Headington Campus, Oxford
OX3 0BP
T 01865 484995
F 01865 484952
E lisa.atkinson@brookes.ac.uk
W www.ah.brookes.ac.uk/art
Contact Lisa Atkinson
Degrees offered BA (Hons): Fine Art. MA: Contemporary Arts and Music; Social Sculpture; Composition and Sonic Art; Contemporary Art.
Admissions policy Successful completion of foundation or Access course in Art and Design. Applicants with alternative qualifications welcomed. UCAS routes A and B.

Oxford University
University Offices, Wellington Square, Oxford
OX1 2JD
T 01865 270000
E undergraduate.admissions@admin.ox.ac.uk
W www.ox.ac.uk
Oxford is the oldest university in the English-speaking world and lays claim to nine centuries of continuous existence. More than 130 nationalities represented in student population of over sixteen thousand.
Degrees offered BFA: Fine Art. MFA: Fine Art.
Admissions policy For undergraduate: UCAS system. All candidates are required to submit a

portfolio of their work (see the Ruskin School of Drawing and Fine Art prospectus for further information). The school is not looking for a particular style or skill, although it is generally felt that a foundation course can be beneficial to a candidate. Should be a sufficient amount of work to demonstrate real commitment and interests, with a good selection of drawings. Must be sent or delivered in a strong standard type portfolio (A1). For postgraduate: entry requirements as outlined in the applications and admissions procedure (completion of a bachelor's degree with a first or upper second-class honours or the international equivalent). Additional: Applicants will be expected to have completed or be about to complete a good honours degree, which would normally be in fine art.

Reading College and School of Art & Design
Crescent Road, Reading
RG1 5RQ
T 0118 9675000
F 0118 9675301
E Admissions@reading-college.ac.uk
W www.reading-college.ac.uk
Merged with Thames Valley University in 2004.
Degrees offered BA (Hons): Three-Dimensional Design.
Other fine-art courses ND: Art and Design (Fine Art). BTEC GNVQ Intermediate: Art and Design. Dip. in Foundation Studies: Art and Design. HND ND: Art, Design and Multimedia.
Admissions policy Through UCAS. See website.

Reigate School of Art, Design and Media (East Surrey College)
Gatton Point North, Claremont Road, Redhill
RH1 2JX
T 01737 788391
F 01737 788392
E afowler@esc.ac.uk
W www.esc.ac.uk
Contact Allison Fowle (Art School Administrator).
Celebrated its 110th anniversary in 2005.
Other fine-art courses Level 4 BTEC HND/HNC: Fine Art; Graphic Design and Illustration; Digital Photography; Textile Design; Modelmaking and Special Effects; Lettering, Calligraphy and Heraldic Art. Level 3 BTEC ND: Fine Art; Graphic Design; Photography; Fashion and Clothing; Multimedia. Level 3 BTEC foundation diploma: Art and Design.
Admissions policy For ND: four GCSEs, grade C and above. For HND: ND in Art or A-level Art. Mature students – acceptable portfolio.

Southampton Institute
East Park Terrace, Southampton
SO14 OYN
T 023 80319000
F 023 80334161
E enquiries@solent.ac.uk
W www.solent.ac.uk
Origins can be traced back to a private school of
art founded in 1856. Made a university college in
2004. Almost eleven thousand full-time students.
Degrees offered BA(Hons): Fine Art; Fine Arts
Valuation; Fine Art Media; Photographic Art
Practices; Design Studies; Graphic Design.
Foundation: Design.

Surrey Institute of Art & Design
(University College)
Farnham Campus, Falkner Road, Farnham
GU9 7DS
T 01252 722441
F 01252 892616
E registry@surrart.ac.uk
W www.surrart.ac.uk
Founded in 1868 as Farnham School of Art, 1870
as Guildford School of Art and 1896 as Epsom and
Ewell School of Art. Offers more than thirty
programmes in art, design, media and
communication.
Degrees offered BA (full-time): Animation;
Arts and Media; Digital Screen Art; Fine Art;
Photography; Textiles; Glass; Ceramics;
Metalwork; Jewelry. BA (part-time): Fine Art.
MA full- and part-time.
Other fine-art courses Access to Art and Design.
Dip. in Foundation Studies: Art and Design. Short
courses also available.
Admissions policy For undergraduate: UCAS
routes A and B. For postgraduate application
information contact the Academic Registry.

University College Chichester
Bishop Otter Campus, College Lane, Chichester
PO19 6PE
T 01243 816000
E C.Ferguson@ucc.ac.uk
W www.ucc.ac.uk/arts/fineart/index.html
Contact Admissions Office at
admissions@ucc.ac.uk or on 01243 816002.
Bishop Otter College was established in 1839 to
train schoolmasters. In 1946 Bognor Regis
Emergency Training College was founded in 'an
emergency' effort to staff the nation's schools in
the aftermath of the Second World War. In 1977
the two colleges merged and became known as the
West Sussex Institute of Higher Education.
In 1999 it became University College Chichester.
Broad artistic interdisciplinarity welcomed as part
of fine-art practice.
Degrees offered BA (Hons): Fine Art. Minor: New
Media Arts. MA: Fine Art.
Admissions policy Qualifications recommended:
art foundation course with pass. Basic requirement:
Advanced GNVQ Art with Merit, or pass in
approved Access course, or two to three A-level
passes, including Art A-level grade C/B, or
equivalent mix of A-levels and AS levels, or
equivalent. Applicants must also present a portfolio.

University of Kent
The Registry, Canterbury
CT2 7NZ
T 01227 764000
E recruitment@kent.ac.uk
W www.kent.ac.uk
The school consists of thirty-three academic staff,
supported in their work by two administrators, four
secretaries and six technicians. Over eight hundred
students from the UK, Europe and beyond. Many
programmes involve practical creative elements,
some involve work placements, and some allow
students to spend a year abroad, in Europe or
the USA.
Degrees offered BA (Hons): Contemporary Art;
Fine Art (one year top-up at South Kent College).
Other fine-art courses HND: Fine Art.

University of Portsmouth
University House, Winston Churchill Avenue,
Portsmouth
PO1 2UP
T 023 92848484
F 023 92843082
E info.centre@port.ac.uk
W www.port.ac.uk
Inaugurated in 1992. The former polytechnic grew
from the Portsmouth and Gosport School of
Science and Arts, founded in 1869.
Degrees offered MA: Art, Design and Media.
Other fine-art courses Dip. in Foundation Studies:
Art and Design; Art, Design and Photography.
Admissions policy Applications through UCAS
where applicable. All other applications by
university application form.

University of Reading
Department of Fine Art, 1 Earley Gate, Reading
RG6 6AT
T 0118 3788050 / 3788051

F 0118 9262667
E FineArt@reading.ac.uk
W www.rdg.ac.uk/fineart/index.htm
Contact Jean Butler
Constituted by Royal Charter in 1926. Has its
origins in the union of the Schools of Art and
Science in 1892, forming a university extension
college of Oxford ten years later. Distinguished
visitors and teachers include Walter Crane, Roger
Fry, Robert Gibbings, Walter Sickert, Claude
Rogers, Sir Terry Frost and Martin Froy.
Degrees offered BA (Hons): Art (also available as a
joint degree with other subjects). MA: Fine Art.
Admissions policy For BA: UCAS route A. For
foundation, BTEC or GNVQ: UCAS route B. For
MFA: application forms available from university.

Winchester School of Art

University of Southampton, Park Avenue,
Winchester
SO23 8DL
T 023 80596900
F 023 80596901
E askwsa@soton.ac.uk
W www.wsa.soton.ac.uk
Founded in 1872 and became part of the University
of Southampton in 1996.
Degrees offered BA (Hons): Fine Art Practice and
Theory (pathways in Painting, Printmaking,
Sculpture, New Media and History and Theory);
Textiles, Fashion and Fibre (pathways in Textile
Design, Fashion, Textile Art, New Media and
History and Theory). MA: Fine Art Practice and
Theory; Textiles Practice and Theory; Museums
and Galleries; Textile Conservation. All BA and
MA programmes are offered as full- or part-time.
Evening drawing class once a week.
Admissions policy Art and design foundation or
three A-levels (ABB, totalling 320 points). Apply
via UCAS, application deadlines for routes A or B.

South-west

Arts Institute at Bournemouth

Wallisdown, Poole
BH12 5HH
T 01202 533011
F 01202 537729
E general@aib.ac.uk
W www.aib.ac.uk
Contact Alison Aspery
Established in 1883.
Degrees offered BA (Hons): Fine Art (full- and
part-time). FdA: Printmaking (part-time).

Other fine-art courses NCFE Cert.: Art and Design
(part-time). Institute Cert.: Fine Art; Life Drawing;
Printmaking (part-time plus short Easter and
summer courses).
Admissions policy Full-time: through UCAS. Part-
time: direct to institute (forms available through
Short Course Department).

Bath School of Art and Design

Bath Spa University College, Sion Hill, Lansdown,
Bath
BA1 5SF
T 01225 875875
F 01225 875666
E enquiries@bathspa.ac.uk
W www.bathspa.ac.uk/schools/art-and-design
Contact enquiries@bathspa.ac.uk
Founded in 1898, becoming Bath College of
Higher Education in 1975 and granted degree-
awarding powers in 1992. Became Bath Spa
University in 1999. About 4,500 students in total.
Degrees offered BA (Hons): Fine Art
(Painting/Sculpture/Media); Creative Arts. MA:
Fine Art. PgCert: Fine Art. PgDip: Fine Art.
Admissions policy For undergraduate courses, a
foundation course in art and design or appropriate
BTEC course plus five subjects at GCSE level (or
one subject at GCE/VCE A-level with three
different subjects at GCSE level; or other
qualifications considered equivalent). If applying
to study Art and Design, looking above all for
creative ability and suitability for chosen course.
Entry also possible via Access courses.

Bristol School of Art, Media and Design

University of the West of England, Bower Ashton
Campus, Kennel Lodge Road, Bristol
BS3 2JT
T 0117 3284716
F 0117 3284745
E amd.enquiries@uwe.ac.uk
W www.uwe.ac.uk
Founded in 1853. More than 1,600 students
studying at all levels.
Degrees offered BA (Hons): Art and Visual
Culture; Drawing and Applied Arts; Fine Art; Fine
Art in Context; Illustration; Illustration with
Animation; Textile Design. MA: Fine Art
(Research); Illustration (Research); Illustration
with Animation (Research); Interactive Media;
Interactive Media (Research); Multidisciplinary
Printmaking. PhD and New Route PhDs.
Other fine-art courses Foundation Studies: Art and
Design. Short courses: Animation; Applied Arts;

Computing for Artists; Drawing; Photography; Printmaking. Also runs Easter courses, evening classes, Saturday workshops and summer schools.

Dartington College of Arts
Totnes
TQ9 6EJ
T 01803 862224
F 01803 861666
E college@dartington.ac.uk
W www.dartington.ac.uk
Contact Margaret Eggleton
Founded in 1961 as a University Sector College for Higher Education, specializing in the performing arts. Alumni include Josie Lawrence, Lavine Booth, Verity Sharp, Mick Jackson and Matthew Strachan. Approximately 500 undergraduates taught by experienced tutors actively involved in contemporary arts practice and research.
Degrees offered BA (Hons) Fine Art (Contemporary Practices); Fine Art (with Digital Arts Practices/Choreographic Practices/Cultural Entrepreneurship/Textual Practices/Theatre Practices/Sound Practices/Community Practices); Art and Performance; Art and Performance (with Digital Arts Practices/Choreographic Practices/Cultural Entrepreneurship/ Textual Practices/Theatre Practices/Sound Practices/Community Practices).
Admissions policy A foundation course in art and design and/or Art A-level/AS or vocational A-level (160 UCAS points). Minimum 140 points from six- or twelve-unit awards. Equivalent experience also taken into consideration. Selection based on presentation of a portfolio and interview.

Exeter College
Victoria House, 33–36 Queen Street, Exeter
EX4 3SR
T 01392 205232
E admissions@exe-coll.ac.uk
W www.exe-coll.ac.uk
The tertiary college for the City of Exeter and surrounding parts of Mid-, East and South Devon. Victoria Yard Studios is the college's centre for higher-level study in art and design. The fully equipped premises have light and spacious studios, facilities for printmaking, photography, wood, metal workshops and IT. Nearby are various gallery venues including the V&A, Phoenix Arts Centre and Spacex Gallery.
Degrees offered BA (Hons): Fine Art.
Other fine-art courses Foundation Studies: Art and Design. HND: Three-Dimensional Applied Arts.

Filton College
Filton Avenue, Bristol
BS34 7AT
T 0117 9312121
F 0117 9312233
E admin@filton.ac.uk
W www.filton.ac.uk
Large range of art and design courses across three sites: Bristol School of Art in the city centre; Western Institute of Specialist Education (WISE); and Filton College at Filton, north Bristol.
Other fine-art courses HND: Fine Art; Graphic Design. Bristol School of Art offers a wide range of open-access part-time courses (varying length across the year): Life Drawing; Ceramics; Painting; Stained Glass; Jewelry; Enamelling; Printmaking; Sculpture; Digital Imaging.
Admissions policy For HND: apply through UCAS. For other courses: apply directly. Phone, email or fax the college for further information.

Plymouth College of Art and Design
Tavistock Place, Plymouth
PL11 2QP
T 01752 203434
F 01752 203444
E enquiries@pcad.ac.uk
W www.pcad.ac.uk
Contact Jean Edmonds
Originally founded as an art school in the nineteenth century and now one of the few remaining specialist art colleges in the country providing both FE and HE. Composed of four subject areas: Three-Dimensional Design; Media and Photography; Design Communications; and Fine Art, Diagnostic Drawing and Painting. The Viewpoint Gallery allows students and local artists to exhibit work.
Degrees offered BA (Hons): Applied Arts; Fine Art.
Other fine-art courses FdA: Fine Art; Applied Arts; Spatial Design. ABC Dip. in Foundation Studies. BTEC ND: Fine Art.
Admissions policy For all HE courses: through UCAS. Selected applicants will then be invited to attend an interview and present a portfolio of work. For FE courses: apply direct to the college.

Somerset College of Arts and Technology
Wellington Road, Taunton
TA1 5AX
T 01823 366331
E enquiries@somerset.ac.uk
W www.somerset.ac.uk
Contact Admissions Office

Formed in 1974 from the Taunton Technical College and Somerset College of Art, institutions with histories going back over a century.
Degrees offered BA (Hons): Fashion; Fashion and Textiles; Interior Textiles; Surface Design; Interior Textiles and Surface Design; Graphic Design (top-up year); Packaging Design (top-up year); Advertising Design (top-up year); Fine Art (top-up year; awaiting validation). Foundation: Graphic Design; Fine Art; Three-Dimensional Design (Product); Interior Spatial Design (awaiting validation).
Admissions policy UCAS routes A and B. Art-related ND, Advanced GNVQ, A-levels or foundation year. Five GCSEs grade C or above (including English Language). Top-ups require relevant art foundation or HND.

Swindon College School of Art and Design
Regent Circus, Swindon
SN1 1PT
T 01793 498308
E fineart@swindon-college.ac.uk
W www.swindon-college.ac.uk/he/artanddesign
Contact Swindon College Admissions on 0800 7312250 (freephone).
Offers a wide range of programmes at HND, first-degree and postgraduate levels.
Degrees offered BA (Hons): Fine Art (Drawing for Fine Art Practice).
Admissions policy UCAS routes A or B. Students should have: foundation or Access (Art and Design); or AVCE/ND (Art and Design); or two A-levels and five GCSEs at grade C or above; or entry to year two with HND in appropriate subject; or other equivalent qualifications or experience.

University College Falmouth
Woodlane, Falmouth
TR11 4RH
T 01326 211077
F 01326 213880
E admissions@falmouth.ac.uk
W www.falmouth.ac.uk
Contact Admissions
Founded as an art school in 1902. Now a leading specialist university college for art, design and media at undergraduate and postgraduate level, having been granted the power to award its own degrees in 2004. An award-winning design centre and broadcast-industry-standard media centre at Tremough in Penryn complement the College's specialist studios in Falmouth.
Degrees offered BA (Hons): Fine Art. MA:

Contemporary Visual Arts. (Full- and part-time.)
Other fine-art courses Dip. in Foundation Studies (full- or part-time): Art and Design. Annual printmaking summer school.
Admissions policy For BA: foundation, ND, AVCE/Advanced GNVQ, qualifications or experience. For MA: degree or relevant qualifications or experience.

University of Bath
Claverton Down, Bath
BA2 7AY
T 01225 383019
E admissions@bath.ac.uk
W www.bath.ac.uk
Received Royal Charter in 1966 but can trace its history back to the Bristol Trade School of 1856.
Degrees offered FdA: Digital Media Arts (Multimedia); Digital Media Arts (Moving Image Production).
Other fine-art courses Workshops include: Contemporary Ceramics; Painting in the Twenty-First Century; Drawing in the Twenty-First Century; Contemporary Flat Glass; Digital Video; Ceramics: Throwing on the Wheel; Ceramics: Figurative Sculpture; Ceramics: Raku Digital Art.
Admissions policy For foundation degree programmes: apply through UCAS. Minimum entry requirements will normally be at least four GCSE passes (at grades C or above), including Maths and English together with one or more of the following: UCAS tariff of 80; one pass at Advanced GCE level; one pass in a six-unit vocational A-level; a broader base of studies incorporating AS level; success in an Access to HE course; formally assessed outcomes acquired by dint of APEL. There may be additional entry requirements for each specific foundation degree programme.

University of Gloucestershire
Pittville Campus, Albert Road, Cheltenham
GL52 3JG
T 01242 532218
F 01242 532207
E bdavison@glos.ac.uk
W www.glos.ac.uk
Contact Bob Davison
Art education began in Cheltenham 150 years ago and became part of the University of Gloucestershire in 2001. Pittville Campus specializes in courses in art, media and design. The fine-art courses build on strong theoretical and practical foundations, incorporating new

media and contemporary practices.
Degrees offered Fine Art; Painting and Drawing
Fine Art; Photography Fine Art; Digital Media.
Admissions policy Applicants interviewed through
UCAS routes A and B would normally have
completed a foundation course or equivalent.

University of Plymouth
Faculty of Arts, 2 Endsleigh Place, Plymouth
PL4 8AA
T 01752 238106
F 01752 238102
E arts.admissions@plymouth.ac.uk
W www.plymouth.ac.uk
Founded as Exeter School of Art over 150 years
ago. Situated on Exeter campus of the university
and moving to Plymouth in 2007.
Degrees offered BA (Hons): Fine Art (full- and
part-time). MA: Fine Art (full- and part-time).
Admissions policy For BA (Hons): through UCAS
routes A and B. Portfolio required.

Weston College
Knightstone Road, Weston-super-Mare
BS23 2AL
T 01934 411411
F 01934 411410
E enquiries@weston.ac.uk
W www.weston.ac.uk
Can trace its origins to private drawing and
painting classes provided by Henry Stacy in Oriel
Terrace in 1859. The School of Art was opened in
1865 and since 1993 the college has been an
autonomous public body.
Degrees offered BA (Hons): Fine Art (in
association with Bath Spa University College).
Other fine-art courses HND: Fine Art (three years
part-time or two years full-time).

Wales

Cardiff School of Art and Design
University of Wales Institute Cardiff, Howard
Gardens, Cardiff
CF24 0SP
T 029 20416647
F 029 20416944
E artdesign@uwic.ac.uk
W www.uwic.ac.uk/csad
There has been a college of art in Cardiff for
over 130 years. School located on two campuses.
The Howard Gardens campus in the city centre
houses the Howard Gardens Gallery, a public
gallery and community resource with a continuous

programme of curated and touring exhibitions.
The second campus is at Llandaff on the northern
edge of the city centre, with purpose-built studios
and a student learning resource.
Degrees offered BA (Hons): Art and Art History;
Art and Creative Writing; Art and Philosophy; Art
and Welsh Culture; Ceramics; Contemporary
Textile Practice; Design for Interactive Media; Fine
Art. MA: Design: Heritage and Modernity;
MA/PgDip: Ceramics; Fine Art.
Other fine-art courses Foundation: Art and Design.
The Cardiff Open Art School offer a wide range of
short courses, aimed both for enjoyment and
progression within the subject of art and design, but
also for experienced professionals wishing to extend
or update their knowledge and skills. Examples of
courses: Life Drawing; Painting in Oil and Acrylic;
Printmaking; Photography and Photoshop.

North Wales School of Art and Design
North East Wales Institute of Higher Education,
Regent Street, Wrexham
LL11 1PF
T 01978 293502
F 01978 310060
E d.loonie@newi.ac.uk
W www.newi.ac.uk/nwsad
Founded as School of Science and Art in 1887. Full
member of the University of Wales since 2002.
Degrees offered BA (Hons): Applied Arts; Fine Art.
MA: Animation; Contemporary Applied Arts.

Swansea Institute of Higher Education
Mount Pleasant, Swansea
SA1 6ED
T 01792 481000
F 01792 481085
E enquiry@sihe.ac.uk
W www.sihe.ac.uk
Can trace its history through 150 years via the
Swansea School of Art. There are four schools:
Contextual Studies and Visual Communication;
Fine and Applied Arts; Photography and Video;
Research and Postgraduate Studies.
Degrees offered BA (Hons): Design for
Advertising; Fine Art (Ceramics); Fine Art
(Combined Media); Fine Art (Painting and
Drawing); General Illustration; Graphic
Design; Art History (Joint Hons); Photography in
the Arts; Photojournalism (Contemporary
Practice); Photojournalism with Journalism;
Surface Pattern Design (Contemporary Applied
Arts Practice); Video. Dip. in Foundation Studies:
Art and Design. MA: Fine Art; Photography;

Visual Arts Enterprise; Visual Communication. MPhil and PhD research degrees.

Trinity College
School of Creative Arts and Humanities, Carmarthen
SA31 3EP
T 01267 676767
F 01267 676766
E registry@trinity-cm.ac.uk
W www.trinity-cm.ac.uk
Degrees offered BA (Hons): Fine Art.
Admissions policy Via UCAS.

University of Glamorgan
Pontypridd
CF37 1DL
T 0800 716925
F 01443 822055
E enquiries@glam.ac.uk
W www.glam.ac.uk
Over twenty thousand students.
Degrees offered BA (Hons): Art Practice; Media Studies and Art Practice. MA: Art in the Community.
Other fine-art courses Foundation certificate: Visual and Community Art.

University of Wales, Aberystwyth
Old College, King Street, Aberystwyth
SY23 2AX
T 01970 622021
E ug-admissions@aber.ac.uk
W www.aber.ac.uk
Founded in 1872. The first university institution to be established in Wales. Over seven thousand registered students, including over 1,100 postgraduates across eighteen academic departments. The school is unusual in the traditional British university context as one of the few places where art practice can be studied along with art history as part of a university degree.
Degrees offered BA (Hons): Art; Art History; Art with Art History. MA: Art; Art and Art History. PgDip: Art. MPhil and PhD: Art History. Art Practice may be taken in Drawing and Painting, Printmaking, Photography, and Book Illustration with Typography.
Admissions policy Normal entry requirement is three A-levels (or combination with AS levels), grades BCD or CCC, together with a portfolio of art work. Applications are welcome from those without the above qualifications or with different backgrounds, such as mature students; all

applications are considered on merit. Entry is primarily through the submission of the portfolio rather than the number or score of A-levels, together with some evidence of academic ability for art-history courses.

University of Wales, Bangor
Bangor
LL57 2DG
T 01248 382016 / 382017
E Admissions@bangor.ac.uk
W www.bangor.ac.uk
Opened in 1884 in an old coaching inn with fifty-eight students and ten members of staff. In 1893 it became one of the three constituent colleges of the University of Wales.
Degrees offered HE Cert. in Fine Art (part-time).
Other fine-art courses Part time courses: Colour in Fine Art; Explorations in Fine Art Drawing and Painting; Drawing and Painting from Life; Fine Art Challenge (Module 2); Modernism; Painting and Composition; Exploring Three-Dimensional and Sculpture; Life, Costume and Portrait Study; Working from Nature; Atelier Life Class; Fine Art Printmaking.
Admissions policy No particular academic qualifications required for the certificate. However, it is only suitable for those with some competence in art e.g. experienced amateur artists, or who have previously attended an art foundation course. Expects to offer a place to anyone it feels would benefit from studying for the certificate. Prospective students with no foundation experience may be offered direct entry if they can produce a satisfactory portfolio of work.

University of Wales, Newport
Caerleon Campus, P.O. Box 101, Newport
NP18 3YH
T 01633 432432
F 01633 432046
E uic@newport.ac.uk
W www.newport.ac.uk
Degrees offered BA (Hons): Animation; Fine Art; Documentary Photography; (Contemporary Media); Photographic Art; Photography. BScEd (Hons): Design and Technology. Dip. in Foundation Studies: Art and Design.
Admissions policy For BA (Hons): through UCAS.

West Wales School of the Arts
College of Carmarthenshire/Coleg Sir Gâr, Graig Campus, Sandy Road, Llanelli
SA15 4

T 01554 74800
F 01554 756088
E admissions@colegsirgar.ac.uk
W www.colegsirgar.ac.uk
Coleg Sir Gâr has five campuses spread
throughout Carmarthenshire, offering courses
from GCSE up to postgraduate-degree level.
Degrees offered BA (Hons): Three-Dimensional
Art in the Landscape; Fine Art Sculpture; Fine Art
Painting; Art and Design Multidisciplinary;
Graphic Design (including pathways in Illustration
and Computer Arts); Contemporary Textiles
(including interpretive pathway in Surface
Decoration); Ceramics; Photography. Many BA
degrees can be taken part-time.
Other fine-art courses Part-time courses in
ceramics, drawing and painting, textile printing,
figurative sculpture, fine art, life drawing,
photography (beginner and advanced). FD: Art,
Design and Craft; Advanced Art; Design and Craft.
ND: Ceramics.

West Midlands

Birmingham Institute of Art and Design
Department of Art, University of Central England,
Margaret Street, Birmingham
B3 3BX
T 0121 3315970
F 0121 3316970
E art@students.uce.ac.uk
W www.biad.uce.ac.uk/home.htm
Contact General admissions enquiries:
info@ucechoices.com. International admissions:
Pauline Burke, pauline.burke@uce.ac.uk.
Provides education for nearly four thousand
students on five campuses located in the centre
and to the north and south of the centre of
Birmingham. The faculty offers a comprehensive
portfolio of courses at all levels from FE to higher
research. The Department of Art is located in
Margaret Street in a newly refurbished grade 1-
listed building, where it first opened in 1885.
Degrees offered BA (Hons): Art and Design by
Negotiated Study; Fine Art; Fine Art (Painting and
Sculpture); Textile Design; Visual Communication;
Multimedia Art. PgCert: Research Practice in
Art, Design and Media. PGCE: Art and Design.
MA: Art and Education; Fine Art; Textiles,
Fashion and Surface Design; Visual Arts:
Critical and Contextual Practices; Multimedia Art;
Artist/Teacher Scheme. MPhil and PhD degrees.
Other fine-art courses BTEC foundation diploma:

Art and Design. HND: Fine Art; Visual
Communication; Textiles. Cert. or Dip.: Art and
Design by Negotiated Study; Fine Art. Short and
leisure courses: Art Club; Watercolour Painting.
Admissions policy See website.

Coventry University
Priory Street, Coventry
CV1 5FB
T 024 76888248
F 024 76888667
E afuture.ad@coventry.ac.uk
W www.coventry.ac.uk
Degrees offered BA: Fine Art; Illustration; Graphic
Design; Contemporary Crafts. MA: Fine Art;
Contemporary Crafts; Design and Digital Media;
Media Arts.
Admissions policy For undergraduate: a minimum
of 180 A-level points, including GSCE English, and
a good portfolio. For postgraduate: a first degree
and a good portfolio.

Dudley College of Technology
The Broadway, Dudley
DY1 4AS
T 01384 363000
E admissions@dudleycol.ac.uk
W www.dudleycol.ac.uk
Other fine-art courses Art and Design (levels 1
to 3); Three-Dimensional Design; Graphic Design;
Photography; Sculpture; Glass Design.
Admissions policy Depends on the course but
generally a portfolio is required.

Herefordshire College of Art & Design
Folly Lane, Hereford
HR1 1LT
T 01432 273359
F 01432 841099
E hcad@hereford-art-col.ac.uk
W www.hereford-art-col.ac.uk
Contact Fiona Watkins
A small specialist arts college, founded 150 years
ago. Offers a range of courses in art, design and
the performing arts – from entry level including
GCSEs or A-levels, through to foundation and
honours degrees, or part-time courses for those
returning as a mature student.
Degrees offered FdA/BA (Hons): Fine and Applied
Arts; Illustration.
Other fine-art courses Portfolio course (part-time).
Many short/evening courses.
Admissions policy All applicants will need to
provide a portfolio of work and attend an interview.

North East Worcestershire College

Blackwood Road, Bromsgrove
B60 1PQ
T 01527 570020
F 01527 572900
E admissions@ne-worcs.ac.uk
W www.ne-worcs.ac.uk
Contact Susan Greetham
Other fine-art courses BTEC HND: Fine Art.
Course was set up in 2001 and aims to offer a
broad-based fine art programme of study. BTEC
HNC: Fine Art.
Admissions policy For HND: through UCAS
routes A or B. For HNC: apply directly to college.

North Warwickshire & Hinckley College

Hinckley Road, Nuneaton
CV11 6BH
T 024 76243000
E the.college@nwhc.ac.uk
W www.nwhc.ac.uk
Degrees offered BA (Hons) in Negotiated Studies:
Art and Design.
Other fine-art courses BTEC FD: Design.
BTEC Introductory Dip.: Art, Design and
Media. Certified Dip. in HE: Art and Design.
Edexcel foundation diploma: Art and Design;
Edexcel ND: Fine Art; Graphic Design. HND:
Visual Communication; HND: Three-Dimensional
Design Practice. Also adult education classes.

Solihull College

Art and Design, Blossomfield Road, Solihull
B91 1SB
T 0121 6787006
F 0121 6787200
E tammy.dennis@solihull.ac.uk
W www.solihull.ac.uk
Contact Tammy Dennis (HE Admissions Officer)
Opened in 1993, the college has purpose-built
painting and sculpture studios.
Degrees offered BA (Hons): Fine Art (three years
full-time or six years part-time; validated by UCE).
Admissions policy Full-time applications via UCAS
(twenty places per year). Part-time applications
direct to the college (five places per year).

Staffordshire University

Faculty of Arts, Media and Design, College Road,
Stoke-on-Trent
ST4 2XW
T 01782 294552
F 01782 294760
E n.a.powell@staffs.ac.uk

W www.staffs.ac.uk
Contact Neil Powell
School of Art established in 1876.
Degrees offered BA (Hons): Fine Art. MA: Fine
Art. Full- or part-time.
Admissions policy Portfolio interview plus 160
points. UCAS routes A and B. Requires English
GCSE at grade C or above. Applications welcome
from those who wish to experience a broad-
based art course and who may already have an
established area of practice and wish to deepen
their knowledge of a particular specialism.

Stourbridge College

Longlands Centre, Brook Street, Stourbridge
DY8 3XB
T 01384 344600
F 01384 344601
W www.stourbridge.ac.uk
Contact Elaine Dunn
Other fine-art courses HND: Fine Arts (full- or part-
time). Course provides a progression route to either
the second or third year of BA (Hons) in Fine Art or
employment in related areas. Emphasis on the
vocational nature of fine art and students gain an
understanding of professional practice.
Admissions policy Art and design qualifications in
either a foundation diploma, ND, AVCE Double
Award or a high level of skill. UCAS route B.

Sutton Coldfield College

34 Lichfield Road, Sutton Coldfield
B74 2NW
T 0121 3555671
F 0121 3550799
E heenquiries@sutcol.ac.uk
W www.sutcol.ac.uk
Other fine-art courses BTEC Dip. in Foundation
Studies: Art and Design. BTEC HND: Three-
Dimensional Design (Crafts); Fine Art; Graphic
Design; Textiles.

Telford College of Arts & Technology

Haybridge Road, Wellington, Telford
TF1 2NP
T 01952 642200
F 01952 642263
E studserv@tcat.ac.uk
W www.tcat.ac.uk
Established over one hundred years ago. Over
16,000 students (1,200 full-time). Courses include
NVQs, professional, preparatory degrees and
tailor-made programmes.
Other fine-art courses GNVQ foundation: Art. Dip.

in Foundation Studies: Art and Design. Foundation diploma: Art and Design. Encaustic art workshop.

University College Worcester
Henwick Grove, Worcester
WR2 6AJ
T 01905 855000
F 01905 855132
E registry@worc.ac.uk
W www.worc.ac.uk
Contact Francesca Fairhurst
Worcester College of Higher Education was founded in 1947 as an emergency teacher training college. Began to offer a wider curriculum in the early 1990s, when degrees in art and design and other subjects were added to the portfolio. Won degree-awarding powers in 1997 and has a strong strategic partnership with Birmingham University. Has eighteen thousand students. Awarded £1m in 2002 from HEFC to develop a digital arts centre.
Degrees offered BA (Hons): Art and Design (Single Hons); Visual Arts (Major Hons); Communication Design (Major Hons); Creative Digital Media (Single Hons); Interactive Media (Major Hons); Communication Design (Major Hons).
Other fine-art courses Three modules available for both part- and full-time students at Malvern Hills and Evesham College, one of which is available as a three-week summer school. These are all level 1 courses and include: Fine Art Practice and Theory; Landscape and Visual Identity; Textile Design.
Admissions policy Grades CC or equivalent. UCAS routes A and B. Portfolio interviews in the spring.

University of Wolverhampton
Wulfruna Street, Wolverhampton
WV1 1SB
T 01902 321000
E enquiries@wlv.ac.uk
W www.asp.wlv.ac.uk
Four campuses covering the West Midlands and Shropshire.
Other fine-art courses Various foundation degrees.

Walsall College of Arts & Technology
St Paul's Street, Walsall
WS1 1XN
T 01922 657000
F 01922 657083
E info@walcat.ac.uk
W www.walcat.ac.uk
Contact Alan Tyler
Other fine-art courses Edexcel Foundation Studies: Art and Design (post-A-level).

Admissions policy Apply November/December for admission the following September.

Warwickshire College
Warwick New Road, Leamington Spa
CV32 5JE
T 01926 318207
F 01926 319025
E jherbert@warkscol.ac.uk
W www.warkscol.ac.uk
Contact John Herbert
The School of Art in Leamington was founded in 1866 and is now a part of Warwickshire College. Alumni include Sir Terry Frost. The Dip. of HE fine-art course is run in conjunction with the Birmingham Institute of Art and Design at the University of Central England.
Other fine-art courses Dip. of HE: Fine Art. A wide range of full-time courses, including studies in fine art plus a variety of short courses in life drawing, painting and sculpture. BTEC Dip. in Foundation Studies: Art and Design. ND: Art and Design.
Admissions policy Applicants must be at least 18 years old at entry. A comprehensive portfolio of work plus one of the following: successful completion of an art foundation; a merit profile at ND in a relevant subject; a merit at Advanced VCE in relevant subject; A-levels (180 points); equivalent qualifications and experience. UCAS routes A or B.

Yorkshire and Humberside

Barnsley College
P.O. Box 266, Church Street, Barnsley
S20 2YW
T 01226 216216
F 01226 216553
E programme.enquiries@barnsley.ac.uk
W www.barnsley.ac.uk
Offers courses from AS, HNC and HND to degree level. Most students come from Barnsley and surrounding areas of Yorkshire. Access courses for mature students with few or no qualifications.
Degrees offered BA: Art and Design (Fine Art).
Other fine-art courses Intermediate and foundation certificates: Art and Design; Ceramics; Drawing and Painting; Photography; Textiles.

Bradford College
Great Horton Road, Bradford
BD7 1AY
T 01274 433333
F 01274 741060
E admissions@bilk.ac.uk

W www.bradfordcollege.ac.uk
Origins go back to 1863 when the School of
Industrial Design and Art was formed. Runs
courses through to postgraduate level. Past students
include David Hockney and Andy Goldsworthy.
Degrees offered BA (Hons): Art and Design;
Fashion Design; Fine Art; Graphic Media
Communication (Graphic Design, Moving Image,
Interactive Multimedia, Illustration); Textile
Design; Photography (stage 3, top-up). PgCert/
PgDip/MA: Photography; Politics of Visual
Representation; Representation in Film;
Printmaking.
Other fine-art courses Most full-time courses may
be taken on a part-time basis. HND: Spatial Design
(Interior Design); Photography (Editorial,
Advertising and Fine Art).
Admissions policy Entry normally based on
portfolio and interview. Entry requirements for
full-time undergraduate courses published in
college prospectus or on UCAS site. Encourages
applications from potential students who can
demonstrate suitable qualifications or experience
in an appropriate area of study.

Craven College, Skipton

School of Art and Media, Aireville Campus,
Skipton
BD23 1US
T 01756 693855
F 01756 797047
E enquiries@craven-college.ac.uk
W www.craven-college.ac.uk
Contact Christine Bailey
Housed in a custom-built centre opened in 2001.
There are fifteen specialist studios including
Three-Dimensional Design, Graphic Design,
Photography, Textiles, Ceramics, Fine Art and
Printmaking.
Other fine-art courses Dip. in Foundation Studies:
Art and Design. HNC: Three-Dimensional Design
(Jewelry); Fine Art. HNC/HND: Graphic Design;
Textiles. Range of full- and part-time art courses.

Dewsbury College

Halifax Road, Dewsbury
WF13 2AS
T 01924 465916
F 01924 457047
E info@dewsbury.ac.uk
W www.dewsbury.ac.uk
The main campus on Halifax Road hosts the
majority of general courses, while the Batley and
Wheelwright campuses (Batley School of Art and

Design) deliver mainly art and design courses.
Degrees offered BA (Hons): Contemporary
Photographic Arts; Creative Imaging; Fine Art and
Design. FdA: Applied Arts; Digital Arts; Graphic
Design.

Doncaster College

Waterdale, Doncaster
DN1 3EX
T 01302 553610
E he@don.ac.uk
W www.don.ac.uk
Contact Joanne Crapper
Degrees offered BA (Hons): Visual
Communication; Combined Design; Art and
Associated Crafts; Art and Design (one-year top-up).
Admissions policy 100 tariff points. Applications
accepted through UCAS right up to clearing.

Hull College School of Art and Design

Park Street Centre, Park Street, Hull
HU2 8RR
T 01482 598754
F 01482 598989
E rmoore@hull-college.ac.uk
Contact Carol Morgan at Hull College, Queens
Gardens, Hull HU1.
Situated close to the city centre, the school plays
a major part in the cultural life of the city and
students enjoy good industry and professional
practice collaborations.
Degrees offered FdA: Creative Arts. Commits
students to two years of degree study with option
of third-year honours top-up at the University of
Lincoln or other institutions. Allows work across
traditional and non-traditional media boundaries.
Other fine-art courses Access to HE: Art and
Design (two days per week for two years). OCN
Drawing and Painting or Printmaking (day or
evening for three hours per week for thirty weeks).
Summer schools of one-week duration in early July
in painting or printmaking.
Admissions policy For foundation: via UCAS
routes A or B for full-time or directly to college for
part-time. Folio of work, interview and an art-
related pre-course for school- and college-leavers.
Mature students welcomed without formal
qualifications. OCN programmes directly to
college; no formal entry requirements.

Leeds College of Art & Design

Blenheim Walk, Leeds
LS2 9AQ
T 0113 2028000

F 0113 2028001
E info@leeds-art.ac.uk
W www.leeds-art.ac.uk
Contact Student Advice Team
Founded over one hundred years ago. Past students include Henry Moore, Barbara Hepworth and Damien Hirst.
Degrees offered BA (Hons): Art and Design (interdisciplinary); Fine Art (part-time).
Other fine-art courses HND: Photography. Dip. in Foundation Studies: Art and Design. College diploma: Design. ND: Art and Design. College certificate: Art and Design. Access to Art and Design A2 levels: Fine Art; Sculpture and Ceramics; Photography. Also a selection of part-time courses both in the day and evening.
Admissions policy Apply through UCAS for BA (Hons) Art and Design (interdisciplinary) and HND Photography. Complete a college application form for all other courses.

Leeds School of Contemporary Art and Graphic Design
Leeds Metropolitan University, Calverley Street, Leeds
LS1 3HE
T 0113 2833108
F 0113 2833094
E t.gray@leedsmet.ac.uk
W www.leedsmet.ac.uk/as/cagd/
Contact Tracy Gray
Evolved from the Leeds College of Art.
Degrees offered BA (Hons): Fine Art; Contemporary Creative Practice.
Admissions policy Admission is by direct entry and UCAS routes A and B. Preference is given to applicants with pre-degree experience of study at FE level.

Park Lane College
Park Lane, Leeds
LS3 1AA
T 0113 2162000
F 0113 2162020
E course.enquiry@parklanecoll.ac.uk
W www.parklanecoll.ac.uk
Runs art-based courses across a range of levels.
Admissions policy See website for details.

Sheffield College, Hillsborough Centre
P.O. Box 3676, Sheffield
S6 5WS
T 0114 2602600
F 0114 2602601

W www.sheffcol.ac.uk
Contact HE Unit
Other fine-art courses HND: Fine Art pathways (Painting, Printmaking, Sculpture, Photography, Ceramics, Illustration). Proposed foundation degree: Fine Art.
Admissions policy UCAS routes A or B.

Sheffield Hallam University
Faculty of Arts, Computing, Engineering and Sciences, Psalter Lane Campus, Sheffield
S11 8UZ
T 0114 2252607
F 0114 2252603
E cultural@shu.ac.uk
W www.shu.ac.uk
Contact Jane Leadston
Founded as Sheffield School of Design in 1843, name changed to Sheffield School of Art some years later. At present location since 1950.
Degrees offered BA (Hons): Fine Art. MA: Fine Art. Part- and full-time.
Admissions policy For BA: Dip. in Foundation Studies (Art and Design) plus portfolio preferred. Apply through UCAS routes A or B.

University of Huddersfield
School of Art and Design, Queensgate, Huddersfield
HD1 3DH
T 01484 422288
E admissions@hud.ac.uk
W www.hud.ac.uk
Degrees offered BA (Hons): Fine Art Painting and Drawing; Fine Art with Community Education; Fine Art with Contemporary Writing.

University of Hull
School of Arts, Scarborough Campus, Filey Road, Scarborough
YO11 3AZ
T 01723 362392
E ssa@hull.ac.uk
W www.hull.ac.uk
Contact admissions@hull.ac.uk
Degrees offered BA: Digital Arts; Design For Digital Media.

University of Leeds
The School of Fine Art, History of Art and Cultural Studies, Old Mining Building, Leeds
LS2 9JT
T 0113 3435192
F 0113 2451977

E fine.art.enquiries@leeds.ac.uk
W www.leeds.ac.uk
Almost one hundred years old. 31,500 students.
Degrees offered BA (Hons): Fine Art; Art History;
Art History with Museum Studies. MA: Fine Art;
Art History; Country House Studies; Feminism
and the Visual Arts; Feminist Theory and Practice
in the Visual Arts; Sculpture Studies.

York St John College
Lord Mayor's Walk, York
YO31 7EX
T 01904 624624
F 01904 716931
W www.yorksj.ac.uk
Contact Fiona Coventry
Founded in 1841.
Degrees offered BA (Hons): Art and Design;
Design and Technology.
Admissions policy UCAS routes A or B applicants.
Minimum entry is 140 to 160 points plus portfolio.

Yorkshire Coast College
Lady Edith's Drive, Scarborough
YO12 5RN
T 01723 372105
F 01723 501918
E admissions@ycoastco.ac.uk
W www.yorkshirecoastcollege.ac.uk
Over ten thousand students.
Degrees offered BA (Hons): Fine Art. FdA: Applied
Digital Media (Design).
Other fine-art courses BTEC Dip. in Foundation
Studies: Art and Design (from level 3). BTEC
HNC: Graphic and Multimedia Design. ND: Art
and Design (level 3).

Foundation studies in art and design

East Anglia

Barking College
Dagenham Road, Romford
RM7 0XU
T 01708 770000
F 01708 770007
Contact John Thurman

Barnfield College
New Bedford Road, Luton
LU2 7BF
T 01582 569637
F 01582 572264

Bedford College
Cauldwell Street, Bedford
MK42 9AH
T 01234 291000
F 01234 342674
Contact Rosie Rigg

Braintree College
Church Lane, Braintree
CM7 5SN
T 01376 321711
F 01376 340799
Contact Allan Drummond

Cambridge Regional College
Kings Hedges Road, Kings Hedges, Cambridge
CB4 2QT
T 01223 418518
F 01223 418519
E skelly@mail.camre.ac.uk
Contact Steve Kelly

Chelmsford College
Moulsham Street, Chelmsford
CM2 0JQ
T 01245 265611
F 01245 266908
Contact Mrs Chris Drane

Colchester Institute
Sheepen Road, Colchester
CO3 3LL
T 01206 518000
F 01206 763041

College of West Anglia
Fennyson Avenue, Kings Lynn
PE30 4EW
T 01553 761144 ext. 319
Contact Paul Setchell

Dunstable College
School of Art and Design, Kingsway, Dunstable
LU5 4HG
T 01582 477776 ext. 314
F 01582 478801
E thecorns@talk21.com
Contact Carol Tarrant

Epping Forest College
Borders Lane, Debden, Loughton
IG10 3SA
T 020 8508 8311
F 020 8502 0186
Contact Robert Bramich

Great Yarmouth College
Southtown, Great Yarmouth
NR31 0ED
T 01493 655261
F 01493 653423
Contact Andy Small

Harlow College
Visual Arts, Velizy Avenue,
Harlow
CM20 3LH
T 01279 868000
F 01279 868260
Contact Lin Hilton

Havering College of Further and Higher Education
Ardleigh Green Road, Hornchurch
RM11 2LL
T 01708 462801
F 01708 462736
Contact Jane Norris

Hertford Regional College
Ware Centre, Scotts Road,
Ware
SG12 9JF
T 01992 411776
F 01992 411885
E ptowers@hertreg.ac.uk
Contact Peer Towers

Isle College
Ramnoth Road, Wisbech,
Cambridge
PE13 0HY
T 01945 582561
F 01945 582706
Contact Ian Coulson

Lowestoft College
St Peters Street, Lowestoft
NR32 2NB
T 01502 583521
F 01502 500031
E p.vivian@lowestoft.ac.uk
Contact Paul Vivian

Luton Sixth-Form College
Bradgers Hill Road, Luton
LU2 7EW
T 01582 877500
F 01582 877501
Contact Jake Robson

North Hertfordshire College
Centre for the Arts, Willian Road, Hitchin
SG4 0LS
T 01462 424242
F 01462 471054
E brianbarton@beeb.net

Norwich School of Art & Design
St George Street, Norwich
NR3 1BB
T 01603 610561
F 01603 615728
E info@nsad.ac.uk
Contact Roderick K. Newlands

Oaklands College
St Albans City Campus, St Peter's Road,
St Albans
AL1 3RX
T 01727 737000
F 01727 737272
E help.line@oaklands.ac.uk
Contact Stephanie Newell-Price

Peterborough Regional College
Creative Studies, Park Crescent, Peterborough
PE1 2QU
T 01733 767366
F 01733 767986
E info@peterborough.ac.uk
W www.peterborough.ac.uk
Contact Rob Fuller

South East Essex College
Carnarvon Road, Southend-on-Sea
SS2 6LS
T 01702 220400
F 01702 432320
Contact James Beighton

Suffolk College
Rope Walk, Ipswich
IP4 1LT
T 01473 296318
F 01473 343657
E cam@suffolk.ac.uk
Contact Malcolm Moseley

Thurrock and Basildon College
Woodview Campus, Woodview, Grays
RM16 2YR
T 01375 391199
F 01375 373356
Contact Steve Bouttell

University of Hertfordshire
Faculty of Art and Design, College Lane,
Hatfield
AL10 9AB
T 01707 285347
F 01707 285350
E a.meredith@herts.ac.uk
Contact Mr A. Meredith

Uxbridge College
Uxbridge Campus, Park Road, Uxbridge
UB8 1NQ
T 01895 853333
F 01895 853377
Contact Ian Hebditch

West Herts College
Hempstead Road, Watford
WD17 3EZ
T 01923 812674
F 01923 812667
E isobelw@westherts.ac.uk
Contact Isobel Warrender

West Suffolk College
Out Risbygate, Bury St Edmunds
IP33 3RL
T 01284 701301
F 01284 750561
E simon.smith@westsuffolk.ac.uk
Contact Simon Smith

East Midlands

Boston College
De Montford Campus, Mill Road, Boston
PE21 0HF
T 01205 365701
E carruth@boston.ac.uk
Contact David Carruthers

Broxtowe College Nottingham
High Road, Chilwell, Beeston, Nottingham
NG9 4AH
T 0115 9175252
F 0115 917500
Contact Mandy Chandler

Burton College
Lichfield Street, Burton-on-Trent
DE14 3RL
T 01283 494400
F 01283 494800
Contact Dave Spooner or Phil Birch

De Montfort University
Faculty of Art and Design, The Gateway,
Leicester
LE1 9BH
T 0116 2506370
F 0116 2506281
Contact Lulu Hancock

Derby Tertiary College, Wilmorton
London Road, Derby
DE24 8UG
T 01332 757570
F 01332 576301
Contact Ena Wright

Gateway College
The Newarke, Leicester
LE2 7BY
T 0116 2553079
F 0116 2549857
E dlovegrove@gateway.ac.uk
Contact Deborah Lovegrove

Grantham College
Stonebridge Road,
Grantham
NG31 9AP
T 01476 400200
F 01476 400291
E enquiry@grantham.ac.uk
Contact Eileen Strange

Grimsby College
Nuns Corner, Grimsby
DN34 5BQ
T 01472 311231
F 01472 315507
E clarksonja@grimsby.ac.uk
Contact Jeff Clarkson

Huntingdonshire Regional College
California Road, Huntingdon
PE29 1BL
T 01480 379180
F 01480 379127
Contact Angela Sanderson

Leicester College
St Margaret's Campus, Grafton Place,
Leicester
LE1 3WL
T 0116 2242002
F 0116 2242150
E ipepperill-clarke@leicestercollege.ac.uk
Contact I. Pepperill-Clarke or R. Pountney

Loughborough University
School of Art and Design, 12 Frederick Street,
Loughborough
LE11 3BJ
T 01509 228941
F 01509 231174
E j.tormey@lboro.ac.uk
Contact Jane Tormey

Mackworth College Derby
Prince Charles Avenue, Mackworth, Derby
DE22 4LR
T 01332 519951
F 01332 510548
Contact Pete Gill

New College Nottingham
25 Stoney Street, The Lace Market, Nottingham
NG1 1LP
T 0115 9554131
F 0115 9553710
E carl.marshall@ncn.ac.uk
Contact Carl Marshall

North Lindsey College
Kingsway, Scunthorpe
DN17 1AJ
T 01724 281111
F 01724 294020
E info@northlindsey.ac.uk
W www.northlindsey.ac.uk
Contact Angie Hodgson

South East Derbyshire College
Cavendish Site, Cavendish Road, Ilkeston
DE7 5AN
T 0115 8492111
F 0115 8492148
Contact Tricia Gardiner

South Nottingham College
Charnwood Centre, Farnborough Road,
Clifton
NG11 8LU
T 0115 9146300
F 0115 9146333
Contact Tim Rundle

Stamford College
Visual Arts Centre, Drift Road, Stamford
PE9 1XA
T 01780 484300
F 01780 484301
Contact Richard Smith

**Tresham Institute of Further and
Higher Education**
Windmill Avenue Campus, Windmill Avenue,
Kettering
NN15 6ER
T 01536 410252
F 01536 524965
Contact Graham Keddie

University College Northampton
St Georges Avenue, Northampton
NN2 6JD
T 01604 735500
F 01604 717813
Contact Clive Ramsdale

University of Lincoln
School of Art and Design, Chad Varah House,
Wordsworth Street, Lincoln
LN1 3BP
T 01522 895088
F 01522 895137
Contact David Armitage

West Notts College of Further Education
Derby Road, Mansfield
NG18 5BH
T 01623 627191
F 01623 623063
Contact Julian Bray

London

Barnet College
Wood Street, Barnet
EN5 4AZ
T 020 84406321
F 020 84415236
Contact Ken Ratling

Bexley College
269 Woolwich Road, Abbey Road,
London
SE2 0AR
T 01322 404280
F 020 83107298
E richardw@bexley.ac.uk
Contact Richard Wight

Blake College
162 New Cavendish Street, London
W1W 6YS
T 020 76360658
F 020 74360049

E study@blake.ac.uk
Contact Robert Persey

Camberwell College of Arts
Peckham Road, London
SE5 8UF
T 020 75146328
F 020 75146310
E enquiries@camb.linst.ac.uk
Contact Peter Nencini

Central School of Speech and Drama
Canterbury Court, 1–3 Brixton Road, London
SW9 6DE
T 020 78208088
F 020 77358967
E b.townsend@cssd.ac.uk

Central St Martins College of Art & Design
Southampton Row, London
WC1B 4AP
T 020 75147000
F 020 75147024
Contact Kate Losty

Chelsea College of Art & Design
Bagley's Lane, London
SW6 2QB
T 020 75147941
F 020 75147944
E h.j.p.davies@chelsea.linst.ac.uk
Contact Hugh Davies

City and Guilds of London Art School
124 Kennington Park Road, London
SE11 4DJ
T 020 77352306
F 020 75825361
E info@cityandguildsartschool.ac.uk
Contact Keith Price

City and Islington College
383 Holloway Road, London
N7 0RN
T 020 77009259
F 020 77004268
Contact Jean Lockett

City Literary Institute
16 Stukeley Street, London
WC2B 5LJ
T 020 72429872
F 020 74053347

E j.sexton@citylit.ac.uk
Contact John Sexton

City of Westminster College
Paddington Centre, 25 Paddington Green, London
W2 1NB
T 020 77238826
F 020 72582700
Contact Jane Baker

College of North East London
High Road, Tottenham, London
N15 4RU
T 020 88024352
E grider@staff.conel.ac.uk
Contact Gordon Rider

Community College, Shoreditch
Falkirk Street, London
N1 6HQ
T 020 76139123
Contact Bo Davies

Croydon College
Fairfield Campus, College Road, Croydon
CR9 1DX
T 020 86865700
F 020 876 5880
Contact Calvin Bunyan

Enfield College
73 Hertford Road, Enfield
EN3 5HA
T 020 84433434
F 020 88055898
Contact Hilary Sleiman

Greenwich Community College
95 Plumstead Road, London
SE18 7DQ
T 020 84884873
F 020 84884899
Contact Philip Crozier

Hammersmith and West London College
Gliddon Road, Barons Court, London
W14 9BL
T 020 87411688
F 020 85638247
Contact Beatrice Movathar

Kensington and Chelsea College
Hortensia Road, London
SW10 0QS
T 020 75735258
F 020 73510956
E p.ritson@kcc.ac.uk
Contact Phillip Ritson

Kingston College
55 Richmond Road, Kingston-upon-Thames
KT2 5BP
T 020 89394601 / 89394618 (direct line)
F 020 89394628
Contact Pat Boyle

Lewisham College
2 Deptford Church Street, Lewisham, London
SE8 4RZ
T 020 86943497
F 020 86943408
Contact Jenny Wiggins

London College of Communication
Elephant and Castle, London
SE1 6SB
T 020 75146500
Contact David Sowerby

London College of Fashion
182 Mare Street, London
E8 3RE
T 020 75147400
F 020 75147484
Contact Andrea Godfrey

London Metropolitan University
Central House, 59–63 Whitechapel High Street,
London
E1 7PF
T 020 73201902
F 020 73201936
Contact John Coleman

Middlesex University
Cat Hill, Barnet
EN4 8HT
T 020 84115085
F 020 84115085
E c.milton@mdx.ac.uk
Contact Chris Milton

Newham College of Further Education
East Ham Campus, High Street South, London
E6 6ER

T 020 82574205
F 020 8254308
E steph.hodges@newham.ac.uk
Contact Mr Steph Hodges

Richmond-upon-Thames College
Egerton Road, Twickenham
TW2 7SJ
T 020 86078307
F 020 87449738
Contact Audrey Simpson

South Thames College
Wandsworth High Street, London
SW18 2PP
T 020 89187092
F 020 89187132
Contact Dave Atkins

Southgate College
High Street, Southgate, London
N14 6BS
T 020 8982 104
F 020 89825051
Contact Paul Schofield

Southwark College
Surrey Docks Centre, Drummond Road,
London
SE16 4EE
T 020 78151526
Contact Mark Trompeteler

Tower Hamlets College
Poplar Centre, Poplar High Street,
London
E14 0AF
T 020 75107510
F 020 75389153
Contact Harry Robertson

Waltham Forest College
Forest Road, Walthamstow,
London
E17 4JB
T 020 85018217
F 020 85018001
E robinp@waltham.ac.uk
Contact Peter Robinson

West Thames College
Art, Design and Engineering, London Road,
Isleworth
TW7 4HS

T 020 83262000
F 020 85699314
E sarah.howat@west-thames.ac.uk
Contact Sarah Howat

Westminster Kingsway College
Kentish Town Centre, 87 Holmes Road, London
NW5 3AX
T 020 75568001
F 020 75568003
Contact Ken Newlan

Wimbledon School of Art
Palmerston Road, London
SW19 1PB
T 020 84085030
F 020 84085050
E foundation@wimbledon.ac.uk
Contact Cally Saunders

North-east

City of Sunderland College
Shiney Row Centre, Houghton-le-Spring
DH4 4TL
T 0191 5116113
F 0191 5116380
Contact Linda Anderson

Cleveland College of Art & Design
Church Square, Hartlepool
TS24 7EX
T 01642 288000
Contact Patrick O'Doherty

Cleveland College of Art & Design
Green Lane, Linthorpe, Middlesbrough
TS5 7RJ
T 01642 288000
F 01642 288828
Contact Sue Dewey

Derwentside College
Park Road, Consett
DH8 5EE
T 01207 585900
F 01207 502434
E ian_holmes@derwentside.ac.uk
Contact Ian Holmes

Gateshead College
Durham Road, Low Fell, Gateshead
NE9 5BN

T 0191 4902308
F 0191 4902313
E karen.little@gateshead.ac.uk
Contact Karen Little (Foundation Art and Design)

New College Durham
Framwellgate Moor Centre, Durham
DH1 5ES
T 0191 3754325
F 0191 3754222
E ray.birss@newdur.ac.uk
Contact Ray Birss

Newcastle College
Rye Hill Campus, Scotswood Road, Newcastle-
upon-Tyne
NE4 7SA
T 0191 2004000
F 0191 2004517
Contact David Lawrence

North Tyneside College
Embleton Avenue, Wallsend
NE28 9NJ
T 0191 2295000
F 0191 2295301
Contact John O'Rourke

Northumberland College
College Road, Ashington
NE63 9RG
T 01670 841200
F 01670 841201
E david.goard@northland.ac.uk
Contact David Goard

Queen Elizabeth Sixth-Form College
Vane Terrace, Darlington
DL3 7AU
T 01325 465602
F 01325 361705
Contact Rita Smith

South Tyneside College
St Georges Avenue, South Shields
NE34 6ET
T 0191 4273535 / 4273500 (direct line)
Contact Doug Veitch

University of Sunderland
Ashburne House, Ryhope Road, Sunderland
SR2 7EF
T 0191 5152142
E ed.tillotson@sunderland.ac.uk
Contact Edmund Tillotson

Northern Ireland

Armagh College of Further Education
Lonsdale Street, Armagh
BT61 7HN
T 01861 522205
F 01861 526011
Contact Carlie Pettigrew

Belfast Institute of Further and Higher Education
Millfield Building, Belfast
BT1 1HS
T 028 90265000
F 028 90265451

Castlereagh College
Montgomery Road, Belfast
BT5 7DU
T 0289 0797144
F 0289 0401820
E castlereagh@tibus.com
Contact Sam Fleming

East Tyrone College of Further and Higher Education
Circular Road, Dungannon
BT71 6BQ
T 028 87722323
F 028 87722323
E etyronecolfe@campus.bt.com
Contact Ann Murphy

Limavady College of Further and Higher Education
Main Street, Limavady
BT49 0EX
T 028 77762334
F 028 77761018
E dhanna@limavady.ac.uk
Contact David Hanna

Newry and Kilkeel Institute of Further and Higher Education
Patrick Street, Newry
BT35 8DN
T 028 30261071
F 028 30259662
E fmccartney@nkifhe.ac.uk
Contact Fiona McCartney

North Downs and Ards Institute
Castle Park Road, Bangor
BT20 4TF
T 028 91276600
F 028 91276601
W www.ndai.ac.uk
Contact Margaret Ravey

North East Institute of Further and Higher Education
Ballymena Campus, Trostan Avenue, Ballymena
BT43 7BN
T 028 25652871 / 2563625 (direct line)
F 028 25659245
E j.maybin@nei.co.uk
Contact John Maybin

North West Institute of Further and Higher Education
Arts Department, Strand Road, Londonderry
BT48 7BY
T 028 71266711
F 028 71260520
Contact Ms Mary Harrigan

Omagh College
2 Mountjoy Road, Omagh
BT79 7AH
T 028 82245433
F 028 82241440
Contact Jane Evason

Upper Bann Institute of Further and Higher Education
2–8 Kitchen Hill, Lurgan, Craigavon
BT66 6AZ
T 028 38326135
F 028 38322762
E bradyd@ubi.ac.uk
Contact Dermot Brady

North-west

Accrington and Rossendale College
Sandy Lane, Accrington
BB5 2AW
T 01254 389933
F 01254 354201
Contact Alan Crabtree

Barrow Sixth-Form College
Rating Lane, Barrow-in-Furness
LA13 9LE
T 01229 828377
F 01229 836874

E colinaldred@barrow6fc.org.uk
Contact Colin Aldred

Blackburn College
Feilden Street, Blackburn
BB2 1LH
T 01254 55133
Contact Gordon Huxley

Blackpool and the Fylde College
Palatine Road, Blackpool
FY1 4DW
T 01253 352352
F 01253 291627
E visitors@blackpool.ac.uk
Contact Norman Travis

Bolton Institute of Higher Education
Dean Road, Bolton
BL3 5AB
T 01204 528851
F 01204 399074
Contact Cassandra O'Connor

Burnley College
Shorey Bank, Ormerod Road,
Burnley
BB11 2RX
T 01282 711200
F 01282 415063
Contact Les Gillon

Bury College
Woodbury Centre, Market Street,
Bury
BL9 0BG
T 0800 0925900
F 0161 2808228
Contact Janice Crowley

Carmel College
Prescot Road, St Helens
WA10 3AG
T 01744 22876
F 01744 453843
Contact Steve Bonati

Chesterfield College
Infirmary Road, Chesterfield
S41 7NG
T 01246 500609
E monkhouc@chesterfield.ac.uk
Contact Charles Monkhouse

City College Manchester
The Arden Centre, Sale Road, Northenden,
Manchester
M23 0DD
T 0161 9571757
F 0161 9459488
E g.robinson@ccm.ac.uk
Contact John Thomas

City of Liverpool Community College
The Arts Centre, Myrtle Street, Liverpool
L7 7JA
T 0151 2524354
Contact Colin Beckett

Cumbria Institute of the Arts
Brampton Road, Carlisle
CA3 9AY
T 01228 400300
E jan.goodey@cumbriacad.uk
Contact Jan Goodey

Deeside College
Kelsterton Road, Connah's Quay
CH5 4BR
T 01244 831531
F 01244 814395
E enquiries@deeside.ac.uk
Contact David Craig

Hugh Baird College
Balliol Road, Bootle
L20 7EW
T 0151 3534419
F 0151 3534420
Contact John A. Horrigan

Isle of Man College
Homefield Road, Douglas
IM2 6RB
T 01624 648206
F 01624 648201
Contact Ian Coulson

Kendal College
Milnthorpe Road, Kendal
LA9 5AY
T 01539 814700
E enquiries@kendal.ac.uk
Contact Matt Burke

Knowsley Community College
Rupert Road, Roby
L36 9TD

T 0151 4775793
F 0151 4775703
E ghwilliams@kcc.mernet.org.uk
Contact Graham Williams

Lancaster and Morecambe College
White Cross Education Centre, Quarry Road,
Lancaster
LA1 3SD
T 01524 382257
Contact Emma Grover

Leek College
Stockwell Street, Leek
ST13 6DP
T 01538 398866
F 01538 399506
Contact Kevin Brown

Macclesfield College
Park Lane, Macclesfield
SK11 8LF
T 01625 410000
F 01625 410001
E info@macclesfield.ac.uk
Contact Lee Burgess

Manchester College of Arts and Technology
MANCAT Openshaw Campus, Ashton Old Road,
Openshaw, Manchester
M11 2WH
T 0161 9535995
F 0161 9533909
Contact Kevin Keane

Manchester Metropolitan University
Grosvenor Building, Cavendish Street, Manchester
M15 6BR
T 0161 2473548
F 0161 2476818
Contact Joan Beadle

Mid-Cheshire College
Hartford Campus, Northwich
CW8 1LJ
T 01606 74444
F 01606 720700
Contact Sue Ainsworth

Nelson and Colne College
Scotland Road, Nelson
BB9 7YT
T 01282 440267
F 01282 440274
Contact Dennis Roberts

Oldham College
Rochdale Road, Oldham
OL9 6AA
T 0161 6245214
F 0161 6244234
Contact David Pugh

Preston College
The Park School, Moor Park Avenue, Fulwood
PR1 6AS
T 01772 225604
F 01772 225007
E giovanni-turner@virgin.net
Contact Ian Turner

Priestley College
Loushers Lane, Warrington
WA4 6RD
T 01925 633591
F 01925 413887
Contact Alan Evans

Runshaw College
Langdale Road, Leyland
PR25 3DQ
T 01772 622688 ext. 2128
F 01772 642009
E crystal.g@runshaw.ac.uk
Contact Gay Crystal

Salford College
Worsley Campus, Walkden Road, Worsley
M28 7QD
T 0161 2115159
E cbarker@salford-col.ac.uk
Contact Mr Chris Barber

South Cheshire College
Creative Arts Department, Dane Bank Avenue,
Crewe
CW2 8AB
T 01270 654654
F 01270 651515
E d-ballantyne@s-cheshire.ac.uk
Contact David Ballantyne

South Trafford College
Manchester Road, Altrincham
WA14 5PQ
T 0161 9524733
F 0161 9524672
Contact Ian Read

Southport College
Mornington Road, Southport
PR9 0TT
T 01704 500606
F 01704 392794
Contact Dave Green

St Helens College
School of Arts, S.K.B. Building, Water Street,
St Helens
WA10 1PP
T 01744 623221
F 01744 623400
E wjrobinson@talk21.co.uk
Contact Wayne Robinson

**Stockport College of Further and
Higher Education**
Foundation Art and Design, Wellington Road
South, Stockport
SK1 3UQ
T 0161 9583507
F 0161 4806636
E foundidea@hotmail.com
Contact Gillian Patterson

Tameside College
Beauford Road, Ashton-under-Lyne
OL6 6NX
T 0161 9086763
F 0161 9086611
Contact Malcolm Young

University of Salford
School of Art and Design, Irwell Valley Campus,
Blandford Road, Salford
M6 6BD
T 0161 2952634
E h.heery@salford.ac.uk
Contact Helen Heery

Warrington Collegiate Institute
School of Art and Design, Padgate Campus,
Crab Lane, Fearnhead, Warrington
WA2 0DB
T 01925 494494
F 01925 816077
E d.fye@warr.ac.uk
Contact Deryk Fye

West Cheshire College
Grange Centre, Regent Street, Ellesmere Port
L65 8EJ
T 01244 670359

F 01244 670380
E a.hirst@west-cheshire.ac.uk
Contact Phil Clarkson

Wigan & Leigh College
School of Art and Design, Parsons Walk, Wigan
WN1 1RS
T 01942 761811
F 01942 761812
Contact Robin Salt

Winstanley College
Winstanley Road, Billinge, Wigan
WN5 7XF
T 01695 633244
F 01695 633409
Contact Sue Cook

Wirral Metropolitan College
Borough Road Campus, Borough Road,
Birkenhead
CH42 9QD
T 0151 5517777
F 0151 5517401
Contact Chris Kelly

Xaverian College
Lower Park Road, Manchester
M14 5RB
T 0161 2241781
F 0161 2489039
Contact Shaun Steele

South-east

Abingdon & Witney College
Northcolt Road, Abingdon
OX14 1NN
T 01235 216209
F 01235 553168
E mike.gaston@abingdon-witneycollege.ac.uk

Alton College
Old Oldham Road, Alton
GU34 1NX
T 01420 592200 ext. 235
F 01420 592253
Contact C. Thomas

Amersham & Wycombe College
Amersham Campus, Stanley Hill, Amersham
HP7 9HN

T 01494 735555
F 01494 735566
E abeaumont@amersham.ac.uk
Contact Anya Beaumont

Ashford School of Art & Design
Tufton Street, Ashford
TN23 1RJ
T 01233 655555
E asad@southkent.ac.uk
Contact Mavernie Cunningham

Basingstoke College of Technology (BCOT)
Worting Road, Basingstoke
RG21 1TN
T 01256 306221
F 01256 306444
Contact Brian C. Stevens

Bracknell & Wokingham College
Church Road, Bracknell
RG12 1DJ
T 01344 460200
F 01344 460360
E study@bracknell.ac.uk
Contact Lorraine Zutshi

Brooklands College
Heath Road, Weybridge
KT13 8TT
T 01932 797700
F 01932 797800
Contact Cherry Solon

Buckinghamshire Chilterns University College
Kingshill Road, High Wycombe
HP13 5BB
T 01494 522141
E swilke01@bcuc.ac.uk
Contact Sarah Wilkes

Chichester College of Arts, Science and Technology
Westgate Fields, Chichester
PO19 1SB
T 01243 786321
F 01243 527884
E bernadette.manning@chichester.ac.uk
Contact Bernadette Manning

City College Brighton & Hove
Pelham Street, Brighton
BN1 4FA

T 01273 667788
F 01273 667703
E info@ccb.ac.uk
Contact Wendy Sherratt

Cricklade College
Charlton Road, Andover
SP10 1EJ
T 01264 360000
F 01264 360010
E info@cricklade.ac.uk
Contact Charmaine Cook

East Berkshire College
Station Road, Langley,
Slough
SL3 8BY
T 01753 793000
F 01753 793316
Contact Diana Rowles

East Surrey College
Claremont Road, Redhill
RH1 2JX
T 01737 772611
F 01737 768641
Contact Tim Daly

Fareham College
Bishopsfield Road,
Fareham
PO14 1NH
T 01329 815372
F 01329 822483
E michael.odonnell@fareham.ac.uk
Contact Michael O'Donnell

Guildford College of Further and Higher Education
School of Art, Design and Media, Stoke Park,
Guildford
GU1 1EZ
T 01483 448500 ext. 4877
F 01483 448603
E s.cross@guildford.ac.uk
Contact Samantha Cross

Hastings College of Arts & Technology
Archery Road, St Leonards-on-Sea
TN38 0HX
T 01424 442222
F 01424 717973
E amsmith@hastings.ac.uk
Contact Jeb Haward

Henley College
Deanfield Avenue,
Henley-on-Thames
RG9 1UH
T 01491 579988
F 01491 410099
Contact Julian Brinsford-Webb

Isle of Wight College
Medina Way, Newport
PO30 5TA
T 01983 526631
F 01983 521707
E judith.salmon@iwightc.ac.uk
Contact Judith Salmon

Kent Institute of Art & Design
New Dover Road, Canterbury
CT1 3AN
T 01227 817527
F 01227 817500
E mstockton-smith@kiad.ac.uk
Contact Mary Stockton-Smith

Kent Institute of Art & Design
Oakwood Park, Maidstone
ME14 1RW
T 01622 757286
E maddison@klad.ac.uk
Contact Mike Addison

Kent Institute of Art & Design
Fort Pitt, Rochester
ME1 1DZ
T 01634 830022
F 01634 820300
E agreen@kiad.ac.uk
Contact Sue Dray

**Medway Adult and Community
Learning Service**
Green Street, Gillingham
ME7 5TJ
T 01634 850235
F 01634 500297
Contact Gary Bassett

Milton Keynes College
Bletchley Centre, Sherwood Drive,
Bletchley
MK3 6DR
T 01908 684444
F 01908 684399
Contact Adrian Pinkard

NESCOT
Reigate Road, Ewell, Epsom
KT17 3DS
T 020 83943261
F 020 83943030
E p.allen@nescot.ac.uk
Contact Philip Allen

Newbury College
Oxford Road, Newbury
RG14 1PQ
T 01635 845243
F 01635 845312
E l-jones@newbury-college.ac.uk
Contact Linda Jones

**North Oxfordshire College and School of
Art and Design**
Broughton Road, Banbury
OX16 9QA
T 01295 252221
Contact Sue Eve

Northbrook College
Union Place Campus, Union Place,
Worthing
BN11 1LU
T 01903 606124 / 606133
F 01903 606125
Contact Geoff Hands

Oxford Brookes University
School of Art, Publishing and Music, Headington
Campus, Oxford
OX3 0BP
T 01865 484951
F 01865 484952
E ccatherton@brookes.ac.uk
Contact Catherine Atherton

Oxford College of Further Education
Oxpens Road, Oxford
OX1 1SA
T 01865 269320
F 01865 248871
E jola_pernak@oxfe.ac.uk
Contact Jola Pernak

**Ravensbourne College of Design and
Communication**
Walden Road, Chislehurst
BR7 5SN
T 020 82894900
F 020 83258320

E l.lidington@rave.ac.uk
Contact Louise Lidington

Reading College and School of Art & Design
Crescent Road, Reading
RG1 5RQ
T 0118 9675404
F 0118 9675301
E hamiltonr@reading-college.ac.uk
Contact Robin Hamilton-Farey

Reigate School of Art and Design
127 Blackborough Road, Reigate
RH2 7DE
T 01737 766137
F 01737 768643
Contact Robert Jones

Richmond Adult Community College
Park Shot Centre, Parkshot, Richmond
TW9 2RE
T 020 89400170
F 020 83326560
E richardbeard@racc.org.uk
Contact Richard Beard

Rycotewood College
Priest End, Thame
OX9 2AF
T 01844 212501
F 01844 218809
Contact Chris Hyde

South Downs College
College Road, Waterlooville
PO7 8AA
T 023 92797979
F 023 92364578
Contact Yvonne Kimber

Southampton City College
St Mary Street, Southampton
SO14 1AR
T 023 80577324
F 023 80577473
E paul.everitt@southampton-city.ac.uk
Contact Paul Everitt

Surrey Institute of Art and Design
University College, Falkner Road,
Farnham
GU9 7DS
T 01252 892770
E pfranckel@surrart.ac.uk
Contact Pauline Franckel

Sussex Downs College
Eastbourne Campus, Cross Levels Way,
Eastbourne
BN21 2UF
T 01323 637504
F 01323 637523
E s.levy-nichols@ecat.ac.uk
Contact Sylvia Levy-Nichols

Sussex Downs College
Mountfield Road, Lewes
BN7 2XH
T 01273 483188
F 01273 478561
Contact Stuart Revill

Thanet College
Ramsgate Road, Broadstairs
CT10 1PN
T 01843 605040
F 01843 605031
E staff-pds@thanet.ac.uk
Contact Paul Seton

Totton College
Water Lane, Totton, Southampton
SO40 3ZX
T 023 80874874
F 023 80874879
Contact Dave Carter

University of Portsmouth
School of Art Design and Media, Eldon Building,
Winston Churchill Avenue, Portsmouth
PO1 2DJ
T 023 92848484
F 023 92843808
Contact Greg Nicholls

West Kent College
Brook Street, Tonbridge
TN9 2PW
T 01732 358101
F 01732 771415
Contact Barbara Giles

Winchester School of Art
University of Southampton New College,
The Avenue, Southampton
SO17 1BG
T 023 80597440
F 023 80597341
E rn1@soton.ac.uk
Contact Roy Naylor

South-west

The Arts Institute at Bournemouth
The School of Art, Wallisdown, Poole
BH12 5HH
T 01202 363283
F 01202 537729
E a.scott@arts-inst-bournemouth.ac.uk
Contact Amanda Scott

Bournemouth & Poole College
North Road, Poole
BH14 0LS
T 01202 205205
Contact Andrew Piesley

Bridgwater College
Bath Road, Bridgwater
TA6 4PZ
T 01278 441292
F 01278 441232
E wrightj@bridgwater.ac.uk
Contact Nichola Kingsbury

Camborne Poole Redruth College
Trevenson Road, Poole, Redruth
TR15 3RD
T 01209 611611
F 01209 616168
E p.lowry@cornwall.ac.uk
Contact Patrick Lowry

City of Bath College
Avon Street, Bath
BA1 1UP
T 01225 312191
F 01225 444213
Contact David Hyde

City of Bristol College
College Green Centre, St Georges Road,
Bristol
BS1 5UA
T 0117 9072858
F 0117 9045139
E roland.goddard@cityofbristol.ac.uk
Contact Roland Goddard

Cornwall College
Trevarthian Road, St Austell
PL25 4BU
T 01726 67911
F 01726 67911

E info@st-austell.ac.uk
Contact David Bartram

Exeter College
Victoria Yard Studios, Queen Street, Exeter
EX4 3SR
T 01392 205290
E c.kennedy@exe-coll.ac.uk
Contact Carol Kennedy

Falmouth College of Arts
Woodlane, Falmouth
TR11 4RA
T 01326 211832
F 01326 211205
Contact Phil Naylor

Ferndown Upper School
Cherry Grove, Ferndown
BH22 9EY
T 01202 871243
F 01202 893383
E school@fernup.dorset.sch.uk
Contact David Pilkington

Filton College
Filton Avenue, Bristol
BS34 7AT
T 0117 9092324
F 0117 9312244
E pratt@filton-college.ac.uk
Contact David Beech

Gloscat
Centre for the Arts, Brunswick Road,
Gloucester
GL1 1HS
T 01452 426602
F 01452 426601
E willis01@gloscat.ac.uk
W www.gloscat.ac.uk
Contact Sally Williams

Highlands College
P.O. Box 1000, St Saviour
JE4 9QA
T 01534 608620
F 01534 608600
E glyn.burton@highlands.ac.uk
Contact Glyn Burton

North Devon College
Old Sticklepath Hill, Sticklepath, Barnstaple
EX31 2BQ
T 01271 338107

F 01271 338121
E appatrick84@hotmail.com
Contact Alan Patrick

Plymouth College of Art and Design
Tavistock Place, Plymouth
PL4 8AT
T 01752 203434
F 01752 203444
E enquiries@pcad.ac.uk

Salisbury College
Southampton Road, Salisbury
SP1 2LW
T 01722 344344
F 01722 344345
Contact David Mackerth

Somerset College of Arts & Technology
Wellington Road, Taunton
TA1 5AX
T 01823 366366
F 01823 366357
Contact Jane Southwell

South Devon College
Newton Road, Torquay
TQ2 5BY
T 01803 400700
F 01803 400701
Contact Keith Bloor

Strode College
Church Road, Street
BA16 0AB
T 01458 844444
F 01458 844411
Contact Mark Tinsley

Stroud College
Stratford Road, Stroud
GL5 4AH
T 01453 763424
F 01453 753543
E enquire@stroudcol.ac.uk
Contact Jen Whiskerd

Swindon School of Art & Design
Euclid Street, Swindon
SN1 2JQ
T 01793 498490
F 01793 422102
E wendyforrest@swindon-college.ac.uk
Contact John Fowler

Truro College
College Road, Truro
TR1 3XX
T 01872 267000
F 01872 267100
Contact Mary Oliver

University of Gloucestershire
Park Campus, P.O. Box 220, The Park,
Cheltenham
GL50 2QF
T 01242 532700
F 01242 532810
Contact Nick Pride

University of the West of England
Faculty of Art, Media and Design, Kennel Lodge
Road, off Clanage Road, Bower Ashton, Bristol
BS3 2JT
T 0117 3444768
F 0117 3444765
E dawn.mason@uwe.ac.uk
Contact Dawn Mason

Weston College
Knightstone Road, Weston-super-Mare
BS23 2AL
T 01934 411411
F 01934 411410
Contact Fiona Hunter

Weymouth College
Cranford Avenue, Weymouth
DT4 7LQ
T 01305 764707
F 01305 208752
E kate-withers@weymouth.ac.uk
Contact David Hamling

Wiltshire College Trowbridge
College Road, Trowbridge
BA14 0ES
T 01225 766241 ext. 304
F 01225 777148
E m.rennie@wiltscoll.ac.uk
Contact Tony Williams

Yeovil College
Mudford Road, Yeovil
BA21 4DR
T 01935 423921
F 01935 429962
E maryj@yeovil-college.ac.uk
Contact Mary Jacobsen

Wales

Barry College
Colcot Road, Barry
CT62 8YJ
T 01446 725000
F 01446 732667
E vhenderson@barry.ac.uk
Contact Val Henderson

Bridgend College
Cowbridge Road, Bridgend
CF31 3DF
T 01656 302302
F 01656 663912
E admissions@bridgend.ac.uk
W Richard Morris

Coleg Gwent
Crosskeys Campus, Risca Road, Crosskeys
NP11 7ZA
T 01495 333456
F 01495 333386
Contact Bryan Smith

Coleg Llandrillo College
Llandudno Road, Rhos-on-Sea, Colwyn Bay
LL28 4HZ
T 01492 546666
F 01492 543052
E r.williams@llandrillo.ac.uk

Coleg Meirion-Dwyfor
Barmouth Road, Dolgellau
LL40 2SW
T 01341 422827
F 01341 422393
E go.rowlands@meirion-dwyfor.ac.uk
Contact Gwyn Rowlands

Coleg Menai
Llys Y Wernen, Ffordd Y Llyn, Parc Menai,
Bangor
LL57 4DF
T 01248 370125
E owein.prendergast@menai.co.uk
Contact Owein Prendergast

Coleg Powys
Llanidloes Road, Newtown
SY16 4HU
T 01686 622722
F 01686 622246
Contact Ian Savage

Glamorgan Centre for Art & Design
Glyntaff Road, Glyntaff, Pontypridd
CF37 4AT
T 01443 663309
F 01443 663313
E r.griffin@pontypridd.ac.uk
Contact Robert Griffin

Gwent Coleg
Pontypool Campus, Blaendare Road, Pontypool
NP14 5YE
T 01495 333134
Contact Dennis Gardiner

Pembrokeshire College
Merlins Bridge, Haverfordwest
SA61 1SZ
T 01437 765247
F 01437 767279
Contact Cath Brooks

Swansea Institute of Higher Education
Alexandra Road, Swansea
SA1 6ED
T 01792 481161
F 01792 481161
E stephen.white@sihe.ac.uk
Contact Stephen White

University of Wales College, Newport
Allt-Yr-Yn Campus, P.O. Box 180, Newport
NP20 5XR
T 01633 432681
F 01633 432682
E g.evans@newport.ac.uk
Contact Gareth Evans

University of Wales Institute, Cardiff
Western Avenue, Cardiff
CF5 2YB
T 029 20416689
F 029 20416640
E dgould@uwic.ac.uk
Contact David Gould

West Wales School of the Arts
Faculty of Art/Design, Jobswell Campus,
Carmarthen
SA31 3HY
T 01554 748204
F 01267 221515
E carol.gwizdak@ccta.ac.uk
Contact Carol Gwizdak

Yale College of Wrexham
Grove Park Road, Wrexham
LL12 7AA
T 01978 311794
F 01978 291569 / 364254
E sab@yale-wrexham.ac.uk
Contact Sheena Bain

West Midlands

Cannock Chase Technical College
Progres Centre, Walsall Road, Bridgetown
WS11 1UE
T 01543 462200
E rachel.holmes@cannock.ac.uk
Contact Rachel Holmes

City College, Birmingham
Heartlands Art College, St Peters Urban Village,
Bridge Road, Sattley, Birmingham
B8 3TE
T 0121 3273608
F 0121 3285884
E darkinstall@citycol.ac.uk
Contact Kevin Hawker

City of Wolverhampton College
Wulfrun Campus, Paget Road,
Wolverhampton
WV6 0DU
T 01902 746800
F 01902 423070
E beesont@wolverhamptoncollege.ac.uk
Contact Tom Beeson

Coventry University
School of Art and Design, Priory Street,
Coventry
CV1 5FB
T 024 7688248
E h.cannatecca@coventry.ac.uk
Contact Howard Cannatecca

Dudley College of Technology
The Broadway, Dudley
DY1 4AS
T 01384 363000
F 01384 363311
Contact Gordon Heath

Herefordshire College of Art & Design
Folly Lane, Hereford
HR1 1LT

T 01432 273359
F 01432 341099
E head@hereford-art-col.ac.uk
Contact Roger Collins

Hereward College
Bramston Crescent, Tile Hill Lane, Coventry
CV4 9SW
T 024 76461231
F 024 76694305
E margarettaylor@hereward.ac.uk
Contact Margaret Taylor

Kidderminster College of Further Education
Art and Design Department, Hoo Road,
Kidderminster
DY10 1LX
T 01562 820811 / 732224 (direct line)
F 01562 748504
Contact Saul Cumiskey

Kingston University
Knights Park, 53–57 High Street, Kingston-upon-
Thames
KT1 2QJ
T 020 85472000
Contact Paul Stafford

Malvern College
College Road, Malvern
WR14 3DF
T 01684 581500
Contact Tim Newsholm

**Matthew Boulton College of Further and
Higher Education**
Sherlock Street, Birmingham
B5 7DB
T 0121 4464545
F 0121 4463105
Contact David Lovegrove

Newcastle-under-Lyme College
Liverpool Road, Newcastle-under-Lyme
ST5 2DF
T 01782 254357
F 01782 254281
Contact Noel Connor

North Birmingham College
Aldridge Road, Great Barr, Birmingham
B44 8NE

T 0121 3603543
F 0121 3250828
Contact Emma Buet

North East Worcestershire College
Bromsgrove Campus, Blackwood Road,
Bromsgrove
B60 1PQ
T 01527 585041
F 01527 572900
E info@ne-worcs.ac.uk
Contact Linda Taylor

North Warwickshire & Hinckley College
Hinchley Road, Nuneaton
CV11 6BU
T 024 76343000
F 024 76328376
E the.college@nwarks-hinchley.ac.uk
Contact Dale Robertson

Rugby College School of Art
Lower Hamilton Road, Rugby
CV21 3QS
T 01788 338601
F 01788 338575
E info@rugbycoll.ac.uk
Contact Roy Job

Sandwell College
High Street, West Bromwich
B70 8DW
T 0121 2536648
E lenoraminto@fsmail.net
Contact Lenora Minto

Shrewsbury College of Arts and Technology
London Road, Shrewsbury
SY2 6PR
T 01743 342342
F 01743 342509
E prospects@shrewsbury.ac.uk
Contact Graham Brownridge

Solihull College
Blossomfield Road, Solihull
B91 1SB
T 0121 6787001
F 0121 6787200
Contact Elaine Cantwell

Stafford College
Earl Street, Stafford
ST16 2QR

T 01785 223800
F 01785 259953
Contact Anne Piercy

Staffordshire University
School of Art and Design, College Road,
Stoke-on-Trent
ST5 4HL
T 01782 294625
F 01782 294873
E artkm@staffs.ac.uk
Contact Keith Malkin

Stourbridge College
The Longlands Centre, Brook Street,
Stourbridge
DY8 3XB
T 01384 344616 / 344600
F 01384 344601
E p.d.caines@wcv.ac.uk
Contact Patrick Caines

Sutton Coldfield College
Design Centre, 90 Upper Holland Road, Sutton
Coldfield
B72 1RD
T 0121 3621158
F 0121 3213180
E jayneb@sutcol.ac.uk
Contact Ian Andrews

Tamworth & Lichfield College
Lichfield Campus, The Friary,
Lichfield
WS13 6QG
T 01543 301100
F 01543 301103
E gill.bailey@lichfield.ac.uk
Contact John Hayward

University of Central England in Birmingham
UCE Birmingham, Perry Barr,
Birmingham
B42 2SU
T 0121 3315800
F 0121 3316740
Contact Frank Johnson

Walford and North Shropshire College
College Road, Oswestry
SY11 2SA
T 01691 688000
F 01691 688001
Contact Graham Cox

Walsall College of Arts & Technology
St Pauls Street, Walsall
WS1 1XN
T 01922 657000
F 01922 657083
E jjenkins@walcat.ac.uk
Contact Alan Tyler or Jed Hoyland

Warwickshire College
Leamington Centre, Warwick New Road,
Leamington Spa
CV32 5JE
T 01926 318118
F 01926 318111
Contact Sue Henderson

Worcester College of Technology
School of Art and Design, Barbourne,
Worcester
WR1 1RT
T 01905 725631
F 01905 725645
Contact Marc Bullock

Yorkshire and Humberside

Barnsley College
P.O. Box 266, Church Street,
Barnsley
S70 2YW
T 01226 730191
F 01226 298514
Contact Maurice Senior

Beverley College
Gallows Lane, Beverley
HU17 7DT
T 01482 868362
F 01482 866784
E pennykealey@hotmail.com

Bradford College
Great Horton Road, Bradford
BD7 1AY
T 01274 753004

Calderdale College
School of Integrated Arts, Francis Street,
Halifax
HX1 3UZ
T 01422 357357
F 01422 399320
Contact Carol South

Craven College, Skipton
Gargrave Road, Skipton
BD23 1US
T 01752 799637
F 01756 794872
E enquiries@craven-college.ac.uk
Contact Bruce Timson

Dewsbury College
Batley School of Art and Design, Wheelwright
Campus, Birkdale Road, Dewsbury
WF13 4HQ
T 01924 451649
F 01924 469491
E clough@staffmail.dewsbury.ac.uk
Contact Mark Clough

Doncaster College
Waterdale, Doncaster
DN1 3EF
T 01302 553553
F 01302 553559
Contact Sharon Jarvis

Hopwood Hall College
Rochdale Campus, St Marys Gate, Rochdale
OL12 6RY
T 01706 345346 ext. 2214
F 01706 41426
E john.brisland@hopwood.ac.uk
Contact John Brisland

Huddersfield Technical College
New North Road, Huddersfield
HD1 5NN
T 01484 536521
F 01484 511885
Contact John Cracknell

Hull College
School of Art and Design, The Riley Centre,
Parkfield Drive, Hull
HU3 6TE
T 01482 351228
F 01482 569918
Contact Ian Carmichael or Andy Dakin

Keighley College
Cavendish Street, Keighley
BD21 3DF
T 01535 618662
F 01535 618665
Contact Pam Brook

Leeds College of Art and Design
Blenheim Walk, Leeds
LS2 9AQ
T 0113 2028000
F 0113 2028001
E info@leeds-art.ac.uk

Leeds Metropolitan University
City Campus, Calverley Street, Leeds
LS1 3HE
T 0113 2832600
Contact Chris Roysse

Rotherham College of Arts and Technology
Eastwood Lane, Rotherham
S65 1EG
T 01709 362111
F 01709 373053
E srhodes@rotherham.ac.uk
Contact Bonita T. Duacuterber

Selby College
Abbots Road, Selby
YO8 8AT
T 01757 211011
F 01757 213137
Contact Roger Silvester

Sheffield College
'Loxley' Centre, Sheffield
S6 5JL
T 0114 2602230
F 0114 2602201
E john.milner@sheffcol.ac.uk
Contact John Milner and Myra Rennie

Wakefield College
Thornes Park Centre, Thornes Park, Wakefield
WF2 8QZ
T 01924 789800
E m.grant@wakcoll.ac.uk
Contact Mandi Grant

Wyke College
Grammar School Road, Hull
HU5 4NX
T 01482 346347
F 01482 473336
E office@wyke.ac.co.uk
Contact Ian Potter

York College
Art, Design and Craft, Tadcaster Road, York
YO24 1UA
T 01904 770284
F 01904 770499
Contact Angela Newdick

Yorkshire Coast College
School of Art and Design, Westwood Campus,
Valley Bridge Parade, Scarborough
YO11 2PF
T 01723 361960
F 01723 366057
Contact K.B. Cunningham

List of abbreviations
ABC Awarding Body Consortium
AHRB Arts and Humanities Research Board
APEL Accreditation of Prior Experential
  Learning
AVCE Advanced Vocational Certificate of
  Education
BA Bachelor of Arts
BScEd Bachelor of Science Education
BTEC Business and Technology Education
  Council
CertHE Certificate of Higher Education
DipHE Diploma of Higher Education
FD First Diploma
FdA Foundation in Art Degree
FE Further Education
GCE General Certificate of Education
GCSE General Certificate of Secondary Education
GNVQ General National Vocational Qualification
HE Higher Education
HEFC Higher Education Funding Council
HNC Higher National Certificate
HND Higher National Diploma
IELTS International English Language Testing
  Certificate
MA Master of Arts
MFA Master of Fine Art
MLitt Master of Literature
MPhil Master of Philosophy
MRes Master of Research
NC National Certificate
NCFE National Council for Further Education
ND National Diploma
NVQ National Vocational Qualification
OCN Open College Network
PGCE Postgraduate Certificate of Education
PgCert Postgraduate Certificate
PgDip Postgraduate Diploma
QTS Qualified Teacher Status
SQA Scottish Qualifications Authority
VCE Vocational Certificate of Education

06

Art fairs
and festivals

The market has landed: The impact of fairs on the UK art scene

Louisa Buck

Frieze ends commercial chill

Over the past decade, London has undergone a dramatic expansion from a relative backwater – albeit one with a clutch of interesting artists and galleries – into a major marketplace for contemporary art, widely acknowledged as the second largest after New York and the undisputed centre of the European art market. Although this success has manifested itself in a range of ways, with galleries large and small opening up in both London's East and West Ends, the most dramatic manifestation of the capital's art market status has been the arrival of the Frieze Art Fair, London's first international contemporary art fair, which was inaugurated in autumn 2003 and is now established as an annual event.

Although Frieze, organized by the eponymous British art magazine, is at pains to promote an edgy, maverick image – by commissioning special artists' projects housed in a tent in Regent's Park specially redesigned by architect to the art world, David Adjaye – it is nonetheless a nakedly commercial enterprise. Art enthusiasts should never forget that its primary purpose is to sell as much top-end art as possible in its four-day run. And as such, Frieze provides a fascinating snapshot of the international market: who the main players are, what they are selling and to whom. Here it is possible to assess the commercial flavours of the moment and to be entertained by the sight of the art market's major dealers – whether Marian Goodman, Nicholas Logsdail or Jay Jopling – strutting their stuff and delivering their sales pitches. Also, there's always some great new art to be seen, even if a maze of booths does not present the most conducive of surroundings.

Zoo: new is improved

Then there are the various satellite events that have been timed to coincide with Frieze, many of which are worth investigating, and which vary from year to year. In 2004 and 2005 the most interesting of these was Zoo, the alternative art fair that took its lead from the criticism that Frieze was too biased towards art-market heavy-hitters and did not give adequate acknowledgment of the vibrant local art scene. Zoo, inspirationally situated in two venues within London's historic zoo, is a mini-fair of young, challenging and mainly London-based galleries and project spaces – and indeed some artists without any representation at all – all of whom may well be making an appearance at Frieze in the future. Such was its initial success (on the inaugural opening night, police had to control the crowds trying to gain entrance) that Zoo is set to continue as an annual event, and forms the perfect youthful counterpoint to its big sister on the other side of Regent's Park.

More mixed in quality is Scope, the contemporary art fair based in a hotel, which also piggybacks on the interest generated by Frieze, just as it coincides with other major fairs in New York, Miami and Los Angeles. Here each hotel room is taken over by individual galleries – mainly from the USA but also increasingly from Europe – but only on rare occasions is a display imaginative enough to hold its own against the hotel decor.

Faithful forerunners

The triumph of Frieze has inevitably eclipsed the other art fairs taking place across the UK, especially the London Art Fair, which, since 1988, has been held every year in the Business Design Centre in Islington. But even in its heyday, the London Art Fair never managed to attract galleries from overseas but instead catered to many of the nation's more conservative galleries as well as those showing more historical British art. Nonetheless, the London Art Fair is always very well attended and consistently makes a concerted attempt to inject a more experimental, cutting-edge presence into its line-up: it has a special subsidized section that, whatever its title (in 2004 it called itself New Projects, in previous years it was START), is devoted to showcasing more challenging work by emerging galleries and artists. For a more explicitly historical approach, the 20/21 British Art Fair at the Royal College of Art presents top-notch British art from 1900 to the present day, from classic pieces at Agnew's and the Marlborough Gallery to Alan Cristea's works on paper. The other high-profile art fair presence in the UK comes in the form of the various Affordable Art Fairs that, as their title suggests, sell a wide range of work, most of which is not especially avant-garde in nature but is reasonably priced, accessible in style and aimed at a wide market.

More modest and selective but also more progressive is the Contemporary Art Society's (CAS) annual ART*futures* fair in London, which features work by recent graduates as well as more established names, all of whom have been picked by the CAS. In its time the CAS has provided an early marketplace for artists such as the Chapman Brothers, Sam Taylor-Wood and Damien Hirst – it is a popular destination for young collectors and a worthwhile place to see and be seen in.

Artists' DIY fairs

When it comes to art fairs and events, size isn't necessarily everything; and this is especially true in the case of the various unofficial, *ad hoc* artist-run events that crop up at regular intervals that combine the chance to buy with the chance to have a good time. Following in the footsteps of the legendary 'Fêtes Worse than Death' organized by the late, lamented curator Joshua Compston in and around Hoxton in the early 1990s, there have been more recent occurrences such as the Art Car Boot Sale and the Art Bring and Buy, all of which have featured various permutations of artist-run stalls

where prizes can be won and/or purchases made of art works and objects for often ludicrously low amounts of money. £1 for an original Bob and Roberta Smith 'concrete rubbing' or £5 for interior artist Abigail Lane's set of Fly stickers, anyone?

Biennial or bust

On a more sober, less commercial note, an air of general artistic vibrancy, if not direct sales, can be whipped up by the timely appearance of an art festival. These generally take place outside the metropolitan art centres and tend to focus on the site-specific and the temporary. Here size usually does matter. A case in point was the 1998 Art Transpennine, an ambitious one-off 'exhibition' stretching across the Pennines in the north of England, consisting of a series of temporary works of art and shows commissioned from thirty-five artists, a third of them British and the rest from abroad, along a 130-mile corridor from Liverpool to Hull. Or there is the now-established Liverpool Biennial, an international series of exhibitions and events that colonizes a wide variety of locations, both official and unorthodox throughout Liverpool, with work by both British and international artists.

However, while these events can give rise to some extraordinary projects and often attract a temporary flurry of attention to an area and maybe even some of its artists, they are primarily for the benefit of the international art world and have little lasting impact on the local scene. Curators and artists may focus on the characteristics of a region, but the engagement rarely does more than scratch the surface, and within a few days of its opening, the art bandwagon moves on, its gaze focused on the next event. For if there is no infrastructure within a region for the making, the showing and the selling of art then no amount of subsidized temporary activities, however well-intentioned, can hope to make a significant impression. This is why it is London that dominates the UK art scene:

it is where most of the galleries are based, the events mounted and the sales made. And despite a scattering of activities elsewhere, this situation shows no significant sign of changing.

Louisa Buck is a writer, contemporary art correspondent for *The Art Newspaper* and author of *Market Matters: the dynamics of the contemporary art market* and *Moving Targets: A User's Guide to British Art Now.*

Art fairs and festivals

20/21 British Art Fair
Royal College of Art, Kensington Gore, London
SW7 2EU
T 020 87421611
F 020 89955094
E organisers@artfairs.demon.co.uk
W www.britishartfair.co.uk
Founded in 1988. The only event to showcase
British art from 1900 to the present day. Some
sixty of the UK's leading dealers exhibit a wide
range of painting and sculpture featuring all the
great names of twentieth-century British art up to
and including the art of today.
Submission policy The fair is only open to dealers
and galleries.
Frequency Annual.

Affordable Art Fair
Unit 3, Heathmans Road, Fulham, London
SW6 4TJ
T 020 73718787
F 020 73710044
E enquiries@affordableartfair.com
W www.affordableartfair.co.uk
Founded in 1999 with the aim of making
original art work more accessible. The ceiling on
price is currently £3,000, but prices are as low
as £30. Attracts not only first-time buyers but
also collectors in search of work by emerging
artists.
Submission policy The fair is for dealers and
galleries (rather than independent artists) that
represent living artists producing contemporary,
original paintings, prints, sculpture and
photography.
Frequency Twice a year in London (March and
October) and annual in Bristol, New York,
San Francisco, Sydney and Melbourne.

Appledore Visual Arts Festival
3 Marine Parade, Appledore
EX39 1PJ
T 01409 281193
E info@appledorearts.org.uk
W www.appledorearts.org.uk
Contact Jane Bartlett
Founded in 1997. Includes exhibitions, artist talks,
open studios, workshops and residencies. Events
for adults and children of mixed ages and abilities.
Several further education establishments involved,
including SCATS, Falmouth, Plymouth and North
Devon College. Featured artists for 2005 included
Richard Long, Sandy Brown, John Pollex, Svend
Bayer, Clive Bowen and Simon Moore.
Submission policy Artists from all art forms are
encouraged to submit proposals for inclusion
in the festival. Stalls allocated by selection.
Frequency An annual four-day festival (on the
weekend after the spring bank holiday).

ART*futures*
Contemporary Art Society, Bloomsbury House,
74–77 Great Russell Street, London
WC1B 3DA
T 020 76120730
F 020 76314230
E cas@contempart.org.uk
W www.contempart.org.uk/artfutures2005.htm
Organized by the Contemporary Art Society, with
a track record of recognizing emerging talent.
Past exhibitors include Damien Hirst, Sam Taylor-
Wood and Douglas Gordon.
Submission policy Entry to the festival is free and
selection of work is by invitation only.

Art in Action
96 Sedlescombe Road, Fulham, London
SW6 1RB
T 020 73813192
E info@artinaction.org.uk
W www.artinaction.org.uk
Contact Patricia Prendergast
An annual exhibition of over 250 participating
artists and craftsmen. Over a four-day period in
the grounds of Waterperry House near Oxford.
25,000 visitors come to watch and speak to
working demonstrators.
Submission policy Application details available
from the above address. Applications are invited in
September and October.
Frequency Annual.

Art London
Burton's Court, St Leonard's Terrace, Chelsea,
London
SW3
T 020 72599399
E ralph@eburyevents.co.uk
W www.artlondon.net
Over seventy-five UK and international galleries
showing twentieth-century and contemporary art
(paintings, sculpture, photography, works on paper
and ceramics), priced from £300 to over £100,000.

Art on Paper Fair

Royal College of Art, Kensington Gore, London
SW7 2EU
T 020 87421611
F 020 89955094
E organisers@artfairs.demon.co.uk
W www.artonpaper.co.uk
For original works of art on paper only (prints,
drawings, watercolour and photography).
Some fifty dealers and galleries from the UK and
Europe as well as work from China and Japan.
Includes works from the seventeenth to the
twenty-first centuries. Accessible price range.
Frequency Annual.

Artists & Illustrators Exhibition

T 020 78128656
E paulh@quarto.com
Contact Natalie Braiden (Exhibitions Manager)
An annual event at the Business Design Centre
in Islington in London for artists, art material
manufacturers, retailers, art magazines, art
societies and galleries to promote, create and sell
work and network.

Artists & Makers

18 Chancton View Road, Worthing
BN11 5JR
T 01903 709471
E rag@artistsandmakers.com
W www.artistsandmakers.com
Founded in 2000. An independent festival
that takes place across West Sussex every July,
featuring artists' open houses and studios
alongside a programme of live literature
and music.
Submission policy Application details are posted
on the website.

ArtsFest

10th Floor, Alpha Tower, Suffolk Street
Queensway, Birmingham
B1 1TT
T 0121 6852605
F 0121 6852606
E mail@artsfest.org.uk
W www.artsfest.org.uk
Contact Sabra Khan
The UK's largest free arts festival, attracting
audiences in excess of 100,000. Over three
hundred performances take place over the
weekend across arts venues and the streets and
squares of Birmingham.

Submission policy West Midlands-based, or
performing in West Midlands in months following
the event.
Frequency Annual.

Asian Art in London

32 Dover Street, Mayfair, London
W1S 4NE
T 020 74992215
F 020 74992216
E info@asianartinlondon.com
W www.asianartinlondon.com
Contact Virginia Sykes-Wright (PR Marketing) or
Antonia Howard-Sneyd (Company Secretary)
Established in 1997, bringing together London's
leading Asian art dealers, major auction houses
and societies in a series of gallery selling
exhibitions, auctions, receptions, lectures and
seminars. These are complemented by exhibitions
at leading museums. Prices range from £5 to over
£500,000. Works span all media and ages.
Submission policy Participants must be dealing in
the London area. Does not personally handle
submissions from artists.
Frequency Annual.

Battersea Contemporary Art Fair

The Grange, Frensham, Surrey
GU10 3DS
T 0870 2860066
E maria@bcaf.info
W www.bcaf.info
Contact Maria Scaman
Founded in 1991 and bought by current directors
on previous organizers' retirement in 2001. Held
at the Battersea Arts Centre in Lavender Hill, SW11.
Features 150 artists, sculptors, printmakers and
photographers. Works priced from £25 to £4,000.
Submission policy Send CV with four examples of
work in hard copy (anything but image files over
the Internet). Artists only; no galleries or agents.
Frequency Twice a year, in May and November.

Belfast Festival at Queen's

8, Fitzwilliam Street, Belfast
BT9 6AW
T 029 90971034
E festival@qub.ac.uk
W www.belfastfestival.com
Every year since 1963, the largest festival of its kind
in Ireland has celebrated the best of international
art and culture. Runs for three weeks.
Frequency Annual.

The Big Draw

The Campaign for Drawing, 7 Gentleman's Row, Enfield
EN2 6PT
T 020 83511719
E info@drawingpower.org.uk
W www.drawingpower.org.uk
Contact Sue Grayson Ford (Campaign Director)
Includes over a thousand events held each October throughout the UK to promote the art of drawing for all. Quentin Blake is campaign patron.

Bow Festival

Space, 129–131 Mare Street, London
E8 3RH
E melanie@spacestudios.org.uk
W www.spacestudios.org.uk
A fortnight of collaborative public-art projects that engage with the community and built environment of Bow. Space project-manages and produces the festival on behalf of the Roman Road Revel Group, which is made up of local volunteers.

Brighton Art Fair

P.O. Box 73, Hove
BN3 1ZE
E info@brightonartfair.co.uk
W www.brightonartfair.co.uk
An opportunity for art buyers to meet with and purchase work direct from artists. Works range from traditional to contemporary and prices are generally from £50 to £1,500.

Brighton Festival

Festival Office, 12a Pavilion Buildings, Castle Square, Brighton
BN1 1EE
T 01273 700747
F 01273 707505
E info@brighton-festival.org.uk
W www.brighton-festival.org.uk
Started in 1966, one of the UK's largest international arts festivals.

Brighton Photo Biennial

E mail@bpb.org.uk
W www.bpb.org.uk
A major photography festival.
Frequency Biannual, in odd-numbered years.

Celf Caerleon Arts Festival

c/o Hambrook Cottage, Isca Road, Caerleon, Newport
NP18 1QG

T 01633 423354
E editor@caerleon-arts.org
W www.caerleon-arts.org
A two-week summer festival started in 2003. The main event is an international sculpture symposium in which around ten sculptors are selected to create new works from wood in public. Sculptors are paid a fee and their work is afterwards sited around the town.
Submission policy Applications from sculptors working in wood are usually invited towards the end of the year for selection in January and February. See website for details.
Frequency Annual, usually in June or July.

Ceramic Art London

Royal College of Art, Kensington Gore, London
SW7 2EU
T 020 74393377
F 020 72879954
E organiser@ceramics.org.uk
W www.ceramics.org.uk
Contact Peter Bradley
The festival's vision is to be the national focus for studio ceramics. Components include a selling fair of ninety of the best potters worldwide (prices range from £30 to £30,000); a major, free events programme; an exhibition of student work; major prizes for potters; full-colour catalogue. Presented by the Craft Potters Association of Great Britain and Ceramic Review Magazine, in association with the Crafts Council.
Submission policy Open to all working studio potters (not students) worldwide, in any ceramic form. Selection of exhibitors is by independent selection panel. Applications via website.
Frequency Annual.

Chelsea Arts Fair

Penman Antiques Fairs, Widdicombe, Bedford Place, Uckfield
TN22 1LW
T 01825 744074
F 01825 744012
E info@penman-fairs.co.uk
W www.penman-fairs.co.uk
Over forty British and international galleries display contemporary and twentieth-century works of art in a relaxed atmosphere. Held in Chelsea Old Town Hall.

Collect at V&A

Victoria & Albert Museum, London
SW7 2RL

T 020 78062512
E collect@craftscouncil.org.uk
W www.craftscouncil.org.uk/collect
Organized by the British Crafts Council. The
only art fair in Europe to showcase contemporary
applied and decorative arts from around the world.

Contemporary Art Fair Edinburgh (CAFE)
Arte in Europa, 77 Poplar Park, Port Seton, East
Lothian
EH32 0TE
T 07740 552375
F 01875 819857
E enquiries@arteineuropa.com
W www.thecafe2005.com
Inaugural festival held in 2005. Over seventy
exhibitors from throughout Europe and the UK,
showcasing over five hundred artists, sculptors
and photographers, from recent graduates and
self-taught artists to established names.

Deptford X
c/o Creative Lewisham Agency, 1 Resolution Way,
Deptford, London
SE8 4NT
E hannah@deptfordx.org
W www.deptfordx.org.uk
A programme of integrated exhibitions for
different sites and venues in and around Deptford.

Dorset Art Weeks
DAWA, P.O. Box 4040, Dorchester
DT2 8YA
T 07974 959550
E admin@dorsetartweek.com
W www.dorsetartweek.com
Began in 1992, following a visit made by furniture
designer and maker John Makepeace to Oxford's
open studios. By opening their own workplaces
and homes to the public, artists get their work on
the show and receive feedback directly from
visitors. Held over sixteen days, featuring 362
venues with almost five hundred named artists
and almost the same number again represented in
groups, art clubs and societies. Does not select on
the basis of the 'quality' of the work nor stipulate
that artists should make their living through their
art, nor that they be art-school graduates.

Dulwich Art Fair
Penman Antiques Fairs, Widdicombe, Bedford
Place, Uckfield
TN22 1LW
T 01825 744074
F 01825 744012

E info@penman-fairs.co.uk
W www.penman-fairs.co.uk
Held at Dulwich College and aimed at art-lovers
who live in south London. Features galleries from
London and across the UK offering contemporary
art from £50 to over £10,000.

Dumfries & Galloway Arts Festival
Gracefield Arts Centre, 28 Edinburgh Road,
Dumfries
DG1 1JQ
T 01387 260447
F 01387 260447
E info@dgartsfestival.org.uk
W www.dgartsfestival.org.uk
Contact Annette Rogers
Started in 1979. Presents a wide range of art
forms, including jazz, folk and classical music,
drama, literature, children's events, films and
exhibitions, in various venues located between
Langholm in the east to Gatehouse of Fleet in the
west of the region.
Frequency Annual.

Edinburgh International Festival
Hub, Castlehill, Edinburgh
EH1 2NE
T 0131 4732001
W www.eif.co.uk
Founded over fifty years ago and one of the
world's leading festivals of the arts. Held in
locations throughout Edinburgh.

Euroart Live Festival
Euroart Studios & Gallery, Unit 22F @ N17
Studios, 784–788 High Road, London
N17 0DA
W www.euroart.co.uk
A festival of live-art performances drawn from a
diversity of cultures. Aims to instigate dialogue
and debate across art forms and cultural borders
and, by presenting work from both mature and
emerging artists, across generations.

F-EST
T 020 74284949
E info@f-est.com
W www.f-est.com
An open weekend for East End contemporary-art
galleries, aiming to introduce visitors and local
people to the proliferation of art projects in the
East End. More than eighty participating galleries
and museums open later than usual for free, and
most hold special events.

Frieze Art Fair
5–9 Hatton Wall, London
EC1N 8HX
T 020 70253970
F 020 70253971
E info@friezeartfair.com
W www.friezeartfair.com
London's largest international art fair launched in
2003 by the publishers of *frieze* magazine. Takes
place in Regent's Park, London and features over
140 of the most exciting contemporary-art galleries
in the world. As well as these exhibitors, the fair
includes specially commissioned artists' projects
and a talks programme.
Submission policy Accepts gallery applications
only.
Frequency Annual, in October.

Glasgow Art Fair
UZ Events, 125–129 High Street, Glasgow
G1 1PH
T 0141 5526027
F 0141 5526048
E artfair@uzevents.com
W www.glasgowartfair.com
Contact Cristina Armstrong
Founded in 1995, with fifty-three selected galleries
showing work in 2005. An opportunity to buy, sell
and view art from over a thousand national and
international artists.

Glasgow International
E marketing@glasgowinternational.org
W www.glasgowinternational.org
Glasgow's first curated and commissioning
festival of contemporary visual art.

Inspired Art Fair
The Bridge, Weston Street, London
SE1
T 020 83747318
F 020 83744566
E jo@inspiredartfair.com
W www.inspiredartfair.com
Contact Jo George
Established in 2003, showcasing up to seventy
independent undiscovered artists. Held at
the Bridge, a new urban venue situated within
the vaulted arches beneath London Bridge
Station. The venue totals over 30,000 sq. ft,
comprising a series of arches of differing
sizes and styles.
Submission policy Go to website to view cost and
stand sizes. Two methods of submitting images:
by post or email. A selection committee chooses all
the artists taking part on the quality, technical
ability and originality of artists' work.
Frequency Annual.

International Ceramics Fair and Seminar
Haughton International Fairs, 31 Old Burlington
Street, London
W1S 3AS
T 020 77345491
F 020 74944604
E info@haughton.com
W www.haughton.com
Founded in 1981, bringing together leading
international ceramics dealers from around
the world to display and sell European pottery,
porcelain, glass and enamels. Includes
lecture series.

Inverness Art Fair
Old High Church Halls, 45 Milton Crescent,
Inverness
IVU
T 01463 220802
E lwjohnson@zoom.co.uk
Contact Len W. Johnson
Founded in 2004 by the Old High St Stephen's
Church of Scotland to increase church funds and
to create a marketing opportunity for artists of all
abilities throughout the Highlands and Islands of
Scotland. Selling prices of paintings vary from
£100 to over £1,000.
Submission policy Visual arts in most
media are acceptable with a restriction on
size over 100cm² (except under previous
agreement).
Frequency Annual, running for the first week
in June each year.

Leeds Art Fair
61a Weetwood Lane, Leeds
LS16 5NP
T 0113 2425242
E info@ytb.org.uk
W www.leedsartfair.org.uk
A contemporary visual arts event, with preference
given to artists with ties to or living and working
in the local area.

Liverpool Biennial
P.O. Box 1200, The Tea Factory, 82 Wood Street,
Liverpool
L69 1XB
T 0151 7097444

F 0151 7097377
E info@biennial.com
W www.biennial.com
Established in 1998. A major international festival of contemporary art.

London Art Fair

Business Design Centre, 52 Upper Street, London
N1 0QH
T 020 72886736
F 020 72886446
E laf@upperstreetevents.co.uk
W www.londonartfair.co.uk
Contact Sarah Monk
Featuring the best in modern British and contemporary art. The 2006 fair will include over one hundred leading UK galleries.
Submission policy Galleries dealing in modern British and contemporary art welcome to apply.
Frequency Annual.

London Design Festival

56 Kingsway Place, Sans Walk, London
EC1R 0LU
T 020 70145313
F 020 70145301
E info@londondesignfestival.com
W www.londondesignfestival.com
The official launch of the London Design Festival took place at Bloomberg in 2003. Festival partners had grown from forty in 2003 to eighty in 2004. In 2004 there were seventy-five different activities listed as part of the festival, including an array of design disciplines, from interior design to sculpture, photography to ceramics.
Submission policy Does not accept submissions from individual artists. Works on a not-for-profit partnership basis with various London organizations, venues, institutions and exhibitions companies to plan content for the period of the festival.
Frequency Annual, though dates vary from year to year.

London Original Print Fair, The

T 020 7439 2000
E info@londonprintfair.com
W www.londonprintfair.com
First held in 1985. Now at the Royal Academy of Arts (Burlington House, Burlington Gardens, London W1). Features forty-five international dealers, showing prints from Dürer to Hockney and Hirst.

Manchester Art Show

P.O. Box 512, Altrincham, Cheshire
WA15 9WL
T 0161 9287353
F 0161 9291537
E info@engagingarts.co.uk
W www.manchesterartshow.co.uk
Contact Valerie McNamara
Founded in 2002 and now established as the north's largest selling contemporary art fair. The show takes place in the MICC-GMEX in the heart of Manchester city centre. No price limit on work exhibited.
Submission policy Applications from artists in all forms of visual arts are welcome.
Frequency Annual.

Margate Rocks

P.O. Box 373, Birchington
CT7 9WY
E info@margaterocks.co.uk
W margaterocks.co.uk
Established in 2001. An eclectic mix of contemporary art, using alternative venues and existing businesses as exhibition spaces. Centred around the Old Town and Harbour area of Margate, with other events happening throughout Thanet. Artists' open-studio programme began in 2005.
Submission policy Work must be inventive, interesting and able to engage the public.
Frequency Annual, in July.

Museums and Galleries Month (MGM)

The Campaign for Museums, 35–37 Grosvenor Gardens, London
SW1W 0BS
T 020 72339796
F 020 7 2336770
E info@campaignformuseums.org.uk
W www.mgm.org.uk
Celebration of the UK's museums and galleries, with special events, workshops and exhibitions in museums and galleries around the country. Organized by the Campaign for Museums, MGM is an opportunity for museums and galleries to try out new events to attract visitors.
Frequency Annual, in May.

National Review of Live Art

New Moves International Ltd, P.O. Box 25262, Glasgow
G1 1YW
T 0141 3575538

E admin@newmoves.co.uk
W www.newmoves.co.uk
Europe's longest-running festival of live art.

Nine Days of Art

T 01803 868805
E anneward@onetel.net.uk
W www.ninedaysofart.co.uk
Contact Anne Ward (Secretary)
A festival organized in the south-west of England
by the Skills Training and Rural Arts Week
(STRAW) Project.

On The Wall Art Fair

Upper Street Events, Business Design Centre,
52 Upper Street, Islington, London
N1 0QH
T 020 72886191
F 020 72886446
E elliotg@upperstreetevents.co.uk
W www.on-the-wall.co.uk
Contact Elliot Gard (Sales Manager)
A major London-based fair providing independent
professional artists and artist studios with direct
routes to consumer and trade buyers.
Submission policy Event open to two-dimensional
originals, limited editions, three-dimensional
sculpture and applied-art objects in traditional or
new media. Vetted.
Frequency Annual.

Oxfordshire Artweeks

P.O. Box 281, Oxford
OX2 9FX
T 01865 861574
F 01865 861574
Contact Caryn Paladina
First held in 1981. Now the largest open-
studio festival of visual art in the country.
Artists invite the public into their homes and
studios. Run by a board comprising artists as
well as other professionals who volunteer time
and expertise. There is also one part-time paid
coordinator.
Submission policy The festival operates a
no-selection policy and welcomes all artists,
commercial galleries, public-art spaces,
schools and any other organization wishing to
take part. To take part, artists must either be a
member, or be part of a larger group that has
membership. Welcomes artists working in
all media and styles. It is up to each participant
to find their own venue and to organize their
exhibition.

photo-london

2nd Floor, 13 Mason's Yard, St James's,
London
SW1Y 6BU
T 020 78399300
E info@photo-london.com
Began in 2004 as London's first international
photography fair. Around fifty exhibitors from ten
countries showing photography, film and video
from throughout the history of the art form. Takes
place in the Royal Academy of Arts' Burlington
Gardens.

Raw Arts Festival

Candid Arts Trust, 3 Torrens Street,
London
EC1V 1NQ
T 020 78374237
E rawartsfestival@yahoo.co.uk
W www.raf2005.co.uk
Contact Piers Midwinter
First held in 2004. An annual exhibition of
international self-taught artists.
Submission policy Artists should submit pictures
and information about themselves. The entry fee
in 2005 was £150 per artist's space.

Redbridge Arts Festival

London Borough of Redbridge Leisure Services,
8th Floor, Lynton House, 255–259 High Road,
Ilford
IG1 1NY
E jacqueline.eggleston@redbridge.gov.uk
A showcase of artistic disciplines held at a range of
locations throughout Redbridge.

Rye Festival

P.O. Box 33, Rye
TN31 7YB
T 01797 224442
E info@ryefestival.co.uk
W www.ryefestival.co.uk
Contact Pat Field info@turtlefineart.co.uk
A festival of the arts founded in 1971 and now
including more than fifty events over two weeks.
Frequency Annual.

scope art fair (London)

521 West 26th Street, New York
NY 10001, USA
T +1 212 2681522
F +1 212 2680123
E info@scope-art.com
W www.scope-art.com

Aims to demystify the buying process of contemporary art by producing international art fairs of cutting-edge art and emerging culture. The fairs bring together up-and-coming dealers, curators and artists in a relaxed atmosphere. Founded in 2002 and currently producing fairs in the USA and London.
Submission policy The fair is vetted for exhibitors. Interested artists should work through an exhibitor.

Somerset Art Weeks
SAW Ltd, Dillington House, Ilminster
TA19 9DT
T 01460 259324
F 01460 259324
E arts@somersetartweek.freeserve.co.uk
W www.somersetartweek.org.uk
A biennial showcase of open studios and exhibitions, residencies, installations and special events. To be next held in September 2006.
Submission policy £15 for artist members; £25 for organizations; £7 to £15 for Friends.

St Ives International
1 Queen's Chambers, 38–40 Queen Street, Penzance
TR18 4BH
T 01736 333024
F 01736 333074
E info@stii.co.uk
W www.stii.co.uk
A partnership organization founded by Falmouth College of Arts, Newlyn Art Gallery, South West Arts and Tate St Ives to present major arts projects in Cornwall.

Zoo Art Fair
164 Fernhead Road, London
W9 3EL
E info@zooartfair.com
W www.zooartfair.com
Showcases London galleries, arts organizations and publications, and represents an in-depth survey of a thriving young cosmopolitan scene. While the fair itself is non-profit, it provides the next generation of art professionals with an international commercial platform.

07

Competitions, residencies, awards and prizes

Open to the possibility: How to submit yourself to an art prize

Sacha Craddock

Although artists may question whether it is worth putting themselves forward for possible and probable rejection by submitting work to an open competition or art prize, an unseen, but nonetheless powerful pressure does start to build up through the inclusion and exposure that such an experience can bring. A confident student on a postgraduate course should definitely feel encouraged to submit a piece that has turned out well as part of an application for open exhibitions such as New Contemporaries or EAST. Not only will participation in one of these opens have been worthwhile as an experience of exhibiting in a prestigious group show, but a photograph and account of the work, along with the artist's details, will now exist in the accompanying catalogue.

Student prospects

These are the two main open-submission exhibitions in Britain but there are a number of other smaller, often more localized shows such as the Mostyn Open. EAST, held annually in Norwich, is selected by a strong pair of selectors or sometimes an individual, often themselves prominent artists. It is truly 'open' and international, in that it accepts submissions from anyone, anywhere in the world.

The annual New Contemporaries is selected by a panel of three or four artists, writers or curators, and produces an exhibition that tours the UK. The exhibition reflects the fundamental role of art school by inviting artists either in, or just out of, a British art school, at either graduate or postgraduate level. Although it used to be open to those who had been out of college for up to two years, by this stage too many up-and-coming superstars are already well on their successful way. Yet the very principle of the show remains a matter for

discussion: does providing a readymade show of student art benefit the contemporary art collector or dealer looking for fresh talent, or more crucially, does it support the exhibiting artists, and don't these ultimately amount to much the same thing? In any case, the overriding principle of the exhibition is to give each individual artist the space, place and proper context in which to show work and be free. The rest inevitably has to follow.

Judge and jury

Prizes are divisive, but that is the whole idea. While it is good to win something, it can be just as advantageous to be included in the exhibition and experience as a whole. The opportunity to see individual work in another context, to understand the principle of the mixed show, to appreciate the free association of work separated from the security of explanation, is a great preparation for a more successful reality. However, it depends at what stage you are in your career, and on the prestige of the prize or exhibition. The board of New Contemporaries decided to stop the somewhat meaningless task of choosing one winner from a group of around thirty-five finalists, selected from some 1,250 applicants.

Selection is key to the exhibition's success. While the application process is anonymous and open, it is essential that the selectors pick artists that represent the most ambitious and exciting art of that particular time. Real attention is paid to properly representing a range of media; but in the end, the judges who perform this long-drawn-out procedure – often in darkness, with the shunt of slide, insistent whirr of backtracked video, and conceptually confusing written statements – gain a tremendous amount of general and abstract insight. A great deal of concentrated faith has to be projected onto each slide, sound piece, video, proposal, moving image, book work and illustration for it to work. It would be a depressing and lonely experience for the selector more dependent on labels and context, schools and trappings – the clues and props of success – than their own self-belief and judgment.

Turner and the present

At some very basic level, art is most democratic and challenging at its point of observation. It can be approached from many different places and positions. Imagine, though, choosing from between just four lots of work, as with the Tate Gallery's annual Turner Prize. The fact that the shortlist is always the result of an immense whittling process, a huge negotiation about worth and worthwhile, is soon forgotten in the judges' huddle. Choose between this and that: between a sculptor who invents the best atmospheric fiction and then makes it real, a photographer who used to film and photograph his family but has taken to photographing a classical landscape, a filmmaker-turned-video-maker who makes fulsome and generous installations, and a minimal gesturalist who shows little to great effect and ultimate victory. This is all very difficult but comes at exactly the other end of success, at the upper echelons of achievement as an artist.

Some prizes, and exhibitions, concentrate on a particular medium. The John Moores Prize, Britain's truly important open painting show, has witnessed many attempts to change its form and function, to give it a different guise. The only real novelty is that the first stage is selected from slides rather than actual paintings. It is difficult to argue that this is perfect, but the transportation of huge paintings from across the country to Liverpool would be inevitably punitive. The tendency to concentrate on subject or content over and above the very quality, volume, sense and significance of paint means that reproduction always provides less than half the story. A painting can equally look much better in slide than it does in reality, and so the juries of the John Moores, EAST and New Contemporaries always have to deal with this disappointment at the first stage of selection.

Free your work

Chance comes in many guises and at very different stages. The Hamlyn Award is unusual in that it is not a prize as such, but a vast encouragement in the form of a serious pot of money spread over three years. It is given, every year, to four artists who have in some way already proved their importance. The opportunity to produce work over a period of time, independently of extreme poverty and desperate part-time work, is fantastic. Ultimately the Hamlyn Award functions as a secure and long-term boost that announces how good you are. The award comes through nomination and is then judged by a panel. There is no exhibition at the end – no accountability, in any case. The Hamlyn Award is a matter of trust, a way of encouraging individual artists to hold on and develop.

While it may still feel a touch soul-destroying to submit that application fee, photograph the work, then title, explain and interpret it for others, it is worth the effort. Without the experience, in equal measures, of criticism and fallibility, the 'isolated' work of art becomes overworked, overloved, overnourished and overprotected, like an only child born to a suffocating parent. Any opportunity for exposure is important. Slides must be of good quality, however, and the statement should be honest without claiming 'to deal with' the terrors of the world. The application process provides an occasion to take stock, stand back, and understand that that very particular image, surface, attitude and approach are good enough to go out and continue to exist.

Sacha Craddock, an independent art critic, postgraduate tutor and curator for Sadlers Wells and Bloomberg Space, has been chair of New Contemporaries since 1997 and judged numerous art competitions including the Turner Prize and the Jerwood Painting Prize.

Competitions, residencies, awards and prizes

1871 Fellowship

Ruskin School of Drawing and Fine Art, 74 High Street, Oxford
OX1 4BG
T 01865 276940
F 01865 276949
E vanda.wilkinson@ruskin-school.ox.ac.uk
W www.ruskin-sch.ox.ac.uk/lab
Contact Paul Bonaventura
Established in 2001 by the Laboratory at the Ruskin School of Drawing and Fine Art and the San Francisco Art Institute to help artists make new work by spending periods of time in Oxford and San Francisco. The fellow devotes two months to research-related activities in England before travelling to San Francisco for up to four months of intensive studio-based production. The fellowship was implemented in 2001. Current value of award is £18,000.
Frequency One award annually.
Entry policy The award is by nomination only.

Abbey Awards in Painting and Abbey Scholarship in Painting

Abbey Council, P.O. Box 5, Rhayader
LD6 5WA
T 01597 810704
E faithclark@netmatters.co.uk
W www.bsr.ac.uk
Contact Faith Clark (Administrator)
Awards enable artists to work in the British School at Rome for two to three months. Exhibition of scholars' and awardees' work held at the end of each academic year. The British School has a Curator (Contemporary Arts Programme) to assist with exhibitions and in making contact with an artistic community in Rome, and an Arts Adviser responsible for direct support of painters.
Frequency Normally at least two to three awards. Abbey Council also offers a yearly scholarship tenable at British School at Rome.
Entry policy Open to mid-career painters who are UK, Commonwealth or US citizens with an established record of achievement. No age limit.

Academy Schloss Solitude

Stiftung des Offentlichen Rechts, Solitude 3, Stuttgart
70197, GERMANY
T +49 711699300
F +49 7116993015
E iw@akademie-solitude.de
W www.akademie-solitude.de
Living and working opportunities within six- to twelve-month scholarships. Includes forty-five individual studios (several for painters and sculptors), workshops, computer units and other technical equipment. Scholarship holders can access library, artists' archive, seminar rooms and cafeteria. Fine arts, literature, music, architecture, performing arts, design, video/film/new media all represented.
Frequency Grants awarded every eighteen months.
Entry policy Open to visual artists, film/video artists, architects, designers, composers, musicians and performing artists of any nationality. Majority of scholarships for applicants under 35.

ACE Award for a Commissioned Artwork in Ecclesiastical Space

107 Crundale Avenue, London
NW9 9PS
T 020 82062253
F 020 82062253
E awards@acetrust.org
W www.acetrust.org
Contact Laura Moffatt
Given for the first time in 2003, the award is presented by the Art and Christianity Enquiry (ACE) in association with the Michael Marks Charitable Trust. The prize goes to the artist and a specially commissioned art work is offered to the client to display for a period of six weeks. The commissioned work, in any medium, must be within the building or grounds of a Christian worship space; it should be permanent, completed and *in situ* by the time of the entry deadline.
Frequency One award of £3,000 every two years.
Entry policy Entries should reflect both theological insight and aesthetic excellence.

ACE/MERCERS International Book Award

107 Crundale Avenue, London
NW9 9PS
T 020 82062253
F 020 82062253
E awards@acetrust.org
W www.acetrust.org
Contact Laura Moffatt
Given by the Art and Christianity Enquiry (ACE) in association with the Mercers' Company for a book that makes an outstanding contribution to the dialogue between religious faith and the visual arts. The subject matter may relate to any major faith tradition, and to any visual medium

(including film, performance arts, design and architecture). Entries should be written in or translated into English.
Frequency One award of £3,000 every two years.

ACE/REEP Award
17 Allan House, 55 Saffron Hill, London
EC1N 8QX
T 020 74046859
F 020 74046859
E gardenawards@reep.org
W www.reep.org
Contact Elizabeth Brooker
Given jointly by the Religious Education and Environment Programme (REEP) and the Art and Christianity Enquiry (ACE) to an artist working with a school to design a garden that includes an art work incorporating text. First presented in 2003 and runs every two years. Artists working on community projects are encouraged to work with a primary or secondary school to design a school garden. This should involve cross-curricular work, especially RE and Spirituality. A specific theme for the art work varies each time. £2,500 goes to the winning artist and £500 to the school.
Entry policy Visit website to register and view curriculum and practical advice. Only submit plans and a proposal for this award.

Adolph & Esther Gottlieb Foundation Grants
Adolph & Esther Gottlieb Foundation, 380 West Broadway, New York
NY 10012, USA
T +1 212 2260581
F +1 212 2260584
Contact Jenny Gillis (Grants Manager)
Ten individual support grants available through an annual juried competition. Grant amounts are determined each year (typically US$20,000 each, awarded end March). The foundation also administers a year-round emergency assistance grants programme, which assists artists suffering from recent catastrophic circumstances such as fire, flood, medical emergency, and who have worked for a minimum of ten years in a mature phase of their art. Grant amounts range from US$1,000 to US$10,000.
Entry policy Open to painters, sculptors and printmakers who have been working for minimum twenty years in a mature phase of their art and have financial need. Application forms available by post in early September. Only written requests for application forms honoured; none sent out in response to telephone/fax requests.

AiR Creative Programme
The Media Centre, 7 Northumberland Street, Huddersfield
HD1 1RL
T 0870 9905007
F 0870 9905000
E info@druh.co.uk
W www.druh.co.uk
Contact Tom Holley (Creative Director)
Focuses on digital and interactive media. The programme comprises Medialounge exhibition space, an international artist residency programme, commissions, Speaker's Corner and Ultrasound Festival (experimental and electronic music). Emphasizes knowledge-sharing, collaboration and partnerships between artists, academics and creative networks regionally, nationally and internationally.
Frequency Four residencies per year.
Entry policy Open submission process. Make initial contact before submitting CV, as the programme encompasses a diverse range of interests.

Alexander Graham Munro Travel Award
The Royal Scottish Society of Painters in Watercolour, 29 Waterloo Street, Glasgow
G2 6BZ
T 01355 233725
Contact Roger Frame (Secretary)
An award of £3,500 to an artist under 30 years of age, to be used in conjunction with travel. Council to be informed of proposed itinerary and benefits to artist.
Entry policy Only work in a water-based medium.

Alice Berger Hammerschlag Trust Award
Visual Arts Department, Arts Council of Northern Ireland, MacNeice House,
77 Malone Road, Belfast
BT9 6AQ
T 028 90385200
F 028 90661715
W www.artscouncil-ni.org
Established in 1970 for practising visual artists resident in Northern Ireland or the Republic of Ireland. Reflecting Alice Berger Hammerschlag's interest, the award is to be spent on travel to enable artists to experience other cultures and thus develop their work.

Apthorp Fund for Young Artists
Arts Service, Old Town Hall, Friern Barnet Lane, London
N11 3DL

T 020 83593152
W www.barnet.gov.uk/cultural_services
Awards purchase prizes from £100 to £5,000
and displays the purchased works in a touring
exhibition and as permanent display in public
buildings. Funded through the Milly Apthorp
Charitable Trust and administered by the London
Borough of Barnet.
Entry policy Open to artists aged 18 to 30 who live,
work or study in the London boroughs of Barnet,
Brent, Enfield, Haringey and Harrow. Closing
date: November to January, depending on borough.

Arcimboldo Award
W www.arcimboldo-award.com
Each year the Fondation d'entreprise HP France
awards a prize of   10,000 to a digital artist.
Established in 1999. Winner chosen on basis of
artistic merit of the contest entry, calibre of the
creative approach and contribution of digital
technology.
Entry policy Closing date: March. Works must be
printed on paper. Candidates must certify that they
hold moral and legal rights to the photographs
submitted.

Arles Photography Book Prize
RP, 10 Rond-point des Arnes, Arles
BP 96–1362, FRANCE
Reinstated in 2000 and awarded to the best
photography book published in the previous year
(from July to June). Shared between publisher and
photographer and awarded in July each year at the
Recontres Internationales de la Photographie in
Arles.
Frequency Annual prize.
Entry policy Closing date: June.

Artes Mundi Prize
Park Gate, Westgate Street, Cardiff
CF10 1NW
T 029 20723562
F 029 20723561
E info@artesmundi.org
W www.artesmundi.org
Contact Tessa Jackson
First awarded in 2004 to celebrate artists who have
gained recognition in their own country and are
emerging internationally. Focuses upon those
who discuss the human form, the human
condition and add to our understanding
of humanity. A shortlist is drawn up by two
international selectors; the shortlisted artists
exhibit a body of work at the National Museum

and Gallery in Cardiff; and a panel of curators and
artists award the £40,000 prize to the artist who
consistently makes work of note and quality, and is
thought-provoking within the criteria of the prize.
Frequency Every two years. Next prize in 2006.
Entry policy Artists considered through
nomination process only. See website for details.

Artist-in-Residence, Durham Cathedral
1 Stafford Villas, Springwell Village, Gateshead
NE9 7SL
T 0191 4194883
F 0191 4194883
E billhalluk@yahoo.co.uk
W www.artschaplaincy.org.uk
Contact Canon Bill Hall
Founded in 1983, the residency offers an artist
time and space to assess their practice and
development while responding to the cathedral
as a powerful creative statement. Should the artist
wish, currently there is also the offer of a short-
term collaboration with another artist, perhaps
from another art form.
Frequency Twelve-month residency beginning
each year in October, in addition to a £16,000 fee.
Entry policy A good first degree/MA. Artists
should be over 25 years old and be able to
demonstrate a continuous theme of exploration.

Artist of the Year by the Society for All Artists (SAA)
AOY SAA, P.O. Box 50, Newark
NG23 5GY
T 01949 844050
F 01949 844051
E AOY@saa.co.uk
W www.saa.co.uk
Contact Susan Leak
The SAA exists to inform, encourage and inspire
all who want to paint, from beginners to
professionals. This competition is open to non-
members and is free to members.
Frequency One main competition per year.
Entry policy Open to paintings not previously
published in the main categories of landscape,
seascape, flowers, still life, abstract and figure,
with prizes for Artist of the Year, Young, Junior,
Beginner, Amateur and Professional.

Artists in Berlin Programme (DAAD)
Deutscher Akademischer Austauschdienst,
Berlinner Kunstlerprogramm, Jagerstrasse 22–23,
Berlin
10117, GERMANY

T +49 302312080
F +49 302292512
To promote the exchange of artists' experiences and the concern for current cultural issues in other countries. Each year fifteen to twenty artists of international reputation are invited to live and work in Berlin for twelve months to present their work to the Berlin public. Invitations issued with grants to allow adequate standard of living and rental of apartments/workrooms.
Entry policy No application process for visual arts; a commission issues invitations.

Arts and Crafts in Architecture Awards
The Saltire Society, 9 Fountain Close,
122 High Street, Edinburgh
EH1 1TF
T 0131 5561836
F 0131 5571675
E saltire@saltire.org.uk
W www.saltire-society.demon.co.uk
Contact Kathleen Munro
Exists to promote art and culture of Scotland. Awards made for works of art and craft designed to enhance and enrich buildings. Examples include sculpture, painting, tilework, mosaic, tapestry, textile hangings, glass, plaster, metalwork and enamel. Artists and craftsmen working in any suitable medium are invited to enter the competition. The society may arrange for members of the panel to inspect selected entries on site. Adjudication will take place as soon as possible after closing date. Awards or commendations, each in the form of a certificate, will be made to the artist or craftsman and commissioning body or person.
Entry policy Work must: (1) be located in Scotland; (2) have been completed the previous year within the period 1 April to 31 March inclusive; and (3) be an intrinsic part of a building or group of buildings. Each entry must be accompanied by a fee of £25. Closing date: April.

Arts Council England
Helen Chadwick Fellowship
Ruskin School of Drawing and Fine Art, 74 High Street, Oxford
OX1 4BG
T 01865 276940
F 01865 276949
E vanda.wilkinson@ruskin-school.ox.ac.uk
W www.ruskin-sch.ox.ac.uk/lab
Contact Paul Bonaventura
Established by the Laboratory at the Ruskin School

of Drawing and Fine Art and the British School at Rome to help artists make new work by spending periods of time in Oxford and Rome. After visiting Italy for a one-month reconnaissance period, the fellow devotes two months to research-related activities in England before returning to Italy for three months of intensive studio-based production. The fellowship was implemented in 1997 and the current value of the award is £7,500.
Frequency One award annually.
Entry policy The award is advertised in the specialist press. Applicants must be British nationals or have been continuously resident in the UK since March 2002. It is expected that the fellowship will attract visual artists who have established their practices in the years following graduation and who have identified a project that could be made possible or enhanced by spending periods of time both in Oxford and Rome.

Arts Council England
Oxford–Melbourne Fellowship
Ruskin School of Drawing and Fine Art, 74 High Street, Oxford
OX1 4BG
T 01865 276940
F 01865 2276949
E vanda.wilkinson@ruskin-school.ox.ac.uk
W www.ruskin-sch.ox.ac.uk/lab
Contact Paul Bonaventura
Established by the Laboratory at the Ruskin School of Drawing and Fine Art and the Victorian College of the Arts to help artists make new work by spending periods of time in Oxford and Melbourne. The fellow devotes two months to research-related activities in England before travelling to Melbourne for up to four months of intensive studio-based production. The fellowship was implemented in 2002. The current value of the award is £7,500.
Frequency One award biannually.
Entry policy The award is advertised in the specialist press. Applicants must be British nationasl or have been continuously resident in the UK since March 2002. It is expected that the fellowship will attract visual artists who have established their practices in the years following graduation and who have identified a project that could be made possible or enhanced by spending periods of time both in Oxford and Melbourne.

Arts Grant Committee (Sweden)
Konstnärsnämnden, P.O. Box 1610, Stockholm
11186, SWEDEN

T +46 84023570
F +46 84023590
E info@konstnarsnamnden.se
Contact Nils Johansson (Director)
The Visual Arts Fund, part of the Arts Grant
Committee, runs a programme called Artists
in Residence in Sweden (AIRIS). Offers an
opportunity for Swedish artists to invite foreign
artists with whom they wish to work/collaborate to
Sweden to participate in workshops, symposia or
to work towards an art exhibition.
Frequency Grants are issued four times a year and
range from £3,500 to £20,000 to cover the costs of
travel, accommodation, fees, materials, premises
and documentation.
Entry policy Approach must be made by Swedish
artists.

Arts/Industry Artist-in-Residency
John Michael Kohler Arts Center, 608 New York
Avenue, P.O. Box 489, Sheboygan
WI 53082–0489, USA
T +1 920 4586144
E kcridler@jmkac.org
W www.jmkac.org
Contact Kim Cridler (Arts/Industry Coordinator)
Provides artists worldwide with access to
plumbingware firm Kohler Co., through two
six-month residencies. Artists-in-residence
are provided with studio space in the factory,
accessible twenty-four hours a day, seven days a
week. Additionally, they receive free materials, use
of equipment, technical assistance, photographic
services, housing, round-trip transportation within
continental USA from their home to the site, and
weekly honoraria. Available media are vitreous
china, iron, enamel and brass.
Entry policy Emerging and established artists in
any discipline are invited to apply for arts/industry
residencies. Closing date: August for the following
year. Send sae for application form or visit website.

Association of Photographers (AOP) Open
The AOP, 81 Leonard Street, London
EC2A 4QS
W www.the-aop.org
Open to professional and amateur photographers,
with a mission to celebrate the diversity of
photography as an artistic medium. The AOP also
administers a Bursary (£15,000), an Assistant
Photographer's Award, Document (awarded for
documentary photography) and Zeitgeist (to
provide an overview of trends and fashions in
published photography).

Entry policy Membership of the AOP is not
necessary and no set themes or categories are
imposed for the open.

Balmoral Scholarship for Fine Arts
Künstlerhaus Schloss Balmoral, Villenpromenade
11, Bad Ems
56130, GERMANY
T +49 260394190
F +49 2603941916
E info@balmoral.de
W www.balmoral.de
Contact Dr Sabine Jung
An international institution for fine arts.
Allocates grants to qualified artists of all ages
in the fields of painting, drawing, sculpture,
installation, graphics and design, photography
and art theory. Not an art college, but a meeting
place where gifted artists can widen their horizons
by meeting colleagues from various art sectors and
different parts of the world. Eight apartments
and eight studios available.
Frequency Monthly grant given for eleven-month
residency.
Entry policy Applicants should have relevant
training/study or degree followed by at least
three-years' experience. Knowledge of at least one
language (German, English or French) is
requested.

Bass Ireland Arts Award
Visual Arts Department, The Arts Council of
Northern Ireland, MacNeice House, 77 Malone
Road, Belfast
BT9 6AQ
T 028 90385200
F 028 90661715
W www.artscouncil-ni.org
This award of up to £5,000 exists to encourage and
enrich the cultural scene in Northern Ireland by
providing financial assistance to aspiring, creative
individuals or groups in all branches of the arts.
There is normally one award each year, but there
may be more than one depending on the merit of
the applications.

Beck's Futures Exhibition and Award
W www.becksfutures.co.uk
A total of £45,000 prize money awarded (£20,000
to the winner and the remainder between five
others). Nominations are by professional
exhibition curators, museum directors, critics and
artists from Britain and Ireland, who propose three
artists each. Run in conjunction with the ICA.

Bellagio Individual, Collaborative and Parallel Residencies

The Rockefeller Foundation, 420 Fifth Avenue, New York
NY 10018–2702, USA
E bellagio@rockfound.org
W www.rockfound.org
Provides a stimulating international environment for month-long study residencies for scholars, scientists and artists. Scholars, artists and others may apply as individual or with one collaborator who is also qualified for the residency.
Entry policy Applicants must be scholars, scientists, policymakers, practitioners or artists who expect their work at the centre to result in publication, exhibition, performance or other concrete product. Request application one year in advance of residency period.

Best of Digital Arts

Jenoptik L.O.S. GmbH - Digital Cameras, Oskar-Von-Miller-Str. 1a, Munich-Eching
85386, GERMANY
T +49 816577475
F +49 816577503
E info@eyelike.com
W www.eyelike.com
A showcase for creativity and design in all areas of photography. The website has a facility for simple submission of images.
Frequency Certificates for US$2,000, US$1,500 and US$500 for the first three winners, which can be used against purchases of equipment/services from Jenoptik.
Entry policy Check website for applications. Closing date to upload images: January.

BlindArt Prize

P.O. Box 50113, London
SW1X 9EY
T 020 72459977
F 020 72451228
E info@blindart.net
W www.blindart.net
Founded in 2004. The competition invites artists in all media to submit work specifically created for blind and partially sighted people. An exhibition is subsequently held at the Royal College of Art.

Bloomberg newcontemporaries

127F Liverpool Road, Castlefield, Manchester
M3 4JN
T 0161 8399453
F 0161 8351698
E ncinfo2004@yahoo.co.uk
W www.newcontemporaries.org.uk
An annual 'exhibition without a building' of work by students and recent graduates from the UK's art colleges. Tours major UK arts venues each year. Normally thirty-five pieces chosen from 1,200 applications.
Entry policy Selection from slides, videos, CDs, photographs and audio tapes through to a shortlist of actual works.

BOC Emerging Artist Award

International Art Consultants/Art for Offices, The Galleries, 15 Dock Street, London
E1 8JL
E laura@afo.co.uk
W www.boc.com
Launched in 2002. Supports promising young artists based in the UK with a grant of £20,000 to the winner, with additional discretionary awards of £1,000 each to runners-up. The winner's award also includes ongoing support from BOC and its art consultant, Art for Offices/International Art Consultants. The award is designed to cover a year's studio rental and materials, a travel bursary and the costs of a London-based exhibition at the end of the award period.
Entry policy Open to suitably qualified UK-based artists working in two dimensions who are under 30 years of age at the award's closing date.

BP Portrait Award

National Portrait Gallery, St Martin's Place, London
WC2H 0HE
T 0870 1126772
W www.npg.org.uk
Contact Beatrice Hosegood
An annual event aimed at encouraging young artists to focus on and develop the theme of portraiture within their work. Many artists shown have gained commissions as a result of interest in the award and resulting exhibition.
Frequency Four annual prizes. First prize of £25,000 in 2005, plus at the judges' discretion, a commission worth £4,000 to be agreed between the National Portrait Gallery and the artist.
Entry policy Open to artists from around the world, aged not under 18 and not over 40 on 1 January of the year of the competition. One entry per artist. Work entered should be a painting based on a sitting or study from life and the human figure must predominate. The work entered must be mainly painted in oil, tempera or acrylic and must be on a stretcher or board.

Braziers International Artists' Workshop

c/o 25 Lavender Grove, London
E8 3LU
T 020 72411326
E info@braziersworkshop.org
W www.braziersworkshop.org
Established in 1995 as an artist-run, non-profit-making initiative. Strives to provide a meeting point for artists working in all visual disciplines. Brings together up to thirty artists of all nationalities. Seventeen-day residential workshop.

British Council Grants to Artists Scheme

Visual Arts Department, The British Council, 11 Portland Place, London
W1N 4EJ
T 020 73893045
F 020 73893101
W www.britcoun.org/arts/index.htm
Contact Katie Boot
Designed to help promote British art by assisting professional British artists to exhibit overseas in public or commercial spaces. Artists who have received a firm invitation to exhibit overseas may apply for a grant to assist them in meeting the costs of the transport, packing and insurance of their work to and from Britain and the country concerned. Grants only give a contribution towards these costs. Artists may also apply for their own travel costs where their presence is essential. Grants are not given to assist with either the production costs of the work or framing and other preparation costs.
Entry policy Submit copy of contract/invitation from overseas galleries, and selection of six 35mm slides showing recent work. Open to British artists resident in the UK. Closing dates: usually 1 August, 1 November and 1 February.

Byard Art Open Competition

Byard Art, 4 St Mary's Passage, Cambridge
CB2 3PQ
T 01223 464646
F 01223 464655
E info@byardart.co.uk
W www.byardart.co.uk
Contact Juliet Bowmaker
Established in 1993. An annual competition with winners selected by professional panel of judges. General public invited to vote for the People's Prize.
Entry policy Open to professional artists living or working within a twenty-five-mile radius of Cambridge. Acceptable media are painting, printmaking, photography, sculpture, ceramics, textiles and glass.

Calouste Gulbenkian Foundation Awards

98 Portland Place, London
W1N 4ET
T 020 76365313
F 020 76373421
The work of the foundation is divided into programmes in arts, education and social welfare, with a separate programme for Anglo-Portuguese cultural relations. The arts programme deals with the arts for adults and young people out of formal education settings. For the past five years it has run a programme offering support to groups of professional artists to undertake short periods of experiment, which will now focus on encouraging British groups to invite international arts practitioners to participate in British or Irish-based research and development activities.
Entry policy Open to UK residents. Closing date: at least three months before project starting date.

Clark Digital Bursary

Watershed, 1 Canon's Road, Harbourside, Bristol
BS1 5TX
E info@watershed.co.uk
W www.watershed.co.uk/bursary
Awarded annually for the creative development and production of new work in digital media. These awards can be for any stage of development and/or completion of new digital work. Technical support on the winning project can be arranged at either Watershed Media Centre in Bristol or PVA Media Lab in Bridport.
Entry policy Open to artists and multimedia producers working in the south-west.

Commonwealth Arts and Crafts Award

The Commonwealth Foundation, Marlborough House, Pall Mall, London
SW1Y 5HY
T 020 79303783
F 020 78398157
W www.oneworld.org/com_fnd/
Contact Andrew Firmin
An award to enable young artists and craftspeople to learn new techniques or enhance existing skills, work with more established artists and mount an exhibition of their work in another region of the Commonwealth. Seeks to encourage sharing of artistic traditions within the Commonwealth and promote excellence in arts and crafts in Commonwealth countries. Each award covers

airfares, living expenses for up to nine months and expenses of mounting an exhibition in the host country. Preference given to talented individuals showing promise of artistic initiative, merit and achievement in their own countries and who seek opportunities for creative work with other artists and craftspeople. Participants are expected to plan, organize and manage their awards.
Frequency Biennial prize worth £6,000.
Entry policy Open to anyone aged between 22 and 25 who is a citizen of a Commonwealth country.

CORE Program

The Glassell School of Art, 5101 Montrose Boulevard, Houston
TX 77006, USA
T +1 713 6397500
W core.mfah.org/home.asp
Awards one- and two-year residencies to highly motivated, exceptional visual artists and art scholars who have graduated but have yet to develop a professional career. Established in 1982 within Glassell School of Art, the teaching wing of Houston's Museum of Fine Arts. Residents engage in ongoing dialogue with each other and with invited guests. Each artist-resident is given approximately 450 sq. ft of private studio space, twenty-four-hour access to school facilities and equipment, and a US$9,000 annual stipend.
Entry policy Send twelve slides of work (include name of artist and practical details of each piece) completed in previous two years. The selection jury views six slides from each applicant in first elimination round. The remaining six slides will only be viewed in the second round. Applicants are encouraged to number their slides 1 to 12, in order of priority. Also include a CV, statement of intent, three letters of recommendation and an sae for return of slides.

Cove Park Residency Programme

Peaton Hill, Cove, Argyll and Bute
G84 0PE
T 01436 850123
F 01436 850445
E information@covepark.org
W www.covepark.org
Contact Alexia Holt
Founded in 1999. Located on a fifty-acre site overlooking Loch Long on the west coast of Scotland. Organizes residencies for national and international artists working in all art forms. Up to seven residencies at any one time, lasting from one week to three months. The programme runs from May to October. Artists receive a fee (determined by the duration of the residency), accommodation and, when appropriate, studio space.
Frequency Up to fifty residencies each year.
Entry policy Selection is by both invitation and application. When applications are required, the residency is advertised nationally and internationally and on Cove Park's website. Requirements vary following open submission and application, depending on the form of the residency itself.

Crafts Council Grants and Lottery Unit

44a Pentonville Road, Islington, London
N1 9BX
T 020 78062509
F 020 78376891
W www.craftscouncil.org.uk
The Setting Up Scheme offers assistance with contemporary craft projects and exhibitions. Range of grants between £1,000 and £25,000.
Entry policy Application pack available from the Crafts Council. Closing dates: March, June, September and December.

Creekside Open

APT, 6 Creekside, Deptford, London
SE8 4SA
E enquiry@creeksideopen.org
W www.creeksideopen.org
Contact Liz May
Launched in 2005 to celebrate the tenth anniversary of the APT Art in Perpetuity Trust. A biannual competition for inclusion in an exhibition at the APT Gallery. Awards of £500 are given. Open to all visual/fine artists living or working in greater London.
Entry policy Entry by slide submission.

David Canter Memorial Fund

c/o Devon Guild of Craftsmen, Riverside Mill, Bovey Tracey
TQ13 9AF
T 01626 832223
F 01626 834220
E jenny@crafts.org.uk
W www.crafts.org.uk
Contact Jenny Plackett (Secretary)
Provides support for special projects, such as setting up a workshop, buying materials and equipment or for research and travel. Grants usually range between £500 and £1,000.
Entry policy Open to artists who have finished formal training, working full- or part-time.

Awards are usually made in the autumn, and the selection process falls into two stages: (1) preliminary application using the application form, for shortlisting; and (2) shortlisted applicants are asked to send further information about their work, together with six slides of recent pieces for final selection.

De Ateliers

Stadhouderskade 86, Amsterdam
1073 AT, NETHERLANDS
T +31 206739359
F +31 206755039
E office@de-ateliers.nl
W www.de-ateliers.nl
Founded in 1963. An international studio programme run by artists at a postgraduate level. Offers twenty young artists at the beginning of their professional career the opportunity to develop their work in a private studio during a maximum of two years, supported with a stipend and the critical guidance from prominent artists who do weekly individual studio visits. Tutors include Rob Birza, Dominic van den Boogerd, Marlene Dumas, Ceal Floyer, Georg Herold, Rita McBride, Steve McQueen, Willem Oorebeek, Willem de Rooij, Marien Schouten, Didier Vermeiren and Marijke van Warmerdam.
Frequency Some ten studios available annually.
Entry policy Application is possible at any time and open to young artists from Holland and abroad at the beginning of their professional career. Ability to speak English is required. Apply by sending documentation of work (slides, CDs, videotapes) and application form. Applications are selected by tutors. Main criteria are visual qualities, artistic ambitions and prospects for future development.

Dedalo Painting Award

Loc. Greppolungo 43–44, Camaiore (LU)
55051, ITALY
T +39 584984258
E info@dedaloarte.org
W www.dedaloarte.org and
www.artcoursestuscany.com
Contact Sarah Baker
Founded by artists in 1996, Dedalo Arte offers residencies primarily to painters, although equipment for ceramics and sculpture may also be available for use. The artists will be present during a season of courses and invited to talk about their work and way of working during informal discussions with fellow participants. The award has a value of around £900 and consists of a fourteen-day stay in Castelfalfi in Tuscany, with full board and shared use of a studio. Materials are not included. The artist is asked to leave behind a piece of work of their own choice.
Frequency One or two per year, during the summer.
Entry policy To apply send one photo of a recent work, a short CV and short artist statement.

Delfina Studio Trust Residencies

50 Bermondsey Street, London
SE1 3UD
T 020 73576600
E admin@delfina.org.uk
W www.delfina.org.uk
The largest residency programme in the UK, awarding studio space to as many as eighteen artists each year for periods ranging from two months to two years. Set up in 1988 as a registered charity with the aim of providing high-quality studio space and related facilities for visual artists. Housed in a renovated factory in the Bankside area of central London, it provides thirty studios in total.

Derek Hill Foundation Scholarship

The British School at Rome at the British Academy, 10 Carlton House Terrace, London
SW1Y 5AH
T 020 79695202
F 020 79695401
E bsr@britac.ac.uk
W www.bsr.ac.uk
Contact Dr Gill Clark (The Registrar)
Founded in 2004 and funded by the Derek Hill Foundation. Open to artists whose work demonstrates proficiency in drawing and who have a commitment to portrait and landscape painting. Offers full board and lodging at the British School at Rome for three or six months, with a grant of approximately £950 per month.
Frequency One each year.
Entry policy Applicants must be of British or Irish nationality and aged 24 or over on 1 September of the academic year in which the scholarship will be held. An application form must be completed. Closing date: mid-December.

Deutsche Börse Photography Prize

5 & 8 Great Newport Street, London
WC2H 7HY
T 020 78311772
F 020 78369704
E info@photonet.org.uk
W www.photonet.org.uk

Aims to reward a living photographer of any nationality who has made the most significant contribution to the medium of photography during the past year. Photographers are nominated for a significant exhibition or publication that took place in that year. Nominations are made by an academy, a diverse group of people invited by the Photographers' Gallery from photography institutions throughout Europe. From these, four shortlisted photographers are selected by a jury and invited to present their work in an exhibition at the Photographers' Gallery. The winner receives £30,000; three runners-up each receive £3,000.
Frequency An annual exhibition and award.
Entry policy Nominations can only be made by the academy, not by by individual submissions.

Deveron Arts Residency Programme
The Studio, Brander Building, The Square, Huntly
AB54 8BR
T 01466 794494
F 01466 794494
E deveronarts@aol.com
W www.deveron-arts.com
Contact Claudia Zeiske
Founded in 1995 to engage artists for short- and long-term residency programmes to work within the community, bringing contemporary art to a wide audience. Aims to work within a theme that is of local significance but also of national and even global concern. Deveron Arts has no dedicated gallery space as 'the town is the venue'.
Frequency Average of three residencies per year.
Entry policy Artists are advised to write or email for further information before submitting CVs.

Discerning Eye
Parker Harris Partnership, P.O. Box 279, Esher
KT10 8YZ
T 01372 462190
E info@parkerharris.co.uk
W www.parkerharris.co.uk
Exhibition of small works, up to 20" × 20". Covers painting, drawing and sculpture, with exhibition at the Mall Galleries in London. There is a purchase prize worth £3,000 and several prizes of £1,000.

Djerassi Resident Artists Program
2325 Bear Gulch Road, Woodside
CA 94062–4405, USA
T +1 650 7471250
F +1 650 7470105
Based in the foothills of Santa Cruz Mountains of Northern California. Visual arts studios and living quarters are located in a twelve-sided barn. The Artists' Barn also houses a choreography studio, darkroom and composers' studio. Artists pay for travel, personal needs, materials and supplies.
Frequency Residencies last for four to six weeks, from April through to October. No residency fee and all meals are provided.

East End Academy
Whitechapel Art Gallery, 80–82 Whitechapel High Street, London
E1 7QX
E info@whitechapel.org
W www.whitechapel.org
Showcases new work from emerging artists living and working in east London. Works on show range from pencil-and-ink drawings to room-sized environments, and include painting, photography, video and installation. First launched in 1932 as an open-submission exhibition for 'all artists living and working east of the famous Aldgate Pump'. There are also off-site commissions. Admission is free and most works are for sale.

East International
Norwich School of Art and Design, St George Street, Norwich
NR3 1BB
T 01603 610561
F 01603 615728
E nor.gal@nsad.ac.uk
W www.nsad.co.uk/gallery
An exhibition open to visual artists working in any medium. Each year one artist is given £5,000. Takes place at Norwich Gallery, the Fine Art Studios of Norwich School of Art and Design and the Sainsbury Centre for Visual Art at the University of East Anglia. Emphasis is on choosing artists from work submitted on slide. Now a major international open exhibition held every summer, selected by a number of distinguished curators and artists including David Tremlett, Helen Chadwick, Konrad Fischer, Marian Goodman, Rudi Fuchs and Richard Long.
Entry policy No rules of age, status, place of residence or medium to limit those who may enter. For entry form and further information contact above address.

Elephant Trust Award
512 Bankside Lofts, 65 Hopton Street, London
SE1 9GZ
T 020 79221160
F 020 79221160

E ruth@elephanttrust.org.uk
W www.elephanttrust.org.uk
Contact Ruth Rattenbury
Founded in 1975. Aims to make it possible for artists and those presenting their work to complete projects when frustrated by lack of funds. Bias towards the visual arts; particularly interested in funding projects that depart from the routine and signal distinct and imaginative sets of possibilities. Value of awards usually about £2,000.
Frequency The trustees meet four times a year to consider applications and decide on awards.
Entry policy Grants not available for students or for educational and other study purposes.

Elizabeth Foundation for the Arts

P.O. Box 2670, New York
NY 10108, USA
T +1 212 5635855
F +1 212 5631875
E grants@efa1.org
Offers a grants programme for individuals in the visual arts. Selection is based on quality of work, financial need, background and dedication to career, and proposals for use of grant. Grant amounts range from US$2,500 and US$12,000 and are targeted to assist artists in creating new work and/or gaining recognition for work. Twelve to fifteen grants awarded per year. Applicant pool averages one thousand applications. Previous grantees not eligible to apply for five years following their grant periods.
Entry policy Open to artists in all media except photography, video/film and crafts. Must be over 30 or have been working for at least six years since completing formal schooling. Closing date: 1 May.

Elizabeth Greenshields Foundation Grants

1814 Sherbrooke Street West, Suite #1, Montreal, Quebec
H3H 1E4, Canada
T +1 514 9379225
F +1 514 9370141
E egreen@total.net
Contact Micheline Leduc (Administrator)
Grants for artists in early stages of career, working in painting, drawing, printmaking and sculpture. Work must be representational or figurative. The award of C$10,000 is tenable anywhere in the world and may be used for any art-related purpose.
Entry policy Applicants must have started or already completed art-school training and/or demonstrate through past work and future plans a commitment to making art a lifetime career.

Erna & Victor Hasselblad Foundation Awards and Bursaries

Ekmansgatan 8, Göteborg
SE-412 56, Sweden
An international photography award selected by jury (no applications accepted). Also stipends and research grants for photographic research and scholarly projects. Bias towards research in photographic theory and history, scientific photography, conservation and restoration of photographic material and experimental projects.
Entry policy Open to photographers, researchers and other professionals working primarily within the field of still photography. Open to all nationalities. Closing date: usually March.

European Association for Jewish Culture Grants

London Office, 79 Wimpole Street, London
W1G 9RY
T 020 79358266
F 020 79353252
E london@jewishcultureineurope.org
W www.jewishcultureineurope.org
Grants in performing and visual arts.
Entry policy Priority given to individual artists, presenters, scholars or small groups. Applicants must be European nationals or long-term residents. Record of artistic or scholarly achievement must be appended to application. Application forms available on website.

European Award for Women Photographers

Dryphoto, CP 1024, Via Pugliesi 23, Prato
I-59100, Italy
T +39 574604939
F +39 574444508
E dryphoto@po-net.prato.it
Started in 1995 and open to all females resident in Europe who use the photographic medium as an expressive instrument of artistic research. Prize worth 2,500.

Federation of British Artists (FBA)

Mall Galleries, 17 Carlton House Terrace, London
SW1Y 5BD
T 020 79306844
F 020 78397830
E info@mallgalleries.com
W www.mallgalleries.org.uk
Of nine member art societies, eight hold their annual open exhibitions in the Mall Galleries. Any artist may submit work for selection. Work for exhibition is selected by a committee of members from the society where work has been submitted.

Entry policy See website or send sae (35p) to Mall Galleries for full details. Indicate the relevant society and address to 'Entry Details' at the above address. A maximum of six works may be entered.

Feiweles Trust
Yorkshire Sculpture Park, West Bretton, Wakefield
WF4 4LG
Established in 1989, supporting work in schools and the community by artists at the beginning of their careers. A sculpture bursary in the region of £10,000 is awarded to a sculptor to work with schools and the community for approximately one hundred days. Some preliminary planning work will need to be undertaken before the bursary begins. It is expected that the appointed artist will use this bursary experience to develop their own artistic practice.

Florence Trust Residencies
St Saviour's, Aberdeen Park, London
N5 2AR
T 020 73540460
W www.florencetrust.org
Established in 1988, offering eleven residencies for artists' professional development (including business planning, marketing, interview and presentation skills and applying to other trusts and foundations for funding) and production of new work. Housed in grade-1-listed Victorian church.
Frequency Annual, lasting twelve months.
Entry policy Closing date: normally June.

Franklin Furnace Fund for Performance Art and Franklin Furnace Future of the Present
80 Hanson Place #301, Brooklyn
NY 11217, USA
T +1 212 3987255
F +1 212 3987256
E mail@franklinfurnace.org
W www.franklinfurnace.org
Contact Dolores Zorreguieta
An avant-garde arts organization founded in 1976. The Fund for Performance Art (supported by Jerome Foundation and the New York State Council on the Arts) awards grants of between US$2,000 and US$5,000 to emerging performance artists, allowing them to produce major works in the New York area. Artists from all areas of the world are invited to apply. The Future of the Present awards artists an honorarium and offers its resources to facilitate the creation of 'live art on the Internet'. Open to artists worldwide.

Frequency Around ten awards per year.
Entry policy See website for full details.

Friends of Israel Young Artists Award
P.O. Box 7545, London
NW2 2QZ
T 020 74356803
F 020 77940291
E info@foi-asg.org
W www.foi-asg.org
Contact John Levy
The award consists of return air passage to Israel, a minimum of six weeks' work on a kibbutz with time for painting/art instruction by the award winner, a ten-day placement at the Bezalel School of Art in Jerusalem, and free time to travel around the country and an exhibition.
Entry policy Open to British students graduating from art school: painters, printmakers and illustrators are invited to apply. Send a CV, academic letter of reference, statement of reasons for wishing to visit Israel and a representative selection of work (transparencies to be submitted initially). Closing date: 1 May each year.

Friends of the Royal Scottish Academy Artist Bursary
The RSA, The Mound, Edinburgh
EH2 2EL
T 0131 2253922
F 0131 2206016
E friends@royalscottishacademy.org
W www.royalscottishacademy.org
Founded in 1995 to enable artists to continue and extend their creative development. The bursary will assist in the cost of a specific developmental project such as travel or research, attending a course or workshop, or to supplement or replace income in order to permit a period of exploration and experimentation. Worth £2,000.
Frequency Annual.
Entry policy Applications invited from artists permanently resident in Scotland, qualified and working within the disciplines of the RSA (painting, drawings, sculpture, architecture and printmaking). Must have completed full-time education (including postgraduate study) at least three years beforehand. Strong preference to those over 35 years old or working professionally for ten years or more. Closing date: 1 July.

Gen Foundation
45 Old Bond Street, London
W1X 2AQ

T 020 74955564
F 020 74954450
E info@genfoundation.org.uk
Provides substantial scholarships and grants to
students and scholars from a broad cross-section
of fields. Aims to further academic research in
both the humanities and natural sciences by
awarding grants to candidates from a variety
of disciplines. In recognition of the importance of
crosscultural exchange in today's global society,
also aims to deepen understanding between Japan
and the rest of the world. Scholarships are one-off,
non-renewable grants of approximately £2,000.
Entry policy The foundation will make preliminary
selection of candidates on the basis of submitted
application forms, then conduct interviews.
Scholarships are awarded annually to candidates
mainly from the UK and Japan.

George Campbell Memorial Travel Grant

Visual Arts Department, The Arts Council of
Northern Ireland, MacNeice House, 77 Malone
Road, Belfast
BT9 6AQ
T 028 90385200
F 028 90661715
W www.artscouncil-ni.org
Instituted to celebrate the strong cultural contact
that the Irish artist George Campbell developed in
Spain. Funded by the Arts Council of Northern
Ireland, the Arts Council/An Chomhairle Ealaíon
and the Instituto Cervantes, and made specifically
to allow for a period of work in Spain.
Frequency One award normally made each year.
Administered on alternate years by the two Arts
Councils.

Getty Grant Program

1200 Getty Center Drive, Suite 800, Los Angeles
CA 90049–1685, USA
T +1 310 4407320
F +1 310 4407703
W www.getty.edu
Provides support to institutions and individuals
throughout the world for projects that promote the
understanding of art and its history and the
conservation of cultural heritage. Projects are
sought that set high standards and provide
opportunities for collaboration.

Gilchrist-Fisher Memorial Award

c/o Rebecca Hossack Gallery, 35 Windmill Street,
London
W1P 1HH

T 020 74364899
F 020 73233182
E rebecca@r-h-g.co.uk
W www.r-h-g.co.uk
Established in 1987 in memory of Alasdair
Gilchrist-Fisher who died of cancer in December
1986 at the age of 24. For work with landscape art
as the broad theme. First prize of £3,000; £1,000
for runner-up. Winner's work is also exhibited at
the Rebecca Hossack Gallery.
Entry policy Applications are invited from artists
under 30 years of age, particularly graduates.
Closing date: usually June.

Global Arts Village

Utsav Mandir, Ghitorni, Mehrauli-Gurgoan Road,
New Delhi
110030, INDIA
T +91 1155657265 / 1126804790
E info@globalartsvillage.com
W www.globalartsvillage.com
Contact Julie Upmeyer
Residencies offered at the Village, an emerging
art centre in New Delhi. Open to emerging,
mid-career and established artists. Encourages
diversity and multicultural exchange among
creative people of all kinds. Practices community
living, sharing meals and evening activities on a
three-acre property that includes: gardens;
ceramics, sculpture and two-dimensional studios;
a meditation hall; a common building; dance
studio; performance spaces; and accommodation.
Caters for studio ceramics, sculpture, photography,
Ikebana, digital arts, arts management, land art,
fibre arts, installation art and public art. Offers five
different types of residency; details on website.
Entry policy Applications to include: a completed
residency application; documentation of creative
work in the form of digital photos attached to an
email; thin frame slides or photographs (twelve
maximum); a brief description of the project (two
hundred words maximum); a brief explanation of
why the project is especially suited to the Village
and India (two hundred words maximum).

Gunk Foundation Grants for Public Arts Projects

P.O. Box 333, Gardiner
NY 12525, USA
T +1 914 2558252
F +1 914 2558252
E gunk@mhv.net
W www.gunk.org
Contact Nadine Lemmon

Provides grants to individuals and organizations as well as national and international projects. At present, concentrating on supporting production of non-traditional public-art projects. Interested in supporting projects that move out into the spaces of daily life. Also favours projects that reach a non-traditional art audience. Likely range of grants is between US$1,000 and US$5,000.

Entry policy Applications in writing. Hesitant to fund production of video or film unless specifically earmarked for public space (such as public-access television or outdoor screenings).

Henry Moore Sculpture Fellowship

The British School at Rome, Via Gramsci 61, Rome 00197, ITALY
T +39 63264939
F +39 63221201
E bsr@britac.ac.uk
W www.bsr.ac.uk
The fellowship at the British School at Rome is funded by the Henry Moore Foundation. Awarded to established sculptors to enable them to spend three months in Rome. Offers a spacious studio with en-suite facilities, board and accommodation at the school, along with a grant of £2,000 per month.
Frequency Annual.
Entry policy Open to Commonwealth and UK citizens.

Hunting Art Prize

Parker Harris Partnership, P.O. Box 279, Esher KT10 8YZ
T 01372 462190
F 01372 460032
E Hap@parkerharris.co.uk
Seven cash prizes for first and second prize, Young Artist (under 25), Runner Up (under 25), Print & Drawing, Most Popular Painting and Outstanding Regional Entry. Worth between £500 and £12,000. Shortlisted candidates shown at a London exhibition.
Entry policy Send sae for entry information.

Iceland, Ministry of Culture and Education Residencies

Solvholsgata 4, Reykjavik
15–150, ICELAND
T +354 5609500
F +354 5623068
Offers artists' studios and residencies to artists from other countries working across various art forms. Travel assistance is not included.

Inches Carr Trust Craft Bursaries

The Inches Carr Trust, 2 Greenhill Park, Edinburgh
EH10 4DW
T 0131 4474847
F 0131 4469520
W www.inchescarr.org
Annual awards to craft workers based in Scotland with a minimum of five years' experience in their craft. Each award is £4,000, to enable the applicant to develop a specific aspect of their work or to undertake a specific project.
Frequency Annual. Maximum of three awards per year.
Entry policy Provide a description of current work, the specific project or aspect for development proposed, and a CV. Closing date: end April.

Indigo Art Prize

Indigo Art Ltd, Brunswick Place, Liverpool
L20 8DT
T 0115 9339779
F 0151 9221524
E kaye@indigoart.co.uk
W www.indigoart.co.uk
Contact Kaye Kent
Founded in 1994. Aimed at professional artists currently practising in the UK. Sponsored by Indigo Art Ltd, suppliers of bespoke art work to the hotel and leisure industry. Opportunity for artists to gain exposure to major interior-design projects, commissions and publishing. £2,000 goes to the winning artist, with £500 each to the runners-up. All entrants are considered for inclusion in the Indigo Collection, a range of published images for contemporary interiors.
Frequency Annual.
Entry policy Refer to website for details of how to enter. Submissions accepted from 1 September.

International Artists' Centre, Poland – Miedzynarodowe Centrum Sztuki

ul. Jackowskiego 5/7, Poznan
60–508, POLAND
T +48 618483777
E artistscentre@dialcom.com.pl
W www.dialcom.com.pl/artistscentre
Residencies open to all artists from various disciplines and cultural backgrounds. Usually last three months.

J.D. Fergusson Arts Award

The Fergusson Gallery, Marshall Place, Perth
PH2 8NU

T 01738 443505
E museum@pkc.gov.uk
W www.perthshire.com
Contact Jenny Kinnear
Inaugural award presented in 1997. Aims to
support artists who have shown a high level of
commitment but have not yet received any awards
or recognition. Value in the region of £2,500.
Frequency Annual award, alternating year-on-year
between an exhibition award and a travel bursary.
Entry policy Artists who are Scottish by birth or
have spent over half their life in Scotland and have
not won any major awards. Closing date: 31 October.

James Milne Memorial Trust

Scottish Trade Union Congress, Middleton House,
333 Woodlands Road, Glasgow
G3 6NG
T 0141 3378100
F 0141 3378101
Grants open to Scots aged 26 and under of
outstanding talent, based in Scotland and who will
be able to extend their skills by a period of study
out of the UK. Study may be formal or informal.
Frequency Annual.

Japan Foundation Fellowship Program

ARK Mori Building 1–12–32, Akaska Minato-ku,
Tokyo
107, JAPAN
T +81 355623511
F +81 355623494
W www.jpf.go.jp
Provides scholars, researchers, artists and other
professionals with opportunities to learn more
about Japan and its people and to conduct research
or pursue creative projects in Japan. Grants are
available for two to six months.
Frequency Monthly stipends plus round-trip
airfare.
Entry policy Recipients of the fellowship are not
eligible to reapply until a full three years have
passed.

Jerwood Applied Arts Prize

Crafts Council, 44a Pentonville Road, London
N1 9BY
T 020 7278 7700
F 020 7837 6891
E reference@craftscouncil.org.uk
W www.craftscouncil.org.uk
Contact Aravec Clarke (Exhibitions Officer –
Touring)
Founded in 1995 and presented in collaboration

with the Crafts Council and the Jerwood Charity.
The most prestigious and significant prize in the
applied and decorative arts. Now in its eleventh
year, it covers six categories: metal, jewelry,
ceramics, textiles, glass and furniture. Prize worth
£30,000.
Frequency Annual: metal 2005, jewelry 2006,
ceramics 2007, textiles 2008, glass 2009,
furniture 2010.
Entry policy Entry requirements on website from
November/December. Shortlisting in February
and exhibition in September. Award presented end
September. The exhibition then tours the UK for
one year (four venues plus Crafts Council Gallery
in London). Open to artists, makers and designers.

Jerwood Drawing Prize

Wimbledon School of Art, Merton Hall Road,
London
SW19 3QA
T 020 8408 5533
F 020 8408 5050
E jerwood@wimbledon.ac.uk
W www.wimbledon.ac.uk/jerwood
Contact Clare Mitten or Rose Heelas
Aims to promote and reward talent and
excellence in contemporary drawing. Every year,
a changing panel of distinguished artists, writers,
critics, collectors and curators select the show
independently, defining their own priorities for
an exhibition of current drawing practice.
Frequency Prizes awarded yearly. First prize of
£5,000; second prize of £3,000; third prize of
£2,000. Student prizes of £500 each.
Entry policy Open to artists resident or domiciled
in the UK.

Jerwood Painting Prize

Parker Harris Partnership, 15 Church Street, Esher
KT10 8QS
T 01372 462190
F 01372 460032
E info@parkerharris.co.uk
W www.jerwood.org
Established in 1994 and, at £30,000, the largest
award given to a single artist in this country for
painting. As well as acknowledging the work of
established artists it has also identified lesser-
known artists.

Jerwood Sculpture Prize

Parker Harris Partnership, 15 Church Street, Esher
KT10 8QS
T 01372 462190

F 01372 460032
E info@parkerharris.co.uk
W www.jerwood.org
A commissioning award for a piece of outdoor sculpture for the Jerwood Sculpture Park. Founded in 2002. Commission worth £25,000.
Entry policy Open to all artists within fifteen years of graduation from a recognized art school. Sculptors are asked to submit drawings, written statements and plans detailing their ideas for the commission.

John Kinross Bequest
Each winning student receives financial assistance to visit and study in Florence for three months, as well as to take a language class while there.
Entry policy Open to students of fine art or architecture from Scotland, in their final or postgraduate years of study, presenting work that would normally relate to their fourth and fifth years. Application forms via heads of department at colleges and art schools in Scotland.

John Moores Exhibition
The Exhibition Assistant, Walker Art Gallery, William Brown Street, Liverpool
L3 8EL
T 0151 4784103
F 0151 4784190
E johnmoores24@liverpoolmuseums.org.uk
W www.liverpoolmuseums.org.uk/walker/johnmoores/
Biennial open exhibition of contemporary British paintings. Artists are invited to submit one painting for display at the Walker Art Gallery. First prize of £25,000 in cash; ten smaller prizes also awarded. The first-prize-winning work is added to the Walker Collection. Previous winners include John Hoyland, Bruce McLean, Lisa Milroy, Peter Doig and Michael Raedecker.
Entry policy For entry form and further information send sae. Handling fee payable on request of an entry form. First phase judged on slides and second phase on actual work.

Kettle's Yard Artist Fellowship and Kettle's Yard Open
Castle Street, Cambridge
CB3 0AQ
T 01223 352124
F 01223 324377
E mail@kettlesyard.cam.ac.uk
W www.kettlesyard.co.uk
Contact Elizabeth Fisher

An artist fellow, normally appointed annually, gets a stipend, studio space and accommodation in Cambridge, and every two years there is an exhibition open to artists in the east of England. Contact Kettle's Yard directly as the nature of the opportunities can vary greatly.

Künstlerinnenhof Die Höge
Högenhausen 2, Bassum
D - 27211, GERMANY
T +49 424993030
F +49 4249930344
E info@hoege.org
W www.hoege.org
Launched an artist-in-residence programme in June 2000, the first of its kind in Europe. Women scholars as well as women artists from all areas of the arts are invited to work experimentally in multimedia. A former farmstead serves as an atelier, forum and common stage for women artists working professionally in the areas of the fine arts, music, literature, multimedia, performance, theatre and dance, and a field station for academic research by women scholars.
Entry policy A jury of three to four members choose the participants, who receive grants to reside at the Höge for one to nine months.

Lady Artists Club Trust Award
McGrigor Donald Solicitors, 70 Wellington Street, Glasgow
G2 6SB
T 0141 2486677
E enquiries@mcgrigors.com
W www.mcgrigors.com
For women artists who either live within thirty-five miles from Glasgow city centre or were born, educated or trained in Glasgow. Students not eligible to apply.

Laing Solo
Laing Art Gallery, New Bridge Street, Newcastle-upon-Tyne
NE1 4JA
T 0191 2327734
F 0191 2220952
E laing@twmuseums.org.uk
W www.twmuseums.sorg.uk/laing
Contact Natalie Frost
A national competition for emerging artists.

Leverhulme Trust Grants and Awards
1 Pemberton Row, London
EC4A 3BG

T 020 78225220
F 020 78225084
E gdupin@leverhulme.ac.uk
W www.leverhulme.org.uk
Established in 1925 at the wish of William Hesketh Lever, the first Viscount Leverhulme. The trust provides academic and education research grants across the UK. In the area of performing and fine arts, there are grants available in the following schemes: artists-in-residence; training and professional development; education.
Entry policy New guidelines published annually accompanied by new application forms and all applicants need to ensure that they use both. Closing dates: vary from scheme to scheme. Study website before applying.

Lexmark European Art Prize

E lexmarkart@redconsultancy.com
W www.lexmark-europe.com/euro-art/gb
The first ever painting prize to be launched on a yearly pan-European basis. Aims to identify and bring to the fore the most exciting, but as yet undiscovered, artistic talent in Europe. Worth 30,000.
Frequency Annual.

Limassol Studios (Cyprus) Residencies

c/o Cyprus College of Art, P.O. Box 304, Leeds
LS6 3YN
T 0113 2743287
F 07092 194514
E enquiries@artcyprus.org
W www.limassolstudios.org
Contact Michael Paraskos
The Limassol Studios were founded in 2001 as an offshoot to the long-established Cyprus College of Art. Offers an opportunity for professional artists and recent graduates to spend an extended period of time making art on the southern European island of Cyprus, and offers artists studio space and living accommodation for periods ranging from one month to a year. The studios are located in the heart of the Old Town area of Limassol, near the medieval castle, cathedral, mosque and hamam. The studio space is simple but is suitable for most art practices, including painting, sculpture, photography, printmaking and some digital work.
Frequency Up to ten at any one time. Artists must be self-funding.
Entry policy Artists should apply directly via the online form on the website. Any additional information required will be requested after this.

London Photographic Awards

23 Roehampton Lane, London
SW15 5LS
T 020 83928557
E kevin@london-photographic-awards.com
W www.london-photographic-awards.com
Contact Kevin O'Connor
Founded in 1997. Started life as an annual international competition for professional, fine-art and keen amateur photographers. Designed to address the breadth of photography's creative potential and the abundance of developments in the medium worldwide.
Frequency Competitions are on an ongoing basis. Approximately nine per year.
Entry policy All entries as jpegs through website.

Manchester Academy of Fine Arts Open

c/o The Portico Library & Gallery, 57 Mosley Street, Manchester
M2 3HY
E secretary@mafa.org.uk
W www.mafa.org.uk
The academy holds an annual open exhibition. Invites submissions from painters, sculptors and printmakers. Prizes range up to £2,000.
Entry policy No restriction on style or subject.

Max Mara Art Prize for Women

Stephanie Churchill PR, 15–17 Huntsworth Mews, London
NW1 6DD
T 020 72986530
F 020 77064730
A prize for female artists, sponsored by the Italian fashion house.

Milliken Brothers Award

Visual Arts Department, The Arts Council of Northern Ireland, MacNeice House, 77 Malone Road, Belfast
BT9 6AQ
T 028 90385200
F 028 90661715
W www.artscouncil-ni.org
An award to enable an artist to develop a body of work prior to an exhibition that may be of significance to the applicant's career. Established by the Arts Council of Northern Ireland, the Arts Council/An Chomhairle Ealaíon and Milliken Brothers, stretched-canvas-makers and suppliers of fine-art materials. Offers £1,000 in kind for the purchase of fine-art materials.
Frequency Annual.

Monagri Foundation Residency

Archangelos Monastery, Monagri
CY-4746, CYPRUS
T +357 5434165
F +357 5434166
E info@mongri.org.cy
W www.monagri.org.cy
The Monagri Foundation invites artists from
all disciplines and nationalities to apply for a
residency. Artists should be prepared to make an
appropriate contribution to the development of
the arts in Cyprus by giving lectures, holding
workshops or other communal activities. Typically
residencies last from two to three weeks to a year.

Montana Artists' Refuge Residency Program

Box 8, Basin, Montana
MT 59631, USA
T +1 406 2253500
F +1 406 2259225
E mtrefuge@earthlink.net
An artist-run residency programme located near
the Continental Divide. Founded in 1993 by four
local artists and area residents to provide living
and work space to artists in all media. Mission is
to further the creative work of artists, to create
residencies for artists, and to provide arts
programmes and art education for both artists and
community members.
Frequency Residencies last three months to one
year (year-round). Only two artists present at a
time.
Entry policy Accepts applications from visual
artists in arts and crafts, book art, ceramics,
clay/pottery, drawing, fibre/textile, film-/video-
making, folk art, installation, jewelry, mixed
media, painting, paper art, photography, and
sculpture. To request application form, send sae.
Closing date: August for winter residencies
(January to March). Applications for other months
accepted on ongoing basis.

Mostyn Open

12 Heol Vaughan, Llandudno
LL30 1AB
T 01492 879201
F 01492 878869
E post@mostyn.org
W www.mostyn.org
Open to artists working in any medium. There is a
prize of £6,000 but selectors reserve the right to
split the prize money if appropriate.
Entry policy No geographical or age restrictions;
size limitations depend on available gallery space.

National Art Library Illustration Awards

Victoria & Albert Museum, Cromwell Road,
London
SW7 2RL
T 020 79422392
E villa@vam.ac.uk
W www.vam.ac.uk/activ_events/events/
illustration_awards/index.html
Contact Annemarie Riding
The National Art Library at the V&A has offered
awards for professional illustration since 1972.
Originally called the Francis Williams Awards
(1972–1982), after their benefactor, they became
annual in 1987. Prizes up to £2,500 in four
categories: Book Illustration; Book Cover and
Jacket Illustration; Editorial Illustration; Student
Illustrator of the Year. Display of the winning
entries is hosted at the V&A.
Entry policy Open to currently practising
illustrators whose work has been published
nationally in the previous year. Send for entry
form. Closing date: usually July.

National Endowment for Science, Technology and the Arts (NESTA)

Fishmongers' Chambers, 110 Upper Thames
Street, London
EC4B 4AQ
T 020 76459638
F 020 76469501
E nesta@nesta.org.uk
W www.nesta.org.uk
NESTA's purpose is to support and promote talent,
innovation and creativity in the fields of science,
technology and the arts. Primary activity is the
support of individuals, rather than organizations,
existing businesses or projects. Each fellow is
supported for between three to five years and
receives a support package of between £25,000 to
£75,000 over the term of the fellowship.
Frequency Fifty to a hundred projects funded each
year.
Entry policy Open to UK residents or
organizations (registered in the UK for three
years). Under-18s must be sponsored by an adult.
Applications assessed throughout year. Forms
available on website or on disk.

National Museum of Women in the Arts (NMWA) Library Fellows Programme

Library and Research Centre, National Museum
of Women in the Arts, 1250 New York Avenue,
N.W. Washington
2000 DC, USA

T +1 202 7835000
F +1 202 3933235
W www.nmwa.org
Contact Leah R. Davis (Library Assistant)
Aims to encourage and promote the art of the
book. Provides funds for creation of new artists'
books by book artists or artists of other media
interested in creating a book. Each year, one
proposal is selected and funding provided for its
creation.
Entry policy The artist responsible for the overall
creation, design and realization of the book must
be a woman. Technical assistance or literary
collaboration in developing the book edition
by both women and men is acceptable.
Only new books considered. Closing date:
31 December.

Nordic Institute for Contemporary Art (NIFCA)

Suomenlinna B 28, Helsinki
FIN-00190, FINLAND
T +358 968643103
F +358 9668594
E residencies@nifca.org
W www.nifca.org
A joint Nordic institution run by the five Nordic
countries (Denmark, Finland, Iceland, Norway
and Sweden) through the Nordic Council for
Ministers. Aim of residency programme is to
promote the mobility of artists and production
of contemporary art by providing work and
accommodation facilities to selected artists in a
foreign country for two to six months. Grant
available for students' rent and living expenses of
840 per month.
Entry policy Applications not accepted from
students. Application can be for a particular
studio or for two different ones, and must contain
a completed, signed application form, CV (on one
sheet) and three slides (or video/CD).

Paisley Art Institute Prizes

c/o 4 Mount Charles House, 36 Mount Charles
Crescent, Ayr
KA7 4NY
E gesso.clark@virgin.net
W www.paisleyartinstitute.org.uk
Paisley Art Institute founded in 1876.
Frequency Drawing competition held every
two years (prizes over £1,000). Other prizes
awarded at annual exhibition (sculpture £500;
painting £1,000; various other awards totalling
£2,000).

Paul Hamlyn Foundation

Sussex House, 12 Upper Mall, London
W6 9TA
T 020 72273500
F 020 72220601
E phf@globalnet.co.uk
Grants usually awarded to large national
institutions, tending not to exceed £25,000.
Categories covered by the foundation are:
General Arts Grants; Increasing Awareness of the
Arts; Art in Education; and Individual Artists.
Entry policy Open to UK citizens. Apply in writing.
Also by nomination.

Pepinières Européennes Pour Jeunes Artistes

Patrice Bonnaffé, BP 13 9/11 rue Paul Leplat, Marly
le Roi cedex
78164, FRANCE
T +33 139171100
F +33 139171109
E info@art4eu.net
W www.art4eu.net
Contact Andrea Cooke, 62 Gabriels Road, London
NW2 4SA; telephone on 020 8450 8257 or fax on
020 8450 8257.
Running for ten years. Offers residencies
for emerging artists to aid advancement and
professional development. The Map Programme is
intended for emerging artists between 20 and 35
years old who are starting their career. The artist is
associated with a professional organization, a city
representative and a coordinator and stays for a
period of three to nine months in a hosting
organization of their choice. Artists in Context –
Artists against Exclusion is intended for artists
aged 18 to 25, taking place in the framework of
European voluntary service. Allows for an artistic
project focused on social realities to be carried out
during a six-month period.
Entry policy Open to artists between 18 and 35
living in a country hosting a Pepinière. Send sae
(A4 size) to request application form.

Pilar Juncosa and Sotheby's Awards

Fundació Pilar I Joan Miró a Mallorca, Joan de
Saridakis 29, Palma, Mallorca
07015 SPAIN
T +34 71701420
F +34 71702102
E premibeques@fpjmiro.org
W www.a-palma.es/fpjmiro
An annual prize for works of art/installations
created for the area of Fundació Pilar i Joan Miró a

Mallorca known as the Cubic Space. The jury gives priority to artistic value of projects entered, technical skills and any other innovative or experimental aspect they deem important. Total of 24,000 awarded to winning project: 12,000 for the project itself, which must later be mounted in the Cubic Space during the following twelve months; and up to 12,000 for the actual creation of the project, following the presentation of a cost estimate. There are also Pilar Juncosa Grants for training, experimentation and creative work in the foundation's graphic art workshops and other grants available (see website).

Entry policy Artists may present one creative project or work designed for the Cubic Space. The project/work must be original and the only one of its kind. Works previously exhibited or entered in other competitions will not be admitted.

Pizza Express Prospects

T 020 78612424
W www.pizzaexpress.co.uk/prospects.htm
Founded in 1999 to recognize the talents of both emerging and established artists and to promote drawing under its widest definition. First prize is worth £10,000 and there is a special student recognition prize of £2,000.

Polish Cultural Institute

34 Portland Place, London
W1N 4HQ
T 020 76366032
F 020 76372190
E pci-lond@pcidir.demon.co.uk
Contact Mrs Aleksandra Czapiewska
The Polish Minister of Culture, in association with the British Council, offers two-week study visits to Poland for people in the field of theatre, dance, music, visual arts, literature, literary translation, conservation of cultural heritage, architecture, musicology, film and photography. Successful applicants are provided with accommodation, per diems and local transportation. The sending country or visitor is expected to pay travel expenses to and from both capitals.

Entry policy Open to UK citizens and residents. Apply in writing. Proposals to be made at least eight weeks in advance to the institution in their own country.

Pollock-Krasner Foundation

863 Park Avenue, New York
NY 10021, USA

T +1 212 5175400
F +1 212 2882836
E grants@pkf.org
W www.pkf.org
Contact Caroline Black (Program Officer)
Established in 1985 to provide financial assistance to individual artists of established ability (painters, sculptors and artists who work on paper). Grants range from US$1,000 to US$30,000.

Entry policy Applications from commercial artists, photographers, video artists, filmmakers, craftsmakers or any artist whose work primarily falls into these categories will not be accepted. The foundation does not make grants to students nor fund academic study. No grants to pay for past debts, legal fees, purchase of real estate, moves to other cities or installation costs, commissions or projects ordered by others. With few exceptions, will not fund travel expenses. Dual criteria for grants are recognizable artistic merit and financial need, whether professional, personal or both. Applications encouraged from artists with genuine financial needs, not necessarily catastrophic. Grants intended for one-year period. Will consider need of applicant for all legitimate expenditures relating to their professional work, personal living and medical expenses. Size and length of grant determined by individual circumstances. Applications year-round.

Queen Elizabeth Scholarship Trust

The Secretary, No. 1 Buckingham Place, London
SW1E 6HR
W www.qest.org.uk
Makes annual craft awards to fund further study, training and practical experience for men and women who want to improve their craft or trade skills. Grants between £2,000 and £15,000. Winners also receive emblazoned certificate and engraved sterling silver medal. The trust looks for well-thought-out proposals that will contribute to excellence in modern and traditional British crafts.

Frequency Scholarships awarded twice a year, in spring and autumn.

Entry policy No age limit. Need to be able to demonstrate a high level of skill and show firm committment to craft or trade. Scholarships not awarded for buying or leasing equipment or premises or for funding courses in general further education. Must live and work in UK to be eligible for a scholarship. Forms downloadable from website or send A4 sae.

Rencontres D'Arles Awards

10 Rond-Point des Arenes, Arles
13200, FRANCE
T +33 490967606
F +33 4900499439
E prix@rencontres-arles.com
W www.rencontres-arles.com
Contact Prune Blachere
Founded in 2002. Five 10,000 awards per year:
Book Award, Discovery Award, Outreach Award,
Project Assistance Grant, No Limit Award.
Entry policy Qualified international jury
determines an artist in each category except for
the Book Award, which is open to all comers.

Rootstein Hopkins Foundation Grants

Rootstein Hopkins Foundation, P.O. Box 14720,
London
W3 7ZG
T 020 73812557
E info@rhfoundation.org.uk
W www.rhfoundation.org.uk
The foundation offers financial support to artists,
art students, lecturers and designers in the form
of travel grants, support grants, sabbatical awards,
mature student grants and exchanges. The trustees
will choose candidates who they feel will make the
best use of the grants to further their careers, and
who can present a plan that seems likely to be
realized within the grant period.
Entry policy Open to British passport-holders only.

Royal British Society of Sculptors

108 Old Brompton Road, London
SW7 3RA
T 020 73738615
F 020 73703721
E info@rbs.org.uk
W www.rbs.org.uk
Hosts annual bursary and bronze-casting award
exhibitions.

Royal Over-Seas League (ROSL) ARTS Scholarships

Over-Seas House, Park Place, St James's Street,
London
SW1A 1LR
T 020 7408 0214 ext.324
F 020 7499 6738
E culture@rosl.org.uk
W www.roslarts.co.uk
Since 2000, five travel scholarships available
each year for artists selected from five
different Commonwealth countries (or former

Commonwealth countries), one each from Africa,
the Americas, Asia, Australasia and Europe.
Artists make a study visit to a country other than
their country of origin, and participate in the ROSL
Annual Exhibition at Over-Seas House in London
and Over-Seas House in Edinburgh. Countries and
regions change each year.
Entry policy Artists must be under 35 years old.
Entry by application form and slide submission,
video (ten minutes and video artists only). Will
consider work in any medium. Application forms
available online or from above address.

Royal West of England Academy (RWA) Student Bursaries

Queens Road, Clifton, Bristol
BS8 1PX
T 0117 9735129
F 0117 9237874
E rwa@rwa.org
The council of the RWA offers two bursaries of
£1,000 each to students in the final year of their
degree course in painting, printmaking, sculpture
or architecture. Postgraduate students in their first
year are also eligible to apply.
Entry policy Closing date: March.

Royal Scottish Academy Alastair Salvesen Art Scholarship

The Competitions Office, Royal Scottish Academy,
The Mound, Edinburgh
EH2 2EL
T 0131 2256671
F 0131 2206016
E info@royalscottishacademy.org
W www.royalscottishacademy.org
Contact Pauline Costigane (Assistant
Administrative Secretary)
A major initiative intended to encourage young
professional painters. Alastair Salvesen is one of
Scotland's foremost benefactors and has offered a
three- to six-month travel scholarship in association
with the RSA since 1989. The £10,000 scholarship
is accompanied by a solo exhibition at the RSA.
Frequency Annual.
Entry policy Open to Scottish painters aged 25 to 35,
currently living and working in Scotland, who have
been trained at any of Scotland's colleges of art but
have worked away from a student environment for
at least three years. Closing date: January.

Royal Society of Arts Art for Architecture Scheme

The Administrator, 8 John Adam Street, London
WC2N 6EZ

T 020 74516871
F 020 78395805
E alex.lucas@rsa.org.uk
W www.rsa.org.uk
Two types of grant offered. Project grants, ranging from £2,000 to £15,000, cover design fees of artists working directly with one other design professional (e.g. architect, landscape architect or engineer) on building projects using new technologies (electronic and digital media, virtual space, etc.). Publications grants are given for publications that significantly address issues and practice relating to collaboration between artists, architects and other design professionals; these may be used to underwrite all or part of publication costs. There should be evidence that publication will be of high standard in both content and production. Not intended for distribution costs, but a detailed strategy regarding distribution is required.
Entry policy Contact Art for Architecture office to discuss project before submitting application. Advisory panel meets three times a year.

Ruth Davidson Memorial Scholarship
RDAM – Elphinstone Institute, Taylor Building, University of Aberdeen, Regent Walk, Aberdeen AB24 3UB
T 01224 272996
E elphinstone@abdn.ac.uk
Offers the successful applicant three months' rent-free accommodation in the Languedoc Roussillon region of the south of France to develop/express new ideas in their work. Also provides £3,000 to cover all costs associated with residency including return travel to France, travel in local area (driving licence essential), materials and living expenses.
Entry policy Open to a painter currently living and working in Scotland of at least four years' experience since graduation or since beginning to exhibit. Students are not eligible. Key criteria used in selecting artists are quality of work, as shown in a selection of slides, and the nature of the proposal for residency period.

Sainsbury Scholarship in Painting and Sculpture
The British School at Rome at the British Academy, 10 Carlton House Terrace, London SW1Y 5AH
T 020 79695202
F 020 79695401
E bsr@britac.ac.uk
W www.bsr.ac.uk

Contact Dr Gill Clark (The Registrar)
Founded in 2001 and funded by the Linbury Trust, open to painters and sculptors who can demonstrate a commitment to drawing within their artistic practice and who can present a well-argued case for the continuation of their studies in Italy and in particular Rome. Offers full board and lodging at the British School at Rome for twelve months (with, at the discretion of the selection committee, an opportunity for a further nine months in the following academic year). There is a grant of approximately £750 per month, plus a one-off travel grant of £1,000.
Frequency One per year.
Entry policy Applicants must be: of British nationality or have been working professionally or studying at postgraduate level for at least the last three years in the UK; under 28 on 1 October of the academic year in which the scholarship will be held; normally in the final year of or already have an MA (or equivalent) in fine art. An application form must be completed. Closing date for applications: mid-December.

Sargant Fellowship
The British School at Rome at the British Academy, 10 Carlton House Terrace, London SW1Y 5AH
T 020 79695202
F 020 79695401
E bsr@britac.ac.uk
W www.bsr.ac.uk
Contact Dr Gill Clark (The Registrar)
Founded in 1990, one of the senior and most prestigious residencies offered by the British School at Rome. Open to distinguished artists and architects to enable them to research and make new work within the historical context of Rome. Offers full board and lodging in a residential studio at the school, a grant of £2,000 per month, and a one-off travel allowance of £500.
Frequency Each year or every other year.
Entry policy Applicants must be of British or Commonwealth nationality, or have been living in the UK or Commonwealth for at least the last three years. An application form must be completed. Closing date: early to mid-January.

Sciart Awards
The Wellcome Trust, 210 Euston Road, London NW1 2BE
T 020 76118538
F 020 76118545
E sciart@wellcome.ac.uk

W www.sciart.org
Contact Bergit Arends
Aims to encourage creative and experimental collaborations between scientists and artists. Award scheme provides a unique opportunity for scientists and artists to research in collaboration, and develop and produce projects likely to result in innovative public engagement.

Scottish Sculpture Workshop Programme
1 Main Street, Lumsden, Huntley
AB54 4JN
T 01464 861372
F 01464 861550
W www.ssw.org.uk
The Scottish Sculpture Workshop has initiated a programme of fellowships funded by the Scottish Arts Council and the PF Charitable Trust.

Singer & Friedlander/Sunday Times Watercolour Competition
Parker Harris Partnership, 15 Church Street, Esher
KT10 8QS
T 01372 462190
F 01372 460032
E info@parkerharris.co.uk
Offers £25,000 in prizes to artists. The first prize of £15,000 is awarded to the finest British watercolour painting. There is no restriction on the subject matter of paintings submitted. The painting should have been carried out in the last three years and not have been previously exhibited. **Entry policy** Open to all living artists born or resident in the UK. The work must be the sole and original work of the entrant, who must own all works entered plus their copyright. For general information and regional receiving days contact the address above.

Skopelos Foundation for the Arts
P.O. Box 56, Skopelos Island
37003, GREECE
T +30 2424024143
F +30 2424024143
E info@skopart.org
W www.skopart.org
Contact Jill Somer (Associate Director)
Founded in 1999. Committed to honouring and sharing the Greek artistic tradition while fostering innovative artistic expression and development. The foundation offers residencies in ceramics, painting, printmaking and screenprinting, from September through to May.
Entry policy An application is required and reviewed by the board of directors. Experience is necessary and college graduates are preferred.

Soros Centres for Contemporary Arts (SCCA) Network Residencies
Bolyai u. 14, Budapest
1023, HUNGARY
T +36 13150303
F +36 13150201
E office@soros.hu
The SCCA is a network of nineteen offices devoted to development of contemporary arts in central and eastern Europe and the former Soviet Union. Runs a residencies scheme. Apply in writing.

St Hugh's Fellowship
The Administrator, The St Hugh's Foundation, Andrew & Company Solicitors, St Swithin's Square, Lincoln
LN2 1HB
E sthughesfoundation@lineone.net
To assist established arts practitioners and animators to develop their careers in the arts and to contribute their knowledge and experience to the wider growth and dissemination of arts practice in the region. Proposals should be for a substantial and sustained programme of work, to be carried out over a period of at least six months (two years maximum). Average grant up to £10,000.
Entry policy Open to individuals working as practitioners in any field of arts (under 30 years old on 1 May); resident and working full or part-time in Lincolnshire or former Humberside area. Application cover sheet and application requirements should be completed and returned by noon on 1 May. Obtain leaflet by sending sae.

Stiftung Kunstlerdorf Schoppingen Foundation
Feuerstiege 6, Schoppingen
48620, GERMANY
T +49 255593810
E kuenstlerdorf@tzs.de
W www.kuenstlerdorf.tzs.de
The foundation offers twenty-four scholarships for artists and writers for a maximum of six months.
Entry policy Application documents should include: a CV, exhibition list, catalogues (no more than three), folder including no more than twenty-five photos or slides (no originals), and the name of the applicant on the folder.

Stockport Art Gallery Annual Open Exhibition
Wellington Road South, Stockport
SK3 8AB

T 0161 4744453
F 0161 4804960
E stockport.artgallery@stockport.gov.uk
W www.stockport.gov.uk/tourism/artgallery
Contact Andy Firth
An annual event with four prizes of £100 each.
Entry policy Information and application forms
available in May each year by sending an A5 sae.

Straumur International Art Commune
v/Reykjanesbraut, P.O. Box 33.222, Hafnarfjordur
ICELAND
T +354 5650128
F +354 5650655
E solar@tv.is
Contact Sverrir Olafsson (Director)
Established in 1988, since when more than eight
hundred artists have visited from twenty-nine
countries and all fields of media and art. Funded
by the city of Hafnarfjordur and Sol-Art, a private
non-profit organization that handles daily
operations in close cooperation with the city's
cultural committee. The commune consists of
five spacious studios of various sizes. Residencies
are one to five months, with a maximum of
twelve months under special circumstances. The
artist has to pay all living and working expenses.
Entry policy Applications are accepted from all
professional artists regardless of artistic media,
citizenship, nationality, sex or race.

Summer Exhibition – Royal Academy of Arts
Burlington House, Piccadilly, London
W1J OBD
T 020 73005680
F 020 73005812
E summerexhibition@royalacademy.org.uk
W www.royalacademy.org.uk
Founded in 1768. The largest open contemporary-
art exhibition in the world encompassing all styles
and media. Over a thousand works, the majority of
which are for sale. Over 130,000 visitors.
Frequency Annual. Over £75,000 in prize money
awarded.
Entry policy Maximum of three works in any
media (£18 per work, non-refundable).

Swansea Open
The Glynn Vivian Art Gallery, Alexandra Road,
Swansea
SA1 5DZ
T 01792 655006
F 01792 651713
E glynn.vivian.gallery@swansea.gov.uk

W www.swansea.gov.uk/glynnvivian/
Open to professional artists as well as to those who
have never had the opportunity to show their work
in a public art gallery. Three winners are selected
from all the entries, with a first prize of £250,
second prize of £150 and third prize of £100.
These are announced at the beginning of the
exhibition, usually held from July to September.

Thouron Awards
University of Glasgow, Glasgow
G12 8QQ
T 0141 3305853
E d.maddern@admin.gla.ac.uk
Contact Deborah Maddern
Up to ten awards for British nationals covering
tuition fees and a monthly allowance of US$1,300
at the University of Pennsylvania. Eligible study
fields include fine arts, art and archaeology of the
Mediterranean world, architecture, and history of
art and music.
Entry policy Open to unmarried UK citizens
qualified to pursue a postgraduate degree.
Proposed study must be in a different field from
their degree. Must not already be in USA or have
studied there. Apply in writing to University of
Pennsylvania for course details and registration
materials.

Turner Prize
Tate Britain, Millbank, London
SW1P 4RG
T 020 78878000
F 020 78878007
W www.tate.org.uk/britain/turnerprize
An annual contemporary art award founded in
1984. Considered among the most prestigious
and influential awards available. Worth £40,000.
Entry policy Nominated artists must be under the
age of 50 and British, which includes artists
working in the UK and British-born artists who
may be working abroad. Need to have had an
outstanding exhibition or display in the twelve
months preceding the competition.

UNESCO Grants Scheme for Young Artists
UNESCO Division of Arts and Cultural Life,
Bureau B10.29, rue Miollis, Paris Cedex 15
75732, FRANCE
T +33 145684328
F +33 142730401
W www.unesco.org
Contact Madeleine Gobeil (Director)
A limited number of grants for young artists in

the field of performance and creation, made for short study tours or projects. Each grant of approximately US$2,000 is intended to cover, for example, the travel costs of the artist. Applicants must organize their own project or course and obtain agreement of the host institution.
Entry policy Candidates' applications must include the following documents: CV, study plan and dates, letters of agreement from the institution where study will take place, estimation of costs.

Virginia A. Groot Foundation
P.O. Box 1050, Evanston
IL 60204–1050, USA
Offers a grant of up to US$20,000 to an artist of exceptional talent with a demonstrated ability in the areas of ceramic sculpture or sculpture.
Entry policy Send sae for application form.

Wingate Rome Scholarship in the Fine Arts
The British School at Rome at the British Academy, 10 Carlton House Terrace, London
SW1Y 5AH
T 020 79695202
F 020 79695401
E bsr@britac.ac.uk
W www.bsr.ac.uk
Contact Dr Gill Clark (The Registrar)
Founded in 1998 and funded by the Harold Hyam Wingate Foundation. Open to painters, sculptors and mixed-media artists who can demonstrate that they are establishing a significant position in their chosen field. Offers full board and lodging in a residential studio at the school for three to six months, plus a grant equivalent to £500 per month.
Frequency One each year.
Entry policy Applicants must be: able to satisfy the selection panel that they need financial support to undertake the work projected; living in the British Isles during the period of application; citizens of the UK or other Commonwealth country, Ireland or Israel – or citizens of another EU country provided that they are and have been for the last three years resident in the UK; aged 24 or over on 1 September of the academic year in which the scholarship will be held. An

application form must be completed. Closing date: mid-December.

Women's Studio Workshop Fellowship Grants
P.O. Box 489, Rosendale, New York
12472, USA
T +1 914 6589133
F +1 914 6589031
E wsw@ulster.net
W www.wsworkshop.org
Fellowship Grants designed to provide concentrated work time for artists to explore new ideas in dynamic and supportive community of women artists. Facilities feature complete studios in intaglio, silkscreen, hand papermaking, photography, letterpress and clay. Two-to-six week sessions available each year from September to June. Fellowships awarded through jury process. Cost to recipients is US$200 per week plus materials (approximately one-fifth of the cost of actual residency). The award includes on-site housing and unlimited access to studios. Artists are given studio orientation but should be able to work independently. Technical assistance available for additional fee.
Entry policy Open to women artists. Fellowship grants applicants should submit an application form, a resume, six to ten slides, letter of interest that addresses the purpose of the residency (explaining areas of proficiency and studio skills) and sae for return of material.

Woo Charitable Foundation Arts Bursaries
The Administrator, Arts Bursaries, 277 Green Lanes, London
N13 4XS
The foundation offers arts bursaries for artists who have finished their formal education. Approximately ten bursaries of £5,000 are awarded to artists working in the visual arts sector (fine and applied).
Entry policy Open to artists who have finished formal education. All applications must include a CV, ten 35mm slides or colour photos, a short A4 written critique, details of a professional referee, and a brief summary of how the bursary would benefit the applicant.

08

Arts boards, councils, funding and commissioning organizations

Arts Council England, the market and the public purse: What do artists get?

Tim Eastop

The boundaries of contemporary art are fluid. Artists need time and space in which to fly, to search and to research. Art cross-fertilizes as never before. Artists are curators and critics as well as makers of film and video, crafts, live art, photography and new media. There is vibrant interplay between fine art, design and architecture, music, media, fashion and games. For artists to realize their potential in this expanded field it is essential they have appropriate professional guidance and support. Through the lens of a public patron this section offers a brief look at the problems artists face and gives some practical tips about studio space, how to apply for funding, and the labyrinth that is the contemporary art market.

Artists don't need to be poor
A recent survey showed that the average gross weekly earnings for visual artists in 2000 was £401, the lowest average earnings for all cultural occupations. Further research in 2004 by Newcastle University, commissioned by a-n The Artists Information Company, has highlighted that many artists' earnings are substantially lower than those in comparable professions such as teachers, who have similar skills and levels of education. In response, a-n The Artists Information Company, supported by the Arts Council, has produced a valuable toolkit for calculating professional fees for artists, now available through its website. The guidance suggests that artists with upwards of ten years' experience could be aiming to earn an annual salary of a mid-career teacher (approximately £34,299 in 2004) or more. A graduate could aim for £21,090 per annum, a daily rate of £176 to £204.

Arts Council England (ACE) research into artists' working lives raises significant issues.

In terms of taxation, there is a need for increased flexibility in reporting both income and employment status. There are inconsistencies in the level of understanding of artists' lives between tax and benefit offices, and regulations need to be applied in a more coherent and sympathetic way. A useful exemplar under examination is the approach taken by the Australian Tax Office, which, after extensive lobbying by artists' organizations, now distinguishes between professional artists and those who are simply making art for their own enjoyment. If this approach were to be adopted in the UK it would make a huge difference to artists' earning patterns.

There needs to be acknowledgment for the significant proportion of time that artists spend on research and development, which is rarely paid for. They therefore have reduced income for long periods. As a result, an artist's career is often characterized by multiple-job-holding, short-term contracts and underemployment. This can have beneficial effects for the arts community, as many artists use these periods of time to undertake teaching, outreach and educational work, giving value through their experience and skills.

Applying for funding
The Arts Council welcomes applications from individual artists to its new, open-application programme called Grants for the Arts. This funding stream is for individuals, arts organizations and other people who use the arts in their field of work. The funds are for activities that benefit people in England or that help artists and arts organizations from England to carry out their work.

As an artist you can apply for grants for arts-related activities that might include: projects and events; commissions and productions; research and development; capital items (such as equipment); professional development and training, including travel grants; bursaries; residencies; and touring exhibitions or events.

It is crucial that you set aside the time to read and fully understand the guidance notes and application form before you start writing. The most common mistake among applicants is not reading this guidance thoroughly. You can download the form you need to make an application from the Arts Council website or call the number listed in this section of the directory for an application pack. It is strongly recommended that, before you apply, you contact and get advice from the Arts Council Office for the region you are based in.

When assessing applications, the Arts Council uses five criteria that can be seen in more detail in a document entitled *Grants for the Arts, Understanding the Assessment Criteria*. It is important to note that not all these factors will apply to every application, but they are the type of things the assessors may look at so you should read this information carefully.

Assessing officers use their judgment as to what issues are relevant in each case, depending on the type of activity and how much you are applying for. The assessments examine: the artistic quality of the activity; how the activity will be managed; how feasible the activity is financially; how the public will benefit from the activity, immediately or in the long term; and the contribution of the activity to meeting the aims of Grants for the Arts.

You only have a limited number of words to describe your proposal, so the more clearly you express your project and how you will meet the stated funding criteria, the more likely your bid is to succeed. You must make sure you allow plenty of time to receive a decision before your activity starts. Currently you have to allow six working weeks for applications under £5,000 and twelve working weeks for applications over £5,000.

Understanding funding criteria and writing project proposals concisely are necessary skills for most applications to other trusts, foundations and even commercial sponsors. Where possible make direct contact to clarify anything you are unsure about. A useful starting point to find the best funding organization for you is the 'Money Map' available on the website of the Department for Culture, Media and Sport (www.culture.gov.uk/moneymap).

Arts Council England and the public purse

As the national arts development agency, Arts Council England is responsible for developing and implementing arts policy and funding on behalf of taxpayers via financing from the Department for Culture, Media and Sport. It makes strategic use of both National Lottery and Treasury grant-in-aid funding, aiming to place the arts at the heart of national life. The Arts Council is placing greater emphasis than ever before on direct support for artists and on helping to enhance the conditions that allow them and their creativity to thrive. It not only provides core funding to established venues for presenting contemporary art, but establishes strategic partnerships further upstream at the point of production, in the art school, the studio complex, new media companies and through artist-run projects and socially engaged practices. The ACE Collection of modern and contemporary British art directly supports artists and the market. This collection began with the foundation of the Arts Council of Great Britain in 1946. Since then, over seven thousand works have been acquired from artists and commercial galleries and the collection is now the largest national loan collection of modern and contemporary art in the world, and the largest loan collection of British contemporary art. It is highly regarded for its quality and range.

The Arts Council has increased its funding and support to individual artists in England and for international activity both for artists coming into the country and for those going abroad. Through its Grants for the Arts programme, ACE is investing £25m in individual artists between 2003–4 and 2005–6. The programme has already allocated £6m for 852 grants to individual visual artists for work ranging from animation, graphic design and new media to fine art, photography, crafts and live arts. In 2002–3 seventy-three organizations regularly funded by ACE commissioned 854 works from

1,217 individual visual artists.[1] The total expenditure for art commissions in the Arts Council's Capital Programme was nearly £70m by the time of completion of most projects in 2004; over £2m was allocated to visual artists development initiatives in 2004–5 compared with £450,000 in 1999.

These figures demonstrate the scale of public investment in artists by ACE and the returns are being seen countrywide. Innovative practice in the commissioning of new work is exemplified through the work of organizations such as Artangel, IXIA (the lead national public art body), Locus Plus and Modus Operandi. New and improving relationships are growing between artists and local authority planners, developers and other regeneration agencies.

The impact of new investment has an international reach. In 2002, the Arts Council entered into a major partnership with the British Council in China to establish an artists' exchange programme supporting up to thirty artists each year across the art forms to develop new work in China. The programme also funds Chinese contemporary artists to visit, research and present work in this country using a range of venues and artist-run organizations as their creative base. The International Artists Fellowships Programme, run directly by ACE, awards special research fellowships to high-achieving artists within different geo-cultural contexts. The programme has provided 175 fellowships in thirty countries within seventy-two different host institutes. Eighty-three of these fellowships were visual artists including those specializing in architecture, craft, new media, photography, moving image and live art.

Artists' workspaces

Many artists have difficulties in finding and affording workspaces with any degree of permanence or reliability. Artists have helped inner-city regeneration but ultimately, as in Hoxton in east London, their presence has increased property prices and forced them out. Through its capital grants, ACE is helping more artists and craftmakers to secure their futures by acquiring the freeholds of properties, and create safer, stimulating workspaces. Over £69m has been invested through its capital funds.[2] Open studios, where artists group together to show their work, have become a cultural attraction. In 2001, for instance, thirty-two open-studio events across England represented three thousand artists and attracted 250,000 visitors, turning over £1.5m in sales. These events are a celebration of creativity among the artistic grass roots, bringing many more artists to a larger and wider public at a time when art and creativity are assuming a new importance within the economy. Again, a-n The Artists Information Company provides vital advice and toolkits for artists seeking to set up studios.

The market for art

The art market is a broad ecology that includes the ways works of art are commissioned, researched, produced, promoted, presented, bought and sold and how creativity is converted into commercial value. Visual art contributes significantly to the UK economy and in recent years London has become the largest market in Europe and the second largest in the world after New York. The total sales for the UK in 1998 were £3,287m or €4,765.1m, representing over 60 per cent of the European Union art trade.[3] The estimated value of sales through contemporary commercial galleries and open studios in England was worth £354.5m in 2003,[4] while a recent ACE publication suggested that the international sales of London-based commercial galleries and agents are likely to be at least double this figure.[5]

To enable more people to enter the art market, ACE launched 'Own Art' in November 2004. The Own Art scheme is currently available through 250 regional galleries and outlets, making it more affordable for the public to buy original contemporary art and craft, through point-of-sale, interest-free loans.

Despite considerable resistance from the UK art market, a new European Union directive will enable visual artists to receive a percentage of the revenue from the resale of their works in the art market. This must be implemented in the UK from 1 January 2006 for living artists and extended to heirs and the estates of the deceased by 1 January 2012. Currently visual artists in the UK are protected only by copyright.

Tim Eastop is Senior Visual Arts Officer, Artists' Development, Arts Council England.

1 Joy, A et al. (2005), *A statistical survey of regularly funded organisations 2002/03*, Arts Council England.
2 Based on all ACE capital awards to visual arts projects over the past ten years to artists' studios/workspaces.
3 Market Tracking International Company Ltd (MTIC) (2000), *The European Art Market 2000*, The European Fine Art Foundation (TEFAF).
4 Morris, Hargreaves and McIntyre (2004), *Taste buds: how to cultivate the art market: executive summary*, Arts Council England.
5 Louisa Buck (2004), *Market Matters: The Dynamics of the Contemporary Art Market*, Arts Council England.

Arts boards, councils, funding and commissioning organizations

'A' Foundation

c/o MacFarlane & Co., Cunard Building, Water Street, Liverpool
L3 1DS
T 0151 7097444
Contact Paul Kurthousen
Established in 1998 with the principal aim of 'helping Liverpool to establish itself as a centre being at the cutting edge of the art world'.
Grants awarded Three art-related grants: Liverpool Biennial Trust, Liverpool Biennial of Contemporary Art Ltd and Liverpool Biennial Fringe.

Art Consultants Ltd – Art For Offices

15 Dock Street, London
E1 8JL
T 020 74811337
F 020 74813425
E enquiries@afo.co.uk
W www.afo.co.uk
Established in 1979, specializing in sourcing and commissioning art. Works with developers, architects and interior designers to provide art work for the corporate, hotel and leisure sectors. Can advise on a consultancy basis through International Art Consultants Ltd or supply art directly through Art For Offices.

Art Point Trust

2 Littlegate Street, Oxford
OX1 1QT
T 01865 248822
F 01865 248899
E info@artpointtrust.org.uk
W www.artpointtrust.org.uk
A creative company working with artists to support new thinking and practice for the built environment and public space. Advocates and establishes opportunities for artists to create new work within public contexts. This includes public-art commissioning, consultancy, research projects and audience engagement activities. Based in Oxford and works throughout the south-east of England.
Grants awarded Has delivered sixty projects worth £2.5m in the past five years.

ART.e @ the art of change

6 Container City, Trinity Buoy Wharfy, 64 Orchard Place, London
E14 0JW
T 020 79879921
F 020 79879922
E pete@artofchange.demon.co.uk
W www.arte-ofchange.com
Contact Peter Dunn
Founded 2001. A visual arts organization concerned with issues of change and, particularly, the transformation of the urban environment and its impact upon quality of life and cultural identity. The practice ranges from strategy through creative development to production. The core team is a combination of visual arts practitioners and strategists, resourced with new technology and administrative backup. Produces art works in the public domain in all its aspects, be they physical, virtual or social, through a process of working with communities of interest and location.
Submission policy Artists can apply to become workshop facilitators. Send a CV and details of experience of running workshops. A disclosure certificate is desirable but the organization can assist if required. Phone or email for further details.

Artangel

31 Eyre Street Hill, London
EC1R 5EW
T 020 77131400
F 020 77131401
E info@artangel.org.uk
W www.artangel.org.uk
Has pioneered a new way of collaborating with artists and engaging audiences in a series of commissions since the early 1990s. Previous projects include Rachel Whiteread's *House*, Janet Cardiff's *The Missing Voice*, Michael Landy's *Break Down* and Jeremy Deller's *The Battle of Orgreave*.

Artists' General Benevolent Institution

Burlington House, Piccadilly, London
W1J 0BB
T 020 77341193
F 020 77349966
Founded in 1814. Aids professional artists whose work has been known to the public for some time and who, through accident, old age or illness, are unable to support their families.

Arts and Humanities Research Council

Whitefriars, Lewins Mead, Bristol
BS1 2AE
T 0117 9876500
F 0117 9876600
W www.ahrc.ac.uk

Various schemes funded, including Core Funding Scheme for Higher Education Museums, Galleries & Collections, Postgraduate Awards in the Arts and Humanities, and Advanced Research Awards in the Arts and Humanities.
Submission policy See website for details of schemes and funding available.

Arts Council England
National Office, 14 Great Peter Street, London SW1P 3NQ
T 0845 3006200
E tim.eastop@artscouncil.org.uk
W www.artscouncil.org.uk
The national development agency for the arts. Supports artists and organizations working professionally in the contemporary arts. 'Visual arts' is an inclusive term to represenat a range of practices including architecture, craft, fine art, live art, moving image, new-media art, public-art and socially engaged practice, including education.
Submission policy Grants for the Arts are for individuals, arts organizations, national touring companies and other people who use the arts in their work. They are for activities that benefit people in England or help artists and arts organizations from England to carry out their work. Organizations and national touring are funded by the National Lottery. The application season runs from 31 October to 31 August. Application packs become available in the late summer. See website for more detailed instructions.
Grants awarded Grants for the Arts worth approximately £50m a year.

Arts Council England East
Eden House, 48–49 Bateman Street, Cambridge CB2 1LR
T 01223 454400
F 0870 2421271
E info@eearts.co.uk
W www.arts.org.uk
Areas covered: Bedfordshire, Cambridgeshire, Essex, Hertfordshire, Norfolk, Suffolk and unitary authorities of Luton, Peterborough, Southend-on-Sea, Thurrock.

Arts Council England East Midlands
Mountfields House, Epinal Way, Loughborough LE11 0QE
T 01509 218292
F 01509 262214

E info@em-arts.co.uk
W www.arts.org.uk
Areas covered: Derbyshire (including High Peak of Derbyshire), Leicestershire, Lincolnshire, Northamptonshire, Nottinghamshire; unitary authorities of Derby, Leicester, Nottingham, Rutland.

Arts Council England London
Elme House, 2 Pear Tree Court, London EC1R 0DS
T 020 76086100
F 020 76084100
E info@lonab.co.uk
W www.arts.org.uk
Areas covered: the thirty-two London boroughs and the Corporation of the City of London.

Arts Council England North East
Central Square, Forth Street, Newcastle-upon-Tyne NE1 3PJ
T 0191 2558500
F 0191 2301020
E amanda.ward@artscouncil.org.uk
W www.arts.org.uk
Areas covered: Durham, Northumberland; unitary authorities of Darlington, Hartlepool, Middlesbrough, Redcar and Cleveland, Stockton-on-Tees; metropolitan districts of Newcastle-upon-Tyne, Gateshead, North Tyneside, Sunderland and South Tyneside.

Arts Council England North West
Manchester House, 22 Bridge Street, Manchester M3 3AB
T 0161 8346644
F 0161 8346969
E info@nwarts.co.uk
W www.arts.org.uk
Areas covered: Cheshire, Cumbria, Lancashire, Merseyside, Greater Manchester; unitary authorities of Blackburn with Darwen, Blackpool, Halton and Warrington. Also has offices in Manchester and Liverpool.

Arts Council England South East
Sovereign House, Church Street, Brighton BN1 1RA
T 0845 3006200
F 0870 2421257
E chloe.barker@artscouncil.org.uk
W www.arts.org.uk
Areas covered: Kent, Surrey, East Sussex, West Sussex, Buckinghamshire, Hampshire, Isle of

Wight, Oxfordshire; unitary authorities of
Bournemouth, Bracknell Forest, Brighton and
Hove, the Medway towns, Milton Keynes,
Portsmouth, Reading, Slough, Southampton,
Swindow, West Berkshire, Wiltshire, Windsor and
Maidenhead, Wokingham.

Arts Council England South West
Bradninch Place, Gandy Street, Exeter
EX4 3LS
T 01392 218188
F 01392 413554
E claire.gulliver@swa.co.uk
W www.arts.org.uk
Areas covered: Cornwall, Devon, Dorset,
Gloucestershire, Somerset; unitary authorities of
Bath and North-east Somerset, Bristol, North
Somerset, Plymouth, South Gloucestershire,
Torbay; Wiltshire and Swindon.

Arts Council England West Midlands
82 Granville Street, Birmingham
B1 2LH
T 0121 6313121
F 0121 6437239
E info@west-midlands-arts.co.uk
W www.arts.org.uk
Areas covered: Shropshire, Staffordshire,
Warwickshire, Worcestershire; metropolitan
districts of Birmingham, Coventry, Dudley,
Sandwell, Solihull, Walsall and Wolverhampton;
unitary authorities of Hereford, Stoke-on-Trent,
Telford and Wrekin.

Arts Council England Yorkshire
21 Bond Street, Dewsbury
WF13 1AX
T 01924 455555
F 01924 466522
E info@yarts.co.uk
W www.arts.org.uk
Areas covered: North Yorkshire; unitary authorities
of East Riding, Kingston-upon-Hull, North-east
Lincolnshire, North Lincolnshire and York;
metropolitan districts of Barnsley, Bradford,
Calderdale, Doncaster, Kirklees, Leeds,
Rotherham, Sheffield and Wakefield.

Arts Council of Northern Ireland
MacNeice House, 77 Malone Road, Belfast
BT9 6AQ
T 028 90385200
F 028 90661715
E info@artscouncil-ni.org

W www.artscouncil-ni.org
Contact Iain Davidson
Under the current five-year arts plan, priority has
been given to extend opportunities for artists to
develop their work and practice. Many employment
possibilities are available for artists under, for
example, the Access Programme. There are also
major commissioning opportunities across all art
forms under the New Work Scheme in areas such
as public art, musical composition, script writing,
etc. As an expansion of the Arts Council's systems
of support for the individual artist, a number of
other specific schemes have been developed
including: Support for the Individual Artist
Programme; Travel Awards Scheme; General
Art Awards Scheme; Major Individual Awards
Scheme; Artists in the Community Scheme;
the Arts and Disability Awards Ireland; Arts and
Artists Abroad; Arts and Disability Networking
Abroad; International Artists' Profile Scheme
Residencies; the British School at Rome
Fellowship; self-arranged residencies.
Submission policy Specific criteria vary according
to scheme, but for all schemes, applicants must
satisfy the following criteria: (1) have made a
contribution to artistic activities in Northern
Ireland for a minimum period of one year; and
(2) be domiciled (as distinct from a national or
resident) in Northern Ireland. Priority is given to
practising individual artists.
Grants awarded Annual awards totalling around
£1.05m.

Arts Council of Wales
9 Museum Place, Cardiff
CF1 3NX
T 029 20376500
F 029 20221447
E information@ccc-acw.org.uk
W www.ccc-acw.org.uk
Contact Angela Blackburn (Communications
Officer)
A national organization with specific responsibility
for the funding and development of the arts in
Wales. Main sources of funds are an annual grant
from the Welsh Assembly and its share of the
'good causes fund' for the arts from the National
Lottery. Also receives funds from other sources,
including local authorities.

Arts Foundation
2nd Floor, 6 Salem Road, London
W2 4BU
T 020 82293813

F 020 82299410
E artsfound@hotmail.com
Contact Shelley Warren (Director)
Funds artists living and working in England,
Scotland or Wales who have demonstrated
commitment to and proven their ability in
their chosen art form. A minimum of five annual
fellowships awarded, worth £10,000 each, in five
specific art forms that change every year.
Submission policy Programme not open to
applications. Seventy established artists and other
professionals nominate individual artists who are
then invited to make an application.

artsadmin

Toynbee Studios 28 Commercial Street,
28 Commercial Street, London
E1 6AB
T 020 72475102
F 020 72475103
E manick@artsadmin.co.uk
W www.artsadmin.co.uk
Contact Manick Govinda
Provides a comprehensive management service and
national resource for contemporary artists across the
spectrum of new theatre, dance, music, live art and
mixed-media work. Develops and promotes artists'
work, from the initial stages of a project through to
its final presentation. Seeks to establish partnerships
with producers, promoters and relevant arts
organizations in Britain and abroad. Based at
Toynbee Studios in east London since 1994,
artsadmin is building up a centre for the creation
and development of new work. Has established a
range of new opportunities for emerging and
unfunded artists with a bursary and mentoring
scheme, a full-time advisory service, school
residencies and a programme of showcases. Toynbee
Studios has a 280-seat theatre, four additional
rehearsal spaces, a café, and technical resources
including video camera and editing facilities.
Submission policy Each bursary scheme has
different requirements and deadlines. See
website for specific application criteria.
Grants awarded Eight early-career bursaries,
eight mid-career bursaries, four digital-media
bursaries for disabled and deaf artists.
Total bursary fund of £63,000.

Awards for All

T 0845 6002040
W www.awardsforall.org.uk
A grants programme for small groups involved
in arts, sports, heritage, education, environment,
health and voluntary and community activities that
need grants of between £50 and £5,000. Criteria
include increasing skills and creativity and
improving quality of life. Operates through a series
of regional offices.
Submission policy Open to small, non-profit
organizations and some statutory bodies such as
parish town councils, schools and health bodies,
but not to fund statutory responsibilities. Priority
given to groups with a lower income. Groups
must spend the money within twelve months of
receiving the grant. No requirement for match
funding.

Belfast Exposed Photography

The Exchange Place, 23 Donegall Street, Belfast
BT1 2FF
T 028 90230965
F 028 90314343
E info@belfastexposed.org
W www.belfastexposed.org
Contact Karen Downey (Exhibitions Manager)
A photographic resource, archive and gallery.
Through its annual programme of exhibitions and
the commissioning of new work, Belfast Exposed
promotes excellence, access and participation
in the arts and aims to raise the profile of
photography as an art form. By developing a policy
of project origination, placing its main emphasis
on the commissioning of new work, producing
publications and generating discussion through
seminars and talks around projects, it aims to aid
the development of an infrastructure in which the
photographic arts can flourish.
Submission policy Only exhibits and supports
photographic projects. There is no formal
application process. Project proposals, artists
statement, examples of work, CVs, etc. should be
submitted to the Exhibition Manager in a Mac-
compatible format.

Bloomberg

City Gate House, 39–45 Finsbury Square, London
EC2A 1PQ
T 020 73307500
F 020 73926000
W www.bloomberg.com/uk
Contact Jemma Read (Head of Arts Sponsorship
and Charitable Investment)
Handles sponsorships and donations together,
with no stated preference between them or
for any particular art form. Policy is to 'support
contemporary arts projects that enrich the
community and involve our employees in new

and challenging cultural areas'. Has a commitment to the arts and young people.

British Council Arts Group
11 Portland Place, London
W1N 4EJ
T 020 73893194
F 020 73893199
E kate.smith@britcoun.org
W www.britcoun.org/arts/index.htm
Contact Kate Smith
Reinforces the UK's role in the international community through cultural, scientific, technological and educational cooperation, working with partners in the UK and overseas (represented in 110 countries). The principal aims of the council's work in the arts, literature and design are: to demonstrate the innovation and excellence of British arts to overseas publics, media, opinion-formers and successor generations; to promote intercultural dialogue and exchange; to stimulate the export of British cultural goods and services; to a create climate for export promotion in non-arts sectors; to contribute to international skills development and dissemination through arts for education projects and training programmes.

Calouste Gulbenkian Foundation
98 Portland Place, London
W1B 1ET
T 020 76365313
F 020 79087580
E info@gulbenkian.org.uk
W www.gulbenkian.org.uk
Contact Sian Ede (Assistant Director, Arts Programme)
Established in 1956. The Arts Programme is principally for professional arts organizations or individual professional artists working in partnerships or groups. Its purpose is to support the development of new art-making in any art form. It excludes activities that are linked to mainstream education. As a general principle the foundation supports projects that are genuinely original in their field and also favours those that take place outside London.
Submission policy For detailed information on grant programmes and exclusions see the foundation's website or free 'Advice to Applicants for Grants' leaflet.

CBAT – The Arts and Regeneration Agency
123 Bute Street, Cardiff
CF10 5AE

T 029 20488772
F 029 20472439
E info@cbat.co.uk
W www.cbat.co.uk
Has been commissioning and managing public art works for both private- and public-sector clients since 1990. Originally worked as the retained consultants to Cardiff Bay Development Corporation but has been working as an independent public art consultancy across the UK since 1998. Initiates approximately ten projects per year.
Submission policy Application forms for registration or artist database on request.

Commissions East
St Giles Hall, Pound Hill, Cambridge
CB3 0AE
T 01223 356882
F 01223 356883
W www.commissionseast.org.uk
A visual arts development agency that works with artists and commissioners to create innovative visual arts projects that place artists' work at the heart of everyday life.

Crafts Council
44a Pentonville Road, Islington, London
N1 9BY
T 020 72787700
F 020 78376891
E reference@craftscouncil.org.uk
W www.craftscouncil.org.uk
The UK development agency for contemporary crafts. An independent organization offering a range of services to makers and the public. The London base includes an exhibition space, shop, reference library, the national register of makers and Photostore, the visual database of makers.

Creative Skills
73 Lemon Street, Truro
TR1 2PN
T 01872 273344
F 01872 260827
E admin@creativeskills.org.uk
W www.creativeskills.org.uk
Contact Jane Sutherland
The professional-development organization for all creative industries practitioners in Cornwall. Set up in 2001 to equip creative practitioners in Cornwall with the skills, knowledge and opportunities they need to develop and share

their creativity and increase their prosperity. Grants depend on funding available.
Submission policy Professional practitioners working within the creative industries who live in Cornwall.

Cywaith Cymru Artworks Wales

Crichton House, 11–12 Mount Stuart Square, Cardiff
CF10 5EE
T 029 20489543
F 029 20465458
E info@cywaithcymru.org
W www.cywaithcymru.org
The national organization for public art in Wales. Established in 1981 to encourage the placing of art in the environment. Regularly gives artists opportunities in public art commissions and artist-in-residence projects. It also offers an artist-initiated residency programme, as well as a mentoring scheme, enabling less established artists to gain experience in residencies.
Submission policy To register to receive details of Cywaith Cymru opportunities, or for further information on artist-initiated projects or mentoring, contact Cywaith.

Elephant Trust

P.O. Box 5521, London
W8 4WA
Aims to 'advance public education in all aspects of the arts and to develop artistic taste and the knowledge, understanding and appreciation of the fine arts'. Support principally given to individuals, art galleries and other organizations in furtherance of these aims. Various grants awarded.
Submission policy Excludes students and any other study-related funding. Send applications in writing together with sae. Guidelines are issued. Trustees meet quarterly.

European Associaton for Jewish Culture

79 Wimpole Street, London
W1G 9RY
T 020 79358266
F 020 79353252
E london@jewishcultureineurope.org
W www.jewishcultureineurope.org
Contact Lena Stanley-Clamp
Established in 2001 with mission to foster and support artistic creativity and achievement, and to promote access to Jewish culture in Europe. Grant programmes include visual arts, performing arts and documentary films.

Grants awarded Approximately twenty grants annually. Total value between £100,000 and £150,000.

Federation of British Artists (FBA)

17 Carlton House Terrace, London
SW1Y 5BD
T 020 79306844
F 020 78397830
E info@mallgalleries.com
W www.mallgalleries.org.uk
Contact John Sayers (Secretary)
The umbrella organization for nine of the country's leading art societies. Objectives are to 'aid, promote, assist, extend and encourage the study and practice of the fine and applied arts'. Aims are met primarily through the organization of, and provision of facilities for, public art exhibitions on behalf of member societies and other organizations and individuals. In addition, the federation also supports workshops, lectures, demonstrations, seminars and educational services.
Grants awarded Various grants, totalling over £400,000.

Freeform

Hothouse, 274 Richmond Road, London Fields, London
E8 3QW
T 020 72493394
F 020 72498499
E contact@freeform.org.uk
W www.freeform.org.uk
Active in urban renewal and regeneration through art- and design-led solutions to humanize the social and physical environment locally, nationally and internationally. Combines the skills of artists, architects and local people on urban regeneration projects.

Helix Arts

2nd Floor, The Old Casino, 1–4 Forth Lane, Newcastle-upon-Tyne
NE1 5HX
T 0191 2414931
F 0191 2414933
E info@helixarts.com
W www.helixarts.com
Specializes in the development of projects and initiatives, including artist residencies and commissions, which explore the role and potential of the arts in a social context.

Henry Moore Foundation

Dane Tree House, Perry Green, Much Hadham
SG10 6EE
T 01279 843333
F 01279 843647
E curator@henry-moore-fdn.co.uk
W www.henry-moore-fdn.co.uk
Contact Timothy Llewellyn (Director)
Established to 'advance the education of the
public by the promotion of their appreciation
of the fine arts and in particular the works of
Henry Moore'. Concentrates its support on
sculpture, drawing and printmaking. Promotes
exhibitions and publications about Henry
Moore, both nationally and internationally.
Submission policy Does not give grants to
individual applicants, nor provide revenue
expenditure. Apply in writing covering the
following: aims and functions of organization;
precise purpose for which grant is sought;
amount required and details of how figure
arrived at; details of efforts made to find other
income, whether firm commitments have been
received and what others are hoped for; details of
budget for scheme and how scheme will be
monitored. Applications considered at quarterly
meetings of the foundation's grants committee.
Grants awarded Grants towards: exhibitions
around the world (at established galleries only);
conferences, workshops and symposia; museum
and gallery acquisitions of sculpture; conservation
work and research; publications which encourage
public interest in sculpture; and minor capital
projects.

Impact Arts

The Factory, 319 Craigpark Drive, Dennistoun,
Glasgow
G31 2TB
T 0141 5753001
F 0141 5753009
E mail@impactarts.co.uk
W www.impactarts.co.uk
Contact Gwen Mackey
A leading community arts company committed
to involving people of all ages and abilities in
innovative, arts-based activities across Glasgow,
Scotland and the UK. Established in 1994, the
company works in partnership with a variety
of community groups, schools, housing
associations and funding agencies, developing
and delivering tailored long- and short-term
projects and events.

International Intelligence on Culture

4 Baden Place, Crosby Row, London
SE1 1YW
T 020 74037001
F 020 74032009
E enquiry@intelculture.org
W www.intelculture.org
Contact Sheena Barbour (Information Officer)
Brings together an experienced multinational
group of experts to work with and for the
international culture sector. Undertakes a range of
activities for public bodies in the UK and overseas,
including policy intelligence, research, consultancy,
project management, training and information
services. Runs tailormade workshops for cultural
organizations, local government, policy-makers
and practitioners on themes such as European
funding, networking, cultural exchange and
cultural politics worldwide. Runs a free enquiry
service and advice surgeries for arts practitioners
on behalf of Arts Council England.

ISIS Arts

1st Floor, 5 Charlotte Square, Newcastle-upon-Tyne
NE1 4XF
T 0191 2614407
F 0191 2616818
E isis@isisarts.org.uk
W www.isisarts.org.uk
Initiates and manages productions, exhibitions
and artist residencies, and works with artists on
collaborative projects and events. Track record of
providing quality arts projects to benefit individual
artists, schools and communities alike, while
promoting the professional status of the artist.
Has a digital facility serving artists in the region
and promotes an interdisciplinary approach to the
use of new media in the arts. Works with around
seventy artists a year on residencies programmes
and a further forty as part of training
programmes.

J. Paul Getty Jr. Charitable Trust

1 Park Square West, London
NW1 4LJ
T 020 74861859
W www.jpgettytrust.org.uk
Contact Bridget O'Brien Twohig (Administrator)
Aims to fund projects to do with poverty and
misery in general, and unpopular causes in
particular, within the UK. With regard to the arts
grants only the following will be considered:
therapeutic use of the arts for the long-term benefit

of groups under social welfare (people with mental illness, communities that are clearly disadvantaged, offenders, the homeless, the unemployed and ethnic minorities); projects that enable people in these groups to feel welcome in arts venues, or that enable them to make long-term constructive use of their leisure. Has made total grants worth over £26m since 1986.

Submission policy Only accepts applications by post. Send a letter no more than two sides long in the first instance, giving an outline of the project and who will benefit, a detailed costing, the existing sources of finance of the organization, and what other applications have been made, including those to statutory sources and the National Lottery. Applicants should disclose if they have applied to or received a grant previously from the trust.

Jerwood Charitable Foundation

22 Fitzroy Square, London
W1P 5HQ
T 020 73886287
F 020 73886289
E info@jerwood.org
W www.jerwood.org.uk
Contact Roanne Dods (Director)
Dedicated to rewarding excellence in the visual and performing arts, and to education. Supports 'outstanding national institutions', along with projects in their early stages that are unable to secure funding from other sources.
Submission policy Applications should be by letter, outlining the aims and objectives of the organization and those of the specific project or scheme for which assistance is sought. Also include a detailed budget for the project.
Grants awarded Various grants, varying from up to £10,000 in the lower range to £50,000.

Lime

St Mary's Hospital, Hathersage Road, Manchester
M13 0JH
T 0161 2564389
F 0161 2564390
E lime@limeart.org
W www.limeart.org
Contact Brian Chapman
Founded as Hospital Arts in 1974. Works to initiate and deliver arts projects within the arena of health and well-being through collaborative and consultative arts practice. Aims to develop sustainable artistic initiatives in healthcare through embedding the expertise of artists and the cultural industries into care planning and delivery and into the social fabric of hospitals. Commissions around thirty artists per year.
Submission policy Send CV and examples of current work for consideration. From this, selected artists will be invited to present to the team.
Grants awarded Ten to fifteen grants worth £450,000.

Locus+

17, 3rd Floor Wards Building, 31–39 High Bridge, Newcastle-upon-Tyne
NE1 1EW
T 0191 2331450
F 0191 2331451
E locusplus@newart.demon.co.uk
W www.locusplus.org.uk
Formally established in 1993 but preceded by the Basement Group (1979–1984) and Projects UK (1982–1992). A visual arts commissioning agency that works with artists on the production and presentation of socially engaged, collaborative and temporary projects, primarily for non-gallery locations. In each project, place or context is integral to the meaning of the art work. To date, the organization has completed over fifty projects touring to a further twenty-five other venues, and produced over twenty publications and nine artists multiples.

Mid Pennine Arts

Yorke Street, Burnley
BB11 1HD
T 01282 421986
F 01282 429513
E info@midpenninearts.org.uk
W www.midpenninearts.org.uk
A north-west arts agency with a diverse variety of projects running at any one time.

National Endowment for Science, Technology and the Arts (NESTA)

Fishmongers Chambers, 110 Upper Thames Street, London
EC4R 3TW
T 020 76459500
F 020 76459501
E nesta@nesta.org.uk
W www.nesta.org.uk
Set up by an Act of Parliament in 1998 to help maximize the country's creative and innovative potential. Funded by an endowment from the National Lottery, using the interest to back people of exceptional talent and imagination. Offers support to explore new ideas, develop new

products and services, or experiment with new ways of nurturing creativity in science, technology and the arts.

Nigel Moores Family Charitable Trust

c/o Macfarlane & Co., 2nd Floor, Cunard Building, Water Street, Liverpool
L3 1DS
Aims to raise the artistic taste of the public 'whether in relation to music, drama, opera, painting, sculpture or otherwise in connection with the fine arts'. Also promotes education in fine arts and academic education in general, as well as providing support for environmental causes, the provision of recreation and leisure facilities, and the promotion of religion.
Has supported institutions that benefit children and young adults, actors and entertainment professionals, musicians, students, textile workers and designers.
Submission policy Apply in writing enclosing a synopsis of aims and funds required, together with financial statements. However, the trust has usually committed its funds for designated projects, making unsolicited applications unlikely to succeed. Trustees meet three times a year.

Public Art Commissions and Exhibitions (PACE)

7 John Street, Edinburgh
EH15 2EB
T 0131 6200445
E pace@ednet.co.uk
W www.paceprojects.org
Contact Juliet Dean
Established in 1996. A public arts agency dedicated to the integration of art into environmental and building projects. Works in a range of sectors including health, education and the environment. Applies for grants for projects on behalf of the client. Recent awards include £350,000 from the arts lottery for the Royal Aberdeen Children's Project.
Submission policy Advertises for artists when opportunities for commissions arise. Works with a range of artists in media such as sculpture, glass, installation, light, photography and new media.

Peter Moores Foundation

c/o Messrs Wallwork, Nelson & Johnson, Chandler House, 7 Ferry Road, Office Park, Riversway, Fulwood, Preston
PR2 2YH
W www.pmf.org.uk

Aim is 'the raising of the taste of the public whether in relation to music, drama, opera, painting, sculpture or otherwise in connection with the fine arts'. Causes that promote education in fine arts, academic education or the Christian religion also attract support from the foundation, as does the provision of facilities for recreation and leisure. Activities supported tend to reflect the personal interests of its founder and patron, Peter Moores, a director of the Littlewoods Organization, the pools and mail-order company.
Submission policy Prospective applicants should note that the foundation will normally support projects that come to the attention of its patron or trustees through their interests or special knowledge. General applications for sponsorship are not encouraged and are unlikely to succeed.
Grants awarded Grants in the following categories: music (performance); music (recording); music (training); fine art; heritage; youth/race relations; social; health; environment; Barbados.

Picture This

40 Sydney Row, Spike Island, Bristol
BS1 6UU
T 0117 9257010
F 0117 9257040
E office@picture-this.org.uk
W www.picture-this.org.uk
Contact Josephine Lanyon (Director)
A moving-image projects agency that commissions contemporary visual art works and produces exhibitions, publications and touring initiatives. Works in partnership with a range of organizations, from galleries and colleges to public sites. The agency develops a range of projects, residencies, research and presentation opportunities as well as providing creative technology services.
Submission policy Aims to provide a range of opportunities for artists to produce new work, for audiences to engage with moving-image projects and for individuals to gain the experience necessary to find paid employment. Each year the agency aims to advertise one to two open-submission schemes.

Prince's Trust

Head Office, 18 Park Square East, London
NW1 4LH
T 020 75431234
F 020 75431200
E webinfops@princes-trust.org.uk

W www.princes-trust.org.uk

A charity aiming to offer young people (14 to 30 years old) practical support including training, mentoring and financial assistance. Focuses on those who have struggled at school, been in care, been in trouble with the law, or are long-term unemployed.

Public Art South West

Arts Council England, South West, Bradninch Place, Gandy Street, Exeter
EX2 4HL
T 01392 229227
E pasw@artscouncil.org.uk
W www.publicartonline.org.uk
Contact Linda Geddes

Recognized as one of the leading public art-development agencies in the UK. Primarily serving the south-west of England, its work extends beyond geographical boundaries in terms of the critical thinking and application of artists' skills and creativity it promotes. Works with artists and national and regional public- and private-sector organizations across Britain, and actively networks with a range of professions within art, design and architecture.
Submission policy Can advise artists on all aspects of the commissioning process but does not act as a project manager nor recommend artists for individual commissions. Organizes two regional network meetings a year, which have a reduced rate for artists.

Rootstein Hopkins Foundation

P.O. Box 14720, London
W3 7ZG
T 020 87462136
E info@rhfoundation.org.uk
W rhfoundation.org.uk
Contact Graham Feldman (Trustee)

Founded as a registered charity in 1990 and provides, among other things, financial support to art institutions, artists, art students, lecturers and designers. The trustees include artists, who are also respected teachers, designers, a visual arts consultant and an accountant.
Submission policy Chooses candidates who will make the best use of the grants to further their careers, and who can present a plan that seems likely to be realized within the grant period. Looking for recent, strong and consistent work from artists wishing to apply for grants.
Grants awarded Various grants, totalling approximately £75,000 annually.

Scottish Arts Council

12 Manor Place, Edinburgh
EH3 7DD
T 0131 2266051
F 0131 2259833
E help.desk@scottisharts.org.uk
W www.scottisharts.org.uk

The national organization with a specific responsibility for the funding and development of the arts in Scotland. Its main sources of funds are an annual grant-in-aid from the Scottish Executive and its share of the 'good causes fund' for the arts from the National Lottery.
Submission policy For detailed guidelines to each fund and the latest information, contact the help desk from Monday to Friday between 9 a.m. and 5 p.m.

Stanley Picker Trust

1 Warren Park, Kingston Hill, Kingston-upon-Thames
KT2 7HX
T 01722 412412

Primarily supports the arts, giving annual grants and fellowships to the arts faculties at the University of Kingston and bursaries to selected schools of music and drama. The trust-owned Warren Park in Surrey is used as a gallery to display the trust's own art works, and is also a major beneficiary, annually receiving the trust's largest grant. Funding is also given in the fields of music, writing, acting, printing and sculpture and a few grants go to arts organizations.
Grants awarded Grants total over £250,000.

Vision in Art

44A Halesworth Road, Lewisham, London
SE13 7TN
T 020 83202099
E office@via.demon.co.uk
W www.via.demon.co.uk
Contact Aileen Ryan

A not-for-profit organization facilitating a London-wide network of visual artists in order to raise the profile of the visual arts and of those who practise them. Provides artist-led professional-development services to enable collaborative mentoring, art-work promotion, exchange of relevant information about artistic opportunities, participation in community projects and events, and networking.

Visiting Arts

11 Portland Place, London
W1N 4EJ

T 020 73893019
F 020 73893016
E melissa.naylor@britishcouncil.org
W www.visitingarts.org.uk
Contact Melissa Naylor (Information Manager)
Jointly funded by national Arts Councils, the Crafts
Council, the Foreign and Commonwealth Office
and the British Council. Aims to encourage the
flow of international arts into the UK in order to
develop cultural awareness and positive cultural
relations between the UK and the rest of the world.
Activities include advice, information, training,
consultancy, publications, special projects and
project development.
Submission policy Applications open to UK-
based arts organizations, promoters and venues
proposing projects that take place in the UK and
involve presenting or working with artists from
any country overseas. See website for more
detailed criteria.

Visual Arts Projects

1st Floor, 14 King Street, Glasgow
G1 5QP
T 0141 5526563
F 0141 5530798
E email@vap.prestel.co.uk
Provides arts research fellowships. Also involved
in arranging seminars and does some publishing.

Wellcome Trust

183 Euston Road, London
NW1 2BE
T 020 76117367
E soss@wellcome.ac.uk
W www.wellcome.ac.uk
A main funder of scientific biomedical research
in Britain, with spending on par with the
government's Medical Research Council.
Within their schemes are the People Awards, a
mechanism for funding initiatives up to £30,000
that encourage and support public engagement
with biosciences, especially novel and imaginative

activities. The scheme is open to academics,
mediators and practitioners (including artists).
Submission policy Applications can be made at
any time during the year and will be subject to
review by referees.

Winston Churchill Memorial Trust

15 Queen's Gate Terrace, London
SW7 5PR
T 020 75849315
F 020 75810410
E office@wcmt.org.uk
W www.wcmt.org.uk
A living tribute to Churchill, running since 1965,
when thousands of people subscribed £3m to
provide travelling fellowships. Since then, the net
income from investments has been used to fund
over three thousand fellowships. Approximately
one hundred are awarded annually for projects
overseas lasting four to eight weeks on
average. The grant awarded covers all fellowship
expenses, return airfare, travel within the
country(-ies) to be visited, daily living and travel
insurance.
Submission policy British citizens may apply.
No formal education or professional qualifications
required. No grants awarded for attending courses,
academic studies, student grants or gap-year
projects.

Woo Charitable Foundation

277 Green Lanes, London
N13 4XS
T 07974 570475
F 020 88863814
Contact John Dowling (Administrator/Secretary)
Established for the advancement of education
through supporting, organizing, promoting and
assisting the development of the arts in England,
together with the specific aim of helping those less
able to help themselves. Funding is usually spread
over a number of years.
Grants awarded Over £250,000 in 'artistic grants'.

09

Societies and other artists' organizations

Society rules:
How letters benefit the artist

Ken Howard RA

To start with, if you are going to become a member of a society, you have to be a society person. For instance, at the Royal Academy we would love to have Lucian Freud as a member, but he will never join – not necessarily because he is disapproving in any way, but simply because he is a very private man and not a 'society' sort of person.

I was, and am, that sort of person, and when I came back from studying in Florence in 1959 and won a prize called the Lord Mayor's Art Award in London, one of the judges happened to be the President of the Royal Institute of Oil Painters (ROI) and he invited me to join. At that time these affiliations were extremely meaningful; letters behind your name were stamps of approval for an artist and it was acknowledged that not everyone could be elected to the societies. Even now, membership of a society gives you a professional status; for example, if someone needs a portrait commissioned, they naturally think of the Royal Society of Portraiture.

I also started to submit work regularly to annual open exhibitions with the New English Art Club (NEAC), as I greatly admired the painters there, such as Bernard Dunstan, Fred Cuming and William Bowyer, and it was reckoned to be among the best. It was not long before they elected me, and although things have changed enormously over the years, that electoral process, for all its flaws, continues to this day. Many societies, including the NEAC, have several exhibitions for their members throughout the year, but one annual, open-submission exhibition from which new members are elected. The process varies, although an artist is usually singled out for their contribution to the show before their nomination has to be countersigned by, say, five society members in order to become a candidate for election.

The Academican shuffle

Unlike the fluid memberships of societies, the Royal Academy (RA) is governed by what we call 'dead men's shoes'. There are only eighty Academicians, and while around fifty of those are painters, at least twelve have to be architects, twelve have to be sculptors and six have to be printmakers or draughtsmen. Within these constraints, which are peculiar to the RA, there is a degree of flexibility, so you can select more than twelve architects or sculptors, but this limits the number of places for painters. There has always been a strict procedure at the RA – even David Hockney had to have his name in the nominations book, find six backers and gain the vote of at least fifty per cent of the members gathered at a general assembly, where we elect all new members. In my case, I exhibited in the RA's Summer Exhibition for thirty-two years from the age of eighteen, so I came in by the traditional route. You remain a lifelong member once you are in, unless you fail to show at the Summer Exhibition for five years without good reason, or you bring the RA into disrepute.

Despite its archaic initiation ceremony where, once elected, you appear before a council, and there are few traditions left over from the nineteenth century. The RA is still alive and well because, to a certain extent, it has moved with the times. However, becoming an Academician nowadays assumes you are an important artist in your field, as was the case with painters Gary Hume and Fiona Rae who were elected in 2001 and 2002 respectively.

New English talents

Different societies cater for different kinds of artists. The NEAC was formed in 1885 in response to the staunch academicism of the RA at the time. The RA was keen on showing the Pre-Raphaelites, but was not interested in French painting of the era, nor in artists who had been influenced by the Impressionists perhaps through studying in Paris, including John Singer Sargent, James McNeill Whistler and, later on, Walter Sickert and Stanley Spencer. The NEAC was a breeding ground for such talents; even Edgar Degas showed there at one point. Gradually the RA caught up and elected the best members of the NEAC, causing the latter to lose its *raison d'être* and prestige during the 1940s and 1950s.

When I became President of the NEAC in 1998 there were many societies that had spread their net far and wide, and I felt it was better to concentrate on figurative painting, rather than trying to be everything to everybody while actually being nothing to anybody. Also, I felt that the British art-buying public is still very conservative; certainly tastes have not changed drastically since the days when people would visit the Summer Exhibition and buy their 'annual picture'. Now they find their annual picture at the NEAC, and this has given impetus to younger members such as Benjamin Sullivan, Jennifer McRae and Peter Brown.

Companions and contacts

One good reason to become a member of a society or organization is to feel the sense of belonging that comes with joining a club and becoming part of a movement. Movements come and go in art, but societies are ongoing – this can be seen as one of their strengths or as a potential weakness – and the RA is the epitome of this persistent, steadying ethos. Besides, painting or art-making of any kind can be a lonely business and once you leave art school you are out on your own. There is a certain amount of socializing attached to society events and dinners, but they should be seen as professional bodies and not social clubs. You have to fit your life around your work, not your work around your life. This is not as constrictive a principle as it sounds; it can be a broadening experience, but if you are committed to being an artist, that is what you must concentrate on.

Apart from the companionship of fellow painters and a seal of professional approval, the society provides a shop window for your work and an environment in which to compare your work with peers and superiors. When I left art school, societies were the best way into the commercial galleries, whereas young painters today increasingly get picked up straight from college, a fact that has made societies less attractive. However, many of the twenty or so London galleries that are interested in figurative painting still keep their eye out for young painters at the NEAC shows. Similarly, if you find friends or contacts to come along and buy pictures from you, then there will inevitably be other buyers, and this creates a sort of collecting club.

Work on walls

Most artists, whether they admit it or not, are concerned about selling their work – we all have to sell in order to paint – and the societies are still a means of getting your work noticed and collected. You have to start getting your work on walls if you are going to live by your art. As soon as you get a picture on someone's wall, that person's friends will see your work and you will start to build up a clientele. Students and young artists have a tendency to rate their work far too expensively. Yet it should be more important to sell than to have a studio full of pictures that you consider to be worth ten times what anybody will pay for them – I sold my first pictures on the railings at Hampstead for £2 each. Once I began to show and sell regularly with a gallery, I automatically developed a price structure that people could believe in.

Another advantage of being a society member is that you don't pay hanging or submission fees to exhibit, as these are subsumed within the cost of membership. When you are trying to get elected, the sending and hanging fees can be expensive if you fail to sell at the show, but many societies are introducing incentives and special terms for newcomers and students. It is also worth noting that societies take much smaller commissions from sales, around thirty-five per cent compared to the standard fifty per cent of a gallery. Also, some galleries burden the artist with hidden charges such as for a private view or for framing and hanging, on top of their already sizeable commission. Societies can supplement a gallery career and provide another umbrella under which to show; certainly they are becoming more active away from their annual open exhibitions.

Finally, you should never apply to be a member unless you have a certain regard for the artists and the work at a particular society, as you are only as good as the company you keep. In a way, the RA is the example that all other societies look to because of the time it has been around, its prestige and its following, what with the support of some ninety thousand Friends of the Royal Academy. Societies are a way of keeping up tradition; they are in a state of constant evolution, not revolution. While it may not get a lot of coverage from art critics or the press, you can base a whole career around showing with a society.

Professor Ken Howard RA is a painter represented by the Richard Green Gallery in London. He was President of the NEAC from 1998 to 2003 and is a member of the Royal West of England Academy, Royal Society of Painters in Watercolours as well as an honorary member of the Royal Society of British Artists and the ROI, among others.

Societies and other artists' organizations

AIM-artists

40 Wolseley Street, Lancaster
LA1 3PH
T 01524 847530
E info@aimartists.fsnet.co.uk
W www.aim-artists.co.uk
Contact Chris Amriding
Based in the Lancaster and Morecambe area.
Formed in 1999 to help develop support and
opportunities for locally based artists and to
organize professional group exhibitions. Now a
small group of artists concentrating on developing
exhibition projects around their individual work in
fine and applied arts including sculpture, painting,
photography and contemporary art in any media.
Admissions policy Members are locally based fine
artists. Group meetings involved. Art work must
be strongly original. Applications welcome but
only a small number of artists required.
Subscription rates Small shared contributions
towards costs when required.

All Arts – The People's Arts Group

52 Toft Street, Kensington, Liverpool
L7 2PS
T 0151 2225410
E allarts@blueyonder.co.uk
Contact Anthony Mantova
Formed in 1998 to promote, support, develop and
create art in all its forms and bridge the traditional
void between different arts and art organizations.
Runs arts, education and employment open days to
show the links between these industries, and has
performed plays and run workshops to encourage
adults and children to participate in the arts. Has a
network of national and international contacts.
Admissions policy Artists in various disciplines are
welcome to become members and all receive a
weekly newsletter.
Subscription rates Annual: £5 for the unwaged;
£10 for the waged; £15 for associates. Suggested
donations from £5 for honorary members.

Alternative Arts

Top Studio, Bethnal Green Training Centre, Deal
Street, London
E1 5HZ
T 020 73750441
F 020 73750484
E info@alternativearts.co.uk
W www.alternativearts.co.uk

Contact Maggie Pinhorn
Founded in 1971 to invest in new artists and ideas
and to make the arts accessible to the public.
Produces a wide range of arts events including
exhibitions, festivals, dance, music, poetry, mime,
theatre, fashion, photography and literature.
Admissions policy Only invites submissions when
necessary.

Anne Peaker Centre for Arts in Criminal Justice (Unit for the Arts and Offenders)

Neville House, 90–91 Northgate, Canterbury
CT1 1BA
T 01227 470629
F 01227 379704
E info@a4offenders.org.uk
W www.a4offenders.org.uk
Contact Carol Clewlow
Set up by Anne Peaker and Dr Jill Vincent in 1992
as part of the Centre for Research in Social Policy
at Loughborough University. Based in Canterbury
since 2000. Supports the development of the
arts within criminal-justice settings. Currently its
work falls within the following broad objectives: to
influence policy; to promote the value of the arts;
to provide clear, up-to-date information, advice and
support to all those interested or involved in this
field of work; to develop a national framework for
continuous professional development for artists
working or wishing to work in criminal-justice
settings; and to put the organization's knowledge
and expertise at the service of the sector.

Art in Perpetuity Trust (APT)

6 Creekside, Deptford, London
SE8 4SA
T 020 86948344
F 020 86948344
E enquiry@aptstudios.org
W www.aptstudios.org
Contact Liz May
Founded in 1995. A charity promoting the value
of creativity through the creative arts. With the
provision of secure studios and high-quality
exhibition space as a cornerstone, it aims to foster
an environment where creativity may flourish.
Admissions policy Supports thirty-seven fine-art
studios. Prospective artists should check the
website for availability.

Art and Spirituality Network

c/o Adam Boulter, Flat 3 Marwell Court,
42 Oakcroft Road, London
SE13 7EE

T 07957 286360
E adam.boulter@virgin.net
Contact Adam Boulter
A small artist-run network of people interested in the arts, spirituality and world religious traditions. Established for ten years. Runs workshops and retreats using the arts to explore spiritual themes. Open to those interested in the arts from all religious traditions and none.

Art Connections
The Art Depot, Asquith Industrial Estate, Eshton Road, Gargrave
BD23 3SE
T 01756 748529
F 01756 749934
E info@art-connections.org.uk
W www.art-connections.org.uk
A project initiated and managed by Chrysalis Arts Ltd, developing and supporting creative businesses in the visual arts, crafts and public art sectors in North Yorkshire. Offers professional artists and makers information, advice, training and marketing support services. Also coordinates a county-wide open-studio programme.
Admissions policy Services only available to professional North Yorkshire-based artists and makers.

Art House
Wakefield College, Margaret Street, Wakefield
WF1 2DH
T 01924 377740
F 01924 377090
E info@the-arthouse.org.uk
W www.the-arthouse.org.uk
Contact Rachael Dent (Art Administrator)
A national visual arts organization established to create equality of opportunity for disabled and non-disabled artists and craftspeople. Founded in 1994 by a group of artists, it is an inclusive organization that believes in enabling all artists to have access to work, training and exhibition opportunities in accessible settings. In 2000, it received £1m from the Arts Council Lottery-funded Capital Programme and is currently working to raise the remaining £2.5m needed to make the Art House building a reality.
Admissions policy Visual artists and craftspeople.
Subscription rates All fees annual: £15 or £7.50 (concessions) per person; £32.50 for group membership; £20 for two persons in the same household.

Art in Partnership
34 Blair Street, Edinburgh
EH1 1QR
T 0131 2254463
F 0131 2256879
E info@art-in-partnership.org.uk
W www.art-in-partnership.org.uk
Contact Lesley Woodbridge
An independent visual arts consultancy and public art-commissioning agency. Provides an advisory, curatorial and project-management service for architects, planners, urban designers and public- and private-sector organizations considering commissioning works of art or developing a collection.
Admissions policy Send current CV and documentation of work, e.g. CD, DVD or slides/publications.

Art Safari
46 Victoria Road, Woodbridge
IP12 1EJ
T 01394 382235
E info@artsafari.co.uk
W www.artsafari.co.uk
Contact Mary-Anne Bartlett
Specializes in taking artists for painting holidays (including art tuition) among the wildlife and landscapes of Malawi and Zambia. Founded in 2003 by travel artist Mary-Anne Bartlett.
Admissions policy Open to artists of all standards. Grants available to professional artists on application. Opportunities to work alongside artists from the host country.

Artists' Network Bedfordshire
26 Russell Drive, Ampthill
MK45 2UA
E melville26uk@yahoo.co.uk
Contact Sue Melville
Founded in 1995 to promote the visual arts in the county. A voluntary artist-led organization promoting exhibitions and studio events. An open-studio event is held every year in September and October over three weekends, during which artists open their houses and studios to the public for free.

Arts & Business
Nutmeg House, 60 Gainsford Street, Butler's Wharf, London
SE1 2NY
T 020 73788143

F 020 74077527
E head.office@aandb.org.uk
W www.aandb.org.uk
A creative network that seeks to help business
people support the arts and the arts to inspire
business people. Fosters long-term partnerships
between business and the arts through an
investment programme, New Partners. Runs a
series of professional-development programmes,
which promote the exchange and development of
skills between the two communities. In association
with the Prince of Wales Arts & Kids Foundation, it
helps businesses develop practical ways of helping
children engage with the arts. Also offers advice,
training, networking and consultancy on a wide
range of issues to business and the arts through a
membership programme.

Arts Catalyst

Toynbee Studios, 28 Commercial Street, London
E1 6LS
T 020 73753690
F 020 73770298
E info@artscatalyst.org
W www.artscatalyst.org
Established for over ten years with a mission to
extend, promote and activate a fundamental shift
in the dialogue between art and science and its
perception by the public. Facilitates collaborative
art–science projects, expanding new territories for
artistic practice and setting up multidisciplinary
research laboratories. Particular current concerns
focus on artists' engagement (practical, artistic,
political) with biotechnology, ecology, space
research, micro- and hyper-gravity research,
astrophysics, biodynamics, and remote
independent research in science, art and tactile
media.

Arts Education Development

16a Broad Street, Bath
BA1 5LJ
T 01225 396425
F 01225 396457
E penny_hay@bathnes.gov.uk
W www.bathnes.gov/arts
Contact penny hay
Runs several major research projects in creative
education: 5×5×5=Creativity, researching creative
learning and teaching strategies in the early years
and primary education; Creative Education for
Disaffected and Excluded Students (CEDES),
researching creative learning and teaching
strategies to engage disaffected and excluded

students, and those at risk of disaffection and
exclusion; The Learning Centre (TLC), academic
research into creative learning and teaching
strategies, including teacher training. Also offers
professional-development courses for teachers to
support arts coordination and creative learning
and teaching strategies.
Admissions policy Open to artists in education.

Arts Project

Northgate Hospital, Morpeth
NE61 3BP
T 01670 394174
E Brian.Scott@nap.nhs.uk
Contact Brian Scott
Operating since 1982. Runs a programme of
participatory arts workshops where visual artists,
musicians, etc. work primarily with people with
learning disabilities. Though based at Northgate
Hospital, workshops also take place in community
venues throughout the region. Special *ad hoc*
projects offer occasional opportunities for
commissioned work.
Admissions policy Keen to hear from artists of
all disciplines who might be able to work in this
demanding field.

ARTS UK

Newburn Enterprise Centre, High Street,
Newburn, Newcastle-upon-Tyne
NE15 8LN
T 0191 2260928
F 0191 2260928
E email@arts-uk.com
W www.arts-uk.com
Contact Steve Chettle
Set up in 2000 as an arts organization to provide
commissioning and other services to private,
public and voluntary sectors. Specializes in public
art commissions.
Admissions policy Artists interested in being
considered for the database should submit a CV
and CD of images.

Association of Illustrators

81 Leonard Street, London
EC2A 4QS
T 020 76134328
F 020 76134417
E info@theaoi.com
W www.theaoi.com
Contact Derek Brazell
Established in 1973 to promote illustration,
advance and protect illustrators' rights and

encourage professional standards. A non-profit-making trade association dedicated to its members' professional interests. Membership consists of freelance illustrators as well as agents, clients, students and universities.

Admissions policy Full members must supply three printed illustrations produced within the last year. Associate membership is for those yet to be commissioned.

Subscription rates £24 joining fee, plus: £120 for full members; £96 for associate members; £42 for student members; £185 for corporate members; £96 for college members.

Aune Head Arts

High Moorland Business Centre, Old Duchy Hotel, Princetown, Yelverton
PL20 6QF
T 01822 890539
F 01822 890539
E info@auneheadarts.org.uk
W www.auneheadarts.org.uk
Contact Nancy Sinclair

A rural-centric arts organization based on Dartmoor. Works with artists and audiences to bring new work to diverse audiences. Aims to: develop projects utilizing traditional and new technologies; engage communities and audiences in aesthetic reflection and debate on issues of rural life; collaborate with organizations engaged in similar work; provide continuing professional development and mentoring to artists within the region; and develop and disseminate models of best practice and innovation for contemporary artists working within a rural context.

Admissions policy Project artists are generally selected via invitation or a commissioning process. Time permitting, it may review unsolicited project outlines that complement the organization's work.

Subscription rates Membership fees range from £5 to £10; artists need not be members to be involved in projects.

Autograph ABP

74 Great Eastern Street, London
EC2A 3JG
T 020 77299200
E info@auto.demon.co.uk
W www.autograph-abp.co.uk

A non-profit photographic arts organization established in 1988. Primary role is to develop, exhibit and publish the work of photographers and artists from culturally diverse backgrounds

and to act as an advocate for their inclusion in all mainstream areas of exhibition, publishing, training, education and commerce. To this end, it produces its own programme of activities, exhibitions, events, residencies, publications, etc. and collaborates with other arts organizations nationally and internationally.

Admissions policy Email up to twelve jpegs of work (each 100 kilobytes or less) plus CV and artist's statement.

Axis

Round Foundry Media Centre, Foundry Street, Leeds
LS11 5QP
T 0870 4430701
F 0870 4430703
E info@axisweb.org
W www.axisweb.org

A not-for-profit organization core funded by Arts Council England and the Arts Council of Wales. The Scottish Arts Council supports activity through project funding. A leading database since 1991 of contemporary artists practising in the UK today. An enquiry service allows commissioners, gallerists, architects and other arts professionals to contact artists with work opportunities. Also researches opportunities and sends them directly to artists.

Bath Area Network for Artists (BANA)

The Old Malthouse, Comfortable Place, Bath
BA1 3AJ
T 01225 471714
E enquiries@bana-arts.co.uk
W www.bana-arts.co.uk
Contact Administrator

An artist-led network established in 1998 to address the needs of the large number of visual artists based in Bath and surrounding areas. It is a non-selective, membership-led organization for artists with a commitment to professional practice. Aims to raise the profile of visual arts activity in the Bath area, establish and strengthen links between artists, artists' groups and art promoters, and advocate increased investment in local arts activities. Members' benefits include a website, newsletter, professional-development opportunities and regular events.

Admissions policy Membership open to visual artists living or working in Bath and North-east Somerset Council or nearby areas.

Subscription rates £15 for individuals; £45 for groups of five or more; £10 for associate members.

Birmingham Artists

Unit 19, Lee Bank Business Centre, 55 Holloway
Head, Birmingham
B1 1HP
T 0121 6436040
E info@birminghamartists.com
W www.birminghamartists.com
Contact Pamina Stewart
Founded in 1987 and formerly known as
Birmingham Art Trust. Committed to the
development of its programme. Uses reclaimed
sites and site-specific venues as alternative gallery
spaces, and has organized several large-scale
international exhibitions, members' shows and
open-studio events. 2004 saw the launch of the
Periscope project space. 'The Window' is a
members' project that exhibits a wide range of
artists and projects throughout the year and
mentors emerging artists. Studio space costs
£2.50 per sq. ft per year.

Bonhoga Gallery

Weisdale Mill, Weisdale, Shetland
ZE2 9LW
T 01595 830400
F 01595 830444
E bonhoga-gallery@shetland-arts-trust.co.uk
The visual arts arm of Shetland Arts Trust, which
celebrated its tenth anniversary in 2004. Open year-
round, showing local, national and international
exhibitions of art and craft. Has a touring exhibition
programme to five satellite venues throughout
Shetland; also runs an education and outreach
programme, community workshops and a
successful residency programme at the Booth in
the nearby village of Scalloway. Housed in an old
converted mill and about twenty minutes to the
west of Lerwick, the main town in Shetland.
The Booth can be rented for £250 per month.

British Academy

10 Carlton House Terrace, London
SW1Y 5AH
T 020 79695200
F 020 79695300
E secretary@britac.ac.uk
W www.britac.ac.uk
The national academy for the humanities and the
social sciences, established by Royal Charter in
1902. An independent and self-governing
fellowship of scholars, elected for distinction and
achievement in one or more branches of the
academic disciplines that make up the humanities
and social sciences, organized in eighteen sections
by academic discipline.
Admissions policy There are Ordinary Fellows,
Senior Fellows (over the age of 70), overseas
Corresponding Fellows and Honorary Fellows
(whose numbers are limited to twenty). Up to
thirty-five new Ordinary Fellows may be elected in
any one year.

British Society of Master Glass Painters

6 Queen Square, London
WC1N 3AR
T 01643 862807
E secretary@bsmgp.org.uk
W www.bsmgp.org.uk
Contact Chris Wyard
Founded in 1926. A society for individuals
involved in the production of stained and painted
glass and other glass treatments (etching,
sandblasting, fusing, etc.), both traditional leaded
methods and non-leaded, for religious and secular
public buildings or private commissions.
Members also involved in research, history,
recording, photography and sale of glass.
Subscription rates £30 per year. Concessions:
£15 for students; £18 for seniors.

Cambridge Open Studios

12A High Street, Fulbourn, Cambridge
CB1 5DH
T 01223 561192
F 01223 561193
E info@camopenstudios.co.uk
W www.camopenstudios.co.uk
Contact Jane Gaskell (Administrator)
Exists to promote the making of original works of
art and craft and to provide an opportunity for the
public to become involved by meeting artists in
their studios, seeing their work and how it is
produced. Started with six artists in 1974 and by
2004 had three hundred.
Admissions policy Must be makers or designers of
original works of art or craft, who live and/or have
a studio in Cambridgeshire.
Subscription rates £25 membership fee;
£5 joining fee for new or lapsed members;
£132 participation fee; £50 non-volunteer fee.

Candid Arts Trust

3 Torrens Street, Angel, Islington, London
EC1V 1NQ
T 020 78374237
F 020 78374123
E info@candidarts.com
W www.candidarts.com

Founded in 1980. A thriving arts centre consisting of three galleries (6,000 sq. ft in total), a café and artists' studios, all available for hire. As a self-funded charity, the trust aims to promote the arts, with an emphasis on newly graduated artists and designers through a marketing package providing exhibition space and artist websites, and acting as an agent for sales and commissions. Also runs the Islington Contemporary Art & Design Fair, regular artists' screenings/film events and life-drawing and painting classes.

Admissions policy Entry requirements for Network AD (Candid's graduate marketing package): a BA or MA certificate; all media and areas are accepted. Welcomes submissions for exhibitions from artists generally.

Subscription rates £60 for annual subscription to Network AD.

Chelsea Arts Club

143 Old Church Street, London
SW3 6EB
T 020 73763311
E secretary@chelseaartsclub.com
W www.chelseaartsclub.com
Contact Dudley Winterbottom
A hundred-year-old members' club for painters, sculptors, architects, designers, photographers and craftsmen. With dining room, bar, garden and thirteen bedrooms (from £37 a night), based in central London.

Admissions policy Proposer and seconder required. Election by committee.

Subscription rates £428 for town members; £298 for country members; £269 for overseas members.

Chrysalis Arts Ltd

The Art Depot, Asquith Industrial Estate, Eshton Road, Gargrave
BD23 3SE
T 01756 749222
F 01756 749934
E chrysalis@artdepot.org.uk
W www.chrysalisarts.org.uk
An artist-led company that has been creating art in public spaces since 1987. Besides working in close collaboration with architects, landscape architects, planners and developers, Chrysalis has pioneered techniques for facilitating community involvement in public art. In 1997, the company built the Art Depot as its base in Gargrave, North Yorkshire, and established an international training centre where artists and others involved in work in public spaces come to learn and work together.

Admissions policy Does not have the capacity to respond to unsolicited applications. See the website for training opportunities, etc.

Community Arts Forum

5 Church Street, Belfast
BT1 1PG
T 028 90242910
F 028 9031264
W www.community-arts-forum.org
Founded at a meeting of community arts activists in Belfast in 1993. A membership-based organization that elects a fifteen-person executive annually. Currently has over three hundred groups and over 150 individual artists affiliated, representing all sections of society in Northern Ireland and all areas, and whose activities cover all art forms. Has been at the forefront of the growth of community arts activity in Northern Ireland over the last ten years.

Contemporary Art Society

Bloomsbury House, 74–77 Great Russell Street, London
WC1B 3DA
T 020 76120730
F 020 76314230
E cas@contempart.org.uk
W www.contempart.org.uk
Founded in 1910. Promotes the collection of contemporary arts through gifts to public galleries and guidance to individuals and companies.

Subscription rates £22.50 including VAT for students; £45 (£40 by direct debit) including VAT for individuals; £50 (£45 by direct debit) including VAT for joint membership shared by two people at the same address.

Contemporary Art Society for Wales – Cymdeithas Gelfydoyd Gyfoes Cymru

1 Court Cottages, St Fagans, Cardiff
CF5 6EN
T 029 20595206
E seccasw@tiscali.co.uk
Founded in 1937. Supports the contemporary visual-art scene in Wales by: annual art-work purchases for gifting to Welsh museums, art galleries and other public institutions; studentship awards; awards to other arts bodies; an annual national Eisteddfod purchase prize; publication awards; lectures and study visits (including abroad); exhibitions.

Subscription rates £4 for students; £24 for single membership; £35 for double membership.

Contemporary Glass Society

c/o Broadfield House Glass Museum, Compton
Drive, Kingswinford
DY6 9NS
T 01603 507737
F 01603 507737
E admin@cgs.org.uk
W www.cgs.org.uk
Founded in 1997 with the dual objectives of
encouraging excellence in glass as a creative
medium and developing a greater awareness and
appreciation of contemporary glass worldwide.
Admissions policy Membership is open to anyone
interested in contemporary glass.
Subscription rates £30 for professional members;
£20 for concessions; £80 for corporate members.

Crafts Council

44a Pentonville Road, Islington, London
N1 9BY
T 020 72787700
F 020 78376891
E reference@craftscouncil.org.uk
W www.craftscouncil.org.uk
The UK development agency for contemporary
crafts. An independent organization, funded by
Arts Council England, that offers a range of services
to makers and the public. London base includes an
exhibition space, shop, reference library, the
National Register of Makers, and Photostore, an
online visual database of selected makers.
Admissions policy Contact the specific fair for
details entry requirements: Chelsea Crafts Fair
T 020 7806 2510 E chelsea@craftscouncil.org.uk;
Collect at the V&A T 020 7806 2507
E collect@craftscouncil.org.uk. For all other
enquiries, see contact details above.

Creative Learning Agency

16a Broad Street, Bath
BA1 5LJ
T 01225 396392
F 01225 396442
E creative_learning_agency@bathnes.gov.uk
W www.creativelearningagency.org.uk
Contact Donna Baber
Established in 2001 as a website resource. Provides
information, signposting and support for artists
and teachers about how to develop creative
learning projects together. Works across four local
authorities: Bath and North-east Somerset, Bristol,
North Somerset and South Gloucestershire.
Forms part of a wider network of arts education
agencies in the south-west. Website is divided into

a searchable online database of nearly one hundred
artists working in all disciplines, an advice and
support section, and opportunities, news and
events sections, which are updated weekly.
Admissions policy Current CRB Enhanced
Disclosure Evidence of three creative learning
projects in last two years, plus two referees.
Subscription rates Free.

Creative Partnerships

T 0845 3006200
E info@artscouncil.org.uk
Provides schoolchildren across England with
the opportunity to develop creativity in learning
and to take part in high-quality cultural activities.
Helps schools to identify individual needs and
enables them to develop long-term, sustainable
partnerships with organizations and individuals
including architects, theatre companies, museums,
cinemas, historic buildings, dance studios,
recording studios, orchestras, filmmakers and web
designers. Currently sixteen Creative Partnerships
areas, due to increase to thirty-six by 2006.

CreativeCapital

3 Wilkes Street, London
E1 6QF
T 020 73752973
E info@creative-capital.org.uk
W www.creative-capital.org.uk
Promotes professional development for artists
and arts practitioners who live and work in London.
A network of arts organizations giving expert
advice to people looking for career development
and information on training, learning and other
relevant services and resources in London. Website
offers up-to-date details of events and opportunities.

Cultural Co-operation

Toynbee Studios, 28 Commercial Street, London
E1 6AB
T 020 74560400
F 020 74560401
E ldc@culturalco-operation.org
W www.culturalco-operation.org
Contact Rizwan Butt
An independent arts charity that promotes
international and intercultural understanding
through the arts. Established in 1987, its
programme includes the summer Music Village,
London Diaspora Capital (an Internet-based
resource that raises the profile of artists from
London's diverse communities), a year-round
education programme for schools, regular

continuing professional development for artists and a number of related projects.

Admissions policy Welcomes contact from artists from London's diverse national and faith communities for possible inclusion on its web database.

Design and Artists Copyright Society (DACS)

33 Great Sutton Street, London
EC1V 0DX
T 020 73368811
F 020 73368822
E info@dacs.org.uk
W www.dacs.org.uk
Contact Janet Tod
Established in 1984. A not-for-profit organization promoting and protecting the copyright and related rights of artists and visual artists in the UK and worldwide. Represents 52,000 artists and their heirs, comprising 36,000 fine artists and 16,000 photographers, illustrators, craftspeople, cartoonists, architects, animators and designers.
Admissions policy Membership is open to any visual creator.
Subscription rates £25 lifetime membership fee.

Design Council

34 Bow Street, London
WC2E 7DL
T 020 74205200
F 020 74205300
E info@designcouncil.org.uk
W www.designcouncil.org.uk
Contact Sandy Gamble
Enhances prosperity and well-being in the UK by demonstrating and promoting the role of design in a modern economy.
Admissions policy Does not welcome submissions from artists.

Devon Guild of Craftsmen

Riverside Mill, Bovey Tracey
TQ13 9AF
T 01626 832223
F 01626 834220
E devonguild@crafts.org.uk
W www.crafts.org.uk
Contact Saffron Wynne (Exhibitions Officer)
The largest contemporary crafts venue in the south-west, representing over 240 makers across the range of craft disciplines. A focus on craft culture for the region, including commissioning, education, professional dvelopment, workshops and lectures. Contact for free mailing.

Admissions policy Members and makers living in the south-west are welcome to apply. Benefits include retail sales, exhibition and marketing opportunities.
Subscription rates £92.50 for full members (associate rate also available).

Dosensos

52 Lavender Grove, London
E8 3LS
T 07932 083337
E info@dosensos.org
W www.dosensos.org
Contact Anna Colin
A curatorial agency since 2002. Has curated and produced international artist-exchange projects, exhibitions and events in collaboration with other curators and venues. Supports artists and projects within the areas of visual arts, sound and new-media art as well as public interventions. Also runs a fortnightly radio programme on visual arts on Resonance 104.4FM and codirects HTTP Gallery.
Admissions policy Welcomes proposals for radio programmes and artists' projects.

East Street Arts (ESA)

Patrick Studios, St Mary's Lane, Leeds
LS9 7EH
T 0113 2480040
F 0113 2480030
E info@esaweb.org.uk
W www.esaweb.org.uk
Contact Anna Gawronska
Founded in 1993 by two artists and now governed by board of directors/trustees. Promotes visual artists' career development through events and by offering high-quality, well-managed studios and facilities on two sites. Artists' support includes professional-development programmes and training sessions tailored to artists' needs. Annual cost of studio space: £9 per sq. ft for Patrick Studios (in city centre); £5.50 per sq. ft for Beaver Studios.

Empowering the Artist (ETA)

11 Markwick Terrace, St Leonards-on-Sea
TN38 0RE
T 01424 461232
F 01424 461232
E info@eta-art.co.uk
W www.eta-art.co.uk
Contact Deborah Rawson (Director)
Established as a limited company in 1998 and now a leading provider of professional-development opportunities for visual artists in the south-east

region of England. One of a network of providers of short courses and mentoring schemes for artists at different stages of their careers.

Admissions policy Any artist can book on the training programme. Access to the mentoring schemes is by application.

Enterprise Centre for the Creative Arts (ECCA)
London College of Communication, University of the Arts London, Elephant & Castle, London SE1 6SB
T 020 75147985
E info@ecca-london.org
W www.ecca-london.org
Contact Deborah Loth
Founded in 2000. Offers advice and information on setting up and running a business or creative practice to London's creative people. Services include free one-to-one sessions with specialist creative-industry business advisers, a calendar of workshops and training, funding guidance and information, and a database of specialist resources. Works across the full range of creative industries, not just the fine arts. Also operates Own It, a free intellectual property advice service.
Admissions policy Does not generally accept submissions but when attending a session with a specialist creative-industry business adviser, it is recommended to bring along any relevant materials such as a portfolio, CV, cards, brochures etc.

Enable Artists
21 Cross Lane, Newton-Le-Willows WA12 9PT
E enableartists@aol.com
W www.enableartists.com
Contact Catherine Taylor Parry (north) or Alice Dass (south)
Started in 2001 to give artists with multiple sclerosis (MS) the opportunity to show their work in a virtual gallery and to exhibit together.
Admissions policy Artists with MS are welcome to apply, as well as other disabled artists who are interested in showing their work in a group. Artists who would like to be involved in finding and organizing exhibition spaces are particularly welcome. Membership from throughout the UK.
Subscription rates Website £12 per year.

engage – National Association for Gallery Education
Basement, 108 Old Brompton Road, London SW7 3RA
T 020 72440110
F 020 73737223
E info@engage.org
W www.engage.org
An international association for gallery educators, artist educators and other arts and education professionals. Promotes access to the visual arts through 'gallery education', i.e. projects and programmes that help schoolchildren and the wider community become confident in their understanding and enjoyment of galleries and the visual arts.
Subscription rates From £29.50 for annual membership.

Euroart Studios and Gallery
Unit 22F @ N17 Studios, 784–788 High Road, Tottenham, London N17 0DA
T 07802 502136
F 020 73544576
E info@euroart.co.uk
W www.euroart.co.uk
Contact Nigel Young
Founded in 2002. A social-action organization working through the arts in Tottenham (Haringey), comprising forty-one studios, a black-and-white darkroom and art gallery. Aims to provide studio spaces, facilities and opportunities for artists and makers and to give people the chance to participate in artistic experiences. Delivers cultural and creative activities to the local community. Gallery programme shows national and international exhibitors. Studio space from £90 to £500 per month.

European Council of Artists (ECA)
Rosenvængets Alle 37, Copenhagen Ø DK-2100 DENMARK
T +45 35384401
F +45 35384417
E eca@eca.dk
W www.eca.dk
An umbrella for national, interdisciplinary artists' councils and artists' organizations, currently in twenty-five European countries. Aims to safeguard the political and cultural position of the arts and artists in Europe and works for the interests of the professional artists in political, economic, judicial and social contexts.

Fabrica
40 Duke Street, Brighton BN1 1AG

T 01273 778646
F 01273 778646
E info@fabrica.org.uk
W www.fabrica.org.uk
Contact Lisa Maddigan
An educational charity with a gallery committed to promoting understanding of contemporary visual art and craft. Opened in 1996 in the defunct Holy Trinity Church in the heart of Brighton. Development was led by a group of artists from Red Herring Studios in Hove. Produces four main exhibition projects a year, in contemporary craft, materials-based installation, lens-based media and digital/interactive art. The Artist Resource, a free information centre for artists, is situated at Fabrica.
Admissions policy Commissions site-specific work. Contact the gallery for more information.

Federation of British Artists (FBA)

17 Carlton House Terrace, London
SW1Y 5BD
T 020 79306844
F 020 78397830
E info@mallgalleries.com
W www.mallgalleries.org.uk
A registered charity and umbrella organization for nine leading art societies. Aims to be the national focal point for contemporary art with timeless values. Has 614 artist-members and over 10,000 artists who submit to open shows. FBA member societies are the Royal Institute of Painters in Watercolours, the Royal Society of British Artists, the Royal Society of Marine Artists, the Royal Society of Portrait Painters, the Royal Institute of Oil Painters, the New English Art Club, the Pastel Society, the Society of Wildlife Artists and the Hesketh Hubbard Art Society.
Admissions policy Submissions should be made to individual member societies (see above).

Figurative Artist Network (FAN)

Unit 112, 62 Tritton Road, West Norwood, London
SE21 8DE
T 020 87613443
E figurativeFAN@aol.com
W www.steveyeates.co.uk
Contact Steve Yeates
An artist-led network set up with the aim of fighting the idea that figurative art is an outdated art form. Seeks to bring together artists who share the same aspirations to encourage and support, discuss and inspire the promotion of innovative work in contemporary culture. Holds group

sessions and encourages the practice and making of figurative art with a view to setting up a collaborative exhibition.
Admissions policy Each member makes contact via email in the first instance and then is invited to submit a current selection of artistic images of the figure on CD or slide.

Florence Trust Studios

St Saviour's, Aberdeen Park, Highbury, London
N5 2AR
T 020 73544771
E info@florencetrust.org
W www.florencetrust.org
Contact Paul Bayley (Director)
Founded in 1989, providing up to twelve studios for one year from August in a grade 1-listed church. An in-house project/gallery space and director are on hand to offer guidance, ensuring artists receive 'much more than just a studio space'.
Admissions policy Annual selection process.
Subscription rates Studios cost approximately £200 per calendar month.

Forma

P.O. Box 637, Newcastle-upon-Tyne
NE99 1JF
T 0191 2304646
F 0191 2306355
E info@forma.org.uk
W www.forma.org.uk
One of Europe's leading agencies for interdisciplinary art. Pioneers new projects with artists internationally. Generates, tours and publishes high-quality work, creating dialogues between artists, audiences and places.
Subscription rates Free regular updates on website.

Foundation for Women's Art (FWA)

55–63 Goswell Road, London
EC1V 7EN
T 020 72514881
E admin@fwa-uk.org
W www.fwa-uk.org
Contact Monica Petzal Director
A networking, adminstrative and educational organization that has as its core activity the promotion of women artists through exhibitions, events and an education programme. The website is a prime UK source of informaton about and of interest to women artists.
Admissions policy Send all proposals to office.
Subscription rates Details of Friends scheme on the website.

Freelance and Self-Employed Disabled People in the Arts (FASED)

P.O. Box 6351, Ripley
DE5 8ZR
T 01773 570077
E co-ordinator@fased.org
W www.fased.org
Contact Kate Rounding (Membership Secretary)
Founded in 2001 with help from Arts Council
England to support the professional-development
needs of freelance arts workers with disabilities.
Provides training, mentoring, skill-sharing and
information distribution on professional
opportunities in the arts.
Admissions policy Membership is open only to
disabled people (broad definition) who freelance,
intend to freelance or are students looking at
working options. Full membership is restricted to
the East Midlands region. Associate members are
welcome from other areas.
Subscription rates £15 for full membership; £12 for
associate membership.

GLOSS

Colwell Arts Centre, Derby Road, Gloucester
GL1 4AD
T 01452 550439
F 01452 550539
E gloss@gloss-aie.co.uk
W www.gloss-artsineducation.co.uk
Gloucestershire's arts education agency. Aims to
provide opportunities for children, their carers and
teachers to engage with a wide range of quality
creative activity. It does this by providing advice,
support and information to schools, youth groups,
artists and arts organizations. Produces a termly
magazine for teachers and artists. Contact the
agency to be added to the mailing list.
Admissions policy See website to register on
online artists' database.

Greenwich Mural Workshop

MacBean Centre, MacBean Street, Woolwich,
London
SE18 6LW
T 020 88549266
F 020 83167577
E steve@greenwichmuralworkshop.com
W www.greenwichmuralworkshop.com
Contact Steve Lobb
Founded in 1975. An artists' cooperative
specializing in the design and manufacture of
murals, mosaics, banners and in the design and
creation of urban parks, gardens and playgrounds.

The group works with local authorities, businesses
and community groups and has a strong
reputation for its collaborative works.
Admissions policy Artists experienced in drawing
and design and interested in working with a variety
of clients should send CV, letter and pictures.

Grizedale Arts

Grizedale, Ambleside
LA22 0QJ
T 01229 860291
F 01229 860050
E info@grizedale.org
W www.grizedale.org
Contact Adam Sutherland or Alistair Hudson
An international research and development agency
for visual artists based in the Lake District National
Park. The programme supports artists in making
new works that relate to the context of the area,
engaging with local communities and events,
integrating artists' thinking and communication
into mainstream and traditional activities. The
emphasis is on developing new approaches to
working and the dissemination of generated ideas.
Up to ten research and development grants are
awarded annually, to develop projects that may
feed into an annual programme of activity.
Grizedale Arts was reconstituted in 2001 as a
successor to the previous residency programme
sited in Grizedale Forest.

Group 75

Tyddyn Squire, Bersham, Wrexham
LL14 4LU
T 01978 757513
F 01978 757513
E m.tietze@btinternet.com
W www.group75.co.uk
Contact Margaret Tietze
A group of professional artists formed in 1975 by
Margaret Tietze. Membership has varied over
time; currently ten members, of whom seven live
in Wales. Work is in mixed media and exhibitions
are toured nationally and internationally with
guest artists invited to contribute.
Admissions policy Artists are invited to join only
on recommendation of group members. A balance
of media and skills is the criterion.
Subscription rates £40 for annual membership.

Guild of Aviation Artists

Trenchard House, 85 Farnborough Road,
Farnborough
GU14 6TF

T 01252 513123
F 01252 510505
E admin@gava.org.uk
W www.gava.org.uk
Contact Susan Gardner
Founded in 1971. Aims to promote, foster
and encourage all forms of aviation art by
providing a forum for discussion of ideas between
members through exhibitions, meetings and
workshops. Holds an annual exhibition at the
Mall Galleries in London, as well as regional
exhibitions.
Admissions policy Aviation art in any hand-applied
medium. Computer-generated or enhanced work
excluded.
Subscription rates £25 entry fee. Membership
rates vary according to status.

Guild of Glass Engravers

87 Nether Street, London
N12 7NP
T 020 84464050
F 020 84464050
E enquiries@gge.org.uk
W www.gge.org.uk
Contact Christine Reyland
Founded in 1975 by a small group of British
engravers. The primary aims are to promote
the highest standards of creative design and
craftsmanship in glass engraving, and to act
as a forum for the teaching and discussion of
engraving techniques.
Admissions policy Membership is worldwide
and open to anyone interested in engraved glass.
The guild welcomes new members, who may or
may not practise engraving. There is a system of
assessment and election within the guild for
practising engravers.
Subscription rates £30 for UK lay members.

here nor there

Bristol
BS
E info@herenorthere.org
W www.herenorthere.org
Founded in 1998 to facilitate international
collaborations in digital-media and audiovisual
performances and events. Projects are developed
through directly participating in international
residencies, events and exhibitions. Utilizes
Internet technology as a resource and as an
arena for project development and creative
collaboration.
Admissions policy Artists are approached through

invitation or project-based calls for submissions
via the website.

Hesketh Hubbard Drawing Society

Federation of British Artists, 17 Carlton House
Terrace, London
SE5 9AX
E info@mallgalleries.com
Runs regular life drawing sessions at the Mall
Galleries. Three models pose, two life and one
portrait, with a choice of short or long poses.
Although not tutored, participants learn from the
company of fellow artists.
Admissions policy Membership is by annual
subscription. A free taster session is offered.
Subscription rates £180 per year.

Independent Art School (IAS)

P.O. Box 304, Hull
HU2 8RR
T 07867 634360
E editor@independent-art-school.org.uk
W www.independent-art-school.org.uk
Contact Pippa Koszerek
An artist-run project set up in 1999, functioning
as a nomadic university. Its online journal contains
writings from past conferences and events. Has
developed as an artistic concept whereby different
artists can take it on.
Admissions policy Welcomes emails from artists
or organizations wishing to collaborate. Artists can
join the e-group via website.

Independent Artists Network (IAN)

23 North Road, Wells
BA52 TL
T 07966 133901 (D. Cameron) /
07775 938500 (C. Black)
E info@independentartists.org.uk
W www.independentartists.org.uk
Contact Duncan Cameron or Carolyn Black
Founded in 1999 by a number of independent
artists in Bristol. Began as a group wishing to
generate new opportunities for exhibiting in the
region. Commissions temporary public art
works on a project basis, both in Bristol and
beyond.

Indigo Arts

9 Cole Road, Aylesbury
HP21 8SU
T 01296 423795
F 01296 392404
E antonia@glynnejones.freeserve.co.uk

Contact Antonia Glynne Jones
A group of artists originally founded by the painter Oliver Bevan. There is no house style but a commitment to making intense, evocative images, whether figurative, abstract or poetic in paint, collage, assemblage and print or drawing media.

Institute of Art & Law
1–5 Cank Street, Leicester
LE1 5GX
T 0116 2538888
F 0116 2511666
E info@ial.uk.com
W www.ial.uk.com
A small independent research and educational organization founded in 1995 to analyze the interface between the world of art and antiquities and that of the law. Main objective is to increase public knowledge concerning the contribution of law to the development of cultural tradition. Organizes seminars and distance-learning courses, and publishes a quarterly periodical and several specialist books.

Institute of International Visual Arts (inIVA)
6–8 Standard Place, Rivington Street, London
EC2A 3BE
T 020 77299616
F 020 77299509
E institute@iniva.org
W www.iniva.org
Founded in 1994. Creates exhibitions, publications, multimedia, education and research projects designed to bring the work of artists from culturally diverse backgrounds to the attention of the widest possible public. Anchored in the diversity of contemporary British culture and society, inIVA engages with culturally diverse practices and ideas, both local and global. Invites artists and audiences to question assumptions about contemporary art and ideas, and acts as a catalyst for making these debates and art works part of mainstream culture.

Ipswich Art Society
Upland, 31 Upland Road, Ipswich
IP4 5BT
T 01473 717521
E enquiries@ipswich-art-society.org.uk
W www.ipswich-art-society.org.uk
Contact Jacqueline Marks
Founded in 1874. Deals with paint, print, sculpture and mixed media. Annual open each May and June, the Anna Airey Award (to young artists aged 16 to 25 and to a mature student) and an exhibition held in February each year.
Admissions policy Membership decided by an election panel that looks at sketchbooks, completed works, work in progress and statement of aims.
Subscription rates £20 for members; £10 for Friends.

Ipswich Arts Association
The Town Hall, Ipswich
IP1 1BZ
T 01473 836448
F 01473 836448
E secretary@ipswich-arts.org.uk
W www.ipswich-arts.org.uk
Contact Vera Rogers (Secretary)
Founded in 1984. Supports the work of arts organizations and individual artists in Ipswich and Suffolk, with over forty member groups. Provides opportunities to discuss matters of mutual concern and acts as a coordinating body for organizations and individuals. Offers advice and information on arts locally and promotes and gives help in presenting events related to arts organizations. Runs talks and workshops, led by professional and amateur practitioners. Works with local authorities and campaigns to secure, maintain and improve facilities for arts organizations.

ixia
2nd Floor, 321 Bradford Street, Birmingham
B5 6ET
E info@ixia-info.com
W www.ixia-info.com
Promotes excellence in public art through information, education and debate. Believes that excellence is achieved through a greater understanding of the nature of public art practice and the impact it has in the public realm. Participants include artists, architects, design professionals, consultants, curators, local-authority officers, researchers and academics.

Kernow Education Arts Partnership (KEAP)
21b Pydar Street, Truro
TR1 2AY
T 01872 275187
F 01872 275182
E hreynolds@cornwall.gov.uk
W www.keap.org
Contact Helen Reynolds
Cornwall's development agency for promoting arts-

in-education activity in learning establishments. Currently works closely with Creative Partnerships Cornwall and plays a significant role in the development of the local programme and partnership. Provides a brokerage role between the arts, cultural and education sectors, and an information service for both artists and schools. Can help schools find practitioners and make the most of them in a school setting, and help artists devise projects, find funding and source training. **Admissions policy** Send CV with education experience and references. KEAP is not an artist employment agency but will recommend artists to schools.

Live Art Development Agency

Rochelle School, Arnold Circus, London
E2 7ES
T 020 70330275
F 020 70330276
E info@thisisliveart.co.uk
W www.thisisliveart.co.uk
Contact Lois Keidan or Daniel Brine
Established in 1999. A leading organization for the support of live art in the UK. Provides practical information and advice, offers opportunities for research, training, dialogue and debate, works in partnership with practitioners and organizations on curatorial initiatives, and develops new ways of increasing popular and critical awareness of live art. The Study Room is a free, open-access research facility used by artists, students, curators and academics and houses one of the largest libraries of live-art-related videos, DVDs and publications in the UK.
Admissions policy Works exclusively with live art.

Luna Nera

Unit 37 Canal Buildings, Shepherdess Walk, London
N1 7RR
T 07949 051908
E mail@luna-nera.com
W www.luna-nera.com
Contact Gillian McIver or Valentina Floris
An artist–curator group since 1997. Has created a number of large-scale live-, visual- and media-art events in disused premises in London and around Europe. Also curates and commissions local and international artists to produce site-responsive works. Aims to stimulate interest in the environmental and architectural heritage of localities.
Admissions policy Interested in strongly site-responsive, collaborative practice only. Does not curate shows for individual artists.

Manchester Academy of Fine Arts

c/o The Portico Library, Mosley Street, Manchester
M2 3HY
T 01457 875718
E cliff.moorhouse@btinternet.com
W www.mafa.org.uk
Contact Cliff Moorhouse (Honorary Secretary)
Founded in 1859. Approximately 120 members covering a broad range of media and approaches. Committed to a developing exhibition programme of members' work and the continuation of the north-west of England's major open exhibition.
Admissions policy £5 registration fee. Submission of up to six works for consideration by council. References and statement also required.
Subscription rates £30 per year.

Media Art Bath

16a Broad Street, Bath
BA1 5LJ
T 01225 396479 / 296440
E sally_shaw@bathnes.gov.uk
W www.mediartbath.org.uk
Contact Sally Shaw
Founded in 1999. Specializes in artist commissions in public contexts in relation to new-media technologies. Also provides training and development opportunities, exhibition and production equipment, advice and support.
Admissions policy Welcomes intelligent, researched, provocative proposals from artists who have a proven capacity to deliver and produce high-quality work. The artist does not have to have prior experience of new-media technologies.

Midwest

P.O. Box 3641, Kidderminster
DY10 2WP
E info@midwest.org.uk
W www.midwest.org.uk
Contact Jason E. Bowman
Since 2003, Midwest has been working with artists, thinkers and organizations in the UK to develop initiatives that encourage artist-led culture on a global level. Hosts an online catalyst project that supports communication and collaboration in the visual arts at a global level. With free membership to date, it allows artists and interested parties to share information and seeks to support artist-led culture.
Subscription rates Free.

Milton Keynes Society of Artists

16 Chalfont Close, Bradville, Milton Keynes
MK13 7HS
T 01908 225290
E katlan@tiscali.co.uk
W www.MKSA.org.uk
Contact Kate East
Founded in 1980. Meets on the last Wednesday
of the month at the Meeting Place in Westcroft
in Milton Keynes. Meetings consist of
demonstrations in all media and a critique.
Members can exhibit four to five times a year with
the society. Monthly newsletter sent to enrolled
members.
Admissions policy Only exhibits original art works.
No prints, digital work or photographs.
Subscription rates £17.50 per year.

Momentum Arts

Bolton's Warehouse, Tenison Road, Cambridge
CB1 2DG
T 01223 500202
F 01223 576307
E info@momentumarts.org.uk
W www.momentumarts.org.uk
Works with a range of partners in east England to
enable the development of best practice in the
arts. Formerly the Eastern Touring Agency, it
changed its name to Momentum Arts in 2003.
Main activities include: networks and forums;
training; delivery of information, advice and
consultancy; capacity building through specific
projects (e.g. in regeneration or in cultural
diversity); action–research projects; dissemination
of best practice theory and research findings;
providing routes to specialist knowledge and
funding sources; making connections between
companies, artists and promoters; and raising the
profile of working partners.

National Association of Decorative and Fine Arts Societies (NADFAS)

NADFAS House, 8 Guilford Street, London
WC1N 1DA
T 020 74300730
F 020 72420686
W www.nadfas.org.uk
Launched in 1968 by Patricia Fay with eleven
societies. Has expanded to over 330 societies in the
UK, nine in Europe, twenty-eight in Australia and
two in New Zealand. With ninety thousand
members worldwide, NADFAS works towards
promoting and preserving the arts. Concerns
include voluntary work to maintain historic

buildings, recording churches and their contents,
working towards developing the arts for the young
and maintaining lecture programmes and tours
for members.

National Campaign for the Arts (NCA)

Pegasus House, 37–43 Sackville Street, London
W1S 3EH
T 020 73330375
F 020 73330660
E nca@artscampaign.org.uk
W www.artscampaign.org.uk
Contact Victoria Todd (Director)
The UK's only independent lobbying organization
representing all the arts. Founded in 1985 to
safeguard, promote and develop the arts and win
public and political recognition for the importance
of the arts as a key element in the national culture.
Relies on subscriptions to sustain its work and
does not receive any public subsidy. Members gain
access to the NCA's information and advice,
networks, seminars, conferences and publications.
Admissions policy Membership is open to
organizations and individuals working in, or with
an interest in, the arts.
Subscription rates £50 for individuals; £25 for
the unwaged. Organizational rates according to
turnover.

National Network for the Arts in Health (NNAH)

The Menier Gallery, 51 Southwark Street, London
SE1 1RU
T 0870 1434555
F 020 72611317
E info@nnah.org.uk
W www.nnah.org.uk
Contact Lara Dose
A membership organization and advocate for the
arts in health field.
Admissions policy To become a member,
complete an application form, which is available
from the NNAH office or online. Membership
includes artists across thirty art forms,
community arts organizations, hospital arts
directors, senior healthcare managers, health
and local authority officers, students, funding
bodies, policy-makers and evaluators. Annual
membership fees are renewable in October and
new applicants will be invoiced on a pro-rata basis
after completion of the membership application
form. All information provided on the form is
recorded in a specially designed database and
used for membership enquiries and requests
from the public and press.

Subscription rates £70 for organizations; £30 for individuals.

National Society of Painters, Sculptors & Printmakers

122 Copse Hill, Wimbledon, London
SW20 0NL
T 020 89467878
W www.nationalsociety.org
Founded in 1930. Holds an annual exhibition in London representing all aspects of art for artists of every creed and outlook. Two newsletters per year for members.
Admissions policy Submission to Honorary Secretary of six photographs of work and CV plus sae for the council's preliminary consideration. Original work will be requested later.
Subscription rates £42.50 for associate members; £85 for full members.

New English Art Club

Federation of British Artists, 17 Carlton House Terrace, London
SE5 9AX
E info@mallgalleries.com
W www.newenglishartclub.co.uk
Contact Bob Brown
Founded in 1885 in reaction to the academic artistic tradition of the time. Members have included John Singer Sargent, Wilson Steer, Walter Sickert, Augustus John, Stanley Spencer, Paul Nash and Duncan Grant. While still rooted in the figurative tradition, today's membership also includes artists who have moved towards abstraction and others whose interests are more narrative. All, however, share a belief in the necessity of good drawing. Holds an annual open exhibition in London.
Admissions policy Membership is by election only but its annual exhibition at the Mall Galleries is open. Details are available from Patricia Renny at the address above.

New Work Network

Top Floor, 449–453 Bethnal Green Road, London
E2 9QH
T 020 77295779
E info@newworknetwork.org.uk
W www.newworknetwork.org.uk
Contact Sophie Cameron (New Work Network Coordinator)
Established in 1997. An artist-led support organization bringing together people working in live art, contemporary performance and interdisciplinary practice in England. Offers a signpost advice service via its searchable website, email and phone. Also advises artists on how to set up artist-led support networks.
Subscription rates £10 per year.

North East Wales Artists' Network (NEWAN)

2 Park Place, Wrexham
LL14 3JD
T 07712 230668
E newan@tiscali.co.uk
W www.newan.co.uk
Contact Jim Duckett
An extended network of artists working across the region since 2001, established in order to provide a support network for recent graduates and other emerging creative talent in the region. Currently comprises eighteen members working across a range of media and at various stages in their careers, from recent graduates to internationally exhibited artists. Primary objectives are the establishment of an artist-run space for the creation and promotion of new works, as well as the development of a vital and energized network of contemporary artists across the region.
Admissions policy Artists must be able to demonstrate a genuine desire to develop their practice. Application is by informal portfolio presentation.
Subscription rates £25 per year.

Nottingham Society of Artists (NSA) and Nottingham Society of Artists Trust (NSAT)

St Luke's House, 71–73 Friar Lane, Nottingham
NG1 6DH
T 0115 9480476
W www.nottinghamstudios.org
Contact Enid Patrick (Honorary Secretary of NSA)
The NSAT aims to promote, maintain, improve and advance education by the encouragement of the arts to include painting, drawing and illustration of all kinds; the whole building is dedicated to art, with two galleries (both for hire) and a well-appointed studio where various study groups attend daily. The NSA (founded in the 1880s) has 260 members and brings together, for mutual help and inspiration, artists and others interested in the visual arts resident in Nottingham and district. Exhibitions held by the NSA take place in St Luke's House.
Admissions policy People wishing to join the NSA as an exhibiting member should submit

three finished works together with a small portfolio of about six items. All work must be signed. Submission twice a year in spring and autumn. People wishing to join the NSAT can join any time without submitting work.
Subscription rates £50 per year. No extra fee to join the society as an exhibitor.

Out of the Blue Arts and Education Trust
The Drill Hall, 36 Dalmeny Street,
Edinburgh
EH6 8RG
T 0131 5557100 / 5557101
E admin@outoftheblue.org.uk
W www.outoftheblue.org.uk
Contact Nicole Lambeng
Founded in 1994 as a gallery space for new artists. Provides studio, production and performance space for Edinburgh's cultural community, while fostering innovative and accessible creative projects (e.g. international tours and exchanges, social inclusion projects, a quarterly arts market). Studio space from £40 to £500 per month.

Organisation for Visual Arts (OVA)
4 Bellefields Road, Brixton, London
SW9 9UQ
T 020 76523937
F 020 76523941
E info@ova-online.org
W www.ova-online.org
Contact Edward Ward
Founded in 1992 as an inIVA franchise, and independent since 1995. A non-venue-based organization that curates exhibitions, conferences and workshops about contemporary art mainly by living artists of non-European descent whose work deals with postcolonial issues. Any medium available for display and presentation in a gallery is suitable. Prefers to work with artists who have some track record but whose work is not part of the European mainstream.
Admissions policy Artists should first look at the website and see if their works are suitable. Then they should make initial contact, which is generally followed by an appointment to visit the studio.

Pastel Society
Federation of British Artists, 17 Carlton House Terrace, London
SE5 9AX
E info@mallgalleries.com
Formed in 1898 with founder members and early exhibitors including Brangwyn, Degas, Rodin, Rothenstein, Whistler and G.F. Watts. Aims to promote the best contemporary work by painters who use the medium for its vibrant colour, immediacy and vitality. Also committed to restoring pastels to the levels of popularity they experienced during the seventeenth and eighteenth centuries and during the time of the Impressionists.
Admissions policy Membership of the society is by election only, but the annual exhibition at the Mall Galleries is open. Send an sae (35p) to 'PS Entry Details', FBA at the above address. Maximum of six works. Acceptable media are pastel, oil pastels, charcoal, pencil, conte, sanguine or any dry medium.

Peacock Visual Arts
21 Castle Street, off the Castlegate, Aberdeen
AB11 5BQ
T 01224 639539
F 01224 627094
E info@peacockvisualarts.co.uk
W www.peacockvisualarts.co.uk
Contact Monika Vykoukal (Assistant Curator)
Peacock Printmakers (Aberdeen) Ltd was established in 1974 by a group of artists. Continues to take pride in the quality of its technical facilities. Aims to bring artists and the public together to share and explore ideas and to make and present art in innovative ways.
Admissions policy Exhibition proposals (any medium) are accepted by letter or email. Mark for the attention of Monika Vykoukal.

Phoenix Arts Association
10–14 Waterloo Place, Brighton
BN2 2NB
T 01273 603700
F 01273 603704
E info@phoenixarts.org
W www.phoenixarts.org
A charitable, non-profit arts organization, offering studio spaces, a gallery and education programme to bring together professional artists and the general public. Offers affordable studio space to over a hundred visual artists working across a range of fine- and applied-art practice, as well as short-term project space for community groups. Phoenix Gallery runs a programme of contemporary visual arts shows in all media. The education programme features workshops in a variety of practices, including life drawing, fine art, art therapy, children's after-school classes, metal jewelry and ceramic sculpture.

photodebut

44 Cheverell House, Teale Street, London
E2 9BN
T 07751 212451
E info@photodebut.org
W www.photodebut.org
Contact Jan von Holleben
Founded in 2003 by the photographers Jan von
Holleben, Esther Teichmann and Andy Porter to
connect and support talented photographers.
Promotes the work of emerging photographers
drawing on their collective strength to develop
group shows, commissions, community projects,
portfolio reviews and educational events. All
photodebut photographers share a continuing
desire to produce critically engaged work within a
variety of contexts.
Admissions policy Send a portfolio, CV and cover
letter with detailed statement of intent, plus sae.

Portland Sculpture and Quarry Trust

Learningstone, The Drill Hall, Easton Lane,
Portland
DT5 1BW
T 01305 826736
F 01305 826736
E psqt@learningstone.net
W www.learningstone.net
Contact Hannah Sofaer MA (RCA) or
Paul Crabtree MA (Ed)
Founded in 1983. The first sculpture quarry in
the UK with work constructed, carved and worked
from the landscape itself. Delivers educational
courses linking the arts to the stone industry,
ecology, earth sciences, architecture and
landscape. Two outdoor workshops: one for
stone carving and sculpture courses from May to
October lasting one to two weeks, for all levels of
skill; the other for more independent work. Indoor
studios and equipment for stone carvers, sculptors
and painters available. Also offers commissioning
opportunities, technical support and an exhibition
hall.
Admissions policy The project and facilities are
open to both established and emerging artists.
Email in the first instance, to be followed up with
telephone call for one-to-one discussion.
Subscription rates £25 per year for Friends
scheme, which offers reduced rates, a newsletter,
an annual Friends exhibition, lectures and events.

Printmakers Council

Ground Floor Unit, 23 Blue Anchor Lane, London
SE16 3UL
T 020 72376789
F 020 72376789
E s.sloss@lcc.arts.ac.uk
W www.printmaker.co.uk/pmc/
An artist-run, non-profit-making association
founded in 1965. Promotes the art form of
printmaking, mostly by exhibitions that show
the public good examples of both the innovative
and skilled use of print. Several shows per year,
selected from the artist members, at different
venues throughout the UK and occasionally
abroad. Most shows include educational activities.
Members receive a newsletter and have the
opportunity to enter shows and be on the council's
website database.
Admissions policy Open to anyone interested in
printmaking. Artist and student printmakers may
enter for selection in shows. Associate members
receive information.
Subscription rates £60 for UK artists; £30 for
students; £35 for associate members; £65 for EU
artists; £70 for non-EU artists.

Prison Arts Foundation (PAF)

Unit 3, Northern Whig House, 2–10 Bridge Street,
Belfast
BT1 1LU
T 028 90247872
F 028 90247872
E office@prisonartsfoundation.com
W www.prisonartsfoundation.com
Contact Mike Moloney
The trust was set up in 1996 with the aim of
putting artists into prison to work with prisoners.
Works in all art forms that are allowable by prison
security in each establishment. Currently has
writers, visual artists, three-dimensional artists,
musicians, dancers, folklore artists, leathercraft
artists, theatre practitioners, filmmakers and
cartoonists engaged in various residencies of
varying lengths.
Admissions policy Operates only in Northern
Ireland; 'If interested, tell us why.'

proof

Unit 6 The Glass House, Royal Oak Yard, London
SE1 3GE
T 020 74070336
F 020 73781585
E multiples@proof.demon.co.uk
W www.metaproof.com
Contact Sue Withers or Andrew Moller
Founded in 1999. An artist-run organization with
three main functions: to create, curate, exhibit, sell

and distribute a range of artists' multiples; to curate and organize exhibitions; and to provide technical help and digital-production facilities for fine artists.

Admissions policy Contact from artists welcomed, but do not send unsolicited materials in any format.

Public Arts

The Orangery, Back Lane, Wakefield
WF1 2TG
T 01924 215550
F 01924 215560
E contact@public-arts.co.uk
W www.public-arts.co.uk

Founded in 1986. Offers professional services and programmes in education and training, public art commissioning, consultancy, general project management and conferencing. The Orangery has been owned and occupied by Public Arts since 1996. A heritage and art site, it includes an exhibition and resource area opened in 2004.

Queens Park Arts Centre

Queens Park, Aylesbury
HP21 7RT
T 01296 424332
F 01296 337363
E qpc@ukonline.co.uk
W www.qpic.org

Contact Louise Griffiths-Kimber or Irene Scott

Founded in 1980. Exists to provide participatory arts activities to the community. Runs over fifty arts and crafts workshops per week including painting, drawing, pottery, woodcarving and willow craft. Also hosts one-off workshops with professional artists. Sells a selection of art materials.

Admissions policy Open-access policy for professional and amateur artists and community groups to exhibit art work in the centre's gallery spaces.

Subscription rates £15 for full members; £8 for concessions.

Realising Art in New Territories (RANT)

12 Sherwood House, 54–58 Station Road,
Ainsdale, Southport
PR8 3HW
T 07971 077406
E craig@craigatkinson.co.uk
W www.craigatkinson.co.uk

Contact Craig Atkinson

Founded in 2003. Aims include promoting contemporary visual arts in and around the north-west, normally using non-standard spaces to exhibit (e.g. old cinemas, the beach, flower beds, houses).

Admissions policy Email in the first instance. Always on the lookout for spaces to use.

Subscription rates Free.

Res Artis – International Association of Residential Arts Centres

Keizersgracht 462 sous, Amsterdam
1016 GE, NETHERLANDS
T +31 206126600
F +31 206126600
E office@resartis.org
W www.resartis.org

An international foundation founded in 1993. The sole worldwide network of residential arts centres. Represents the interests of more than two hundred centres and organizations that offer art facilities and conditions conducive for making art. Membership includes residential arts centres, individuals, artists' unions and organizations that represent numerous residential arts centres themselves.

Royal Academy of Arts

Burlington House, Piccadilly, London
W1J 0BD
T 020 73008000
E info@royalacademy.org.uk
W www.royalacademy.org.uk

Founded by George III in 1768. Governed by artists to 'promote the arts of design' and the first institution in Great Britain devoted solely to the promotion of the visual arts. Receives no public funding and is completely independent.

Admissions policy Annual Summer Exhibition (June to August) welcomes applications in February of each year. Details available on the website or on the number above.

Subscription rates £50 per year for Friends.

Royal Birmingham Society of Artists

4 Brook Street, St Paul's, Birmingham
B3 1SA
T 0121 2364353
F 0121 2364555
E secretary@rbsa.org.uk
W www.rbsa.org.uk

Contact Marie Considine

Founded in 1814. Membership now stands at approximately two hundred professional artists. Aims to promote the arts through holding exhibitions by both regional and national artists. Artists have included Millais, Leighton, Burne-Jones and David Cox.

Admissions policy Membership by election.
Subscription rates £22 per year for Friends.

Royal British Society of Sculptors

108 Old Brompton Road, London
SW7 3RA
T 020 73738615
F 020 73703721
E info@rbs.org.uk
W www.rbs.org.uk
Contact Florencia Guillen
A membership society for professional sculptors,
founded in 1904 by a collective of eminent
sculptors of the day. First granted royal patronage
in 1911. A registered charity that exists to advance
the art of sculpture, ensure a widespread
understanding and involvement in contemporary
sculpture, and promote the pursuit of excellence in
the art form and its practice. Leading sculptors
involved over the years include Sir Hamo
Thorneycroft, Alfred Gilbert, Ivor Roberts-Jones,
Dame Elisabeth Frink, Michael Kenny, Sir
Anthony Caro, Eduardo Chillida, Richard Serra,
Philip King, Allen Jones and Michael Sandle.
Admissions policy Membership categories are:
bursary membership (awarded to a recent graduate
or artist of potential; after two years, automatically
awarded full associate membership); associate
membership (awarded to established sculptors);
fellowship (awarded to associate members who
present a proven track record of distinction and
high achivement); non-selective listing (open to all
practising sculptors based in the UK).
Subscription rates £125 per year.

Royal Glasgow Institute of the Fine Arts

5 Oswald Street, Glasgow
G1 4QR
T 0141 2487411
F 0141 2210417
E rgi@robbferguson.co.uk
W www.rgiscotland.co.uk
Contact Mrs Lesley Nicholl
Founded in 1861 to promote art by means
of annual exhibitions (in Glasgow) of oils,
watercolour, sculpture, etc. Membership of 1,200.
Open to all artists and small gallery available for
solo or group exhibitions.
Admissions policy Works in most media
acceptable. Information available from June each
year. Small gallery also available to rent.
Subscription rates £35 for first year; £25 annually
thereafter. No differentiation between artist and lay
members.

Royal Institute of Oil Painters

Mall Galleries, 17 Carlton House Terrace, London
SW1Y 5BD
T 020 79306844
F 020 78397830
E info@mallgalleries.com
W www.mallgalleries.org.uk
Founded in 1882 and dedicated to promoting the
art of painting in oils. Annual exhibition takes
place at the Mall Galleries in central London.
Admissions policy Open submission to the annual
exhibition. A maximum of six works can be
submitted, of which a maximum of four will be
selected.
Subscription rates Gallery tours are held during
the annual exhibition at the Mall Galleries. £2.50
entry fee (£1.50 concessions).

Royal Institute of Painters in Water Colours

Federation of British Artists, 17 Carlton House
Terrace, London
SW1Y 5BD
T 020 79306844
F 020 78397831
E info@mallgalleries.com
W www.mallgalleries.org.uk
Founded in 1831. A registered charity aiming to
encourage diversity and innovation in the use of
watercolours and water soluble medium. From
its beginning, the society showed non-members'
works alongside that of members.
Admissions policy Artists are invited to submit to
its annual open exhibition. Up to six works in a
water-soluble medium. No metal frames. Send sae
(35p) or see website for details.

Royal Photographic Society

The Octagon, Milsom Street, Bath
BA1 1DN
T 01225 462841
F 01225 448688
E reception@rps.org
W www.rps.org
Formed as the Photographic Society in 1853
and granted Royal Decree in 1894. Mission is
'to promote the Art and Science of Photography'.
Admissions policy Membership open to everyone
with a real interest in photography.

Royal Scottish Academy of Art and Architecture (RSA)

The Mound, Edinburgh
EH2 2EL
T 0131 2256671

F 0131 2206016
E info@royalscottishacademy.org
W www.royalscottishacademy.org
Contact Bruce Laidlaw (Administrative Secretary)
Founded in 1826. An independently funded
institution led by eminent artists and architects
whose purpose is to promote and support the
creation, understanding and enjoyment of the
visual arts through exhibitions and related
educational events. Core exhibitions include the
RSA Annual Exhibition, the RSA Students'
Exhibition and the Alastair Salvesen Scholarship
Exhibition. Also a continuous and changing
programme of new shows. The RSA administers
scholarships, awards and residencies for artists
living and working in Scotland and has an
collection of important historical art works and
an extensive archive.
Admissions policy Offers a number of
scholarships and awards. Check the website or
contact directly for application details and dates for
open exhibitions.

Royal Scottish Society of Painters in Watercolour

5 Oswald Street, Glasgow
G1 4QR
T 0141 2487411
F 0141 2210417
E rsw@robbferguson.co.uk
W www.thersw.org.uk
Contact Mrs Lesley Nicholl
A registered charity founded in 1878 to promote
watercolour painting. Currently has 122 members.
Holds annual exhibitions (usually in Edinburgh)
open to all artists. A major showcase for
watercolourists.
Admissions policy Submissions to exhibitions
must be in water-based media and are subject to
selection. Information available from October each
year. Membership by election.

Royal Society of Arts (RSA)

8 John Adam Street, London
WC2N 6EZ
T 020 79305115
E general@rsa.org.uk
W www.rsa.org.uk
Founded in 1754, today the RSA is an
independent, non-aligned, multidisciplinary
registered charity with over 22,000 fellows.
Encourages sustainable economic development
and the release of human potential through a
programme of projects and a national lecture

programme consisting of over one hundred
events every year. The RSA journal is published
bimonthly and automatically sent to all fellows.

Royal Society of British Artists (RBA)

Federation of British Artists, 17 Carlton House
Terrace, London
SW1Y 5BD
E info@mallgalleries.com
Established in 1823 by a small group of artists
who wished to form an alternative to the Royal
Academy. Granted Royal Charter in 1887. Society
has had thirty-six Presidents, including James
McNeill Whistler, Walter Sickert and Peter
Greenham RA. The society has developed a
strong commitment to issues of education and in
September 1995 supported the foundation of a
new fine-art course based around figurative art,
run by Northbrook College in Worthing. Annual
open exhibition held at the Mall Galleries.
Admissions policy Send sae (35p) to 'RBA Details'
at the above address. Maximum of six works in any
medium, including sculpture and original prints.
The galleries cannot hang works taller than 8ft.

Royal Society of Marine Artists

17 Carlton House Terrace, London
SW1Y 5BD
T 020 79306844
F 020 78397830
E info@mallgalleries.com
W www.mallgalleries.org.uk
A registered charity devoted to the encouragement
and display of contemporary marine painting,
drawing, sculpture and printmaking of the
highest standard. Founded in 1939, but the Second
World War curtailed activity and the society's first
exhibition took place in 1946. Granted royal title in
1966. Annual exhibition moved to the Mall
Galleries in 1981.

Royal Society of Miniature Painters, Sculptors and Gravers

1 Knapp Cottages, Wyke, Gillingham
SP8 4NQ
T 01747 825718
E pamhenderson@dsl.pipex.com
W www.royal-miniature-society-org.uk
Contact Pam Henderson (Executive Secretary)
Founded in 1895. Aims to promote the fine art of
miniature painting or any allied art. Seeks to
provide facilities for the exhibition of works by
artists in these fields.
Admissions policy Apply for an exhibition and

information sheet to the Executive Secretary.
Subscription rates £90 for associate membership;
£100 for full membership.

Royal Society of Painter-Printmakers

Bankside Gallery, 48 Hopton Street, London
SE1 9JH
The Society of Painter-Etchers was founded in
1880 and granted its Royal Charter eight years
later. It changed its name to the Royal Society of
Painter-Printmakers in 1989. Holds an annual
exhibition of members' work at Bankside Gallery
and is involved in group exhibitions and mixed
watercolour and print shows throughout the year.
Committed to raising awareness of printmaking as
an art through education, demonstrations and
talks.

Royal Society of Portait Painters

Federation of British Artists, 17 Carlton House
Terrace, London
SW1Y 5BD
E info@mallgalleries.com
A registered charity that seeks to promote,
maintain, improve and advance education in
the fine arts and in particular to encourage the
appreciation, study and practice of the art of
portraiture. Founded in 1891 with the principal
aim of overcoming the 'uncertainty attending the
acceptance of portraits, however well painted,
by all but academicians'. Became a Royal Society
in 1911. Holds an annual exhibition at the Mall
Galleries. Many substantial prizes are awarded
through the exhibition, and exhibiting artists
frequently receive commissions.
Admissions policy For the open, artists may
submit up to three works in any two-dimensional
medium. Send sae (35p) to 'RP Entry Details' at the
above address.

Royal Watercolour Society

Bankside Gallery, 48 Hopton Street, London
SE1 9JH
Founded almost two hundred years ago. The
first institution in the world to specialize in
watercolours. Members include John Sell
Cotman, David Cox, Edward Burne-Jones,
Helen Allingham, Leslie Worth, Pamela Kay
and Ken Howard. Programme of exhibitions at
Bankside Gallery includes two members'
exhibitions (spring and autumn) and several
joint exhibitions. Also runs an open exhibition
during the summer and a series of educational
activities.

Scottish Artists' Union

c/o Equity, 114 Union Street, Glasgow
GI 3QQ
T 07849 637546
E info@sau.org.uk
W www.sau.org.uk
Contact Executive Committee
The representative voice for artists in Scotland
since 2001. A membership organization
representing visual and applied artists in
Scotland, run by a voluntary committee.
Registered as an official Scottish Trade Union.
Involved in lobbying, defending rights, improving
working conditions and payments, and speaking
up for artists.
Admissions policy Four criteria for full
membership; two criteria for associate
membership. Selected from a generous list.
Subscription rates £35 per year.

Scottish Sculpture Trust

6 Darnaway Street, Edinburgh
EH3 6BG
T 0131 2204788
F 0131 2204787
E info@scottishsculpturetrust.org
W www.scottishsculpturetrust.org
An independent trust that aims to offer advice
and opportunities to sculptors throughout
Scotland. Maintains a database of Scottish
artists working in sculpture, provides information
on national and international projects and
organizations, and advises on funding,
copyright, commissioning, purchasing
and exhibiting. Also arranges events and
conferences, and publishes *Sculpture Matters*
magazine.

Silbury Group of Artists

Westbury Farm Studios, Foxcovert Road,
Milton Keynes
MK5 6AA
T 01980 501214
E admin@silburygroup.org.uk
W www.silburygroup.org.uk
Contact Hayley White
Founded in 1991 as a handful of artists eager to
make connections, find studios and have a place
to show their work. Has evolved into one of the
longest-running artist collectives in the country.
Admissions policy As a members-based collective,
the group is always looking for inspirational
visual artists. Notify interest by email in first
instance.

Society for All Artists (SAA)

P.O. Box 50, Newark
NG23 5GY
T 01949 844050
F 01949 844051
E info@saa.co.uk
W www.saa.co.uk
Founded in 1992. Has over thirty thousand
members in sixty countries and exists to inform,
encourage and inspire all who want to paint.
Welcomes anyone to join, whatever their ability,
and provides benefits including a full art materials
catalogue with five thousand-plus products, the
Paint newsletter, which appears six times a year,
and the chance for artists to promote their work
through the website.

Society of Botanical Artists

1 Knapp Cottages, Wyke, Gillingham
SP8 4NQ
T 01747 825718
E pam@soc-botanical-artists.org
W www.soc-botanical-artists.org
Contact Pam Henderson (Executive Secretary)
Founded in 1986 to promote the fine art of
botanical painting or any allied art and to provide
facilities for the exhibition of works by artists
practising such art. Also seeks to promote the
appreciation and conservation of natural habitats
and plant life, especially endangered species.
Admissions policy Apply to the Executive Secretary
for an exhibition information form and schedule
for the annual open exhibition.
Subscription rates £120 per year.

Society of Catholic Artists

Garden Flat, 36 Warham Road, South Croydon
CR2 6LA
T 020 83617633
E mj.sibtain@virgin.net
W www.catholicartists.co.uk
Contact Mary Davey
Founded in 1929. Aims to supply artists and
craftsmen for the creation and restoration of
church art and fellowship for Catholics interested
in the visual arts. Skills of members include
painting, sculpture, stained glass, ceramics,
metalware, woodcarving and pottery.
Admissions policy Membership is open to any
Catholic interested in the visual arts, though artists
joining for commissions will need assessment.
Subscription rates £15 for members within fifty
miles of central London; £11 for members outside
London; £5 for full-time students.

Society of Portrait Sculptors

T 01825 750485
F 01825 750411
E sps@portrait-sculpture.org
W www.portrait-sculpture.org
Contact David Houchin (Honorary Secretary)
A representative body of professional sculptors
committed to making portrait sculpture
accessible to a wider public. Has an annual open
exhibition and seeks to encourage education and
training in the art through lectures, prizes and
events.

Society of Scottish Artists (SSA)

18 Clarence Street, Edinburgh
EH3 5AF
T 0131 2203977
E ssa@soroka.plus.com
W www.s-s-a.org
Contact Joanne Soroka, Secretary
Founded in 1891. Represents 'the more
adventurous spirit in Scottish art'. Welcomes
members from every country and in all media.
Hosts an annual open exhibition of contemporary
art, held in the Royal Scottish Academy building in
Edinburgh.
Admissions policy Anyone may join as an ordinary
member. Professional membership is by election.
Subscription rates £40 for ordinary members; £50
for professional members.

Society of Wildlife Artists

Federation of British Artists, 17 Carlton House
Terrace, London
SE5 9AX
E info@mallgalleries.com
Founded in 1962. A registered charity aiming to
foster and encourage all forms of wildlife art. The
society's eighty members produce most of the
work on display at the annual exhibition at the
Mall Galleries, but non-members are invited to
submit their work to be judged by the council for
inclusion in the exhibition and outstanding artists
are put forward as candidates for membership.
Admissions policy Send sae (35p) to 'SWLA Entry
Details' at the above address. Maximum of six
works in any medium.

Society of Women Artists

1 Knapp Cottages, Wyke, Gillingham
SP8 4NQ
T 01747 825718
E pamhenderson@dsl.pipex.com
W www.society-women-artists.org.uk

Contact Pam Henderson (Executive Secretary)
Founded in 1855. Aims to promote visual arts
undertaken by women.
Admissions policy Acceptable categories: painting,
drawing and sculpture in all media; miniature
work; engraving, lithography, etc.; ceramics of a
non-utilitarian nature.
Subscription rates £110 for associate members;
£130 for full members.

Spike Island

133 Cumberland Road, Cumberland Basin, Bristol
BS3 4NZ
T 0117 9292266
F 0117 9292066
E admin@spikeisland.org.uk
W www.spikeisland.org.uk
Combines working and exhibition spaces for the
contemporary visual arts. Aims to provide gallery
spaces for 'the making and showing of ambitious
new work'. Also offers seventy affordable studios
and an international programme of residencies.
Admissions policy Artists are welcome to apply for
annual residency programme (see website).
Applications for studio space are also welcome
(forms and details available online or by post).
A selection committee sits four times a year to
select artists for the available spaces.

Suffolk Art Society

Woodview, Watery Lane, Little Henny, Sudbury
CO107NG
T 01787 269432
E moira.orton@btinternet.com
Contact Moira Orton
Founded in 1954, with a membership of around
110 from Suffolk and surrounding counties.
Both professional and amateur artists, mostly
working in watercolour and oils but some
three-dimensional work. Holds three to four
exhibitions annually, visiting important local
churches including Holy Trinity, Long Melford
and Sts Peter and Paul, Lavenham. Awards an
annual prize at Suffolk College to a Fine Art
student on the BA (Hons) course, under
21 years old, showing the most progress in
their studies. Regular newsletters, previews
of exhibitions and an annual general meeting
keep members in touch.
Admissions policy Membership by selection
annually in spring. Applicants (both professional
and amateur) should submit three recent works in
any medium for consideration.
Subscription rates £10

Suffolk Open Studios

46 Victoria Road, Woodbridge
IP12 1EJ
T 01394 382235
E sos@artsafari.co.uk
W www.suffolkopenstudios.co.uk
Contact Mary-Anne Bartlett
Founded fifteen years ago. Attracts over seven
thousand visitors to see the work of two hundred
artists in studios across Suffolk. Aims to provide
an artistic network for artists and public alike,
giving opportunities to artists and helping to
promote their work through publications,
exhibitions and publicity. Studios are open
to the public during the weekends of June
each year and throughout the year by
appointment.
Admissions policy Open to all artists living or
working in Suffolk.
Subscription rates £70 per year.

TotalKunst at the Forest

3 Bristo Place, Edinburgh
EH1 1EY
T 0131 2204538
E committee@totalkunst.com
W www.totalkunst.com, www.theforest.org.uk
Started in 2000, the Forest is a not-for-profit,
artist-led initiative run by volunteers and
financed through a vegetarian café. The
funds are committed to providing a free events
space, exhibition gallery, resource centre, free
broadband, film nights, workshops, garden, live
bands, etc. TotalKunst, the visual-art programme,
launched in 2003.
Admissions policy Applications are accepted
throughout the year. Places an emphasis on
risk-taking works, collaborations and site
specificity.
Subscription rates See website for details:
groups.yahoo.com/group/totalkunst/.

Trans Artists

Keizersgracht 462 sous, Amsterdam
1016 GE, NETHERLANDS
T +31 206127400
E info@transartists.nl
W www.transartists.nl
Contact Director: Maria Tuerlings
An independent information centre for artists,
artist-run initiatives and cultural institutions.
Offers details of cultural exchanges, artist-in-
residence programmes and work opportunities
worldwide.

UK Coloured Pencil Society

c/o Pat Heffer (Secretary), White Meadows, Horton, Devizes
SN10 3NB
T 01380 860205
E secretary@ukcps.co.uk
W www.ukcps.co.uk
Contact Pat Heffer (Secretary)
Founded in 2001 to promote the versatile medium of coloured pencils as well as to support and educate all artists who use it.
Admissions policy Open membership. Art work submitted for the juried annual exhibition must be one hundred per cent coloured pencil; rules vary for other exhibitions.
Subscription rates Within the UK: £25 for full members; £17.50 for associates. Outside the UK: £30 for full members; £22.50 for associates.

Vane

P.O. Box 792, Newcastle-upon-Tyne
NE99 1TX
T 0191 2618281
E info@vane.org.uk
W www.vane.org.uk
Established in 1947. An artist-led organization creating opportunities for artists in the Newcastle area, often with artists and curators from outside the region. Seeks to provide a regional, national and international platform. Manages projects conceived by Vane and by individual artists and curators. Presents projects in a variety of formats and locations.

Visual Artists' Association of Northern Ireland

Flaxart Studios, Edenderry Industrial Estate, Crumlin Road, Belfast
BT14 7EE
T 028 90740465
F 028 90740465
A non-sectarian, non-racist lobbying organization for Northern Irish artists. Hosts workshops and meetings and produces a newsletter.

Visual Arts and Galleries Association (VAGA)

The Old Village School, Witcham, Ely
CB6 2LQ
T 01353 776356
F 01353 775411
E admin@vaga.co.uk
W www.vaga.co.uk
A membership body open to organizations and individuals concerned with the exhibition, interpretation and development of modern and contemporary visual art on behalf of the public. Functions as a catalyst, sharing expertise and knowledge and campaigning for a healthy visual arts sector fit to meet the needs of audiences, creative practitioners and the broader public agenda.

Visual Arts Scotland (VAS)

c/o 4 Mount Charles House, 36 Mount Charles Street, Ayr
KA7 4NY
T 01292 442977
F 01292 442977
E gesso.clark@virgin.net
W www.visualartsscotland.org
Contact Karen Clark
Founded as SSWA in 1920s (evolved to admit men) and became known as VAS. A rapidly expanding society of 370 artists, 160 of whom have been selected to professional membership. Annual exhibition in the RSA building in Edinburgh.
Admissions policy See website, posters or advertisements for annual open exhibition and various awards.
Subscription rates £10 for associate members (students, students graduated in the last three years and artists under 25); £30 for ordinary members.

Visual Images Group

6 Dolphin Place, Aylesbury
HP21 7TG
E vi-group@btconnect.com
W www.bucks-open-studios.org.uk
Contact Sally Bulteel (Chairman elect)
Aims to promote public awareness of the diversity of visual arts and crafts throughout Buckinghamshire and surrounding counties. Representing over four hundred artists, craftspeople and art lovers, the group has run Bucks Open Studios for the past twenty years, when participating artists open their studios to the public.
Subscription rates £12 for individual membership; £18 for family or joint membership.

Vital Arts

Royal London Hospital, Whitechapel, London
E1 1BB
T 020 73777127
F 020 73777317
E info@vitalarts.org.uk
A groundbreaking programme of integrated arts projects for the comfort, healing and well-being of patients, staff and the hospital community. Arts

projects are designed to involve and engage hospital staff, patients, relatives and the local community. Develops commissions and residencies, and shows art by artists, staff and community groups at a number of locations.

Voluntary Arts Network

P.O. Box 200, Cardiff
CF5 1YH
T 029 20395395
F 029 20397397
E info@voluntaryarts.org
W www.voluntaryarts.org
The UK development agency for the voluntary arts, working with policy-makers, funders and politicians to improve the environment for everyone participating in the arts. Provides information and training to those who participate in the voluntary arts sector. Has headquarters in Cardiff and four teams working in England, Ireland, Scotland and Wales.

Wales Arts International

28 Park Place, Cardiff
CF10 3QE
T 029 20383037
F 029 20398778
E info@wai.org.uk
W www.wai.org.uk
Established in 1997. A partnership between the Arts Council of Wales and British Council Wales to promote contemporary culture from Wales and encourage international exchange and collaboration.

Watercolour Society of Wales – Cymdeithas Dyfrlliw Cymru

4 Castle Street, Raglan
NP5 2JZ
T 01291 690260
Formed in 1959 to promote the practice of painting in water-soluble media. Membership of mainly professional artists either living in or from Wales. Members include Ivor Davies, Bert Isaac, Jonah Jones, Mary Lloyd Jones, Richard A. Wills, Des Hawkins and David Tress.

Welfare State International

Lanternhouse, The Ellers, Ulverston
LA12 OAA

T 01229 581127
F 01229 581232
E claire@welfare-state.com
W www.welfare-state.org
Founded in 1968 by John Fox and Sue Gill. A loose association of freelance artists aiming to pioneer new approaches to the arts of celebration and ceremony in the UK and internationally. Advocates a role for art that 'weaves it more fully into the fabric of everyday life'. Designs and constructs performances that are specific to place, people and occasion. Artists are involved as members of small creative teams, project directors, associates, and as members of the artists' forum.

Women's Arts Association

54a Bute Street, Cardiff Bay, Cardiff
CF10 5AF
T 029 20487850
F 029 20487850
E info@womensarts.demon.co.uk
W www.womensarts.demon.co.uk
Contact Ruth Cayford
Aims to provide opportunities for and increase recognition of women in the arts in south-east Wales. Also seeks to increase awareness of the special needs of women in the arts.
Admissions policy Any women over 18 who are artists or have an interest in the arts are welcome.
Subscription rates Membership is free to any woman over 18. Subscription to the quarterly newsletter is £10 per year.

YOlk

49 Harcourt Road, Forest Fields, Nottingham
NG7 6PZ
E info@yolkart.org
W www.yolkart.org
Contact Elaine Speight
Founded in 2003 with the aim of establishing links and promoting collaboration between young artists in Nottingham and its twin cities in Europe. Has since expanded to include artists from any cities who are interested in exploring ideas of place and the city. Works predominantly in live art in public spaces but interested in collaborating with artists from all disciplines.
Admissions policy Artists who are interested in working collaboratively to produce site-responsive art.

10

Art magazines and public relations

The hard sell:
Advancing as an artist through public relations and the media

Ben Rawlingson-Plant and
Helen Scott-Lidgett

Many people are daunted by the thought of public relations or PR – the industry has come under attack in recent years and is distrusted by certain sectors of the media that view it as 'spin'. However, PR is generally recognized as a vital part of the success of any endeavour or business venture, whether it is the latest consumer product on the market or an artist at the beginning of their career, looking to attract a gallery, buyers and positive reviews.

Traditionally, art was a profession or trade learnt through skill and apprenticeship, while artists' guilds, the church or nobility provided support and patronage. However, the history of art is also littered with figures that broke away from their workshop or community to establish their individual reputations as artists. While some artists are well-practised in spreading the word about an upcoming project or exhibition or naturally gifted in the art of self-promotion, others are publicity-shy, perhaps fearful that they may be misquoted or misrepresented in some way.

Happily, there is a middle ground in which an artist can feel comfortable explaining his or her practice, without recourse to force-feeding complex meanings underlying their work to anyone prepared to listen. Art is often deeply personal and it is sometimes helpful to have an outside voice to help communicate the messages – this can be in the form of a curator or dealer, or is often told most eloquently through the words of an arts journalist. After all, PR is the communication of messages, not only through various media, but also through people and objects.

Successful PR for an artist could result in glowing accounts of an exhibition by the country's leading art critics. It could also lead to unwanted headlines, so shock tactics are best avoided unless you have a strong constitution for any potential backlash in the media. The tabloid press is particularly cynical and quick to criticize contemporary art, often portraying it as meaningless and devoid of talent.

Many of the larger commercial galleries and most state-funded public galleries will have press officers or work with PR agencies to achieve the desired level of press coverage for an exhibition. For those not fortunate enough to have this support – which accounts for the vast majority of artists – it is worth noting that there is a standard procedure that should be applied to achieving this goal. The six essential techniques and tools of the trade are as follows.

The press release

Keep it to one side of A4 with a snappy headline and the project title, dates and venue at the top of the page. The first paragraph should be a succinct summary of what the project involves, who the artist is and where the work is being shown. The second paragraph should offer more detail on the work, incorporating names and dates of the pieces to be exhibited. We would advise making the release as factual as possible, as descriptions of art works tend to be overly wordy and off-putting. The final paragraph should briefly summarize what the show is trying to achieve. Contact details should follow with a name, phone number (one that is constantly manned) and an email address. Get someone to proofread all written material. A short quote relating to the artist's work by a recognized name could really help. Any complementary or additional information that may be required by a journalist at a later stage, particularly a standard CV or biography, should be prepared before the release is sent out.

Contacts

Contact details for the numerous art magazines can be found in the next few pages and the more general arts press can be contacted by ringing the switchboards of the national, regional and local papers and asking for direct lines and email addresses. Depending on time, resources and language skills, international press can also be researched, though this is less likely to pay dividends unless the artist is from abroad and targets their country of origin. On national papers it is worth logging the details of the arts editor, the person who commissions reviews in the paper, the art critic, the person who reviews shows for the paper, and the arts correspondent, the person who writes art news stories for the paper. It is also worth contacting the listings pages – some publications use agencies such as PA News to provide details of where an exhibition is taking place, but most national papers have in-house teams who compile this information. Regional or local papers sometimes use one person to cover a number of roles but some will have a specially appointed art critic. Local papers can respond well and this can be a useful tool in driving traffic into a gallery or art space.

Images

It is a good idea to have as many images of the art works as possible available before an exhibition opening. Long-lead publications – all glossy magazines, art magazines and colour supplements – commission articles and art round-ups approximately three to four months in advance and therefore must have access to good-quality, high-resolution images. The simplest way of sending these is as digital images (jpegs) by email. Clear colour shots of the work are preferable and can often be a deciding factor on whether a show is featured. With listings (often working four weeks in advance of an opening) it is advisable to send a couple of images through with the press release. Also, on a practical level, don't send more than two high-resolution jpeg images at one time or you might crash the computer system of whoever is receiving them. If a work is really striking and photogenic it may be worth considering inviting picture desks of national, regional and local papers to send a

photographer down to photograph the work *in situ*. Monitor the papers to get a good sense of the type of image they go for.

Timing

It is worth keeping abreast of the cultural calendar and making sure that your exhibition, project or opening event does not clash with major events at major museums or galleries. It's also worth considering other events such as significant anniversaries that could be linked with the exhibition to give the press an extra reason to cover the exhibition. For example, new art works that are based on human relationships and love could be launched on St Valentine's Day for maximum impact.

Follow-up

Once the press releases and images have been sent out, it is vital to follow up, by email and phone, to ensure that everything is in the right hands and to find out if more information is required. However, never hassle – this will have an adverse effect and guarantee that your show is absolutely not reviewed. It might be worth asking a friend (maybe in exchange for a work of art) to follow up. It is much easier and more effective for a third party to chase any potential press coverage, as many people can be daunted by the prospect of having to promote their own show, particularly during the often stressful run-up to opening a new exhibition. On the other hand, direct contact with the media is to be encouraged, as relationships fostered with journalists or writers can encourage them to write again or may lead to a contribution to a future catalogue essay. Arts media will often adopt emerging artists and provide support and practical help by spreading the word. If and when articles appear, they should be compiled and put into a cuttings folder that could be useful when approaching galleries or collectors.

The opening

Make the most of an evening opening or private view by reaching out to new audiences such as collectors, commercial galleries who may be on the hunt for new talent, or curators from national and regional museums and galleries. Busy art-world grandees are asked to several events in any one evening, but if you have an original, exciting invitation card and can create a buzz of excitement around your project then even the presence of one powerful person on opening night could act as a springboard to greater things.

Ben Rawlingson-Plant and Helen Scott-Lidgett are Senior Arts Manager and Managing Partner, respectively, of Brunswick Arts Consulting, an agency established in 2001 that focuses on the communication needs of arts and cultural organizations and charities.

Art magazines

a–n Magazine
1st Floor, 7–15 Pink Lane, Newcastle-upon-Tyne
NE1 5DW
T 0191 22418000
F 0191 22418001
E subs@a-n.co.uk
W www.a-n.co.uk
A monthly UK magazine for professional artists
and their collaborators. Includes news, reviews,
artists' stories and networks, extensive UK and
international opportunities and art jobs, listings, a
directory, plus a new annual programme of special
subscriber publications focused on key UK and
international visual arts debates, trends and issues.
Current issue and archive since 2001 on website.
Editor(s) Gillian Nicol

AA Files
Architectural Association, 36 Bedford Square,
London
WC1B 3ES
T 020 78874021
F 020 74140783
E publications@aaschool.ac.uk
W www.aaschool.ac.uk
Since 1981, the Architectural Association's (AA)
journal of record, reflecting the current thoughts,
practices and preoccupations of the school's
academic and studio programmes, its tutors and its
students. Published twice a year, AA Files contains
articles on architectural theory, history and
criticism, work by contemporary practitioners and
industrial designers, photography, painting,
sculpture and music, and cross-disciplinary
collaborations. Substantially informed by the AA's
lecture and exhibitions programmes, the journal
publishes original scholarship and projects by those
who visit the school over the course of each year.
Editor(s) David Terrien

Afterall
Central St Martins College of Art & Design,
107–109 Charing Cross Road, London
WC2H 0DU
T 020 75147212
F 020 75147166
E london@afterall.org
W www.afterall.org
Founded in 1999. A journal of contemporary art
published twice a year in London and Los Angeles,
providing analysis of significant art of our time.
Each issue brings together five international artists

whose work seems pertinent to the wider cultural
debates of the moment, considered through a
variety of texts and accompanied by high-quality
reproductions.
Editor(s) Charles Esche, Thomas Lawson and
Mark Lewis

Another Magazine
112–116 Old Street, London
EC1V 9BG
T 020 73360766
F 020 73360966
E info@anothermag.com
W www.anothermag.com
Founded in 2001, covering art, fashion and culture.

Apollo Magazine
20 Theobalds Road, London
WC1X 8PF
T 020 74301900
F 020 74047386
E editorial@apollomag.com
W www.apollo-magazine.com
A monthly international fine- and decorative-arts
and antiques magazine. Founded in 1925 and
relaunched in 2004 in full colour, with a more
topical, contemporary flavour. Specializes in
the publication of new scholarly research. Also
publishes book and exhibition reviews, news and
comment.
Editor(s) Michael Hall

Art & Architecture Journal
70 Cowcross Street, London
EC1M 6EJ
T +33 145670334
F +33 145670334
E editor@artandarchitecturejournal.com
W www.artandarchitecturejournal.com
Specializes in contemporary art and architecture
collaboration, delivering professional information
on public art commissions and projects as a
multidisciplinary activity. Founded in 1980 and
published quarterly.
Editor(s) Jeremy Hunt

The Art Book
Laughton Cottage, Laughton, nr Lewes
BN8 6DD
T 01323 811759
F 01323 811756
E ed-exec-theartbook@aah.org.uk
Published quarterly on behalf of the Association
of Art Historians. Details newly published books

on decorative, fine and applied art, art history, photography, architecture and design. Includes feature articles, reviews of exhibitions and their catalogues, reviews of artists' books and interviews with key figures in the art world. At least fifty reviews in each issue on art, photography and architecture books.
Editor(s) Sue Ward (Executive Editor)

Art History

c/o AAH, 70 Cowcross Street, London
EC1M 6EJ
E ed-arthistory@aah.org.uk
W www.aah.org.uk/pubs/arthistory.html
The journal of the Association of Art Historians, providing an international forum for original research relating to all aspects of the historical and theoretical study of painting, sculpture, design and other visual imagery.

Art Monthly

4th Floor, 28 Charing Cross Road, London
WC2H 0DB
T 020 72400389
F 020 74970726
E info@artmonthly.co.uk
W www.artmonthly.co.uk
A leading journal of contemporary art founded in 1976. Ten issues a year. Includes interviews, features, reviews and reports. For 'anyone with a serious interest in contemporary art'. Reviews of mid-career and up-and-coming artists as well as the leading lights.
Editor(s) Patricia Bickers

The Art Newspaper

70 South Lambeth Road, London
SW8 1RL
T 020 77353331
F 020 77353332
E contact@theartnewspaper.com
W www.theartnewspaper.com
A leading paper for the international art world.
Editor(s) Cristina Ruiz

Art Quarterly

7 Cromwell Place, London
SW7 2JN
T 020 72254821
F 020 72254807
E info@artfund.org
W www.artfund.org
The magazine of the National Art Collections Fund (Art Fund). Covers all aspects of the visual arts and

includes a news section, opinion pieces, features by celebrated art experts, writers and personalities, book reviews, and exhibition listings. Published four times a year.
Editor(s) Caroline Bugler

The Artist

Caxton House, 63–65 High Street, Tenterden
TN30 6BD
T 01580 763673
F 01580 765411
W www.theartistmagazine.co.uk
Founded in 1931. Aims to provide inspiration, instruction and ideas for all artists, professional and amateur. Each monthly issue contains masterclasses and 'in conversation' features with leading artists, reports on materials, events, exhibitions and news relevant to all practising painters.
Editor(s) Sally Bulgin

Artists & Illustrators

226 City Road, London
EC1V 2TT
T 020 77008500
F 020 72534370
E aim@quarto.com
W www.aimag.co.uk
Established in 1986. The UK's best-selling magazine for practising artists. Also organizes Europe's biggest art materials exhibition.

ArtReview

Hereford House, 23–24 Smithfield Street, London
EC1A 9LF
T 020 72364880
E info@art-review.co.uk
W www.art-review.co.uk
A monthly magazine with articles on the visual arts of the twentieth and twenty-first centuries written by international art critics and writers, novelists and cultural historians including Luc Sante, Geoff Dyer, Gordon Burn, Jonathan Lethem, Matthew Collings and Natasha Walter.

Arts Research Digest

Holy Jesus Hospital, City Road, Newcastle-upon-Tyne
NE1 2AS
T 0191 2333856
F 0191 2333857
E hc.ard@unn.ac.uk
W arts-research-digest.com

A specialist journal providing up-to-date details about current and recent research in the arts and cultural sector around the world. Published three times a year and available by subscription only.
Editor(s) Nessa O. Mahony

Audio Arts

6 Briarwood Road, London
SW4 9PX
T 020 77209129
E editor@audio-arts.co.uk
W www.audio-arts.co.uk
Since 1973, the only art magazine regularly published on audio cassette, bringing listeners into contact with contemporary artists and the critical discourse surrounding contemporary art. Each year there are cassette and CD editions of up to 120 minutes' duration, accompanied by supporting texts and colour images.

Blueprint

ETP Ltd, 6–14 Underwood Street, London
N1 7JQ
T 020 74900049
E vrichardson@wilmington.co.uk
W www.wdis.co.uk/blueprint/
A magazine of contemporary architecture, design and culture.

British Journal of Aesthetics

Department of Philosophy, University of York, York
YO10 5DD
F 01904 433251
E P.V.Lamarque@york.ac.uk
W bjaesthetics.oupjournals.org
Founded in 1960. An international forum for debate in aesthetics and the philosophy of art. Published to promote the study, research and discussion of the fine arts and related types of experience from a philosophical standpoint. Appears quarterly and includes a substantial reviews section.
Editor(s) Professor Peter Lamarque

British Journal of Photography

Incisive Media, Haymarket House, London
SW1Y 4RX
T 020 74849700
F 020 74849969
E bjp.editor@bjphoto.co.uk
W www.bjp-online.com
Founded in 1854. The world's longest-running weekly photography magazine. Focusing on professional photography, the magazine contains international news, listings, reviews and features including interviews, market reports, book and exhibition reviews and business-related matters. Covers all areas of professional photography, from fine art, advertising and fashion, to editorial, industrial, weddings, scientific and medical.

The Burlington Magazine

14–16 Duke's Road, London
WC1H 9SZ
T 020 73881228
F 020 7388229
E burlington@burlington.org.uk
W www.burlington.org.uk
Has appeared every month since its creation in 1903. Selects concise, authoritative articles from internationally renowned scholars presenting new works, discoveries and fresh interpretations in painting, sculpture, architecture and the decorative arts, from the antiquity to the present day. Contains main articles, shorter notices, exhibition and book reviews, and a calendar of forthcoming exhibitions. Also contains advertisements with details of works currently on the market.

Ceramic Review

25 Foubert's Place, London
W1F 7QF
T 020 7439 3377
E editorial@ceramicview.com
W www.ceramicreview.com
The international magazine of ceramic art and craft, founded in 1970. Published six times a year. Illustrated in full colour throughout, it includes practical and critical features on ceramic works from the UK and around the world. Also carries news of events and exhibitions as well as reviews of exhibitions and books, plus a comprehensive 'What's On' listing. Aimed at anyone working or involved in the world of ceramics and studio pottery, as well as libraries, collectors, curators and museums.
Editor(s) Emmanuel Cooper

Circa

43–44 Temple Bar, Dublin
2, IRELAND
T +353 16797388
E info@recirca.com
W www.recirca.com

Ireland's leading magazine for contemporary visual arts. Published quarterly and includes news, reviews, previews, interviews, feature articles and a host of images.

Contemporary

K101, Tower Bridge Business Complex, 100 Clements Road, London
SE16 4DG
T 020 77401740
F 020 72523510
E info@contemporary-magazine.com
W www.contemporary-magazine.com
Relaunched in 2002. A monthly magazine with an estimated readership of over 75,000. Covers visual arts, news, books, trivia, architecture, design, fashion, film, music, new media, photography, dance and sport.
Editor(s) Brian Muller (Publisher/Editor)

Crafts Magazine

44a Pentonville Road, Islington, London
N1 9BY
T 020 72787700
F 020 78376891
W www.craftscouncil.org.uk/crafts/index.htm
A decorative- and applied-arts magazine published by the Crafts Council. The only British magazine to cover all craft forms, from studio work to public commissions, and from modern experimental work to traditional and historic designs. Published on alternate months.

Dazed & Confused

112–116 Old Street, London
EC1V 9BG
T 020 73360766
F 020 73360966
W www.confused.co.uk
Monthly magazine founded in 1992, dealing in cutting-edge art and fashion.

EI8HT magazine

foto8., 18 Great Portland Street, London
W1W 8QP
T 020 76360399
F 020 7636 888
E info@foto8.com
W www.foto8.com
A picture-led magazine presenting photo reportages by award-winning photographers and exclusive essays written by leading journalists. Published quarterly.
Editor(s) Jon Levy

Flux Magazine

42 Edge Street, Manchester
M4 1HN
T 0161 8320300
F 0161 8191196
E mike@fluxmagazine.com
W www.fluxmagazine.com
A UK-based magazine covering fashion, music, art and culture.

frieze

5–9 Hatton Wall, London
EC1N 8HX
T 020 78135555
E editors@frieze.com
W www.frieze.com
A magazine of contemporary art and culture from the organizers of the Frieze Art Fair.

Galleries

Barrington Publications, 54 Uxbridge Road, London
W12 8LP
T 020 87407020
E artefact@artefact.co.uk
W www.artefact.co.uk
The UK's largest-circulating monthly arts listings magazine, describing current exhibitions and the stock of over five hundred commercial and public art galleries, galleries for hire and art services.

The Good Gallery Guide

The Art House, Wakefield College, Margaret Street, Wakefield
WF1 2DH
T 01924 377740
F 01924 377090
E info@the-arthouse.org.uk
W www.goodgalleryguide.com
Aims to make visiting galleries easier for everyone. Initially started as a guide to help disabled people plan visits to art galleries but can now be used by all visitors. For each gallery there are details of how to get there, what facilities exist and a personal review of the gallery. Aims to work with galleries to improve their access.
Editor(s) Stuart Bolton

I-D Magazine

124 Tabernacle Street, London
EC2A 45A
T 020 74909710
F 020 72512225
W www.i-dmagazine.com

Began as a fanzine dedicated to the street style of punk-era London in 1980. Has metamorphosed into a glossy magazine that documents fashion.
Editor(s) Terry Jones (Editor-in-Chief)

icon

Media 10 Limited, National House, High Street, Epping
CM16 4BD
T 01992 570030
F 01992 570031
E info@icon-magazine.co.uk
W www.icon-magazine.co.uk
A major monthly international design and architecture magazine.

Irish Arts Review

State Apartments, Dublin Castle, Dublin 2, IRELAND
T +353 16793525
E sperkins@irishartsreview.com
W www.irishartsreview.com
Founded in 1984. Ireland's leading art magazine, published four times a year. Each edition runs to 150 fully illustrated pages and features articles on printing, sculpture, design, architecture, exhibitions and photography.
Editor(s) John Mulcahy

The Jackdaw

88 Leswin Road, London
N16 7ND
T 020 72544027
E dg.lee@virgin.net
W www.thejackdaw.co.uk
Founded in 2000. A newsletter for the visual arts published ten times a year.

Journal of Visual Art Practice

Nottingham Trent University, Nottingham
NG1 4BU
E richard.woodfield@ntu.ac.uk
W www2.ntu.ac.uk/ntsad/nafae/publications.shtml
Founded by the National Association of Fine Art Education in 2000 and published by Intellect. Aimed at tutors and students in the fine-art sector. Addresses issues of contemporary debate in fine-art studios, in matters of both content and practice. Particularly welcomes contributions from studio tutors and students undertaking the Fine Art PhD.

Journal of Visual Culture

Joanne Morra, Central St Martins College of Art & Design, London
WC1B 4AP
E g.morra@csm.arts.ac.uk
Published three times a year. Aims to promote research, scholarship and critical engagement with visual cultures from a range of methodological positions, at various historical moments, and across diverse geographical locations.
Editor(s) Marquard Smith, Raiford Guins, Joanne Morra, Onayra Cruz, Mark Little, Simon Ofield, Vivian Rembere and Rob Stone

Marmalade Magazine

Kent House, 14–17 Market Place, London
W1W 8BY
T 020 76121139
F 020 76121112
E mail@marmaladeworld.com
W www.marmaladeworld.com
Aimed at a readership from the creative industries, from art and design, fashion and advertising, to music and the media in general. Carries a mix of new ideas and trends, as well as being a committed showcase for new creative talent.
Editor(s) Kirsty Robinson and Sacha Spencer Trace

Modern Painters

3rd Floor, 52 Bermondsey Street, London
SE1 3UD
T 020 74079244
F 020 74079242
E info@modernpainters.co.uk
W www.modernpainters.co.uk
A monthly art publication founded in 1988. Covers visual and performing arts and culture.
Editor(s) Karen Wright

n.paradoxa

38 Bellot Street, London
SE10 OAQ
T 020 88583331
F 020 88583331
E k.deepwell@ukonline.co.uk
W web.ukonline.co.uk/n.paradoxa/index.htm
The only international feminist art journal dedicated to contemporary women (visual) artists and feminist theory. Contributions are published by women writers, curators, artists and critics from around the world. In print since 1998. A separate edition started online in 1996. Online and print

versions contain different contents. Print editions are organized thematically.
Editor(s) Katy Deepwell

NADFAS Review
NADFAS House, 8 Guilford Street, London
WC1N 1DA
T 020 74300730
F 020 72420686
E nadfasreview@nadfas.org.uk
W www.nadfasorg.uk
The quarterly magazine of the arts-based educational charity, with over 330 member societies and ninety thousand members worldwide. Offers in-depth articles on the decorative arts, current exhibtions listings and showcases of many of the volunteer projects that members are involved in.
Editor(s) Judith Quiney and Glyn Wilmhurst

Next Level
95 Greenwood Road, London
E8 1NT
T 020 79232117
F 020 79232117
E sheyi@nextleveluk.com
W www.nextleveluk.com
An independent photography publication launched in 2002 and released twice a year during May and October. Aims to showcase new and established photographic artists from around the world and to bring awareness and debate to contemporary issues from a visual and text-based perspective.
Editor(s) Sheyi Antony Bankale and Jimo Salako

Object – Graduate Research and Reviews in the History of Art and Visual Culture
History of Art Department, University College London, Gower Street, London
WC1E 6BT
T 020 76797545
F 020 79165939
E e.richardson@ucl.ac.uk
W www.ucl.ac-uk/art-history/objectmagazine.htm
Founded in 1998. An annual journal produced and edited by postgraduate students from the History of Art Department at UCL, featuring articles drawn from ongoing research alongside reviews of recent exhibitions and publications. Contents represent the diversity of issues and methodologies with which the postgraduate students in the department are engaged.
Editor(s) Emily Richardson (Editor-in-Chief)

Oxford Art Journal
Mary Hunter, Department of Art History, University College London, Gower Street, London
WC1E 6BT
W oaj.oupjournals.org
Has an international reputation for publishing innovative critical work in art history. Committed to the political analysis of visual art and material representation from a variety of theoretical perspectives, and has carried work addressing themes from antiquity to contemporary-art practice. Also carries extended reviews of major contributions to the field.

Performance Research
Linden Elmhirst (Administrative Assistant), Dartington College of Arts, Totnes
TQ9 6EJ
T 01803 861683
E performance-research@dartington.ac.uk
W www.performance-research.net
Founded in 1995 and published quarterly. A specialist journal that promotes the dynamic interchange between scholarship and practice in the expanding field of performance. Interdisciplinary in vision and international in scope, its emphasis is on research in contemporary performance arts within changing cultures.

Portfolio – The Catalogue of Contemporary Photography in Britain
43 Candlemaker Row, Edinburgh
EH1 2QB
T 0131 2201911
F 0131 2264287
E Info@portfoliocatalogue.com
W www.portfoliocatalogue.com
A magazine for innovative photographic art created and shown in the Britain. Published in June and December, combining the contemporary interests and current reviews of a magazine with the quality reproductions and detailed information of an exhibition catalogue. Features the work of established photographers and artists, accompanied by in-depth essays, a series of portfolios by emerging artists, and reviews from esteemed writers and curators. Large-format publication (295mm × 245mm), containing seventy-two pages of colour and duotone photographs.

Print Quarterly
52 Kelso Place, London
W8 5QQ
T 020 77954987

F 020 77954988
E admin@printquarterly.co.uk
W www.printquarterly.co.uk
Has a mission to advance, promote and encourage education and research in the field of art history and the contemporary arts, in particular in the medium of prints.
Editor(s) David Landau

Printmaking Today

Cello Press Ltd, 99–101 Kingsland Road, London
E2 8AG
T 020 77398645
E mikesims@pt.cellopress.co.uk
W www.printmakingtoday.co.uk
First published in 1990. The authorized journal of the Royal Society of Painter–Printmakers. Aims to provide a forum for printmakers, collectors and curators.

RA Magazine

Royal Academy of Arts, Burlington House,
Piccadilly, London
W1J 0BD
T 020 73005820
F 020 73005882
E ramagazine@royalacademy.org.uk
W www.ramagazine.org.uk
Founded in 1983. Published quarterly in association with the Royal Academy of Arts (RA) in London, and distributed to the ninety thousands Friends of the RA as part of their membership benefits. In addition, ten thousand copies of the magazine sell in the academy shop, on specialist news stands and by subscription. Editorial covers art, exhibitions and events at the RA and by Royal Academicians, as well as art, architecture, books and culture more broadly in Britain and abroad.
Editor Sarah Greenberg

Raw Vision

1 Watford Road, Radlett
WD7 8LA
T 01923 856644
F 01923 859897
E info@rawvision.com
W www.rawvision.com
Founded in 1989 to bring Outsider art to an international audience. Has since moved on to cover subjects that fall into the fields of Art Brut, Outsider art, contemporary folk art, visionary art and the marginal arts of the world. Produced quarterly but going up to five issues from 2006.
Editor(s) John Maizels

Royal Photographic Society Journal

Finsbury Business Centre, 40 Bowling Green
Lane, London
EC1R 0NE
T 020 74157099
F 020 74157133
E mail@rpsjournal.co.uk
The journal of the Royal Photographic Society. Published ten times a year. Promotes the art and science of photography, covering all aspects of the medium, and featuring interviews with key photographers, equipment and book reviews, comment and analysis.
Editor(s) David Land

RSA Journal

8 John Adam Street, London
WC2N 6EZ
T 020 74516902
E amanda.jordan@rsa.org.uk
W www.thersa.org/journal/index.asp
The bimonthly journal of the Royal Society for the Encouragement of Arts.

Sculpture Journal

Liverpool University Press, 4 Cambridge Street,
Liverpool
L17 0AB
T 0151 7942234
F 0151 7942235
E lup@liv.ac.uk
W www.liverpool-unipress.co.uk
Founded in 1997. Britain's foremost scholarly journal devoted to sculpture in all its aspects. Disseminates information, scholarship and knowledge in the international field of sculpture from the late-medieval period to the present day and provides an international forum for sculptors, writers and scholars. Published twice a year (March and October), the journal includes illustrated scholarly articles on all aspects of sculpture, reviews of exhibitions and publications. Published for and reflects the aims of the Public Monuments and Sculpture Association.
Editor(s) Katharine Eustace

Selvedge

P.O. Box 40038, London
N6 5UW
T 020 83419721
F 020 83419721
E enquiries@selvedge.org
W www.selvedge.org

A magazine of textiles in all forms, including fine art, fashion and interiors. Six issues per year.

Source Magazine

P.O. Box 352, Belfast
BT12WB
T 028 90329691
E info@source.ie
W www.source.ie
A quarterly magazine founded in 1992, providing informed critical debate around contemporary photographic culture. Reproduces sections of individual photographers' work alongside exhibition and book reviews, and in-depth essays on photographic culture.

Tate Etc

20 John Islip Street, London
SW1P 4RG
T 020 78878724
F 020 78878729
E tateetc@tate.org.uk
W www.tate.org.uk/tateetc
Published three times per year, with a circulation of eighty thousand. Features in-depth articles by leading writers in their fields such as Alain de Botton, Paul Farley, Alison Gingeras and Lynne Cooke, and has a strong emphasis on giving a voice to artists. While a certain percentage of the magazine is devoted to exhibitions at the four Tates (Modern, Britain, Liverpool and St Ives) it also includes polemical, thematic features. Within these articles the magazine aims to blend the historical, modern and contemporary.
Editor(s) Simon Grant

things magazine

P.O. Box 35095, London
NW1 7WN
T 020 72675891
E editors@thingsmagazine.net
W www.thingsmagazine.net
Originally founded in 1994 by a group of writers and historians based at the Victoria & Albert Museum and the Royal College of Art in the belief that objects can open up new ways of understanding the world. The magazine is both online and an occasional print publication.
Editor(s) Hildi Hawkins and Jonathan Bell

Third Text

2G Crusader House, 289 Cricklewood Broadway, London
NW2 6NX
T 020 88307803
E thirdtext@btconnect.com
W www.tandf.co.uk/journals/titles/09528822.html
An international scholarly journal dedicated to providing critical perspectives on art and visual culture. Examines the theoretical and historical ground by which the West legitimizes its position as the ultimate arbiter of what is significant in this field. A forum for the discussion and (re-)appraisal of the theory and practice of art, art history and criticism, and the work of artists hitherto marginalized thorough racial, gender, religious and cultural differences.
Editor(s) Rasheed Araeen

Time Out

Universal House, 251 Tottenham Court Road, London
W1T 7AB
T 020 78133000
F 020 78136001
W www.timeout.com
A guide to what's happening in London. First published in 1968.

V&A Magazine

V&A, South Kensington, Cromwell Road, London
SW7 2RL
T 020 79422000
E vanda@vam.ac.uk
W www.vam.ac.uk
The quarterly magazine of the Victoria & Albert Museum. Subject matter includes contemporary design, interior design, photography, fashion, art, architecture, craft and textiles.

Variant

1/2 189b Maryhill Road, Glasgow
G20 7XJ
T 0141 3339522
E variant@ndirect.co.uk
W www.variant.org.uk
An independent critical arts and culture publication published three times a year, with a circulation of ten thousand copies. Aims to widen the involvement of its readership in debate, discussion and awareness of social, political and cultural issues that are otherwise ignored, hidden, suppressed or censored. Looks to its readership to provide, inform and generate content for the magazine. All articles are free on the website.
Editor(s) Daniel Jewesbury and Leigh French

Visual Culture in Britain
University of Northumbria, School of Arts and Sciences, Squires Building, Sandyford Road, Newcastle-upon-Tyne
NE1 8ST
T 0191 2273235
E ysanne.holt@unn.ac.uk
W www.manchesteruniversitypress.co.uk:
Founded in 2000. Aims to locate the range of visual culture – art, design, print, photography, the performing arts, etc. – in relation to the wider culture (historically and geographically), from the eighteenth century to the present. The journal addresses visual culture in the context of debates such as racial, ethnic and gender identities, nationality and internationalism, high and low culture, and models of production and consumption.
Editor(s) Ysanne Holt

Wallpaper*
T 020 73221592
E editor@wallpaper.com
W www.wallpaper.com
A magazine 'for urban modernists and global navigators'. Aimed at an international audience, covering interiors, industrial design, architecture, entertaining, fashion and travel.

Public relations

Arts Marketing Association
7a Clifton Court, Clifton Road, Cambridge
CB1 7BN
T 01223 578078
F 01223 245862
E info@a-m-a.co.uk
W www.a-m-a.co.uk
Supports the professional development of its members via a range of tools including a mentoring scheme, an accredited certificate in arts marketing, publications (many available free to members), a website, and a broad programme of events.

artsinform
Farncombe House, 16 Market Street, Lewes
BN7 2NB
T 01273 488996
F 01273 488497
E jessica@mediacontacts.org.uk
W www.mediacontacts.org.uk
A marketing consultancy and public relations agency working exclusively within the visual arts

sector. Set up in 1994 by arts journalists Jessica Wood and Rosie Clarke.

The Artspost
Lewisham Library, 199–201 Lewisham High Street, Lewisham
SE13 6LG
A free publicity distribution service available to arts and community organizations throughout the borough. Distributes to over ninety venues in Lewisham.

Bolton & Quinn Ltd
10 Pottery Lane, Holland Park, London
W11 4LZ
T 020 72215000
F 020 72218100
E erica@boltonquinn.com
Offers public relations services in the arts and culture sector.

Brower Lewis Pelham PR
74 Gloucester Place, London
W1U 6HH
T 020 79353414
F 020 79352739
E jasmin@blppr.com
W www.blppr.com
Works with art galleries, arts organizations, art fairs and independent artists to provide strategic public relations campaigns. With over ten years' experience.

Cawdell Douglas
10–11 Lower John Street, London
W1R 3PE
T 020 77340985
F 020 72875488
E press@cawdelldouglas.co.uk
Offers public-relations services for the art world.

Hobsbawm Media + Marketing Communications Ltd (HMC)
15 Doughty Street, Bloomsbury, London
WC1N 2PL
T 020 74309444
F 020 74309595
E julia@hmclondon.co.uk
W hmclondon.co.uk
An independent London-based communications consultancy with over a decade of experience.
Editor(s) Julia Hobsbawm (Chief Executive and Founder)

Idea Generation
10 Greenland Street, London
NW1 0ND
T 020 74284949
F 020 74284948
E frontdoor@ideageneration.co.uk
W www.ideageneration.co.uk
Set up in 2000, specializing in public relations for
the arts and entertainments sectors.

media contacts
Farncombe House 16 Market Street, 16 Market
Street, Lewes
BN7 2NB
T 01273 488996
F 01273 488497
E info@mediacontacts.org.uk
W www.mediacontacts.org.uk
A press information service in book and online
format, researched specifically for the visual arts.
Provides a continuously updated list of over four
thousand visual-arts journalists working in all
areas of the UK and international press. Also
provides detailed insider information for each
entry, including lead times, deadlines and
preferred method of contact. Online service
allows user to select own press list, paste in a press
release and image and send it out. Published since
1995 by artsinform PR.
Editor(s) Laura Charlton

Parker Harris Partnership
15 Church Street, Esher
KT10 8QS
T 01372 462190
F 01372 460032
E info@parkerharris.co.uk
W www.parkerharris.co.uk
Founded by Emma Parker and Penny Harris in
1990, specializing in the creation, organization,
marketing, press and public relations of fine-art
exhibitions and events.

Pippa Roberts Publicity & Communications
101 Mapledene Road, London Fields, London
E8 3LL
T 020 79233188
E pr@pipparoberts.com
A public relations company founded in 2001,
specializing in press relations, marketing
communications and corporate activity for
art and antiques fairs, events and retailers, art
exhibitions, competitions and shows. Clients
since 2001 include Olympia Fine Art and Antiques
Fairs, the London Silver Vaults, Olympia Loan
Exhibitions (Augustus John, Edward Burra, Keith
Vaughan, Graham Sutherland, Prunella Clough,
Wyndham Lewis), Decorative Antiques and
Textiles Fairs, BlindArt (charity) competition and
exhibition, HALI Carpet Textile and Tribal Art Fair.

Rebecca Ward
33 Wellington Row, London
E2 7BB
T 020 76133306
E press@rebeccaward.co.uk
W www.rebeccaward.co.uk
A freelance public relations consultant with more
than ten years' experience of promoting the arts
and fashion. Current and past clients include the
V&A, SHOWstudio, eyestorm.com, the Women's
Library, London College of Fashion, Camberwell
College of Arts, Theatre Museum, English
Heritage, Heritage Lottery Fund and the Iranian
Heritage Foundation.

Sue Bond Public Relations
T 01359 271085
F 01359 271491
E info@suebond.co.uk
W www.suebond.co.uk
Established in 1982, specializing in fine arts,
antiques and cultural events.

Theresa Simon Communications
Stratton House, 1 Stratton Street, London
W1J 8LA
T 020 76299645
E pr@theresasimon.com
W www.theresasimon.com
An agency specializing in public relations and
marketing for visual and performing arts, design
and architecture organizations. Recent clients
include the Wallace Collection, the London
Architecture Biennale, Archives Libraries
Museums London, Arts Council England, Zoo Art
Fair and Modus Operandi Art Consultants.
Editor Theresa Simon (Director)

General index

Alphabetical index to all entries.
All companies and organizations are listed according to
their full names, e.g. Henry Moore Institute is found under
'H' and Paul Hamlyn Foundation can be found under 'P'.

Subject index

Selected entries by category.